THE MINERAL RESOURCES
OF BRITAIN

Frontispiece: Drilling the working face in preparation for blasting at Britain's main underground limestone mine, Middleton-by-Wirksworth, Derbyshire

THE MINERAL RESOURCES
OF BRITAIN

A study in exploitation and planning

JOHN BLUNDEN

HUTCHINSON OF LONDON

HUTCHINSON & CO *(Publishers)* LTD
3 Fitzroy Square, London W1

London Melbourne Sydney Auckland
Wellington Johannesburg Cape Town
and agencies throughout the world

First published 1975
© John Blunden 1975

Set in Monotype Baskerville
Printed in Great Britain by The Anchor Press Ltd
and bound by Wm Brendon & Son Ltd
both of Tiptree, Essex

ISBN 0 09 119990 5

CONTENTS

PLATES

FRONTISPIECE Drilling the working face in preparation for blasting at Britain's main underground limestone mine, Middleton-by-Wirksworth, Derbyshire. *(Geoffrey B. Platts)*

PLATE 1A Gravel extraction in progress at Thorpe, near Chertsey, Surrey. *(Leisure Sport Ltd.)*

PLATE 1B Worked-out areas at Thorpe reinstated to leisure use as a water park. *(Leisure Sport Ltd.)*

PLATE 2A Merehead, the largest limestone quarry in the Mendip Hills, Somerset, producing four million tonnes a year. The rail link is used to supply most of the output of clean stone to a distribution depot at Botley in Hampshire. *(West Air Photography, Weston-S-Mare)*

PLATE 2B The cement works at Hope in the Peak District National Park. Sited because of the favourable proximity of raw materials, the scale of the plant makes it an obtrusive element in the Hope valley. *(Associated Portland Cement Manufacturers Ltd.)*

PLATE 3A The largest chalk quarry in Britain at Swanscombe in Kent, producing 8·5 million tonnes a year. The working is bounded in the north by the Thames estuary and the urban areas of Swanscombe and North-fleet and in the south by the A2 and the M2 serving London and the Channel ports. *(Associated Portland Cement Manufacturers Ltd.)*

PLATE 3B An industrial estate at Coulsden, Surrey, developed inside a disused chalk quarry by the former extractive company and the local authority. *(Neil Maurer)*

PLATE 4A A Bedfordshire brick clay pit after the usable material has been won leaving conical heaps of clay rejects. The saplings in the foreground are an attempt at screening the excavation. *(Bedfordshire County Council)*

PLATE 4B Broughton Moor slate quarry in the Lake District National Park, specializing in the production of decorative cladding materials. *(Aerofilms Ltd.)*

PLATE 5A Slate waste at the disused Dorothea quarry, Llyffni valley, Snowdonia National Park. Although its boundaries were drawn to avoid the worst areas, such tips represent a major dereliction problem within the park. Dorothea is being developed for recreational purposes. *(C. G. Down)*

PLATE 5B A typical open pit china clay operation at West Carclaze, St Austell, Cornwall. The working tips of quartz waste can be seen in the centre background; other disused tips in the area have become vegetated. *(English China Clays)*

PLATE 6A Crushed gypsum being carried by aerial ropeway from the underground working at Mountfield, Sussex, to the processing plant over three miles away. *(British Gypsum)*

PLATE 6B Opencast fluorspar working on Longstone Edge in the Peak District National Park. Some worked-out sections are now being filled, contoured and revegetated by Laporte Industries. *(Peak Park Planning Board)*

PLATE 7A Ridges of overburden produced by the opencast working of iron ore at Cranford St John, Northamptonshire. *(Northamptonshire County Council)*

PLATE 7B The same area as above restored by the local authority to agricultural use from finance provided by the Ironstone Restoration Fund. *(Northamptonshire County Council)*

PLATE 8A Shaft head gear at the new Wheal Jane tin mine near Truro, Cornwall. *(Kenneth M. Trathen)*

PLATE 8B An opencast coal working at Tinings, County Durham. Rock overburden and soil are tipped separately adjacent to the site for subsequent reinstatement of the landscape which is achieved with the level of success of that following ironstone extraction. *(National Coal Board Opencast Executive)*

FIGURES

PREFACE

THIS book is concerned with the identification of the range of minerals that are worked in Britain, their location and the economic circumstances under which they are worked. However, much of the argument also deals with the land-use planning problems that arise when a decision is made to exploit a particular mineral and the circumstances under which a decision may be taken not to do so.

It would be wrong to believe that there are any circumstances under which a mineral might be worked which would have no impact on the land surface. Even the smallest underground working implies headgear and limited facilities for processing and despatch. A large quarry, on the other hand, producing stone at a rate well in advance of one million tonnes a year, must have considerable impact not only on the immediate landscape because of the size of the excavation, but on the surrounding area because of traffic and pollution. The implications of such a quarry in terms of environmental disturbance and the transfer of the use of land from, say, agriculture to mineral extraction are therefore considerable for the community at large, particularly when the multiplicity of locations is borne in mind.

Thus, this book seeks not only to define the straight economic gain attached to the working of a particular location for a mineral, but tries to consider the alternative value that the site may have in other uses. Under what circumstances may the transfer of that land from such a use to the working of a mineral be legitimately required? This becomes a particularly important consideration with respect to many of the hard rock aggregate materials and the working of non-ferrous metals since these are frequently found in just those areas where land has been set aside primarily for recreation—Britain's National Parks.

This book also questions whether the quality of the decision-making process in respect of changed land use might be improved and whether enough attention is being given to mitigation of the impact of an operation during its active life, and to the restoration or rehabilitation of land when the mineral has been exploited and the land becomes available again for yet another use.

The range of minerals discussed, the variations in the level of output, the differences in degree of difficulty which the initial application to work may raise with the appropriate planning body depending on location, mode of working, the amount of waste produced etc., have all made for problems in the preparation of this text. Some difficulty has also on occasion been found in obtaining information at the level of the individual operator: although the commercial reasons for the secrecy which often surrounds and indeed constrains the availability of such information can be appreciated, it has to be said that in the long run such a situation can only be prejudicial to a true understanding of an important sector of Britain's industrial life. Furthermore, the official statistics may suffer on two counts: there is a time-lag before the more specialized statistics become available and they are then in some cases too aggregated to permit of sufficiently detailed analysis. In order to contend meaningfully with some of these problems it has been necessary to relate the discussion mainly to data collected and analysed at the beginning of this decade. In spite of the fact that these figures do not give a totally up to the minute picture, I have been concerned to use this data together with earlier information in such a way as to indicate continuing trends in the pattern of extractive development.

A notable exception to this general approach comes in the section dealing with hydrocarbons. The recent and far-reaching implications of the 1973 Middle East War demonstrated by the Arab oil producers' attitudes to individual western powers and their capacity to raise prices by a factor of four, has led to a major re-appraisal of the value of Britain's off-shore oil reserves, the rate at which oil will be brought ashore, and an intensified search for further fields. It has also given a fillip to the coal industry by making this alternative source of power more competitive and therefore the subject of increased demand, at least in the short term. These developments have justified the updating of the sections on hydrocarbons to 1974.

The work involved in the preparation of this volume is beyond anything that could have been achieved without the dedicated assistance of others. Here I would like particularly to pay a warm tribute to the county planners in England, Wales and Scotland who, with only one exception, very willingly co-operated in the completion of a detailed questionnaire concerning the planning implications of mineral extraction, which must have made considerable inroads in their time and that of their hard-pressed staffs.

I must express gratitude to the many companies who willingly subjected themselves to an intensive scrutiny of their extractive operations without immediately suspecting me of wishing to subvert their operation on behalf of what they might call the planning lobby. I particularly wish to thank the following people who read those sections of the book relevant to their own expertise and made many helpful comments and in some cases put right factual errors: Sand and gravel— E. G. Sibert (Surrey County Council), J. P. R. Jordan (Sand and Gravel Association); Limestone and sandstone—P. Leslie (British Quarrying and Slag Federation); Igneous rocks—M. W. Mason Smith (Associated Roadstone Corporation Ltd); Chalk—M. J. Greer (Associated Portland Cement Ltd); Brick clay—Michael Drown (London Brick Company Ltd); Slate—J. W. Roberts (Penrhyn Quarries Ltd), Harold Ogden (Broughton Moor Green Slate Quarries Ltd); China clay—N. R. Leonard, Clare Bradley (English China Clays Ltd); Ball clay—C. D. Pike (Watts, Blake Bearne and Company Ltd), Fuller's earth—R. M. Raikes (Laporte Industries Ltd); Salt—K. A. Whittaker (Cheshire County Council); Gypsum and anhydrite—D. Skilton (British Gypsum Ltd); Celestite—P. J. C. Brooksband (Rogers and Cooke Ltd); Fluorspar—Dr J. V. Bramsley (Laporte Industries Ltd); Barium minerals— A. R. D. Orr (Athole G. Allen Ltd); Refractories—P. G. Lamb, G. Jago (National Coal Board Opencast Executive), C. S. Hedley (Steetley Ltd); Silica and moulding sands—A P. Lovat (British Industrial Sand Ltd); Diatomite—P. S. Williams (Cape Insulation Ltd); Tin— J. H. Trounson (Cornish Mining Development Association); Coal— H. J. Lowe (Nottinghamshire County Council), I. R. Oldfield (National Coal Board); Hydrocarbons—W. J. Browne (Institute of Petroleum).

Members of staff from the Department of the Environment also proved most helpful and I am especially grateful to Dr Michael Barratt for his encouraging attitude.

I also owe a considerable debt of gratitude to my colleague, Professor Andrew Learmonth, for his forbearance and encouragement at a time when it was not propitious to embark on a work of this magnitude. To Christopher Hamnett who visited many local authorities and undertook interviews with planning officers on my behalf and to John Hunt who was responsible for the preparation of the maps and diagrams, I give my sincere thanks.

Most of all I must pay tribute to the burden carried by my wife who, on the basis of the strategic plan of the book, carried out so much of the collection of data and the collation of other evidence both documentary and oral, besides performing other invaluable organizational tasks without which this volume would merely have been conceived but never born.

In a text as wide ranging as this, there must inevitably be errors, omissions and inadequacies. For these the responsibility is entirely mine.

I

THE EXPLOITATION ENVIRONMENT

GREAT BRITAIN contains rocks which are representative of almost all the identified geological systems from the oldest which occur in the north and west and include many igneous and metamorphic types, to the youngest which predominate in the south and east and include the softer sedimentary rocks. Besides giving rise to a remarkably varied and often extremely attractive range of landscapes, these rock types provide an extensive source of mineral products which are widely mined or quarried and which are vital to the economy. These extend from sand and gravel to celestine; from brick clay to fuller's earth; from limestone to gypsum and anhydrite; from ironstone to tin and from granite to coal, natural gas and oil.

A minerals categorization

So wide is the range that it at once becomes necessary to draw these together under broad category headings in order that they may be considered in a rational and orderly way. The arrangement of the chapters attempts to do this: individual minerals fall under headings of ubiquitous non-metalliferous minerals, localized non-metalliferous minerals, non-ferrous metals, ferrous metals, and carbon and hydrocarbon fuels. Clearly the parameters applied here distinguish the separate identity of those mineral substances which are utilized as a source of heat and power; the iron-bearing ores; the ores of tin, lead, zinc and others, such as copper, which are likely to become more important in Britain in the immediate future. Finally there is the category of non-metalliferous minerals and although these are here subdivided according to their occurrence, either in a few limited areas or widely scattered across Britain, such a broad spectrum of minerals with widely differing characteristics and usages can, for the purposes of greater comprehension, be further distinguished by a categorization which takes account of economic criteria. These are value per unit of material extracted; value added by on-site processing; the importance of market location with reference to the points of primary supply (this may be termed their place value); and the volume of production needed to make operations economic. This last criterion is particularly significant in the case of those non-metalliferous minerals which carry a low potential margin of profit. The values which follow are those for January 1971 for the various minerals as they left the extraction site, i.e. the value added by on-site processing is included.

The lowest group—those extracted and sold at less than £1·50 per tonne ex works[1]—mainly includes those relatively ubiquitous non-metallics which are used as aggregates in road and building construction, e.g. sand and gravel, limestone, igneous rocks and sandstone. These minerals mainly undergo only the simplest type of processing such as washing, screening or, if necessary, crushing. All these processes produce little weight loss or added value. The exceedingly high place value of these minerals result from the high cost of transport in relation to their unit value, and means that they are ideally worked in close proximity to their markets. The localization of markets determined the traditional dispersed pattern of aggregates extraction, from numerous pits or quarries of only small or moderate size. However, a complex of interrelated factors in the 1960s caused these low value aggregate minerals to be transported over much greater distances than previously, on an interregional or even international scale. These factors included the very rapidly rising demand for aggregates, tightening technical specifications and the exhaustion of some of the more easily won deposits in high demand areas. The higher costs attendant on wider market radii for these essentially low value minerals have been partially contained by improved means of transport, and to some extent by the growing practice of further on-site processing such as tar or bitumen coating. In the case of marine dredged sand and gravel, the comparatively low transport costs for conveyance by sea to the point of landing give an added marketing flexibility, and can mean that the material is actually exported. The widening market radii for aggregates has made possible the growth in the average size of pits and quarries, a marked feature of the 1960s, which brings substantial benefits in economies of scale.

In the second group are these minerals which command between £1·50 and £6·50 per tonne, e.g. chalk, limestone, clay and shale for cement manufacture and brick clay for brick manufacture. These minerals are relatively ubiquitous and in their raw state are no more valuable than aggregates; they are in consequence almost always worked in very close proximity to their manufacturing plants. However, they gain in value substantially as a result of their on-site manufacture and can be marketed nationally. In the case of bricks, this national marketing pattern is a recent development, stemming largely from the cost advantages of one particular deposit. The high level of investment in capital equipment required for the manufacturing plant, especially in the case of a modern cement works, means that large-scale extraction is necessary to cover overheads and bring about economies of scale. Also in this second category are minerals of more localized occurrence than aggregates, and which undergo less expensive processing than the cement and brick materials. Since economies of scale are consequently less important and the volume of reserves substantially smaller, these minerals are often extracted by production units of small to moderate size. Among these minerals are the speciality building materials such as gypsum and anhydrite, the primary refractory raw materials such as fire-clay and dolomite, silica sand for foundry use or glass manufacture, rock salt for winter road clearance purposes, and ball clay, an important raw material for the ceramics industry. Ball clay, although a comparatively low value mineral, is exported in large quantities as a result of the excellent quality of the English deposits and their proximity to ports in Devon and Dorset which offer relatively cheap transport by sea. In this price category should also be included other more highly processed forms of group one minerals, such as ground and calcined limestone for steelmaking flux, and the cheap by-products of basically dearer products, such as slate powders from slate quarries geared primarily to the production of sheet slate.

The third group, £6·50–£10 per tonne, is concerned mainly with the chief raw materials of the chemical and fertilizer industries, salt and potash, and with a mineral which is mined on a much smaller scale, lump barytes, used for barium chemicals and X-ray-resistant concrete, etc. The value of these minerals, in contrast to that of aggregates, lies in their chemical rather than their physical properties. These minerals, except barytes, are produced on the whole from large units: in the case of salt this results not only from the proximity of a very large chemical market to the chief Cheshire deposits, but to the development of a new and sophisticated method of extracting the salt in the form of brine. This is known as the Imperial Chemical Industries (ICI) controlled pumping method by which 17 700 million litres per year are removed at one site. Potash, which sold in 1971 at between £6 and £8 per tonne, is also produced, or planned to be produced, in fairly large volume with specific plant running at over

3

100 000 tonnes a year, since the capital costs of its extraction by deep-mining need to be spread over a large output volume. Although the Cheshire salt deposits were a major factor determining the location of the British chemical industry, the higher unit values for this mineral are now of more significance than place value. Brine extraction, heavily concentrated on Cheshire, is also carried out to a limited extent from other deposits near Fleetwood; a working at Droitwich came to an end in 1972. Potash is confined exclusively to the North York Moors and barytes to one working also in the North Riding. Brine, in particular, lends itself to pipeline transportation over short to medium distances, which can involve substantial savings in transport costs.

The fourth group is made up of a substantial group of non-metallics which are characterized chiefly by moderate to high unit values of between £10 and £20 per tonne, moderate to low place value and relatively small volume production. Some of these are the less pro-cessed varieties of relatively localized minerals which can with more elaborate treatment command substantially in excess of £20 per tonne. These include natural fuller's earth used, for instance, as a bonding agent in foundry sands, china clay used as a filler for paper or in other industrial processes and fluorspar of metallurgical grade used for flux. In all these cases, the value added from processing is smaller than in the case of their more expensive grades and consequently transport costs are still of considerable significance. Their restricted occurrence, in the case of fuller's earth to a small area of Surrey and sites near Bath and Woburn, in that of china clay mainly to the St Austell and Bodmin Moor areas of Cornwall and Lee Moor in Devon, and in that of fluorspar mainly to the Pennines, involves necessarily larger market radii than might otherwise be economic for these comparatively inexpensive grades of product. Two other minerals in this price category, namely celestine and talc, are of even more restricted occur-rence, celestine being worked solely at one site in Gloucestershire and talc only in the Shetland Islands.

The fifth and final group, reserved for non-metallic minerals of the highest unit values of more than £20 per tonne, contains the more expensively processed forms of fuller's earth (acid-activated and sodium-exchanged varieties with enhanced bleaching and bonding qualities); china clay, selling mainly as a coating for paper; and acid grade fluorspar for the chemical and aluminium industries. Both coating grade china clay and acid grade fluorspar, of which Britain produces a surplus, can be competitively exported as a result of their low transport costs per unit value. Perhaps surprisingly, roofing slate must also be included in this category: although Britain contains vast

4

reserves of this mineral, notably in North Wales, Cornwall and the Lake District, and although it is not particularly difficult to quarry and requires no processing, the very labour-intensive task of splitting slates of the required thickness from the quarried blocks means that the average ex-works price for roofing slate at one large North Wales quarry in 1971 was £38·40 per tonne. This is probably not untypical.

This categorization of non-metalliferous minerals seeks then to emphasize not only the wide range of types and use but the interrelationships between value per unit of minerals produced, frequency of deposits, degree of processing, scale of working and market radii. Where size of operating unit is not restricted by the extent of reserves or extent of planning permission, the main determinant of maximum size of workings is size of market. The overall trend in extractive industries in Britain has been towards larger mines, pits and quarries. This process has been dependent, particularly in the case of the cheap aggregates, on improved transport resulting from motorways, larger vehicle size, greater use of company-owned fleets and the greater use of sea transport. There has even, in the case of chalk, been the introduction of slurried transportation by pipeline. However, the overall pattern which emerges is greatly complicated by special factors in different cases, which will be examined in detail later.

No attempt is made here to extend this method of categorization to metalliferous minerals, although iron, tin, lead and limited quantities of tungsten and zinc are at present produced in Britain. However, a broad distinction may be drawn between ferrous and non-ferrous ores. Most non-ferrous ores have a much lower metallic content than do the ores of iron, and non-ferrous ores with a metallic content of less than 1 per cent may be worked given the appropriate extraction techniques and if found in sufficient quantity in a relatively accessible deposit. But their working also presupposes that certain conditions prevail in terms of world supply and demand, the climate of international politics and the socio-economic climate at home; all these factors will be looked at in more detail later. Suffice it to say at present that the right factor mix now exists to explain the current expansion of tin mining in Cornwall. However, as in the above categorization, the cost of transport from extraction site to the consumption location remains a pertinent one. For this reason these low grade tin ores are upgraded at the minehead from less than 1 per cent tin content to between 65 and 70 per cent per unit by a concentration process before they are transported to smelting plants. The financial gain to be made by the avoidance of carrying unnecessary amounts of bulky low grade ore by minehead concentration is brought home when it is realized that in 1968–9 the South Crofty mine, situated between Camborne and Redruth, needed one tonne of mined ore to produce 10.37 kg of concentrates with a 70 per cent tin content.[2] Thus the concentration not only reduces volume and weight but increases value, so diminishing to the point of insignificance any place value which tin ore might otherwise be deemed to have. Furthermore, since the metal itself was in January 1973 priced at over £1600 per tonne,[3] the question of place value for tin at the smelter is equally irrelevant.

An exact parallel can be drawn in the case of lead for the small quantities produced as a by-product of fluorspar extraction in Derbyshire and in Weardale in County Durham are concentrated close to the point of extraction. Their resultant greatly enhanced values per unit means that they can be readily carried to smelters even on the Continent of Europe.[4] Similarly the lead and small quantities of zinc mined in Flintshire at Olwyn Goch are concentrated at the mine and despatched to South Wales for smelting.[5]

Iron ore, however, presents a very different picture. Not only do some of the factors which have at present resulted in an upsurge in the extraction of home tin ore not apply here, thus resulting in a falling off of British output (discussed further on pp. 335–340), but the iron content of home produced ores, the bulk of which are extracted from the Jurassic sequence of rocks in England, averaged in 1969 about 28 per cent.[6] Although by world iron ore standards this would not be considered high, it is clearly greatly in advance of those for British non-ferrous metals. As a result, it has been worth while to transport unconcentrated ores internally from extraction sites in Northamptonshire as far as Scunthorpe in north Lincolnshire and Middlesbrough.

It is quite apparent that in the case of many of the non-metalliferous minerals the question of alternative overseas supplies must be of limited importance. Whilst categorization relationships are significant, certainly internally, most of the non-metallic minerals would not be imported simply because of transport costs (which would include break of bulk as well as multi-media transport charges) and the relatively high percentage they would make up of total unit costs. There are, however, minor exceptions for specialized products—e.g. some very high quality silica sands for crystal or optical glass have been imported but only from the deposits adjacent to the canal system connected to the Rhine. Potash is a mineral which has only just begun to be worked in Britain with the successful completion of the Boulby works in north Yorkshire. There it has been necessary to import supplies from Saskatchewan. However, transport costs to the eastern seaboard of Canada and then shipping across the Atlantic meant prices of around £13·30 a tonne landed in Britain. As the Boulby mine can adequately meet the home market demand at between £6 and £7,[7] these imports will shortly cease.

Like the metalliferous minerals these non-metallic commodities are broadly in a state of rising demand though wide variations in the nature of the mineral and the use to which it is put cause differences in the degree to which increase is taking place. Certainly production of these increased by 125 per cent between 1950 and 1968 with the greatest single rise, a quite exceptional one, taking place in the production of rock salt now used mainly for winter road clearance. Total output of rock salt rose by 2553 per cent between 1950 and 1968.[8]

The carbon and hydrocarbon minerals bear a very different relationship to British industrial life since, unlike those other commodities so far considered which form some part of the tangible output or fabric of manufacturing plant, these fuel minerals respond primarily to their energy needs (with perhaps the exception of coke which may be considered as a raw material in the iron and steel industry). In this respect coal has played a major part and in 1969 still maintained a 51 per cent hold on the total domestic energy market. That this had fallen from 77 per cent[9] only ten years earlier was indicative of the increasing importance of oil and natural gas as alternative supplies of energy in terms of competitiveness. Although the continuing growth of motor and air transport would inevitably have meant greater demands on oil and its derivatives, the fact that coal has lost so much ground in spite of being for a considerable period of time Britain's only major fuel reserve, was explained by its increasing failure to compete with its substitutes in terms of price and convenience of transport and conversion. Changes in the cost structure of coalmining will be discussed in detail in Chapter 6, but in the ten-year period from 1960, though there was increasing concentration on mechanization with a halving of the workforce to 300 000 men, greater emphasis on the larger, more easily mined fields with the closure of 300 of the least economic of the 700 pits, and increasing productivity with a rise in output per man year of 156 tonnes to 471 tonnes,[10] the competitive position of coal worsened. Only occasionally was the National Coal Board (NCB) able to secure private contracts of any substance, for example in 1968 when it agreed to deliver one million tonnes of coal a year to Associated Portland Cement at 1·7 pence a therm. But this was only achieved by selling off at uneconomic rates part of a coal surplus of 30·5 million tonnes.[11] The important gas market was increasingly turning to sources other than coal even before the discovery of North Sea gas. In the early 1960s oil-based gas was being produced in large quantities and the Gas Council began to import at Canvey Island in Essex liquid methane in specially built refrigerated tankers from Algeria to meet part of its demand. The coal industry, however, was further disadvantaged in the mid-1960s by the discovery of an immense supply of natural gas from the Permian anticlinal structures under the North Sea. At a beach price of 2·1 pence a therm, agreed in 1967 between the extraction company, British Petroleum and the Gas Council, this was 0·4 pence lower than the Algerian imports.[12] All these alternative sources of gas undercut coal-based gas in price. At the same time as gas was discovered in the North Sea, substantial reserves of oil were located there, mainly in those sections of it divided between Norway, Holland and Britain. The oil industry is optimistically talking of the North Sea as the major oil province to be discovered anywhere in the world this century,[13] but whatever the estimated reserves finally prove to be, it is clear that Britain will increasingly turn to these in the late 1970s and 1980s. Though undersea exploration and development costs are bound to be high, cost per barrel of crude oil beached on the East Coast will not exceed those of similar supplies delivered at British oil refineries from Middle Eastern fields, in spite of transport economies effected by the use of larger tankers.[14] Indeed governments in these areas have now demanded what they would term more realistic prices for their oil and in November 1973 the six major Middle Eastern producing countries increased their prices per barrel to the twenty-two international oil companies by a factor of four, thus adding very substantially to the balance of payments problem in Britain.[15] At the same time, political stability and the continuity of supply have been increasingly in doubt. In December 1971, for example, Libya expropriated British Petroleum's holdings in that country, depriving it of 4 per cent of its crude oil supplies. Thus it is likely, even allowing for market growth, that by the 1980s the North Sea will be able to meet at least 80 per cent of British demands.[16]

Recent trends in British mineral exploration and development

It was this background of British over-dependence on Middle East oil with its political uncertainties and ever increasing drain on our balance of payments, coupled with the rising cost of indigenous coal and the continual growth in the fuel market that stimulated the search for hydrocarbons in the North Sea area.[17] The factors influencing the recent indigenous development of hydrocarbons bear some similarity to those which have catalysed current interest in prospecting for non-ferrous metalliferous minerals. Unlike that of hydrocarbons, however, the extraction of non-ferrous metals has a very long and important history in Britain, dating back at least to Roman times, and involving mainly the base metals of tin, lead, copper and zinc rather than the precious metals, gold and silver. There are about 4000 disused lead mines in Derbyshire alone, while in the early nineteenth century Devon and Cornwall were producing about 50 per cent of the world's output of copper ore. Non-ferrous metal mining as a whole reached its peak in Britain in the mid-nineteenth century but was drastically curtailed in the 1870s and 1880s. During these years of economic depression at home, the discovery of large and accessible overseas deposits produced a slump in world base-metal prices; British mines, where conditions were becoming steadily more unfavourable, were unable to compete with foreign ores, and concentrates, imported more cheaply than ever before by steam shipping. Although substantial non-ferrous metal reserves probably remain in Britain, their extraction has never subsequently reached anything approaching nineteenth century levels. During the 1960s, however, interest in British non-ferrous metal deposits of all kinds was revived by not only the availability of new techniques for the extraction of lower grade ores but by the need to maintain a favourable balance of payments (the import bill for metalliferous ores in 1969 was about £681 million a year),[18] the need to ensure continued supplies in the light of the prevailing uncertain political situation in some of the countries exporting to Britain, as well as the desire to exploit new supplies of ore as the richer overseas deposits become worked out. This has to be seen against a background of rising world prices and demand. Indeed, extrapolation from historical growth in demand which can be shown graphically to be exponential, gives an alarming projection of the size of future needs, even for the next thirty years, and it is likely that lower grade, deeper or more remote deposits will have to be exploited.[19] Increasing re-use of metallic ores will probably also become more and more essential. This revival of interest in Britain first manifested itself in the early 1960s in Cornwall where tin working had never ceased entirely, and the results have already come to fruition in the immense expansion at the South Crofty and Geevor mines in the Penwith Peninsula, and in the opening of Consolidated Goldfield's Wheal Jane mine near Truro in October 1971.

With other minerals, particularly, though not exclusively, metalliferous minerals, interest has been continuous and widespread since 1971. It covers most of the rest of Highland Britain since these are the areas which like the South-West are most likely to give rise to workable deposits, particularly of metallic ores. In that year alone 28 companies had agents or staff geologists exploring 80 sites as Fig. 1.1 shows.[20]

Apart from tin, the South-West would seem likely to be a source of tungsten and a number of companies were in the process of locating workable deposits. In Wales, particularly Snowdonia National Park, copper for opencast working was being sought by Rio-Tinto Zinc (RTZ) in the Coed-y-Brenin area; by the Union Corporation of South Africa who were also prospecting other base metals in the Lleyn Peninsula; and Intermines of Canada who were also actively looking for copper in Anglesey at Parys Mountain, the site of former mining activities which died out about a hundred years ago.[21] In the National Park, RTZ had also concerned themselves with the possibility of extracting gold from the Mawddach Estuary,[22] whilst Geochemical Remining, a firm of mineral agents, had an agreement to act on behalf of the owners of 8100 hectares north-west of Snowdonia and stretching towards the coast.[23] Further south in Cardiganshire, three Canadian companies were prospecting for lead, zinc and silver.[24] Andex Mines of British Columbia were studying the old lead mines of the Plynlimon massif inland from Aberystwyth. In the north-east of Wales, Charter Consolidated, through its associate Minera Mines, had rights in the Minera Mountain near Flint, where Courtaulds were then mining small quantities of lead, and expansion seemed likely in the near future.[25]

RTZ, one of the most active prospectors in Britain, were also exploring for base metals in the Isle of Man as well as in the Lake District (around Thirlmere and Haweswater).[26] Here Coniston Copper Mines of Toronto had just begun to look for copper in an area of about 20·7 square kilometres around Lake Coniston where it is known that about fifteen copper veins exist.[27] Force Crag Mines Ltd., were also at work in this National Park searching for barytes, lead and zinc. Across the Pennines in the North York Moors area, exploration for a non-metallic potash has already been mentioned, but between these two National Parks in the vicinity of Weardale, Allenheads and Rookhope, ICI and Swiss Aluminium were searching for non-metalliferous fluorspar whilst Acmin Ltd. were looking for lead and zinc.

Scotland had in 1971 become the scene of intensely active metalliferous exploration. In Ayrshire drilling for nickel had been undertaken jointly by American Metal Climax Inc. and Selection Trust and the results were being appraised.[28] Within easy reach of Glasgow, Loch Fyne had been examined by Consolidated Goldfields for copper and nickel. The remaining sites in this area had recently been taken up by RTZ, Charter Consolidated and the Canadian partnership Noranda–Kerr. Noranda–Kerr had also been active to the north-east around the

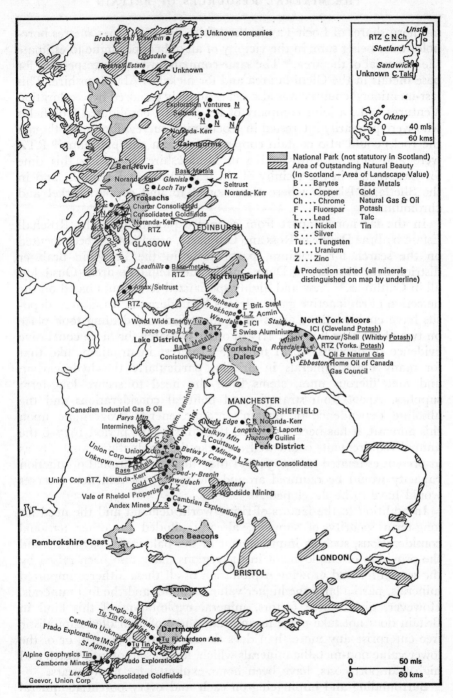

Fig. 1.1 *Mineral prospecting in Britain, 1971*

southern shores of Loch Tay in Perthshire. Here ten 91·5 metres bore-holes were being sunk in the vicinity of an old copper mine to estimate the potential of the area.[29] The same company was also prospecting for base metals in the Glenisla area and for nickel in Aberdeenshire. This last-mentioned country was also being actively explored by Exploration Ventures Ltd., a joint company of RTZ and Consolidated Goldfields who were primarily interested in geochemical surveys for nickel, though the rocks could also contain copper, chromium and platinum.[30] RTZ were also independently active in Lanarkshire, searching this time for base metals in the vicinity of old lead mines at Leadhills, and in the Shetland Islands where they hoped to find copper, nickel and chromium.[31]

In the far north, apart from copper exploration on the Rosehall Estate by Brae Doune in Ross and Cromarty, attention has been focused on the search for uranium, particularly in the Brawlbin–Brabster district, near Houstry of Dunn and in the Helmdale area (Ousdale), all in Caithness.[32] New and highly specialized techniques based on the detection of radioactive gases released by underground uranium deposits have enabled these areas to be identified and drilling took place on two of the sites (see Fig. 1.1) in order to search for more conclusive evidence of deposits worth mining.[33] Interest in uranium, like that for many other minerals in Britain, particularly the hydrocarbon and metalliferous ones, stems from the need to secure long-term supplies. Apart from strategic and political considerations and the absolute dependence of Britain's atomic energy programme upon this mineral, it has been predicted that 'during the period 1977–8 the annual requirements could well overtake the production capability as at present estimated for 1975', and that 'further additional production capacity would be required around the mid-1970s and new reserves would have to be developed'.[34]

In addition to the factors of rising world demand and the need for long-term security of supplies, already alluded to, other national considerations, such as improvement in the balance of payments and the provision of employment in the regions, have also been raised by the search for and growing exploitation of all these hitherto imported minerals, particularly the higher value metallics and the fuel minerals. However, given these factors, mineral exploitation of this kind in Britain does not take place in an atmosphere of unbridled capitalistic free enterprise any more than does the exploitation of coal, or of the lower value non-metallic minerals which, for reasons of unit worth and high transport costs, have been home-exploited for many years.

Surrounding and impingeing on each and every potential mineral extractor is a body of legislation which, though in part designed to assist in the winning of mineral resources, is certainly aimed at limiting the effects of extractive production on the environment and ensuring that wherever possible major restoration of the landscape takes place when the mineral is exhausted.

The legislative framework

This legislative framework within which minerals are extracted can be divided into three main sections, all of which act as constraints upon the operation of the industry as a whole, though in the case of fiscal legislation the impact is the most variable and the most uneven in its effect. Of the other two sections, governing mineral rights and aspects of town and country planning, the latter may be said to be of major and critical significance. With the exception of gold, silver, petroleum and coal, all minerals in the UK are in private hands. Thus in most instances the potential mineral extractor can negotiate with the mineral rights owner of an area the purchase or lease of these for a suitable sum once the presence of a particular mineral has been established by trial borings or by resistivity tests. These preliminary arrangements would be undertaken by arrangement with the mineral rights owner, though in the case of scout drilling it is open to question whether or not other permissions from the local planning authority are needed. RTZ had in 1971 just such an argument as a result of the tests they were conducting for copper in the Coed-y-Brenin of Snowdonia National Park.[35] Planning permission is however unquestionably required both for the more intensive drilling necessary to evaluate a deposit and for its exploitation. The sale of mineral rights will be dependent on the necessary planning permission for extraction being obtained and the figure finally agreed will be determined by the likely quantity of minerals present as well as their quality, the estimated time taken to extract them and the area involved. Unfortunately the task of obtaining such rights was made more difficult by the Labour Government of 1964–70 since their Land Commission Act made mineral rights owners liable to pay 40 per cent of the development value of the land exploited and this to be forthcoming in advance of their receiving any royalties.[36] Extractors were pleased, however, when in May 1970, the Government announced some tax concession by way of compensation to owners of mineral rights. Hitherto royalties from these rights had been treated as income for tax purposes. The increasingly high-speed mining techniques, which have shortened the period during which minerals are likely to be exploited, meant that land owners could have been faced with the situation of receiving their royalties in a period so short as to make payments received more like a capital sum, a sum then taxed as income bunched together in a few years.[37] By a new clause to the 1970 Finance Bill, these royalties were for tax purposes to be treated half as capital, half as income.[38] Mining interests were even more gratified later that year, for when the Conservatives were returned to office, they abolished the Land Commission Act.[39] However, other legislation of direct benefit to mineral producers was lost or amended as a result of this change of government. First of all, the Labour Party, had they remained in power, proposed to introduce legislation enabling mineral operators to obtain access to land for exploration purposes and also to acquire the mineral rights for possible exploitation where it was impossible to reach agreement with the owner or to discover his name or whereabouts.[40] This would have gone some way beyond the Mines Acts of 1923, 1934 and the Town and Country Planning Act of 1947, which permitted in certain circumstances a potential extractor of specified minerals (mainly coal, celestine, fluorspar, barytes, oil shale or the ores of iron, tin, lead, zinc, copper and tungsten) the possibility of acquiring rights from uncooperative or impossibly demanding owners by application to the High Court.[41] For this procedure to be employed, the planning authority had to have exercised its option to gain such access to the High Court under the original acts in its designation of land for potential mineral working. In the event few authorities, probably only two, ever made such access possible.[42] Gloucestershire, for example, designated an area containing celestine deposits in such a way as to allow a potential extractor this access should it ever be needed.[43] Any action taken as a result of the very much more permissive legislation the Labour Government had in mind would have been dependent on their acceptance of the view that the exploitation of the minerals involved was in the national interest and following the application by the operator for a minerals acquisition order. Certainly the extractive industries had welcomed this proposal—indeed many had argued that similar legal provisions had in part made possible the minerals boom in the Irish Republic, a point discussed in Chapter 5. The loss of this legislation (though there has been talk by both parties of taking the matter up again in the future),[44] was followed by almost as serious a blow in the field of mining finance where new operations are concerned.

In October 1970, the Chancellor of the Exchequer announced that investment grants which had met up to 40 per cent of the capital costs of new mines in Development Areas and 20 per cent elsewhere were to be eliminated and replaced by improved depreciation rates. In

Development Areas mining industries would have free depreciation for plant (i.e. immediate write-off), but in other areas plant would receive a 40 per cent first-year allowance followed by 25 per cent a year on the reducing balance.[45] Clearly the mining industry, particularly that part of it engaged in metalliferous mining as well as natural gas and oil, has been disadvantaged, for under the previous arrangement, the Government had provided cash through investment grants at just the time when risk is greatest for a mining concern, i.e. the period when resources are being proved. Subsequently, if and when it was decided to mine, the availability of further grants could become an essential part of the cash flow. The change in legislation no longer distinguishes the essential differences in the capital investment structure of the mining industry compared with other types of industrial concern. However, whilst it is true to say that some operators had not liked even the earlier arrangements of the Labour Government which had involved them in financial risk-taking and had argued in favour of a complete tax holiday (discussed further in Chapter 5), Consolidated Goldfields, with a substantial investment in a new tin mine in Cornwall, suggested that this new legislation involved the company in finding a further £1·25 millions for its project at Wheal Jane. Furthermore another major company, Cleveland Potash, publicly expressed disquiet over the additional finance that was required before production could begin at their site in the North York Moors National Park.[46]

A 2½ per cent cut in corporation tax made at the time of these changes has been helpful particularly to long-established British-based mineral extractors working in areas where reserves are known and assured in the long term (the china clay industry is a good example), though they are clearly of little value to foreign-based companies (e.g. Noranda–Kerr) who have been engaged in metalliferous mineral exploration or in natural gas and oil exploration in Britain in recent years.

More recently, the Act of Mineral Exploration 1971 has sought to make £50 millions available from the Government in the form of loans which could cover up to 35 per cent of the cost of exploration in the case of approved projects. However, these are only loans, to be repaid out of profits when extraction gets under way either for tin, potash, copper, zinc, gold or other non-ferrous metals from land or the British section of the continental shelf. At the second reading of this bill (10 November 1971) the Opposition spokesman probably echoed the feelings of the mineral extractors when he said that 'this measure . . . is merely an attempt to retract a step backwards the Government took when it abolished investment grants'. He added that it made no attempt to remove unnecessary obstacles in the way of mineral working and whilst welcoming the meagre provision it made for operators in the non-ferrous field he criticized its 'complacency towards the problem of the sedimentary mineral operators'.[47] Taking a general view, mineral extractors, particularly those newly operative or about to become so, have said that 'with high risk operations such as theirs, where future earnings must be discounted heavily, replacement of cash investment grants today, by rapid depletion (if any) when profits are made, must make mining investment in Britain less attractive'.[48] They have added that it was no coincidence that the revival of interest in many of Britain's minerals, which took place in the five years up to 1970, occurred when financial support from the Government at the 'vital early stages in exploration and development was forthcoming'.[49] However, although one further step back down the road towards the situation which existed under the former investment grant policy was taken in the 1972 budget when a regional development grant of 20 per cent for plant, machinery and mining was made, the fact remains that interest in the possible expansion of non-ferrous metal mining in Britain had not moved from the high level evident at the beginning of the decade. On the contrary, if anything it had increased with RTZ's explorations in Snowdonia, the Lake District and in Scotland, just one case in point. Furthermore, throughout the period of development that has so spectacularly manifested itself in many sections of the extractive industries, no legislation to sort out the knotty problem of mineral rights has found its way on to the statute books. It is perhaps reasonable then to consider that whilst the matters so far discussed cannot be described as marginal to the progress of the mineral extractive industries, they are best considered as cost factors which limit the achievement of greater profits, but which in the present wider international climate of resource exploitation still make new exploration and development in Britain a viable proposition.

Perhaps more significant to the extraction of minerals is that legislation which governs the planning and development of mining and quarrying operations since it determines not only the physical limits of individual production units but whether minerals shall be extracted from a particular site at all.* Thus not only is the spatial disposition of a particular extractive industry determined within those limits already laid down by the geological extent of its deposits, but also the number of component units of that industry and its overall scale. Certainly from the point of view of the land use geographer, this body

* It is, of course, necessary for all extractive operations to be licensed by the Department of Trade and Industry in order that they comply with safety and other regulations administered by the Mines and Quarries Inspectorate.

of legislation is of major importance and stems initially from the Town and Country Planning Act 1932. This enabled planning authorities for the first time to bring mineral extraction within some degree of control, though few exercised their option. It was for this reason that in 1946 an Interim Development Order was added to the Act of fourteen years earlier which made it obligatory for planning permission to be sought by any firm wishing to begin working minerals at a specific site. In 1947 the Town and Country Planning Act made controls on mineral extraction even more explicit and though existing workings begun before or during the Second World War remained outside planning constraints, this new legislation recognized the need for some element of forward planning for all land uses.[50] The 1947 Act, which was further consolidated in 1962 and modified in 1968, essentially charged the local authorities with the task of preparing development, or since 1968 Structure Plans* for their areas which were supposed to zone districts for various classes of development including mineral extraction.

From a minerals stand-point, however, the 1947 Act has been variously applied since that date. Many planning authorities, both in their initial Development Plans and in subsequent revisions, scheduled zones for mineral working only where planning permission had been granted. In some counties after the 1947 Act freeholders of land were able to apply for permission to exploit minerals without producing proof of the existence of workable reserves and received consent with few, if any, conditions of workings being imposed. As a result some county Development Plans show substantial areas designated for mineral extraction which are unlikely ever to be worked. Certainly in more recent years planning authorities have become more reluctant to grant permission for mineral working outside zones designated for that purpose in the Development Plan and where this has been forthcoming, the conditions imposed for working have been very restrictive for the mineral operator. But in order to at least allow counties to more readily adjust areas designated for mineral working, the 1968 Act[51] stipulated that working permissions not taken up inside five years of the beginning of the Act must lapse. The idea was to avoid in future the state of affairs where some counties said that no new permissions could be given since areas already designated for minerals but not worked were ample to meet future demands.[52] Welcome as this might seem to mineral extractors, they have not found this change to their liking since it does not allow *bona fide* mineral untertakings to hold on to permissions which they consider to be their long-term reserves. For this reason the Government

* Development Plans were until 1968 essentially Plans showing only proposed land use. The Structure Plan however must express the authority's planning policies.

is being pressed to apply this enactment only to permissions to work which are in the hands of individuals outside the industry. Although legitimate extractors can, of course, always reapply for previous permissions lost under the 1968 amendment, they are concerned that if granted, the restrictive conditions will be more onerous. Thus, while extractors feel disadvantaged by this change in the legal framework within which they work, amenity conservationists may well consider that the new legal situation benefits their interests at a time when the dangers to the environment seem at their greatest.[53]

The framework of law necessitates the mineral extractor, when wishing to exploit new ground, submitting a detailed application to the planning authority for the area in which the site is located. This has to show the direction of working, the situation of the proposed plant and buildings, as well as details of the mineral to be extracted, the rate of extraction, the life of the deposit and, not least, that a genuine demand for the mineral exists which cannot be economically met elsewhere. In this respect, a ministry publication, setting out for the industry some of the parameters in which it must work, makes a pertinent point when it states that

minerals may be of no less importance to the national economy for being relatively low value per tonne. It is indeed often the low value minerals that need to be most carefully considered (in planning applications) because haulage charges usually form a high percentage of the cost to the consumer and the addition of even a few miles to the distance between the point of production or processing and the main markets may have a serious effect on price levels in the district. As much attention requires to be given to supplies of such substances as sand, gravel and chalk, which are in general economically marketable only near to the source of production, as to the more expensive or less common types of minerals.[54]

This clearly refers, then, to those non-metalliferous minerals making up group one.

If the extractor wishes to break new ground not already designated for mineral working his application will have to be referred to the Secretary of State for the Environment or the Secretaries of State for Wales or Scotland if those countries are concerned, since a major change in land use contrary to that set out in the Development Plan is involved. In such situations the planning authority will certainly make its own views known to the Secretary of State concerning the application. However, in all planning permissions for mineral extraction, the Secretary of State, knowing the local authority view, will decide whether to 'call-in' the application, which means he will deal with it himself, or whether to leave it to that planning authority to make a decision on its own.

Certainly he or the local authority will not agree to allow land previously designated for other uses, to be used for mineral extraction without consulting one or more of the Ministry of Agriculture, the Forestry Commission, the statutory water undertakings, river conservancy boards, the Minister for Transport and perhaps the Countryside Commission, the Nature Conservancy and the Inspectorate of Ancient Monuments. Not only may they have a view as to the desirability of such a working but their representations can result in the making of conditions of working which take account of amenity interests.[55] For example, the river authority, under the River (Prevention of Pollution) Acts 1951 and 1961, might demand that the disposal of mine and quarry waters should not alter the mineral content of streams or rivers or their degree of acidity in a way that unduly affects the interests of riperian owners below the extractive operation.*

In spite of these controls and contrary to the view often held, the planning legislation described is not designed unreasonably to restrict the activities of extractors or to fight a running battle for the preservation of amenity. As the *Control of Mineral Working* stated,

in considering whether or to what extent mineral working should be permitted, it is important to bear in mind that the mineral industries are fundamental to the national economy and that many of the other industries of the country are in greater or less degree dependent upon them. The fundamental concern of planning policy must therefore be to ensure a free flow of mineral products at economic cost.[56]

Similarly, all planning authorities are bound to protect the interest of the extractive industries as a whole by safeguarding mineral deposits against sterilization by urban encroachment. Certainly, some authorities have taken very seriously their obligations towards mineral extraction. In Devon, Cornwall and Dorset, for instance, the areas containing workable deposits of china and ball clays are not only

---

* Other legislative controls may have an impact on the extractive industries but will be of less significance. The Noise Abatement Act 1960, administered by the local authority, and designed to eliminate or reduce noise nuisance, may in certain circumstances be deemed a minor constraint upon an extractive activity. The work of the Alkali Inspectorate (set up under the Alkali Act of 1893) in the field of air pollution control, together with the provisions of the Clean Air Act 1956, are, however, only likely to have significance in respect of the secondary processing activities of certain extractive industries. These constraints are referred to again, as appropriate, in later chapters.

allocated for that purpose on the Development Plans, but are adjoined by zones referred to as 'consultation areas'. A similar area adjoins the ironstone workings in the Lindsey area of Lincolnshire. This is because such areas are deemed to be of great importance to the working of these minerals. Therefore, a consultation procedure takes place between the industries in question and the planning authority whenever an application for a development is received within these areas that does not bear directly on the working of the minerals concerned. Should the extractors object to the development, the local authority will not let it go ahead without referring it to the Secretary of State who will undoubtedly 'call-in' the application for a decision by himself. Other authorities have in recent years initiated complex exercises in phased planning for particular minerals, based on the best available assessments of future demand, the estimated size of workable deposits and the optimum location of workings to supply the demand. The formulation of such special plans as that of Staffordshire for sand and gravel, or of Somerset County Council for quarrying in the Mendips, has been welcomed by leaders of opinion amongst the extractive industries.[57] However, many operators are far from satisfied with the planning policies of local authorities as a whole.[58]

In recent years, increasingly stringent conditions have been imposed on mineral operations. In the 1960s, the emphasis had been more heavily placed on the role of planning authorities (using the legislation they have at their disposal) in the *resolution* of conflicting demands on land, a reconciliation between mineral extraction and amenity interests, although this had always been accepted to some degree as an aim. Thus, when permission for mineral extraction has been granted, increasing weight has been placed on the need for the restoration of land to a stipulated standard, adequate disposal of waste materials and the minimization of disturbance to other amenities and land use functions. Conditions can be imposed which, for example, require a phased programme of extraction in order to limit the disturbance to agriculture, or a planned programme of working and restoration. An extractor can be required to restore land to a specific state, although he cannot be asked to put the land to any particular use after the mineral has been removed. Many amenity organizations are, however, dissatisfied with the present state of restoration after mineral workings, which is far from complete.[59] There is, in any case, a great backlog of unrestored land from workings which pre-date planning controls, or which received planning permission in the late 1940s and 1950s when conditions were much less stringent than they would be if imposed now. Moreover, restoration is not always practicable. To begin with, the extent to which reclamation is possible must depend on the physical nature of the area quarried. More than 30 per cent of land quarried is taken up by gravels extracted under wet working conditions, i.e. material is removed from beneath the water table. A similar amount is taken up by quarried hillsides or deep holes in the ground or a combination of both. Over 16 per cent of land is quarried in the form of shallow workings whilst the remainder takes the form of the extraction of thin seams of material from beneath a thick overburden.[60] Wet gravel pits and other excavations from beneath the water table can only be reclaimed when suitable non-toxic filling material is available at an economic cost. Apart from this, the lakes which remain can be landscaped and used for recreational purposes such as fishing, yachting and so on. Other deep holes can only be restored if enough waste materials can be obtained locally. Sometimes the problem of filling in holes can be solved at the same time as that of disposing of waste and each year well over 77 million cubic metres of refuse are got rid of by local authorities in this way.[61] The Central Electricity Generating Board also uses pulverized fuel ash for filling in worked-out quarries,[62] but the spatial distribution of disused workings does not match the distribution of suitable filling materials and the cost of long-distance transport has often proved too great. Shallow quarries and those on hillsides can be less of a problem since, where the floor is not far below that of the adjoining land, recontouring can be effective in the restoration process even without the use of filler materials. Perhaps easiest of all to restore are those excavations where only thin seams are worked beneath a thick overburden for the end result is usually only a slight lowering of the land level as is the case after most bedded ironstone or opencast coal working.

The imposition of special statutory regulations which apply specifically to ironstone and coal over and above the provisions of other planning legislation has a connection with their mode of occurrence as well as the ease with which land from which they have been extracted may be restored. In the case of both minerals, the deposits occur over very extensive areas and consequently the damage to amenity and loss of agricultural land which would result from untreated workings would be of very serious proportions. Opencast coal extraction began during the Second World War under emergency legislation and was therefore not subject to planning controls. This continued up to the passing of the Opencast Coal Act 1958, when it was made necessary for the NCB to serve notice on a planning authority of a planned new working. If the authority raised objections, the Minister had to hold a public inquiry. Under the 1962 Town and Country Planning Act, however, all planning decisions on opencast coal workings became vested in the Minister though he would consult with local authorities and all other interested parties and objections of any kind would result again in a public inquiry. Once permission is granted to proceed with working, conditions of the sort normally applied to planning permission are then imposed. If the land was formerly in agricultural use it is obligatory that it be restored in a condition fit for immediate stocking or cropping.[63] The standard of restoration achieved by the Opencast Executive is considered by many planning authorities to be of a very high order.[64] Regulations applying to the opencast winning of ironstone are different inasmuch as the Mineral Workings Act 1951 established an Ironstone Reclamation Fund to assist in financing the reclamation of land exploited by opencast methods. Under this scheme, a sum of 3·308 pence per tonne was raised for this purpose,[65] part of it a contribution from the Exchequer. One great merit of this scheme is that it has virtually eliminated the backlog of dereliction from opencast ironstone workings although the industry has a long history pre-dating planning controls. Specific statutory regulations also cover another mineral, salt, which is now mainly extracted in solution as brine. The case of brine pumping is in some ways different from the other two previously discussed, for although special provisions were made at an early date because of the catastrophic damage which could be caused through surface subsidence, little beyond compensation could (at that time) be done about it. The 1891 Brine Pumping (Compensation for Subsidence) Act provided for payments to owners of property thus damaged from the proceeds of a levy of 3 old pence per ton (1·23p per tonne) of white salt produced within the Northwich area of Cheshire.[66] The Cheshire Brine Pumping (Compensation for Subsidence) Act 1952 increased the levy to 6 old pence per ton (2·46p per tonne) and extended the area over which it operated.[67] A built-in incentive encouraged the use of controlled pumping methods which very substantially reduce the degree of subsidence caused. Subsidence can, however, also result from the winning of coal from deep-mines. These problems became the sole responsibility of the NCB under the Coal-mining (Subsidence) Act of 1957 though some provision was made from Treasury funds in the period from 1950.[68]

All these acts covering opencast coal, ironstone and salt are considered in more detail in later chapters. A similar principle underlies the first two—that land exploitation carries with it the responsibility of restoration. In a period of increasing environmental consciousness, it is now being argued that the principles embodied in the ironstone scheme should be extended to other mineral extractors. The practicability of the blanket application of such a scheme is looked at critically in Chapter 7. Demands from the Council for the Protection of Rural England and others[69] are typical of the pressures being brought to bear on decision-makers in the field of planning at local and national level. Thus more and more attention is being given to questions of amenity and indeed the Countryside Act of 1968 imposes a definite duty on such decision-makers to have regard for natural beauty and amenity in exercising their statutory functions in relation to land.[70] Certainly conservationists would accept the view that landscaping conditions associated with a planning consent often result in the ultimate restoration of the land in a satisfactory way. But since permission for mining as recommended in the Ministry's publication *Control of Mineral Working* should 'afford [not] less than fifteen years' working' and in some cases 'a working life of up to sixty years or sometimes longer',[71] it is not surprising that those concerned with the quality of the environment should feel that it is the loss of amenity during the quarrying operation that is of most significance. On these grounds they would argue that in many more cases applications to extract minerals should be refused. The contention of damage to amenity is one which the extractive industry finds difficult to refute, in spite of the fact that they are already heavily constrained by planning legislation.[72] Almost all applications for mineral workings are now opposed by amenity interests of some kind, whether local or national, and the industry is alarmed at the rate of refusal of consent by local authorities, leading to the expensive and time-consuming process of appeals to the Secretary of State and the holding of public inquiries.[73] These have proved to be both lengthy and a far from effective instrument of decision-making. Since 1968 a more elaborate and searching investigation, a Planning Inquiry Commission, has been statutorily possible, although the power to set up such a commission has not yet been used.

Mineral exploitation and amenity conservation

The shortcomings in practice of the present system of mineral extraction decision-making is well illustrated by the case of the potash workings in Yorkshire. The clash of opposing forces in this case was made the fiercer because the area it was proposed to work was mainly in the North York Moors National Park and this raised issues concerning the whole ethos of the designation of such parks which enjoy no special protection under the 1949 Act setting them up.

These soluble potash deposits were accidentally discovered in 1939 when a subsidiary of British Petroleum, the D'arcy Exploration Company, was boring for oil. Although some preliminary investigation of the deposits was subsequently undertaken in the post-war years by ICI and Fisons,[74] these first proved unsatisfactory in that there were geological difficulties attached to the extraction of the chemical. But later ICI resumed investigations in the Staithes area and found workable deposits[75] at about 1220 metres and calculated that the field had a productive potential of 0·86 to 1·27 million tonnes a year.[76] Meantime RTZ and the Armour Chemical Company had also made what seemed to be promising discoveries, the former at Hawkser near Robin Hood's Bay and the latter just inland from Whitby.[77] All these investigations were carried out on the assumption that if home production did begin for the very first time, there would be a balance of payments saving on imports from Canada of £14 million, a figure based on a productive capacity of one million tonnes a year,[78] and that the European market could be successfully tapped by bulk carriers working out of nearby Teesside. Indeed, it was suggested that since Canadian supplies come from Saskatchewan, English producers could compete on the eastern seaboard of North America.[79] Thus in 1968 at the time of their proving investigations, ICI, through their subsidiary set up for this purpose, Cleveland Potash, were forecasting profits of £7 million a year if the mine went ahead, with development costs being met to the extent of 45 per cent by the Government, because of their location within a Development Area. Under the circumstances it was not surprising that planning permission was sought for the construction of a twin shaft mine and a refining plant on a 81 hectare site at Boulby near Staithes,[80] but perhaps even less surprising that the matter at once became a contentious one which led the Minister of Housing and Local Government to set up a public inquiry which began in August 1968. F. H. B. W. Layfield, QC for the mining company, said however that the inquiry was unique in having such a massive volume of support and such an insignificant volume of objections.[81] Certainly on the grounds of the money and employment they thought it would bring to the area, a number of local authorities as well as the Teesside Industrial Development Board favoured the application.[82] Furthermore even the National Parks Commission admitted that the site had been chosen in order to minimize the effect on the surrounding countryside. However, they did ask that, if the scheme went ahead, careful attention be given to the effects on the coastal environment by the planned scheme of offshore waste disposal; to landscaping of the area well beyond the 81 hectare site; and to further investigations into the possibility of solution mining so that the material could be piped away and processed outside the Park.[83] In the event, the Minister found in favour of the mine in November 1968, and apart from insisting on the restoration of the site when mining ended, imposed seven major conditions to reduce its harmful effects on the environment from gases, the discharge of liquid effluent into the sea, noise and the visual impact of the plant on the scenery. In this last respect the company were in 1970 said to be spending £100 000 on landscaping the minehead complex so that it blended with its background and nestled behind man-made hills and trees. Indeed, a company spokesman said 'we are behaving very carefully. There are pheasant in the woods and trout in the streams and there will continue to be. The only effect from waste material would be that the sea one mile off Whitby would be a little more salty.'[84]

All this was reassuring to the newly formed Countryside Commission (which had replaced that for the National Parks) though they expressed regret that the application by Cleveland Potash had not been the occasion for a more comprehensive and far-reaching inquiry into the implications of potash extraction in the Park area. Their regrets and fears were justified in their eyes for shortly afterwards, RTZ and the Armour Company, now operating respectively as Yorkshire Potash Limited and Whitby Potash Limited, put in applications to mine in those areas where they had been prospecting. Yorkshire Potash submitted their application at the end of 1968 and in February 1969 Whitby Potash applied to extract the mineral by solution from 486 hectares with a 34 hectare processing plant at Broomfield Farm, Whitby,[85] where they would refine about 406 000 tonnes a year.[86] The Whitby Company's scheme involved land almost entirely within the National Park except for the processing area. Two mines were proposed with nine separate sites to cover a hundred hectares or so, each site being a 0·8 hectare square fenced field, with a 7·6 metre pump house. A 30·5 metre rig would move between the twenty-eight well heads, each of which would be plugged and restored after eight years. The overall application was for fifty years. The refinery would have structures 24 to 40 metres high with a 79·3 metre chimney for waste gases which would easily be seen within the Park. Rail transport would be used to carry away the potash and the 510 000 or so tonnes a year of waste material to Whitby Harbour for dumping at sea. The Yorkshire Potash scheme covered 6075 hectares plus another 36·5 hectares at Hawkser Bottom for refining, etc.; there was also to be mining over 21 000 hectares offshore. The operational zone would only be a 400 metres inland from the coastal section of the Cleveland Way long-distance footpath. Structures 46 metres high would be required with 132 kW pylons and a new access road. Rail transport would carry away refined potash with waste discharged at sea by pipeline over the cliffs.[87]

This time, intrusion into the National Park would be very great and both the Countryside Commission and the county council united in opposing the two applications. In fact the Countryside Commission succinctly summarized their position when they wrote in advance of any inquiry to the Minister for Housing and Local Government:

The Commission wish to express to the Minister their great concern at these major industrial proposals to win and work minerals on a very large scale in the National Park which are wholly inconsistent with and alien to the purposes for which the National Park was established. The Commission doubt that landscaping and other ameliorative measures will prevent irreparable damage to the amenity and natural beauty of the Park. They strongly support the case put by the North Riding County Council in their letter of 12 February 1969, for the need to establish a general policy in relation to the further potash mining proposals in the area. It is the considered view of the Commission that mining on the scale envisaged in the National Park raises major questions of planning and economic policy involving technical and other considerations of an unfamiliar character. These questions are of national rather than regional importance. They cannot be satisfactorily investigated and resolved except by means of a planning inquiry commission.[88]

These counsels did not prevail and the two planning applications were the subject of two separate inquiries on the reports of which the Minister decided to act in May 1970. His decision can best be seen in the light of political expediency for with the prospect of the Boulby construction about to employ a 1000 men with a forecast of 500 permanent jobs remaining at that mine alone, he said that the other two projects should go forward. Fred Lee as Minister with Special Responsibility for the North had already just said of the potash schemes that jobs must come before scenery,[89] whilst Peter Shore, Secretary of State for Economic Affairs, had emphasized the possibility of saving £40 million a year in terms of balance of payments by the mid-1970s and of Britain being a net exporter with three mines in operation.[90] Both these points were made by the Minister in support of his own case to which he added comment on the uniqueness of this potash deposit as far as Britain is concerned.[91] However, it was interesting to note that immediately after these findings the two companies concerned announced that they would be delaying any further action on their sites in view of adverse conditions in the world potash market. This was not as surprising as it may seem for *Industrial Minerals* had already commented in the autumn of 1969 that

26

while a single [potash] mine and refinery stands a good chance of disposing of its exportable surplus at reasonable prices, it poses insurmountable problems for three and the real issue is whether three separate mines in Yorkshire within close proximity of one another are justified at all. If over the lives of the mines, which might be fifty years, producers have to dump 50 per cent of their production overseas, a wasting asset will truly have been wasted. No doubt some export revenue, however hard won, is better than none, but it would seem sensible to exercise some form of control over the UK potash industry's development even if it means government intervention.[92]

In their pursuit of a balanced and more rational approach to decision-making in conflict situations such as this, the Countryside Commission had sponsored an independent evaluation of the economic aspects and implications of the proposed mining projects from the Economist Intelligence Unit.[93] This had been presented at the Whitby Potash inquiry[94] and had made much the same point as *Industrial Minerals*. Given, then, that the Minister had this information available to him as part of the expert evidence provided at one of the inquiries and that he himself recognized that the proposed development must inevitably result in some damage to amenity upon which it is difficult if not impossible to set a value,[95] the essentially political nature of his final decision can only again be underlined. As the Countryside Commission had done at the Cleveland Potash inquiry, the Economic Intelligence Unit report drew attention to the important and difficult questions of social and economic planning, both regional and national, which ought to be explored in public before far-reaching decisions are taken. It seems that when a planning decision which concerns land use conflicts between amenity and mineral extraction has to be made, such criteria have yet to be employed. Indeed, whilst admitting the great complexity of making planning decisions, there seems little point in ignoring the important criterion of the short- and long-term situation with regard to world supply and demand for potash. This would equally apply to any other mineral in which international trade occurs and should be a factor which is carefully weighed by decision-makers. Certainly from the evidence of the potash case, it is clear that companies submitting planning applications are themselves not always the best judges of trade conditions, an argument supported in Chapter 5 which deals with a similar situation concerning the working of ironstone in Oxfordshire. The controversy aroused by the Yorkshire potash workings contains many of the main elements in the discussion aroused by proposals to work, either for the first time or by new methods, high value minerals in areas of high scenic quality in Britain.

27

One should not assume that the well-publicized problems caused by proposals to work minerals such as potash or high value non-ferrous metals in National Parks constitute the most severe planning problems amongst extractive industries. It could well be argued that the problems caused by the working of sand and gravel, a mineral with a high annual output and a very heavy annual land take—much higher than that of any other mineral—are much more serious. Well over half the planning appeals held in the decade 1960–70 related to sand and gravel.[96] However, the controversy surrounding the working of minerals such as potash or the more costly non-ferrous metals has attracted particular attention precisely because more choice is felt to exist about their working in Britain, because they are new enterprises, and because their extraction is particularly likely to occur in the mineralized zones of Highland Britain, in areas which are also exceptionally valued for their landscape quality. The discovery of copper deposits in the Coed-y-Brenin area of North Wales, within the Snowdonia National Park, is, for instance, not an unfortunate coincidence, but an example of a highly typical combination of circumstances arising inexorably from the nature of British geology. Their coincidence does, in the light of the already mentioned boom in exploration for such minerals in Britain, involve some discussion of the status of National Parks in Britain, and of other areas designated as being of particular amenity value.

The ten National Parks in England and Wales, averaging more than 1290 square kilometres each,[97] were set up under the 1949 National Parks and Access to the Countryside Act 'for the preservation and enhancement of natural beauty in England and Wales' and 'for encouraging the provision or improvement . . . of facilities for the enjoyment thereof and for the enjoyment of the opportunities for open air recreation and the study of nature afforded thereby'.[98] The National Parks include a high proportion of open, mountainous country and occur predominantly in Highland areas. Elsewhere in England and Wales areas of highly valued landscape are more likely to be designated as Areas of Outstanding Natural Beauty, which are mostly smaller than National Parks and include a higher proportion of improved farmland.[99] The National Parks were not set up, as were those in most other countries, as areas where economic development and human settlement were specifically excluded; indeed, such areas would not be conceivable in a densely populated country like Britain where large tracts of wild, empty country do not exist. Designation as a National Park had no direct effect on land ownership, which remained largely in private hands. But while existing land uses and certain new economic developments were envisaged within the National Parks, these were intended to be subject to more stringent control than economic developments elsewhere. Decisions on planning matters were to be taken initially at local level, in most cases by the relevant local planning authority but in two cases, that of the Peak and Lake District National Parks, by special National Park plannings boards, and ultimately by the Ministers, acting with the advice of the National Parks Commission (now the Countryside Commission). Ministerial decisions may go, and indeed have gone against the advice of both the local planning authority and the Countryside Commission, as is clear from the cases of Yorkshire Potash Ltd. and Whitby Potash Ltd. The possibility of new mineral extractive operations within National Parks was specifically envisaged by the sponsors of the National Parks Bill. The Minister stated during the second reading that

It may be necessary to utilize the mineral wealth which lies in those areas for the purpose of ensuring the economic life of our people. I do not think anybody would seriously suggest that we should ignore the existence of this mineral wealth and fail to utilize it, subject to a number of conditions. The first condition is that it must be demonstrated quite clearly that the exploitation of those minerals is absolutely necessary in the public interest. It must be clear beyond all doubt that there is no possible alternative source of supply and if those two conditions are satisfied then the permission must be subject to the condition that restoration takes place at the earliest opportunity.[100]

Whilst the National Parks themselves do not enjoy any specific immunity from mineral development, they do contain a very wide variety of land endowed with different kinds of special status. Certain categories of land in fact enjoy a degree of protection not given to National Parks as a whole: national nature reserves were accorded Crown Land Status under the 1949 Act, while land held inalienably by the National Trust enjoys immunity from compulsory purchase orders and the character of the scenery there is probably more effectively protected than any other.[101] There are, in addition, certain areas, such as those owned by archaeological trusts, which have no legal protection but whose preservation, one may assume, would be particularly zealously guarded. The very wide variety of different types of land designation within the National Parks may be illustrated in the case of Snowdonia, which contains National Trust land (inalienable), National Trust land (covenanted), national nature reserves, areas of special scientific interest and forest parks with restricted access,[102] some of them overlapping.

In addition to the National Parks of England and Wales, whose legal status has been outlined above, there are five areas of Scotland, known as National Park Direction Areas, which were recommended in 1947 as being suitable for National Parks. In general much less of Scotland, where the pressures of recreational use are less severe than elsewhere in Britain, is subject to special safeguards. However, planning in the National Park Direction Areas is more strictly controlled than elsewhere in Scotland, and all applications are called in for decisions at ministerial level.

As measured in even such crude terms as number of visitors, the National Parks are now more highly valued than when they were established in 1949. A rising overall standard of living has created both a more leisured and a more mobile society. This same factor of a rising overall standard of living has, however, also created a rapidly escalating demand for minerals, some types of which are, as we have seen, disproportionately likely to be located in high amenity areas. Furthermore, the methods of mineral extraction which can now be envisaged in such areas are very different from what was, one may confidently assume, envisaged in 1949. The extraction of low grade, disseminated ores, such as those of copper at Coed-y-Brenin, made possible by the rapid developments in modern opencast equipment and made economic by the rising world demand for minerals, is quite unlike the underground working of a rich mineral vein a metre or so wide, which is more like the hitherto familiar type of non-ferrous metal extraction in Britain. Large strip mines have not yet been operated in Britain and are at present overwhelmingly located in remote and underpopulated parts of the world. A low grade disseminated deposit of a size which might be found and worked in Britain, with a total ore reserve of 61 million tonnes, could require between 600 and 1200 hectares of land, depending on the topography of the site.[103] This is a hypothetical case, and smaller opencast workings or underground mines can be envisaged which would each have a much smaller surface impact.

The changed circumstances relating to the actual and potential usage of National Parks since 1949 have inevitably brought with them changed attitudes. There are those who now feel that the provisions made in the 1949 Act for certain stringently controlled types of new development were regrettable (there are also those who would have it believed that the protection for National Parks is in fact greater than the 1949 Act provides). C. J. Tuck, chief planning officer of Merioneth, has suggested that acceptance of RTZ's application to drill for copper in the Snowdonia National Park (see Fig. 1.2) could 'establish that the National Parks and the protection supposedly afforded to them by the National Parks Act has no real significance in the mind of the Secretary

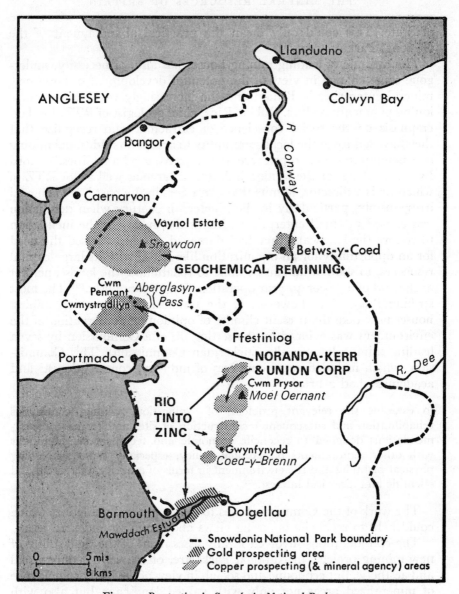

Fig. 1.2 *Prospecting in Snowdonia National Park, 1971*

of State. This could only mean the practical abandonment of the National Park concept.'[104]

The attitude of leading mining houses has also, of necessity, undergone some change in view of the potential development of large new mineral enterprises in Britain and the increasingly vociferous championing of amenity values. Robert Rice, chief geologist of RTZ, has laid emphasis on the social conscience of extractors who recognize that they have a duty to the local community to accept an additional mining cost penalty in order to preserve and improve local amenities.[105] Lord Byers, speaking for the mining industry at large as well as for RTZ of which he is a director, admits that extractors in the past have behaved irresponsibly, particularly in the nineteenth century when dereliction was caused by small enterprises without the money or the inclination to restore the landscape they had damaged. He has stressed the need for an opportunity for an organization like RTZ, with its large capital resources, to show what can be done to rehabilitate the landscape, not at the end of a 30- or 40-year operation, but continuously.[106] The most striking illustration, however, of the seriousness with which mining houses now take the present climate of opinion on conservation of the environment was evinced by the setting up of a Commission by seven leading mining houses (the Zuckerman Commission). This Commission, which included representatives of industry, conservationists and academics, had a brief

to examine the relevant problems of exploration, mining, continuous rehabilitation and subsequent reconstruction of sites and to make recommendations designed to reconcile economic and technical considerations with other requirements of national policy, especially those concerning physical planning and the environment in terms of amenity, recreation and scientific and historical interest.[107]

The work of the Commission was to define general guidelines which could help to reconcile opposing views about mining and land use.

The considerations involved in any assessment of the desirability of new mining projects in National Parks are, of course, not only visual and aesthetic, but economic and social, in view of the likely coincidence of mineralized areas not only with valued landscape but also with areas of exceptionally high unemployment. The questions to be resolved in this connection are complex. The actual amount of employment to be generated by any given mining project is exceedingly difficult to predict before the preparation of a detailed feasibility study for each particular instance. Whilst one may point to the general rapidly diminishing number of wage-earners employed in mining and quarrying (see Table 7.3, p. 440) and the tendency of predictions of employment at new projects to be overestimates,[108] it must be recognized that the amount of indirect employment generated by such projects, through stimulus of the local economy, is likely to be an important factor. In this connection, the instance of English China Clay's operations at Lee Moor in Devon has been cited: although in 1971 only 950 people were directly employed at the working, it has been estimated that half as many jobs again were created in the Plymouth area as a result of the operation.[109] Whilst there clearly cannot be any studies of the employment created by a large opencast non-ferrous operation in Britain, a theoretical study has been carried out by the Department of Economics at the University College of North Wales, Bangor, based on their model of the economy of Anglesey. This is in effect a working model of a representative rural economy, which would predict the net effect, in both incomes and total output, of each activity consequent upon a change in any other activity.[110] A hypothetical working with an annual output of about 25 000 tonnes of copper per year and an operating life of 15–20 years was postulated. This was calculated to occupy 162 hectares with 324 hectares waste and tailings area, 81 hectares for a clear-water dam and 41 hectares of buildings. The labourforce during the construction phase for such a working was estimated to be 840 during the construction phase (60 from outside the area) and 375 during the stage of full production (90 from outside the area). During the construction phase it was shown that £6 000 000 of development of the type envisaged would raise the total output of the regional economy by £8 007 000 approximately, i.e. £2 007 000 of production had been called forth by the £6 000 000, when all the interacting increases had worked their way through the local economy. Total increase in incomes was £1 483 000. At the operating stage, the addition of output of £5 000 000 from the mine raised the total output of the island's economy by £6 016 244, i.e. approximately £1 016 244 of further production was created. The total increase in incomes at this stage was £452 173.[111] The largest percentage increases in output by sector at the construction stage were timber, quarrying and postal and telecommunications, and at the operating stage, road transport, water and electricity. This study unfortunately offers little guidance on the crucial question of the impact of a large new mining development on tourism, which is not in any case a major industry in Anglesey.

Although no comparable study has been done on the economic effects of an increase in tourism, opponents of mining development in areas of high landscape quality have tended to stress the superior economic effects of this industry. It has been argued that money from tourism tends to remain in the local community and quickly be distributed to the advantage of hoteliers, guest house proprietors and numerous other service and retail outlets, while the profits from mining development, for instance by North American companies, would not all remain in either the local community or necessarily even in the country.[112] Furthermore, it has been argued that tourism gives rise to particularly labour-intensive forms of secondary employment, such as the making of woollen goods or pottery. It is suggested that the economic value of land left in its wild state is infinitely greater than that under mineral exploitation, particularly in a country where the number of such places is very limited. Whilst these points merit very serious consideration, one cannot necessarily assume that tourism and large-scale mining developments are mutually exclusive. While certain types of mineral extraction and associated plant and traffic generation are likely to deter tourists from their locality, other types are proving to be of undoubted interest to visitors. Not only has an upsurge of interest in industrial archaeology led to the profitable re-opening of a slate mine for visitors, but current operations such as tin mining in Cornwall or china clay extraction there and in Devon are attracting a large number of sightseers. It is difficult to be precise about what specifically attracts visitors to, or deters them from, tourist areas, and what statistics are available with a bearing on this are out of date.[113]

The authors of the Bangor study considered that, apart from the economic benefits to the local community from a mining project, there would be important social benefits; they assert that 'even if in the short-run skills have to be imported into a region, the future opportunities for local youth are still widened, as vacancies occur due to staff turnover. The effect of this is to maintain a greater level of social cohesion.'[114] The Zuckerman Commission postulated that such projects might help to stimulate social diversity by attracting more professional practition-ers to the area.[115] It is, furthermore, argued that the employment offered by opencast mining is nothing like as seasonal as that afforded by the tourist industry. One has, however, to bear in mind the more limited duration of such developments, unless some later adaptation is made to replace the working, which could well do little to improve the long-term employment prospects for such areas. Nevertheless, there are those who appear to feel that mining or quarrying development is less intrinsically damaging to the character and social structure of remote areas than is a large influx of tourists, who may also make very heavy demands in environmental terms.

The economic benefits to the national as opposed to the local community are generally considered in terms primarily of the balance of payments. It has been argued that the metals which would appear to offer prospects of the largest potential import savings are copper and nickel. At 1972 price levels, 50 000 tonnes of refined copper produced from UK sources would reduce the country's import bill by £25 million per year, and 10 000 tonnes of refined nickel by £12 million.[116] (Against this would have to be set any possible losses to the balance of payments from a reduction in the inflow of foreign tourists, or an increase in British holidays taken abroad.) However, bearing in mind the extremely volatile nature of the world's non-ferrous metal markets, and the high element of risk attached to any new development for extraction of such metals in Britain, predictions of this kind have to be treated with great caution. Indeed, the bankruptcy of the recently established Pendarves tin mine in Cornwall is a reminder that the economic benefits, both to local and national communities, of new non-ferrous operations can never be guaranteed for the period specified.

In the last analysis it comes down to the value that should be put on the extraction of a wide range of minerals, some of which must be extracted in Britain because of their low unit or rarity value, and others for which a case can be made out in terms of balance of payments, employment, etc., and the value that should be put on scarce resources of outstandingly attractive tracts of countryside, in some instances with the status of National Parks, which in themselves have economic importance as recreation and tourist areas. It is easy to state the equation in these terms—its resolution is much more difficult, though it is hoped that the discussion of individual minerals and the problems they present in land use terms which now follows is a contribution to this end. In conclusion, Chapter 7 examines the more striking recent trends in mineral extraction and suggests some options which are now open for national decision.

UBIQUITOUS NON-METALLIFEROUS MINERALS (1): THE AGGREGATES MARKET

An aggregate is a high volume granular material used loose or bound to provide bulk, strength or protection.[1] It forms the basis of concrete and the main materials used for road construction and railway ballast. Aggregates can be made up of any hard material, natural or artificial, which is tough (i.e. able to withstand shock or continuous pressure), resistant to weathering and physically and chemically inert. By far the largest proportion of aggregates used in Britain are heavy duty aggregates derived from the minerals sand and gravel, limestone, igneous and metamorphic rocks and sandstone. All of these minerals are used, to varying extents, for other purposes as well. However, light-weight aggregates (i.e. those with a low density used in structural design and some kinds of insulating concrete) can be obtained from clay, shales and slate; small quantities of vermiculite and diatomite are also used for this purpose. Artificial aggregates, like lightweight aggregates, supply only a minor part of the total aggregates market in Britain, and consist for the most part of what may be termed 'waste materials', notably blast furnace slag, pulverized fuel ash, boiler-house clinker, crushed brick and colliery slag.

The main types of natural, heavy duty aggregate are to a large extent interchangeable and a complex of factors will determine which type is used in any given market. For most of the bulk aggregate market, where special factors of quality are not involved, price may be considered the major determinant in the selection of materials. Price reflects the three main elements of costs of extraction, costs of processing and costs of transport. The cheapest aggregate to extract is sand and gravel (essentially the same mineral differentiated only by size), the only natural aggregate which occurs ready granulated. The hard rock aggregates, which require crushing to resemble the natural granular form of sand and gravel, each involve heavier costs both of extraction and of processing (including usually blasting and primary and secondary crushing) than does sand and gravel. There are, however, substantial differentials in extractive and processing costs between the hard rock aggregates: limestone is a comparatively non-abrasive material which rarely needs more than two stages of crushing and can, when required, be particularly easily coated with tar and bitumen for the production of coated macadam. Igneous and metamorphic rocks, by contrast, involve much more wear and tear on extractive and processing machinery, and usually require three to five stages of crushing. The term 'sandstone', as used by the Ministry for official output figures, includes a wide range of minerals varying from those which crumble readily to quartzite, one of the hardest minerals known; consequently, the extractive and processing costs of sandstone also vary very widely. Apart from these considerations, a further factor affecting extractive and processing costs is the size of unit concerned: amongst the many factors affecting average sizes of operating unit, one may be singled out for mention at this stage. The higher average size of limestone compared with igneous rock or sandstone quarries in Britain is related to the essential role played by this mineral in other non-aggregate markets. (Although limestone has a lower overall percentage of non-aggregate usage than sandstone, the tonnages involved are substantially larger.)[2] The much higher average size of limestone than of igneous rock or sandstone quarries (an estimated annual output of 154 854 tonnes for limestone quarries, 77 519 tonnes for igneous rock quarries and 61 839 tonnes for sandstone quarries in 1969)[3] means that ex-pit prices for limestone more closely resemble those of sand and gravel than those of the costlier igneous rocks and sandstone.[4]

The differentials in the processing and extractive costs of the minerals concerned are clearly one important factor in accounting for the differences in output levels as indicated in Table 2.1. Differences in transport costs from pit to market are also a vitally important factor: since aggregates are low value minerals, with ex-pit prices for the most part falling below £1 per tonne at 1968 levels, transport costs are liable to make up a high percentage of delivered costs, and hence differentials in transport costs can readily cancel out differentials in extractive and processing costs. As a broad generalization, most aggregate materials (uncoated) double in price at about 48 kilometres from the pit. Consequently, the two factors of proximity to market and type of transport available will be significant elements in determining both the choice of aggregate for any given market, and the total output levels of the various aggregate minerals. Neither of these two factors are in fact static. The aggregate demand of any given region of Britain is determined primarily by size of population and will change as population balance changes. Such alterations are of course only of significance over the long term: the South-East constitutes the largest single market for aggregates for construction and roadworks and its dominant position is clearly unlikely to alter in the foreseeable future. The levels of aggregate demand in particular areas may however be heavily affected for specific periods of time by such special circumstances

Table 2.1. UK production (in thousand tonnes) of the principal aggregate minerals, 1960–70

	Sand and gravel	Limestone	Sandstone	Igneous and metamorphic rocks
1960	71 502	40 720	5 038	16 525
1961	83 015	42 584	4 981	17 672
1962	83 175	44 758	5 322	18 574
1963	86 937	47 876	5 395	19 266
1964	103 675	57 991	6 502	23 315
1965	102 160	60 545	6 925	25 213
1966	104 230	67 846	7 668	28 710
1967	109 547	77 403	9 614	34 220
1968	109 369	81 185	13 464	34 073
1969	105 951	83 931	16 635	35 804
1970	105 168	87 822	16 648	36 684

as the building of a motorway, or the realization of a large-scale project such as the Channel tunnel, as well as by local oscillations in the building industry. Even where the relative position of a given market remains static, however, changes in transport technology may alter sharply the competitive position of various suppliers to that market, and the level of demand from the various supply areas. During the 1960s, for instance, reduced unit costs made possible by innovations in rail transport (bulk haulage and merry-go-rounds) and by road (increased lorry size and motorways) could not be matched by sea transport in those cases where the ports concerned were unable to accommodate large coasters. Consequently, the competitive position, for example, of igneous rock from the port of Newlyn in Cornwall to the London/South-Eastern market deteriorated vis-à-vis that of land hauled igneous rock from Leicestershire or land hauled limestone from the Mendips.[5]

Although market size and the cost of transport to market are in a dynamic state, certain broad generalizations may be made about the relationship between proximity to market and overall output levels of the various aggregate minerals. Sand and gravel's predominant position amongst British aggregate minerals (in terms of output) is intimately connected with the proximity of the greatest concentration of available resources to the greatest single market, the Greater London area. There are no large deposits of the hard rock aggregates within the South-East. Of these hard rocks, igneous rock is particularly heavily concentrated in remote and inaccessible parts of north and west Britain, and this is one factor (amongst several of at least equal importance) in its low overall output total relative to limestone.

The third major factor affecting overall output levels of the various types of natural aggregate, and the choice of a particular aggregate for a given market, involves the variations in quality and properties of these minerals. Not only do the properties of the different types of aggregate differ, but there are very wide variations of property within each type. Sand and gravel, which originated in the disintegrating action of weathering on a wide variety of different parent rocks, has no standard chemical properties. Limestone has varying chemical and physical properties, only partially accounted for by geological age and method of formation.

Igneous rocks may be differentiated according to chemical composition, mineral composition, texture, structure, mode of occurrence and age. The term 'sandstone' as used in the official statistics covers a wide variety of rocks which differ in chemical composition, particle size and shape, degree of compaction and the related question of period of formation. The category of sandstone as used here may include wider variations in properties than any other of the major types of aggregate minerals. Certain broad generalizations about the suitability of particular minerals for particular commercial purposes can again be made. Sand and gravel and limestone are the aggregate minerals preferred for use in the concrete market. This is a factor of some significance since concrete constitutes the largest single part of the aggregates market; in 1970 it was estimated to have consumed about 55 per cent of the total aggregates produced.[6] Igneous rocks may be preferred for high stress concrete, or that subjected to an exceptional degree of exposure and weathering, but such concretes make up only a small percentage of the whole. Certain igneous rocks (of the medium and fine grained variety) are also used in a comparatively specialized field, that of road surfacing, especially of major roads, since their durability is specially suited to providing wearing courses able to withstand modern traffic densities. The gritstones (a category of sandstone) provide the highest number of known sources of skid-resistant aggregate[7] required for surfacing specially vulnerable sites such as roundabouts, but many varieties which have good skid-resistant properties are not sufficiently resistant to abrasion. The section of the roadstone market where aggregate of this quality is required is, however, only a small percentage of the total roadstone market.[8] In general, properties commonly attributable to aggregates are required—e.g. capacity to bear the load above, frost resistance and ability to act as a drainage layer—and factors of cost are consequently more important than those of quality. However, the exceptionally wide variations in the properties of sandstone, and hence its comparative unpredictability for commercial usage, is one factor in its lower rate of extraction than any other aggregate mineral.

The distinctions between the properties of different types of aggregate minerals, and between different deposits, are becoming of more significance as research into the effect of these variations on performance progresses and as the specifications of consumers tighten. The progress of such research in the 1960s is likely to have been one factor, amongst several, in the faster growth rate of sandstone, hitherto the most unpredictable of the aggregate minerals, than of the others. Substantially more work is required to define the characteristics required of sandstone for particular uses and the effect of such work could be to increase further the disproportionately high growth rate of this mineral.

The factors affecting the usage of artificial aggregates, as by-products for the most part of other processes, are necessarily different from those outlined above. Artificial aggregates, which are not extracted in that form, are not considered in detail in the following sections. Certain points may however be noted, since the usage of these materials affects the level of demand for the naturally occurring aggregates. The supply of the artificial aggregates is affected by the processes of which these are a by-product, and for reasons of this kind, two types are diminishing, notably blast furnace slag and boilerhouse clinker. Blast furnace slag is the more important of the two: this is believed to be the major artificial aggregate in current use in Britain, where about 10 million tonnes of the total of 12 million tonnes produced in 1970 is used for this purpose, mainly for roadstone,[9] and smaller amounts for Portland blast furnace cement and lightweight concrete. The amount of blast furnace slag being produced is decreasing slowly as the iron and steel industry makes use of higher grade ores. By contrast, increasing quantities of pulverized fuel ash (from coal fired power stations) and colliery shale are being put to aggregates use. Increasing usage of these materials relates primarily not to increasing supply but to questions of marketing and research into their commercial properties. The Central Electricity Generating Board, which is prohibited by statute from surface dumping of pulverized fuel ash, has every incentive to maximize sales for aggregate purposes (which in 1969 amounted to about 40 per cent of the total) in preference to waste disposal schemes which can be very costly.[10] The NCB, although not prohibited by statute from dumping, adopted a substantially keener marketing policy for colliery shale in the late 1960s, when a special division was set up for this purpose. One of the major determinants of this new policy is likely to have been increasing hostility to surface dumping, as exemplified by the increasing difficulty the NCB have had in obtaining planning consent for waste tips.[11] However, the progress of research into the use of colliery shale for specific aggregate purposes was also a contributory factor: such material could not, for instance, be used for bulk fill for the construction of the M1 but has subsequently been passed as acceptable for this purpose in motorway building.

Research is also in hand to widen the range of artificial aggregates with high resistance to polishing and abrasion, and hence suitable for surfacing particularly difficult road sites. The most satisfactory aggregate in this respect is calcined bauxite, which in 1970 was sold at about £40 per tonne, excluding delivery charges.[12] The Transport and Road Research Laboratory is investigating the possibility of producing comparable material at considerably lower cost, e.g. a calcined bauxite/slag mixture which might be produced at about £5 per tonne ex-works.[13] The NCB have also obtained promising results in the production of an artificial aggregate with high resistance to polishing based on colliery shale. Research of this type could affect the overall levels of particular artificial aggregate consumption, although the market concerned is a specialized one.

The overall level of artificial aggregate usage is primarily limited by questions of cost. Although the artificial aggregates, as waste products, are of very low cost ex-works, their final price is likely to be more expensive than that of natural aggregates as a result of the processing which may be required; e.g. pulverized fuel ash has to be pelletized and sintered, blast furnace slag to be cooled and crushed. The amount of artificial aggregates used in Britain for aggregate purposes is substantially lower than that of Japan, the United States, France or Germany, and the chief factor at work here appears to be the cheapness and availability of the natural aggregates in Britain. The level of usage of artificial aggregates is, however, highly susceptible to changes in official policies, in such matters as planning constraints on waste tipping, preferences for such materials built into motorway contracts, or fiscal changes (e.g. removing the rates payable on sales of colliery shale). Changes in any of these policies could increase the percentage of the aggregate market made up by artificial materials and hence affect the level of demand for the natural materials.

Thus a prediction of the overall level of aggregate demand in Britain is a highly complex operation. The overall demand depends on the level of activity in the construction industries, which is in turn heavily affected by the growth rate in the economy. The construction industries react very quickly to expansion or contraction in the economy. In times of recession, both buildings and roads (new and repairs) tend to be early targets for economy, while the need to make good the backlog causes a rapid resurgence of construction activity when the recession passes. Accordingly, both the level of activity in the construction industries and the associated level of demand for aggregates fluctuates more widely than the general movements in the economy.[14] (For example, the years 1958–69 were in general a period of economic expansion, until the small recession of 1969, and the growth rate for the construction industries was almost double that of the Gross National Product.[15] The impact of this expansion on concrete, in particular, was striking: the UK output of ready mixed concrete more than trebled between 1961 and 1970[16] although this reflected increasing diversity of use as well as expansion in the construction industries.) However, if the time factor is extended to cover a longer period, when such fluctuations cancel each other out, it can be seen that the growth in the Gross National Product is practically the same as the growth in output of the construction industries, and hence of the aggregate industries.[17] Other factors which need to be included in any estimate of a future overall demand for aggregate materials include those of population growth, aggregate consumption per head and number of vehicles per head. While short-term predictions of demand (both overall and for particular minerals) by the industry and others have been comparatively successful, longer term assessments of demand for particular aggregate minerals (notably by the former Ministry of Housing and Local Government) have invariably been underestimates.

Amongst the most detailed published estimates of long-term aggregate demand is that of Somerset County Council (apropos of quarrying in the Mendips). By using population projections, relating future demand to past trends, an estimated demand of 762 million tonnes by the year 2010 was obtained. This compares with a total aggregate output of 237 million tonnes in 1969. Estimates of demand based on various possible growth in the Gross Domestic Product produced assessments ranging from 813 million tonnes to well over three times that figure. 'Straight line' projections based on past five-yearly growth rates gave estimates varying from 335 million to 813 million tonnes; by accepting a 'mean' and allowing for population growth, a figure of 843 million tonnes was arrived at. If a growth in the number of road vehicles was allowed for, an estimate of more than 710 million tonnes was reached. The most likely figure adopted was 762 million tonnes.[18] This may be compared with the estimate of G. J. Mortimer, chairman of Amey Roadstone Corporation Ltd.; working on the basis of a population of 75–80 millions by the end of the century and a continuation of the current upward consumption per head, he calculated a total annual demand for aggregates of 2032 million tonnes by the year 2000.[19]

The increasing demand for extraction of aggregate minerals involved in the concept of a trebling or quadrupling of aggregate demand in 30 to 40 years must be seen against a background of other mounting demands on the land, for housing development, for recreation, for water catchment, etc., and seen in terms of processing and transport as well as extraction. A consideration of the likely scale of aggregate demand and of the likely distribution of demand amongst the various aggregate minerals is of immediate relevance. First, quarry size is increasing and hence length of planning permission being sought is increasing, and consequently planning permissions being considered now may well be concerned with the level of demand for the products of a given deposit at the end of the century. Second, a considerable degree of choice could in fact be exercised to determine the relative expansion of the component parts of the aggregates industry, in view of the very large scale of the resources, the partly overlapping markets, and the possible use of artificial materials for some purposes. An overall strategy designed to implement such choice, based on all the economic and social and environmental considerations involved, would be a complex undertaking. It was clear in the early 1970s that there was no single collecting agency at Ministry level for all the relevant information[20] and the Standing Conference on London and South-East Regional Planning was one of the organizations urging the need for action at national level. The particularly complex planning and environmental difficulties posed by the extraction of aggregate minerals was recognized at national level in 1972, when the Department of the Environment announced the formulation of an Advisory Committee on Aggregates to estimate demand and appraise sources of supply and environmental problems, and a research project at the Royal School of Mines to look into the environmental implications of large-scale stone quarrying.

SAND AND GRAVEL

The output of sand and gravel, the major source of aggregates, has increased spectacularly in the course of the present century. Before

1919, the material was used mainly for road metal, mortar, brickwork, masonry and plastering and the recorded annual output for Great Britain was less than 1·5 million cubic metres.[21] The growth of concrete as the raw material of the construction industry has been the major factor in the rise of British sand and gravel production to a total of 71 241 000 cubic metres or 109 000 000 tonnes in 1969.[22] In 1970 sand and gravel output was officially predicted to show an annual increase of between 4 and 5 per cent, which means that during the late 1970s or early 1980s it will overtake coal, with an expected stable output of some 152 400 000 tonnes, as the largest British extractive industry. This development would follow the pattern of the United States, where sand and gravel became the largest extractive industry by volume in 1954.[23]

Since the end of the Second World War predictions of demand for sand and gravel have been difficult to formulate and subject to constant revision. The Advisory Committee on Sand and Gravel, set up by the Minister of Town and Country Planning under the chairmanship of Major (later Sir) Arnold Waters, which submitted 18 reports between 1948 and 1953, estimated that up to the end of the century the national demand for sand and gravel would average 28 million cubic metres per year. Annual output exceeded this figure as early as 1952, however, and the increase did not, as expected, prove to be a shortlived phenomenon reflecting the needs of post-war reconstruction. In 1961 the Minister of Public Building and Works published new forecasts that by 1965–70 the level of output in England and Wales would rise to about 57 million cubic metres per year. In 1964 sand and gravel production once again outstripped the estimates for the 1965–70 period, and in 1965 a forecast for the period 1975–80 was issued which predicted that the huge amount of 136 860 000 cubic metres annually would be required by Britain during that time.[24] In the event, these estimates have now been revised downwards. In 1968 and 1969 production levels fell, in 1969 by nearly 3 per cent, in response to diminished demand and a reduction in building activity resulting from a less buoyant economy, and the 1965 estimates are now considered to be more applicable to the mid-1980s than to 1975–80.[25] This is consistent with an expected annual increase in the long term of between 4 and 5 per cent.* While this estimate is taken as the basis of calculations in this chapter, it is clear that all predictions on future sand and gravel demand, which is closely tied to the economic health of the country, have to be viewed with caution.

* More recently the official forecasts of the rate of growth of demand for sand and gravel have been revised downwards, to 3·5 per cent.

Although sand and gravel output increased very substantially during the period 1950–70, it was in fact increasing less rapidly than output of the major hard rock aggregates. The respective percentage increases (UK figures), 1970 on 1950, were: sand and gravel 162; limestone 246; igneous rocks 223 and sandstone 296.[26] The chief factor in the relatively lower percentage increase of sand and gravel was the sterilization or exhaustion of many of the more easily worked reserves, or of those most able to obtain planning permission, in the major South-Eastern producing region. Since sand and gravel may in a sense be considered the primary aggregate mineral—that with the largest annual output, the cheapest average price and occurring in closest proximity to the major metropolitan market—these difficulties, which are explored in detail later, had repercussions on the output of hard rocks, notably a greatly expanded output from those deposits within easy access of South-Eastern markets.

In spite of an exceptionally high degree of concentration of production since 1922, sand and gravel remains a more dispersed industry than most of the hard rock aggregates industries. Between 1922 and 1964 the average size of British quarries of all types increased approximately 9-fold (from 6000 quarries producing 41 million tonnes in 1922 to less than 4000 quarries producing 254 million tonnes in 1964). Over this same period the average output per sand and gravel pit increased 25-fold.[27] In 1969, however, there were still some 1450 sand and gravel pits in Britain, with an average output of only 67 784 tonnes,[28] i.e. less than the average output per quarry of any of the major hard rock industries except sandstone (see Fig. 2.1). Sand and gravel remains relatively dispersed, largely because it is the simplest of all extractive operations. Although treatment plants for sand and gravel have, in common with all the aggregates, become more elaborate as consumer specifications have tightened, its extraction and processing remain relatively less complicated than that of hard rocks. It involves relatively simple washing and grading, and occasionally the crushing of oversize gravel, compared with the blasting and up to five stages of crushing required for the hardest of hard rocks. Because of the relatively low overheads, small firms, with insufficient capital for hard rock processing, can operate satisfactorily in sand and gravel. Because of the relative simplicity of the extractive and treatment processes, sand and gravel can, in spite of the small average size of producing units, still undercut the hard rocks, on the basis of average ex-pit prices. In 1968 the average prices per tonne in the roadstone (aggregate) market were: sand and gravel 63 pence per tonne; limestone 74 pence per tonne; igneous rocks £1·20 per tonne; and sandstone 95 pence per

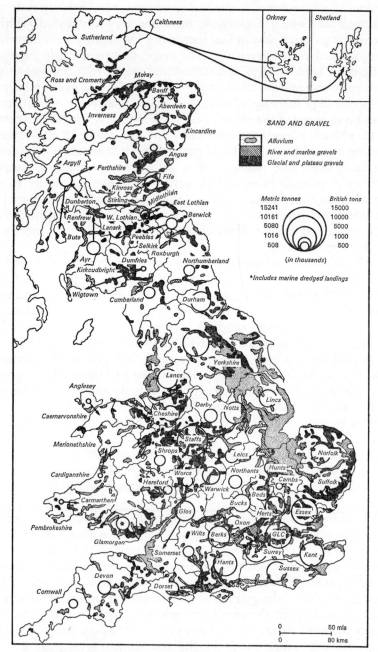

Fig. 2.1 *Sand and gravel*: output by county, 1969
Arrows indicate location of counties whose totals are grouped
Source: Department of the Environment

tonne.[29] This is in spite of the fact that the cost of acquiring reserves of sand and gravel in the late 1960s was about four times as high as that of acquiring hard rock, in view primarily of the occurrence of sand and gravel in areas of acutely competing land use, especially in the South-East, and the premium value of deposits with planning permission for working.

The sand and gravel industry, in spite of its continuing dispersed structure, with more than 1000 firms operative in 1971,[30] had not of course escaped the widespread trend towards amalgamation in the 1960s. During that decade the industry had come to an unprecedented extent to be dominated by a small number of very large producers: in 1969 the estimated production of the five largest sand and gravel producers amounted to 32·9 per cent of national sand and gravel output[31] and subsequent mergers have raised this percentage. The high cost of acquiring reserves means that small companies face considerable difficulties in keeping up the level of investment necessary to maintain their capacity in the future, and hold on to their share of the growing market. Apart from horizontal mergers between sand and gravel operators, there has been an increasing number of vertical mergers integrating extractive and consuming interests. These have been both backward and forward integrations, i.e. aggregate companies have moved into manufacturing partly to safeguard their outlets, and manufacturing companies have moved into extraction partly to safeguard their supplies. The integration with manufacturing operations has been more marked in the sand and gravel industry than in crushed stone, and has been most marked in terms of integration with ready mixed concrete manufacture. All the large sand and gravel companies now have interests in ready mixed concrete, an expanding and profitable field of operations in the 1960s. The largest sand and gravel producer in 1971 was Ready Mixed Concrete Ltd., whose operations centred on the South-East where the company produced 8·8 million tonnes or more than 25 per cent of the local market, and who used about 45 per cent of their production within the group for ready mixed concrete.[32] The mergers of the 1960s also strengthened the organizational links between sand and gravel extraction and that of other types of aggregates: all the larger producers market more than one type of aggregate. However, the fact that market radii are still limited means that large firms have to have a large number of producing and distributing units.

In spite of the mergers and amalgamations, bringing some degree of rationalization, productivity in the sand and gravel industry in 1950–70 increased less rapidly than that of the major hard rock aggregates. During

47

this period, productivity in sand and gravel extraction more than doubled, in limestone extraction more than quadrupled, in igneous rock extraction more than quintupled, while that in sandstone extraction increased by more than seven times.[33] The lower productivity advances in sand and gravel extraction would appear to be linked to the exceptionally dispersed structure of the sand and gravel industry. Furthermore, sand and gravel, as a large-scale extractive industry of long standing, had smaller potential in the 1950s and 1960s than, for instance, sandstone for both expanded output and productivity advances. Sandstone had both the highest percentage increase in output and the most striking productivity advances during this period, and sand and gravel the lowest percentage increase in output and the lowest productivity advances. Sand and gravel alone, of the major aggregate minerals, was worked by an actually expanding labourforce during the period 1950–70.[34]

In England and Wales there are four main sources of sand and gravel, residual, glacial, fluvial and marine. The oldest, the residual deposits, are the Bunter Pebble beds of Triassic age, which are directly related to their underlying parent rock, from which they have become separated by weathering. That is, unlike other sources of sand and gravel, the residual deposits have not been transported and in consequence the particles remain sharp and the beds are unstratified mixtures of boulders, pebbles, sand and clay. The pebble beds outcrop in three main areas: to the west, south-west and north-east of the south Staffordshire coalfield; on Cannock Chase; and in a discontinuous belt bordering the southern margin of the Pennines and the Cheadle and Potteries coalfields.[35] There is also a small and intermittent outcrop of Bunter beds in east Devonshire known as the Buddleigh Salterton Pebble beds. The residual deposits, the thickest found in Britain, vary in depth from 7·6 to more than 30·5 metres. An average yield per hectare of 122 800 cubic metres is the norm for the Bunter beds— much higher than for any other type of deposit—and within the Cheadle Common and Cannock Chase areas yields are of the order of 188 900 cubic metres per hectare. However, the Bunter beds are a comparatively small source of national output, contributing some 10 per cent of the England and Wales total[36] because of constraints on their commercial exploitation. The deposits, being unstratified, vary widely in composition, some being commercially unworkable, whilst the availability of water for washing in the upland areas where they occur is a further limiting factor.

The other two major land-won sources of sand and gravel in England and Wales are of geologically more recent origin, i.e. the drift deposits dating from the glacial and post-glacial periods. The chief distinctions between the two categories of drift deposits are their mode of occurrence, the method of working required and the degree to which they have been sorted. High level or glacial gravels, spread over relatively elevated areas above the water table and consequently worked dry, contribute about 25 per cent of the sand and gravel output of England and Wales.[37] These deposits are found extensively in East Anglia and Central and Northern England. They also provide by far the largest proportion of sand and gravel output in Scotland, particularly Lanarkshire.[38] The high level deposits are less sorted than any other transported form of sand and gravel and vary considerably in quality. The poorest of them contain a high percentage of clay and have poor shrinkage values, i.e. they are unable to counter the natural shrinkage of the cement as it dries out, thus allowing cracks to form. However, appropriate structural design can now in many cases accommodate this problem. The high level deposits of the area around Glasgow suffer from a deficiency of gravel in the deposits, those in central Lanarkshire averaging 36 per cent gravel content of total output in 1967[39] compared with the desirable figure of 50 per cent. Yield per hectare from high level or glacial gravels is rarely more than 28 300–37 800 cubic metres.

Fluvial deposits, or drift deposits in the river valleys, a comparatively minor source of sand and gravel in Scotland, constitute the most important source of the material in England and Wales, accounting for some 60 per cent of output.[40] The oldest, most extensive deposits occur in the deltas and flood plains of rivers, while the more recent fluvial deposits occur in river beds where they are still being replenished. These deposits are generally more rounded and more sorted than high level glacial gravels, with resultant advantages in terms of the reduced treatment required. River-bed gravels are worked by dredging; the much more extensive valley deposits produce mainly wet pits as the excavations normally take place below the water-table. Average yield per hectare from fluvial deposits is 28 300–37 800 cubic metres.[41] The most important areas of workings of this kind are in the Thames and Trent valleys. In the former, the predominantly flint gravels of the river terraces are of particularly high quality.

In 1969 a provisional figure of 6 689 000 cubic metres of gravel was obtained by marine dredging from shallow coastal waters,[42] constituting 9·3 per cent of total production. Shoreline deposits result from the eroding effects of the sea, while deposits further out are the remains of earlier shore levels, subsequently submerged. The material is both rounded and well sorted, and some natural replacement of the worked-out beds may occur by the further action of the sea. However, the higher operating costs than for land deposits means that large-scale exploitation is comparatively recent. Marine deposits have been worked since the early part of this century, initially by horse and cart at low tide, then by hand-loaded barge and finally by dredger. The bulk of current output is obtained by suction dredging at depths of less than 23 metres. From 1948 marine operations have been carried out under licence from the Crown Estate Commissioners but annual output increased very little until about 1956. Since that time, and especially during the 1960s when the annual output more than doubled, marine dredged production has expanded more rapidly than sand and gravel from onshore deposits.[43] The factors influencing this high growth rate included the allaying of doubts about the technical properties of the material; increasing difficulties in obtaining planning permission for land-based workings and increasing cost of acquiring land-based reserves; the exhaustion of pits in certain areas; and the rising aggregates demand. Although marine-dredged material is generally only marketed within about 8 to 11 kilometres of the point of landing because of heavy overland freight costs, it can economically be transported considerable distances by sea, and is virtually the only source of exported sand and gravel. Exports have, with official encouragement, risen from 355 600 tonnes in 1967 to 3 403 600 tonnes in 1970,[44] the major part supplied to Rotterdam for the construction of the Europort. However, the shell content of marine deposits causes some problems and the presence of clay in large quantities makes extraction uneconomic in what were previously thought to be promising dredging areas. Exploitation of marine deposits is at present only known to be commercially possible in a few areas, of which the main ones are as follows: the southern areas of the North Sea and especially Essex coastal waters for London; Liverpool Bay for Liverpool and Manchester; around the Isle of Wight and especially the Solent Bank for Southampton and other parts of the south coast; the Humber estuary for Hull, north Lincolnshire and parts of the North-East; and the Bristol Channel for the south coast of Wales. In 1969 no marine-dredged sand and gravel was recorded for Scotland[45] where widespread marine gravel deposits similar to those off the southern coasts of England do not seem to occur. This is because, in general, the relics of earlier Scottish beaches and sub-aerial deposits lie above rather than below sea level. However, some uncertainty exists and in 1970 a preliminary statement, issued as a result of the marine study of the Institute of Geological Sciences, covering the Firth of Forth Approaches, the Firth of Clyde south to Mull of Kintyre, Sea of Hebrides and Minch and the

Moray Firth,[46] recommended that further investigations should be concentrated within specific areas where geological conditions were most favourable. Apart from the marine workings listed earlier, the Crown Estate Commissioners have in recent years, since the passing of the Continental Shelf Act in 1964, given licences for marine working outside territorial waters, in some cases more than 48 kilometres out in the North Sea, although none of these has as yet resulted in production.

Thus it can be seen that sand and gravel extraction is overwhelmingly concentrated in England. 1969 records show that 89·0 per cent of total British production came from England and a small part of North Wales (Flint and a section of Denbighshire lying south-east of Denbigh).[47] Within this area the greatest concentration of workings occurs south and east of a line from the Wash to the Dorset/Devon boundary. In 1969 approximately half the output for England and Wales came from this zone. The chief reason for heavy demand here, apart from the large market of the Greater London area, is the absence of alternative sources of aggregate: there are no outcrops of hard stone suitable for the production of heavy building aggregate close to London, apart from the small limestone deposits in the Maidstone and Sevenoaks district.[48] This situation may be contrasted with that prevailing in northern England where, with suitable outcrops of limestone, sandstone and igneous rocks, crushed rocks form 70 per cent of all aggregates.[49]

The Greater London region provides the greatest single market for sand and gravel in Britain and, at least until recently, the greatest concentration of available resources.[50] The very extensive nature of land deposits have, however, been substantially reduced during this century both by sterilization and as a result of intensive working. The Advisory Committee on Sand and Gravel estimated that in the London area between the First and Second World Wars 20 250 hectares of land, representing 765 million cubic metres of sand and gravel, were made inaccessible by building development. Since the advent of planning controls, sand and gravel in this area is often worked before building development takes place. As the metropolis has spread the pits have moved steadily away from its core. The main centres of production by areas as defined by the Advisory Committee are: the western area (the Thames valley from Walton to Datchet and the Colne valley from Staines to Rickmansworth); the Thames valley area of south Essex; the Lea valley from Enfield north to Ware; the Cray and Darenth valleys of Kent; and the Vale of St Albans between Ware and Rickmansworth. The western area, where the Thames

C

terrace deposits are exceptionally wide, was still in 1969, as it had been in 1946, the most important source of supply within the Greater London gravel region, although its percentage contribution had fallen from 43 per cent to 31·9 per cent of Greater London regional output during that time.[51] The declining percentage of output from the West London area is indicative of a serious trend. In 1966 it was estimated that output from the existing pits in this area, as well as from south Essex, the second largest area in the London region, and from the Cray and Darenth valleys of Kent was likely to decline during the 1970s unless high quality agricultural land, hitherto protected, was worked.[52] Land of this type forms part of a total of 3 240 hectares which the Advisory Committee, working on the basis of a much smaller estimated demand throughout this century, recommended should be reserved in perpetuity for agriculture and horticulture. Subsequent scaling down of sand and gravel forecasts have postponed this difficulty—it is believed, for instance, that there is sufficient environmentally acceptable gravel-bearing land in the western area to meet demand during the 1970s[53]—but the demands of agriculture and of gravel production are likely seriously to conflict during the 1980s.

The likelihood of future shortages, unless deposits underlying high quality land were worked first, became apparent when the high estimates of demand were made in 1965. Consequently, the then Minister for Housing and Local Government reviewed the question of supplies within the area covered by the six South-Eastern gravel regions (see Fig. 2.2) in 1967 in the light of the then current estimates of demand for the period up to 1980. The starting point of this review was that 'the gravel resources of Greater London are within sight of exhaustion and a marked decline in production can be expected shortly. Gravel will have to be transported from further away.'[54] Of the five other gravel regions within the South-East, the Kent and East Sussex gravel reserves were expected to be exhausted by the late 1970s. The extent of reserves in East Anglia was relatively unknown, and the possible contribution they might make to the London market was the prime factor in their selection as the first topic of investigation in the national economic survey of minerals announced in 1965. The preliminary conclusions of the review were then that additional supplies for the London market by the late 1970s would have to come from the three remaining South-Eastern gravel regions, i.e. from the Wessex gravel region with hauls of 97 to 129 kilometres; from the Middle and Upper Thames gravel region with hauls of well over 81 kilometres; and from the Middle Anglia gravel region.[55] The areas particularly envisaged as making a large contribution to the Greater London market were the fen gravel areas south Lincolnshire and the gravel spreads south and west of Oxford.[56]

However, the maximizing of output from the whole of this South-East region also involves difficult choices. There were in 1966 calculated to be 20 250 hectares of gravel-bearing land remaining in the South-Eastern gravel regions, excluding the Greater London region, apart from the high quality agricultural land, and all of this was

Fig. 2.2 *Sand and gravel regions of England and Wales and marine-dredging areas*
Metric tonnages shown are for 1970
Source: Crown Estates Commission

expected to be worked within the ensuing 12 years.[57] There were in addition gravel reserves underlying high quality agricultural land, hitherto protected, which could satisfy rising demand for a further 10–12 years. The crucial question within the South-East gravel regions, as within the Greater London gravel region, is how far these high quality agricultural lands should be worked in the interests of minimizing aggregate costs in Greater London. Although the urgency of the supply situation and its attendant difficult choices is not as great as was previously thought, as a result of the scaling down of predicted demand in 1970, the dilemma is merely postponed for some five years or so.

The Ministry of Housing and Local Government's recognition that these problems demanded a special degree of planning coordination led to the decision to set up working parties to study the situation in each of the gravel regions within the South-East (including Greater London). By 1971 three such working parties, covering one quarter of the South-East and containing representatives of the local authorities and the Sand and Gravel Association (representing the sand and gravel industry), had been established. The terms of reference were 'to make a detailed assessment of the likely demand for sand and gravel up to 1980 and of the supply potential of the area, taking into account agriculture, amenity and other planning considerations'.[58] The three interim reports, published in 1971, estimated demand and available supply in their respective areas but did not at that stage decide upon the most suitable locations for extensions to workings. The central decision about the working of high quality agricultural land within the South-East had not, therefore, been taken, although the Minister of Agriculture has indicated, in certain specific instances, sections of the agricultural reservations which he might be prepared to consider releasing for gravel working.

Although final decisions on this issue had not yet been taken, the general attitude of most of the parties concerned had already been made clear. The Sand and Gravel Association held that there was in fact no shortage of supplies within the South-East gravel regions if the necessary planning permission for workings was given.[59] Representatives of the industry invariably stress the importance of working the nearest available source of this high bulk/low cost mineral to hold prices. The better prospects of obtaining fill for restoration, the provisions of available tipping space near to the metropolitan centre, and the 'decongestion of public roads' have also been put forward as arguments in favour of working the deposits nearest to the centre.[60] This line of argument was apparently endorsed in an official statement made on behalf of the Minister of Public Building and Works at a regional planning conference in 1969, which is worth quoting at length:

In our view it is right that the material with the cheapest delivery price should be selected. At present, and certainly in most areas of the South-East, local won sand and gravel is the cheapest form of aggregate. Marine gravel is only competitive at comparatively short distance from the point of landing and, in general, artificial aggregate (i.e. crushed rock) is much more expensive because of the distance it has to be transported. It follows therefore that there is and will be a continuing demand for all local sources of sand and gravel in this area. Two things are clear . . . during the period under review (i.e. the next ten years) the demand for aggregates will continue to rise: the only difference of opinion can be the speed with which this may happen. And the second is that it will be necessary to extract all the local won sand and gravel in the South-East which can be made available.[61]

This statement has been much quoted by representatives of the industry. The local authority representatives on one of the three existing working parties, however, took issue with this view. They placed on record their opinion that the alternative sources of supply, ruled out by the Ministry of Works statement, must in fact 'be regarded as desirable sooner rather than later to lessen the impact of surface gravel working in large areas . . . because, in any case, when the gravel has all been exhausted, alternatives will have to be found'.[62] The release of parts of the agricultural reservations raises serious considerations. It has not so far been proved that the very high quality brick-earth market garden land, such as that overlying gravel deposits in the London Boroughs of Hillingdon and Hounslow, can be restored to market garden quality after working.[63] Gravel extraction on such land, particularly within the Greater London gravel region where population densities are high, may create problems of traffic congestion, noise and unsightliness which the stringent planning consents almost universal in such areas cannot entirely mitigate.[64] Furthermore, the proportion of pits being filled, even within areas close to London, was falling in the 1960s because of the larger areas being extracted as output rose. In 1966 the percentage being filled was about 50 per cent, compared with the earlier post-war level of 60 per cent,[65] although the problems of a lessening rate of restoration were partly offset by the increasing demand for wet recreational areas. But it is the essentially temporary nature of meeting supply from these areas—a short-term measure providing supplies for an additional ten to twelve years— which, as the local authorities stressed, make it necessary to examine in greater detail the alternative to sand and gravel from within the South-East for the Greater London aggregates market.

The question of costs caused by longer haulage distances is a crucial one to a consideration of supplying the Greater London market from sources outside the South-East. Clearly, as a high bulk/low value mineral, with an estimated average ex-pit price of 63 pence per tonne in 1968, the transport costs of sand and gravel were very high in relation to its value. However, there are indications that, during the 1960s, the mineral was being transported much greater distances than hitherto, into areas of high demand. In 1966 Staffordshire County Council reported that 'changes in demand and the supply of sand and gravel have already resulted in more flexibility in movement of supplies between Service Areas than was anticipated by the Waters (Advisory) Committee'.[66] As a result, sand and gravel from the Cheadle area had for many years been sold in Liverpool and Manchester and from the Cannock Chase Service Area beyond Birmingham and the Black Country. In 1970 McLellan reported that resources in the formerly 'remote' areas of Peeblesshire, Perthshire and Stirlingshire, more than 72 kilometres from Glasgow, were supplying the large market of the Clydeside conurbation.[67] Increasing demand was not, however, the only factor involved in the lengthening supply lines of the 1960s. Engineers and architects were giving tighter specifications for the mineral, as a result of the growing appreciation of the differing structural-strength characteristics of the various deposits. In 1967 McLellan noted that only two active sand and gravel pits in Central Lanarkshire would be able to tender for the Kingston Bridge and Erskine Bridge projects in the Glasgow area, which required gravel of 0·05 per cent and 0·06 per cent shrinkage or less, respectively.[68] These two pits were approximately 56 kilometres from Glasgow. More surprisingly, the imperfect operation of competition and the market also contributed to lengthening hauls of sand and gravel. McLellan noted that in 1967 sand and gravel was being supplied from Carstairs to Killearn, a road journey of 81 kilometres, even though there was a sand and gravel pit only five kilometres from Killearn, the products of which were at least the equal of those at Carstairs,[69] and no more expensive.

Developments in transport have been a factor in the lengthening supply lines. The larger lorries now in use and the existence of motorways has helped to contain the inevitable rises in price resulting from longer hauling of a low value, bulk mineral. All the same, in spite of the fact that transport was improving, the overall percentage of delivered prices made up by transport costs was increasing, at least in the 1940s and 1950s. In Central Scotland, transport costs rose from 23·5 per cent of gravel prices in 1940 to 38 per cent in 1956 and from 41 per cent of sand prices to 48·3 per cent.[70] The Advisory Committee estimated in 1948 that the cost price of gravel nearly doubled at 21 kilometres from the pit.[71] In 1966 Dunstan noted that a journey of 24–36 kilometres in urban areas or as much as 81 kilometres in country districts doubled the ex-pit price.[72] Since from 1948 to 1966 the average ex-pit price of sand and gravel increased from approximately 26 pence per tonne to an estimated 60·5 pence per tonne,[73] these figures represent a substantial increase in transport costs per tonne mile (although considerably less steep than it appears because of the factor of inflation). Recent legislation on vehicle safety and driving hours has subsequently further increased transport costs. However, further improvements in the road network and a greater practice of double hauling* might conceivably help contain increasing transport costs, whilst the use of strategically placed stockpiles might also play a part. The application of this general view of the transport costs of sand and gravel to the problem of supplying Greater London is probably as follows: although longer hauls to the capital would inevitably mean higher prices, the rise in transport costs can probably be reduced somewhat by further transport improvement. In spite of its great bulk and low value, the market area for sand and gravel was wider than might have been expected in the 1960s, and other factors could well operate to lengthen hauls even if permission were given for the working of all the closest deposits.

The uneconomic nature of bringing other sources of aggregate, i.e. crushed rock, from outside the South-East to serve the Greater London market was similarly not as clear cut as the Ministry of Public Building and Works 1969 statement suggested. In 1966 limited quantities of igneous rock from the Charnwood Forest district of Leicestershire and limestone from the Mendips (160 kilometres from London), and the even more distant Carboniferous limestone of the Peak District of Derbyshire and igneous rock from the coastal quarries of west Cornwall were being brought to London,[74] in the last instance by sea. These 'imported' aggregates were used mainly for specialized purposes such as road surfacing and their delivery costs, justified by their specialist value, was about three times that of locally won gravel. However, since then the volume of these transported materials has grown to include non-specialist aggregate material: e.g. limestone aggregates. Economics of scale in production at the largest quarries, the existence of the M1 and M4 motorways and of large liner trains have in fact[75] meant that limestone can be hauled to London to compete on almost equal terms with locally produced gravel, especially as rising demand and falling

* That is, carrying a return load of some kind. This is not easily achieved since the types of materials that can be carried in aggregate lorries are very limited.

supply force prices up. Other transport innovations, such as the transport of slurried material by pipeline, might conceivably become possible, although such techniques have only been tried up to now over short distances.

While the transportation of crushed rock for aggregate for the London market cannot be entirely ruled out on the grounds of cost, it would, however, if adopted on a large scale, pose considerable planning problems. The planning difficulties associated with limestone and igneous rock extraction are no less formidable than those of sand and gravel, although generally different in kind. A further expansion of extractive output from the Charnwood Forest district of Leicestershire, the Peak District, the Mendips or, less probably, south-west Cornwall to help meet aggregate demand in the South-East is likely to pose planning problems as severe as the extended extraction of local won sand and gravel in the regions of the South-East themselves.

A greatly increased contribution of marine-dredged sand and gravel to the greater London market, already the largest market for this material, does, as the Ministry of Public Building and Works' statement indicates, involve difficulties. Only a comparatively few areas of limited extent are at present known to be commercially workable, and the increased level of output achieved during the 1960s will, when continued throughout the 1970s, result in the exhaustion of some of the better known dredging areas. The ideal policy of balancing the rate of extraction with what is thought to be the natural replacement rate is not practicable everywhere; the important Solent Bank dredging area, for instance, has scarcely any natural replacement.[76] The Sand and Gravel Association does not expect that output of marine-dredged material will grow as rapidly during the 1970s as it has in the past decade. They have no information which would indicate a growth rate of more than 5 per cent per year, compared with about 15 per cent per year during the 1960s, thus doing little more than keeping pace with the expected increase in overall demand.[77] Although advances in dredging and discharge systems are revolutionizing the economics of the industry, capital investment in marine-dredged operations may be as much as 300 per cent higher than in land-based ones, and this may increase even further as operators are forced to work to greater depths. The heavy operating costs indicate that it is not economic to incur heavy additional costs by transporting the material long distances from the point of landing. However, it is possible to transport the material very considerable distances by sea. In 1969 firms dredging off the Humberside coast, for instance, had contracted to supply 5.4 million cubic metres to Europort in Holland[78] and in that year the Crown

Estate mineral agent was instructed at the highest level to encourage exports of gravel to the Continent to improve the balance of payments.[79]

Clearly, sea-dredged sand and gravel from a wide area could economically be delivered to the Port of London if the supplies were available. The planning problems of marine-dredging are, however, complex. Marine-dredging may involve possible damage to fishing grounds, Post Office cables or gas pipes. The dredgers may interfere with nagivation. The major Solent Bank, the biggest source of marine-dredged gravel in the Wessex gravel region, has a limited life because the Crown Estate Commissioners will not permit expansion of the current dredging areas on the grounds of fishery and Trinity House objections. It is also understood that the Commissioners will no longer consider issuing licences for any part of the Thames estuary. In fact, permission for marine-dredging is probably now no easier to obtain than permission for land-based operations. Also some coastal local authorities are worried that there is insufficient information about the effect of continual dredging which could, they fear, cause coastal erosion and changes in the character of beaches. Planning authorities within the South-East believe that local planning authorities should be associated with the grant of licences for marine-dredging by the Crown Estate Commissioners,[80] but this procedure, which clearly has merits from a planning point of view, could if adopted result in even further restrictions on the number of licences issued. Most of the planning difficulties associated with marine-dredging do not, however, apply to the more distant North Sea areas within the British sector of the continental shelf, for which licences have been granted since 1964, but the contribution which such areas might make in the future to the Greater London market is at the moment speculative.

It is clear that the supply of aggregates from outside the South-East to the Greater London market—both land-won and marine-dredged sand and gravel and crushed rock—cannot entirely be ruled out on the grounds of cost. At the same time, it is manifestly desirable that consumers should draw on the nearest working in existence providing the required material, and some rationalization of marketing is necessary. At present, the industry is prevented by the Restrictive Trade Practices Act from taking any action to set up the means to arrange that distribution is from the nearest source of supply. Similarly, it is clearly undesirable that high quality material should be used when lower quality would suffice. It is not uncommon for high quality gravel to be used to considerable depths for the sub-base of road construction if it happens to be close at hand, when a less valuable material would be equally effective. Lightweight aggregates made from blast furnace slag, sintered pulverized fuel ash or colliery slag should be used to the full whenever they can replace heavy aggregates based on sand and gravel or crushed rock. The Department of the Environment has now initiated further research in this field, not only on the technical side, where some work has already been done, but in the economies of production and distribution. It is vital that the utilization of alternative sources of aggregate, which simultaneously remove waste and help to relieve pressures on sand and gravel and crushed rock reserves, should be maximized. However, the transport of china clay sand from the South-West to the markets of the South-East, an attractive idea for these reasons, is not at the present time economically feasible, since it is calculated that the gap between local-won sand and gravel prices and those of Devon china clay sand, delivered to this area, could be £1·38 per tonne, with a range of £1·28 to £1·92, for places between Newbury and London.[81] There are also doubts about its acceptability: sand from china clay operations is a fine aggregate in which none of the accompanying coarse aggregate needed for concreting is present. However, the rise in sand and gravel prices in the South-East likely during the 1980s and beyond might make possible, unless large areas of agricultural reservations were released, some sales of china clay sand in this market. This would particularly be the case if research had made possible production of an accompanying coarse aggregate, if transport improvements had lowered unit coasts of transport and possibly if fiscal changes encouraged the sale rather than the on-site tipping of this sand.

The rationalization of marketing within the aggregates industry, and control of the type of aggregates used, do of course raise delicate questions and could require modifications of existing legislation against monopolies. The Middle and Upper Thames Gravel Region Working Party concluded in 1971 that 'it is realized that detailed control of the destination of the material and of the specifications which are included in contracts, presents many difficulties, but it is considered that nonetheless some effort should be made to deal with this problem.'[82] The specification of materials for contracts in the very important public sector of the construction industries (i.e. roads and other public works) needs to be rationalized. Thus it should be ensured that high grade material is used only when strictly necessary and that substitute aggregates are used whenever these can adequately perform the task required. Within the private sector, the more efficient dissemination of information might at least make possible more completely rationalized marketing, thus eliminating unnecessary journeys. No source of aggregates is limitless, and the potential demand, if one attempts to look ahead to the end of the century, might conceivably be as high as

2030 million tonnes per year,[83] compared with some 237 million tonnes in 1969. Whatever difficulties and inaccuracies may be involved in such long-term forecasting, the need to preserve resources from unnecessary waste must be evident.

The planning problems posed by sand and gravel extraction in the South-East are particularly great because of the exceptional size of the market, but the difficulties associated with their working are present in areas covered by virtually every British local planning authority, sand and gravel being the most ubiquitous of all minerals extracted in Britain. More planning authorities surveyed, cited sand and gravel as posing problems in land use competition or amenity than any other extractive industry. This lends support to the view of Dunstan[84] that it is in the sphere of sand and gravel that 'the most urgent surface mineral planning problems are likely to arise and intensify in the years ahead'. Sand and gravel extraction is first and foremost an extravagent user of land: the average yield per hectare is 37 800 cubic metres of sand and gravel compared with 188 900 cubic metres per hectare from large stone quarries.[85] Although yields in London's western Service Area are commonly above 37 800 cubic metres per hectare, there are many areas where yields are well below this level, thus increasing the 'land-take'. The total acreage consumed by sand and gravel extraction annually is not only growing, but its percentage of the annual take of all extractive industries is also growing. In 1953 the Advisory Committee estimated that sand and gravel in England and Wales was consuming 860 hectares per year or 50 per cent of the annual total take of all extractive industries, excluding opencast coal. By 1966 the area (in hectares) taken annually for quarrying, excluding opencast coal, in England and Wales had reached 2430, of which about 1620 or 66 per cent was consumed annually for sand and gravel extraction. If the present forecast of a rise to a total of 136 859 000 cubic metres annually for Britain by the mid-1980s proves correct, the annual take for sand and gravel in England and Wales will rise to 3240 hectares or more than 31 square kilometres,[86] and sand and gravel will consume more than the current 66 per cent of annual take for the extractive industries.

Although approximately half the pits in Britain are worked wet and half dry,[87] wet pits occupy more than half the area taken annually for sand and gravel. Workings which would result in wet pits occupied almost 1013 hectares of the 1620 hectares in England and Wales being taken annually for sand and gravel in 1966 and will probably consume approximately 18 of the approximately 31 square kilometres of the annual take estimated for sand and gravel by the mid-1980s.[88] It is likely that the proportion of total output derived from wet pits is actually growing. The valley gravels have certain economic advantages deriving from the natural sorting and washing which has taken place and which eliminates much costly processing, but their waterlogged condition can cause operating problems. Improved techniques of wet working may result in an even greater concentration of production on this advantageous type of gravel deposit so that the area of wet pits could be even greater than that estimated above.

Many planning permissions still stipulate that pits should be filled subject to suitable filling material becoming available. Generally, proximity to urban areas has been the largest single factor in determining whether pits are filled. Several hundred hectares of filled pits in the Greater London Area have subsequently been used for building. Indeed in 1966 about 60 per cent of the land excavated for sand and gravel since 1945 in West London had been filled.[89] As is to be expected, the percentage of wet area being filled falls within the South-East as distance from London increases. In the Middle and Upper Thames gravel regions, the total area restored after sand and gravel working and being used for other purposes in 1971 was 507 hectares, the total area not refilled but put to other use was 878 hectares, and the total not restored or refilled was 1166 hectares (including areas forming part of workings still being excavated).[90] That is, of the approximate total area of pits of all types in the region, only 19 per cent had so far been filled. The main type of fill used in most areas is rubble or other inert waste: in spite of some generally encouraging research into filling wet pits with domestic refuse,[91] no satisfactory method of eliminating the risk of polluting underground water supplies has been found. Clearly, whichever of these media were in fact used, proximity to large urban areas would remain the determining factor in availability of filling material.

In the Trent valley, however, a number of wet pits have been filled with pulverized fuel ash supplied by the heavy concentration of coal fired power stations in the area. (In some instances, this results in the creation of productive land where none existed before: at the Meering quarry of Redland Gravel Ltd. about 4 million tonnes of fly ash from High Marnham power station were deposited between 1956 and 1969, and served to create new agricultural land from the gravel excavations in the riverside marshlands.)

It is possible that, with the creation of more very large pits in the Thames and Trent valleys, the percentage being filled will fall. In the West London area, this percentage had in 1966 already dropped to 50 per cent from the earlier 60 per cent figure.[92] This is not, however, the case in every part of the Home Counties: in Surrey the rate of filling in the county has at least matched the rate of extraction in recent years.[93] Any decline in filling rate in areas close to London could conceivably be arrested if domestic refuse could be used. In the Trent valley the supplies of ash becoming available will probably not grow as fast as the rate of sand and gravel extraction, especially if the Central Electricity Generating Board succeeds in selling significantly more than the approximately 40 per cent of total ash sold in 1969.[94] The declining rate of filling is not, however, a major cause for concern since a significant change in public attitude towards wet pits has come about since 1945. In the immediate post-war years, the public demanded filling of these pits whenever possible, whereas in recent years they have been greatly in demand for wet recreational areas.

In the course of the 1960s the water using activities, especially sailing and fishing, were growing at unprecedented rates. This growth is expected to continue and in many areas the demand for facilities is rapidly exceeding supply. There is also growing interest in the provision of wet or partly wet nature reserves. In 1962, 871 hectares of disused wet gravel pits were used for angling and 556 for other water sports,[95] mainly as a result of private initiative or improvisation. On a number of other disused pits, water birds and other wildlife had spontaneously established themselves. The White Paper, Leisure and the Countryside, and the ensuing Countryside Act of 1968 emphasized that local authorities should pay close attention to the provision of new water facilities for the public. Already a number of large-scale local authority schemes for the recreational use of complexes of wet pits had been initiated, notably the Lea Valley Regional Park Plan in the Greater London gravel region[96] and the plan for a major water sports complex at Holme Pierrepoint in Nottinghamshire.[97] The plan for the major Cotswold Water Park differs from these, partly in its scale and more importantly in the extent to which considerations of after-use, provision of roads, etc., were incorporated at the earliest stage of planning, rather than mainly improvised afterwards.

The Cotswold Water Park will consist of two sections, one in the neighbourhood of Ashton Keynes and one near Fairford.[98] Sand and gravel have been worked here since the 1920s and in the 1960s reached more than 1·5 million cubic metres per year. During this last decade, when some 365 hectares of worked-out pits existed, many of them already used for various recreational activities, the Gloucestershire and Wiltshire County Councils, together with rural district councils involved, formed a joint committee to maintain and develop the proper after-use of the area as a water park. The draft plan for the park, which could eventually extend to some 567 hectares, attempted to rationalize treatment and use of existing worked-out areas and co-ordinate these with permitted future workings and their after-use. The various recreational uses, and the areas for wildlife study, are to be segregated as far as possible, and two areas, one in each section of the park, were proposed as Country Parks, financed partly by the Countryside Commission and partly by ratepayers.

While the Cotswold Water Park is clearly a project of exceptional scope, other local authorities are in increasing numbers giving consideration to questions of after-use at an early stage in the planning procedure. As far as wet gravel pits are concerned, this may involve certain difficulties. The planning authority cannot stipulate the after-use, but only the condition in which pits should be left. The authority can therefore provide that a pit should be left in a suitable state, for example sailing, but it is for the landowner to decide whether it is actually used for this purpose, unless the local authority is able or willing to acquire the site. The Cotswold Water Park is only made possible by the cooperation of a large number of private landowners—the percentage of the area owned by the councils concerned is small. There is, in general, the further difficulty of time-scale; most permissions are for 15–20 years, and though it is hard to predict future land use requirements for the site at the end of such a period, the question of after-use should always be considered since permission for mineral extraction, unlike that for building, is in fact permission for two changes of land use rather than one. The director of the Sand and Gravel Association has warned that 'we must be careful not to reach the position where the possible forms of after-use become the dominant factor in the formulation of mineral planning policy'.[99] Nevertheless, the second change of land use may well be equally as important as the first and, if not the dominant consideration, it needs always to be given due weight.

The Sand and Gravel Association have done a valuable job in recent years in impressing upon their members the advantages of tidiness, tree planting and amenity preservation, and an annual trophy is awarded for the best example of restoration of after-use of worked-out pits. On the other hand, the Association's director has expressed the view that planning authorities are now tending to impose unreasonable stipulations on workings. He wrote in 1970 that 'it is neither fair nor far-sighted to attempt to saddle the industry with the cost of creating new facilities for recreation on the scale which the community may require'.[100] It would appear to be reasonable for a planning consent to stipulate grading, contouring and some tree planting at a worked-out site, but not landscaping over wide areas, or the provision of facilities such as roads for the ensuing land use. As long ago as 1953 the Advisory Committee recommended an after-treatment fund, based broadly on the Ironstone Fund; one of the purposes of this was 'to make grants towards the cost of landscaping or similar treatment of lagoons for the purposes of amenity or in consequence of a decision to dedicate the land as open public space'. Such a fund, which would receive a contribution from the Exchequer, might well still have a valuable part to play in these particular circumstances although the more stringent planning consents introduced during the past 20 years have weakened the case for such a fund in other respects.

Dissatisfaction about the part being played by the local authorities can be found elsewhere in the industry. John Taylor, formerly of Associated Portland Cement Manufacturers, would like to see planning of minerals on a regional basis, as a step towards the ultimate aim of direct control by a Minister of Minerals.[101] There were in fact during the 1960s moves towards greater regional consultation on sand and gravel planning, of which the South-Eastern working parties were one manifestation, and as far back as the period of the Advisory Committee the local authorities were given particular official guidance in the planning of this mineral. The Advisory Committee defined the gravel regions of England and Wales, estimated demand for each area and recommended the districts from which extraction to meet demand could most appropriately be drawn. During the 1950s the policy of most local authorities was to restrict new sand and gravel workings to the areas specified by the Advisory Committee and, within that general framework, to treat each application on its merits.[102] During that decade, when it quickly became apparent that the Advisory Committee's estimates of demand were much too small, the Ministry of Housing and Local Government began a procedure for reviewing the position in some areas advising the local authorities of the larger areas which would be needed. The first review was of the Trent valley and other reviews of some of the more important South-East gravel regions followed. Some monitoring of output in relation to forecasting was in progress, but the majority of authorities continued to base their policy on the Advisory Committee's recommendations, and *ad hoc* decisions on applications, in spite of the fact that the annual sand and gravel returns made clear that these recommendations were based on underestimates, and the areas recommended for extraction were coming under increasing pressure. Few Development Plans actually allocated land for working, other than the land already being worked or with planning permission. As far as stipulations of working were concerned, planning authorities concentrated on the need to minimize dereliction and, where possible, fill wet pits. Little attempt was made, apart from through the Advisory Committee recommendations, to influence the location of gravel pits in accordance with an overall view of all relevant considerations such as demand, amenity, agricultural value or recreational after-use. Planning authorities did not feel sufficiently informed to be able to suggest other, more environmentally acceptable sites to those applied for. That is, in most areas the planning authorities were relying on outdated estimates and allocations and following an essentially passive, *ad hoc* role. In the course of the 1960s several factors operated to produce in a number of key areas a more dynamic approach based on the estimate of new forecasts of local demand, areas required and their most desirable location. In other words, planning authorities in several important areas began to take the initiative in the 1960s. Among these factors was the vastly increased estimate of future demand published by the Ministry of Public Building and Works in 1965, subsequently reduced, which indicated the excavation of very large acreages in the major sources of supply. The increasing professionalism of planning departments and the growing practice of appointing specialist mineral officers within them, probably contributed to the appearance of more ambitious local authority policies.

The change from an *ad hoc*, pragmatic approach, guided only by the broad outlines of the Advisory Committee, to an overall strategy attempting to influence the location of sand and gravel deposits on a large scale is a fundamental one. A very few counties have, in recent years, attempted to initiate such a policy for all minerals, based on estimates of reserves and demand, and the whole range of factors relevant to optimum location of workings. Three counties attempting the complex formulation of such a policy for mineral extraction as a whole are the West Riding of Yorkshire, Somerset (for the Mendips) and Denbighshire. A few more authorities have attempted or are attempting such a policy for sand and gravel alone. Such projects are probably due to the very heavy land demand for sand and gravel, the widespread existence of problems connected with this mineral and the fact that the extensive deposits of the mineral permit more flexibility of choice of extraction areas than, for instance, minerals of very restricted occurrence such as fuller's earth. In this last respect, some authorities have come to the opposite conclusion from that of the director of the Sand and Gravel Association that 'to a great extent freedom of choice does not exist where the operations of the sand and gravel industry are concerned'.[103] The belief that there was a choice of site location, and that only a local planning authority initiative could make possible the weighing of all relevant factors in the making of that choice, was the prime motive force behind the local authority special sand and gravel plans.

The Policy for Sand and Gravel Working in the County of Huntingdon and Peterborough,[104] published in 1964, attempted to select areas for future working taking into account such considerations as agricultural land values, visual amenity and extending the use of existing plant. It was stated that these areas 'would have to be tested by trial borings and, if acceptable to the planning authority, would be no more than areas in which planning permission is likely to be given and indications of the direction in which extension should take place'. It was thus a cautious document and the suggested areas, all on the river terrace gravels of the Great Ouse valley, were in every case close to already worked areas. That is, no radical reorientation of working areas was attempted. The new policy document of 1970[105] similarly suggested areas for expansion in the north of the county, all of them extensions to existing pits with the exception of a possible excavation in a new area before a lake was constructed.

The 1966 Staffordshire policy document,[106] still in 1974 not yet approved by the Minister, was a more radical document. Staffordshire is a major source of supply to both the Liverpool and Manchester and the Birmingham and Black Country conurbations. In 1969 it had the largest sand and gravel output of any British county. On the basis of the 1965 Ministry of Public Building and Works forecast, the total demand from the county for 1965–81 would be 153 million cubic metres, compared with a total of 38 million cubic metres over the previous 12 years.[107] Meeting this target would involve, in addition to the 1819 hectares already worked or with planning consent in 1966, new areas of extraction in the county of more than 1215 hectares[108] up to 1981. (In the light of the subsequent scaling down of estimates, 1986 should be substituted for 1981 in each case.) The scale of the problem facing the county was massive, and the planning committee argued the advantages of its taking the initiative and allocating areas, subject to normal planning procedure, rather than leaving it to the industry 'to make suggestions which may be entirely unsuitable as far as the environment and locality is concerned'.[109] This initiative in allocating large areas to meet demand was to be complemented by much greater efforts at restoration—in 1966 only a very limited proportion of the areas worked had been reclaimed. The proposed allocations were, whenever possible, adjacent to existing pits but the main negative provision was that no new permissions would be granted within the Cannock Chase Area of Outstanding Natural Beauty, where restoration of the dry Bunter Pebble pits was virtually impossible in the absence of suitable fill. The chief positive provision was the selection of an entirely new area of extraction in the Trent/Tame valley. During the final stages of the preparation of the report however when three possible areas for the new excavation complex were being considered, the Minister gave permission for a new working of 203 hectares in one of these. Unfortunately this was not the area finally adopted by the local planning authority on the grounds of high yield per hectare, good transport facilities, ease of restoration and the possibility of a comprehensive approach to workings. Since then further modifications to the plan have been made at the behest of the Secretary of State but it is regrettable that in 1974 approval still awaited the outcome of a public enquiry at which further objections to the inclusion of two sites were made. However, the general welcome extended to the plan by the sand and gravel industry was encouraging. Although he considered the time-scale of the plan too short, and deplored its further shortening pending ministerial approval, Taylor wrote that:

Understandably I don't entirely accept the conclusions which Staffordshire County Council reached as to the location of reserve gravel areas to cover the plan period. On the other hand, I commend the foresight and work of the county council in achieving this survey, whatever its imperfections, as being the first real attempt in England to achieve a phased plan of a particular mineral linked to the best available estimates of demand likely to arise within a given period.[110]

Clearly, advance knowledge of the areas most likely to receive permission for working can save potential extractors time and money; any unnecessary uncertainty about future grants of planning permission puts a premium price on deposits for which planning permission is assured and the cost of acquiring reserves rises accordingly. The system of informal advance discussion operated by many other authorities only partially replaces an official written policy indicating areas where planning permission is likely to be given.

By far the most radical of the country sand and gravel plans was that of Northumberland.[111] The aim of the policy document was to examine the factors which determined the most appropriate location for sand and gravel workings in the county, bearing in mind the need to maintain the output of sand and gravel and ensure the least disturbance to amenity and land uses. At the time of the report 59·6 per cent of total county production was obtained from river-bed deposits,[112] a clean, well-sorted easy source to work; 8·6 per cent of the county's production came from beach deposits: these sand dunes, formed by wind-blown sand, are already clean, harmful salts having been leached out by rainfall over a long period. The third source, providing 31·8 per cent of the county total, was land deposits, either river terrace gravels which are often overlain by loam and require screening and washing, or high level glacial sand and gravels of variable quality also generally requiring screening and washing. The survey found weighty objections to the extraction of the first two types of deposit. River bed working was found to have produced flooding, undermining of banks and bridges and grave damage to fishery interests, especially those of salmon fishing. River bed working appeared to be totally incompatible with fishing.[113] The coastal workings were said to produce coastal erosion and to be incompatible with the authority's policy of preserving the coastline as 'a notable asset to the county'. Consequently the policy document proposed the radical step of refusing any further applications to work river bed or coastal deposits and raised the possibility of taking action to end existing permissions in these areas which had no expiry date. The area proposed for expanded working to replace output from river bed and coastal sources was the extensive glacial deposits within the lowland south and east of the county, close to the biggest urban developments. These deposits, already containing 7 of the county's 30 workings, had the initial disadvantage of heavy capital costs for screening and washing plant, but the authority proposed to at least partly outweigh this by granting long-term permissions to enable the investment in plant to be recovered. The crucial question, however, was the extent and quality of the approved deposits: if some 70 per cent of the county's output was to be redirected to this area, assurance was needed that reserves would sustain production. Apart from isolated information such as that from existing workings, the survey was only able to report that 'it is thought that the glacial deposits provide the necessary alternative source of supply but in the absence of detailed geological examination of each deposit it is not possible to give operators any more information than is provided by the Geological Survey maps'.[114] The Geological Survey maps give the location of sand and gravel deposits (not always wholly reliably)[115] but no indication of the crucial questions of quantity and quality. At or shortly after the time of the Northumberland survey, the only area where such information was available on more than a local (pit) basis was central Lanarkshire, where McLellan had estimated the distribution, volume and quality of sand and gravel reserves. Since that time, the preliminary survey of parts of Essex and East Anglia had been completed by the mineral assessment unit of the Institute of Geological Sciences. Hence Northumberland County Council were largely working in the dark. In spite of this, in

1974 it was decided to update the document this time as a co-operative venture with Durham and the North Riding planning authorities.

The problem of lack of knowledge of deposits has in the past and still does deter some authorities from attempting any genuine policy or overall strategy for mineral workings. County after county claimed, in the author's survey, to 'follow a pragmatic policy'—surely a contradiction in terms—considering each application on its merits. Leicestershire claimed that its 'pragmatic policy allows flexibility especially as the knowledge of deposits is not adequate. If more were known a more rigid policy might conceivably be evolved.'[116] However, for all its difficulties, the taking of initiative by local planning authorities or groups of authorities in those areas of mineral extraction where a choice of sites is available, and influencing location towards the optimum sites from all points of view, provides the best chance of truly coordinated planning with a policy really worth the name. If such policies help to stimulate the faster assessment of the quality and quantity of mineral reserves, so much the better.

However informed the policies of individual authorities may be, there is still an increasing need for greater coordination amongst groups of such bodies on the lines of the working parties existing in some areas. As the supply lines of sand and gravel lengthen and the supply of aggregates becomes short in some areas, the need for the fullest collaboration between counties, or even regions, grows. It is significant that the Standing Conference on London and South-East Regional Planning has urged the Department of the Environment to set up a committee at national level to study and report with recommendations on the use of sand and gravel, substitute materials, marine gravel, restoration and after-use. They are probably correct in thinking that the problems facing the nation in terms of sand and gravel are now just as acute as at the time of the Advisory Committee. The Department of the Environment implicitly recognized this when it announced in 1972 the establishment of a new Advisory Committee, to advise on supply and demand in the field of aggregates as a whole.

LIMESTONE

Limestone is economically the most important hard rock quarried in Britain. It is both the largest single source of crushed rock for aggregates and an indispensable raw material in an extremely wide and growing range of industries. Indeed, there is hardly a major industry in Britain in which limestone in some form is not used. Its extraction by

70

volume is exceeded amongst extractive industries only by sand and gravel and coal: in 1969 the total output of limestone, including its Cretaceous form of chalk, was 94 096 000 tonnes (76 543 000 tonnes of limestone excluding dolomite,[117] and 17 553 000 tonnes of chalk). Chalk, however, although a form of limestone, is used in only minor quantities for aggregates, and is dealt with separately: in this chapter the term 'limestone' excludes chalk.

During the decade 1960–70, UK output of limestone grew by 115 per cent.[118] The most important single factor in this high growth rate was its increasing use for aggregates, currently the largest single market. This is perhaps surprising since, of all the major limestone markets, the aggregates one, which utilizes the physical rather than the chemical properties of the mineral, can most readily make use of alternative materials such as sand and gravel, igneous rocks or sandstone. However, the rate of growth in demand for aggregates well exceeded that of the Gross National Product during the 1960s, and was considerably greater than the growth of any other major limestone market. The largest reserves of limestone do not usually coincide with those of the major aggregate source, sand and gravel. High transport costs ensure that limestone is used in the greatest quantities for aggregates in those areas of high demand where reserves are large and those of sand and gravel comparatively small. In the North of England,[119] for instance, where the regional demand for road aggregates was in the 1960s second only to the South-East,[120] crushed rocks, principally limestone, have the largest share of the aggregates market, while the reverse is true of England as a whole. Output of limestone was growing much more rapidly than that of sand and gravel in the UK in the 1960s, with increases in output of 115 per cent and 41 per cent over the decade respectively.[121] This primarily reflects the exhaustion of some of the more easily won sand and gravel deposits, especially in the South-East. The reserves of limestone are of very large proportions. Although extractive costs for limestone are higher than those of sand and gravel, it has a slightly wider range of aggregate usage. Sand and gravel, which has less binding power than crushed rock, is not generally suitable for either the wearing course or the base course (the second layer from the top) of most roads. Limestone, by contrast, can be used extensively for base courses, and for the wearing course of minor roads: gritty limestones have a high resistance to polishing by traffic but few are sufficiently strong to withstand the pressures imposed by modern traffic on major road wearing courses.[122]

Limestone was in 1970 extracted on a much larger scale than either of the other hard rock aggregate minerals, igneous rocks and sandstone (with total UK output figures in that year of 87 822 000 tonnes of limestone, 36 684 000 tonnes of igneous rocks and 16 648 000 tonnes of sandstone). The higher output level of limestone reflects partly the very large tonnages required annually for non-aggregate purposes, but is also due to certain advantages which limestone possesses over the other hard rocks in the aggregates market. Neither sandstone nor igneous rocks can be extracted and processed as cheaply as limestone. Limestone, as a comparatively non-abrasive mineral, very rarely needs more than two stages of crushing and sometimes only one; in any event, the secondary crushing need only be small. It may even be easier to crush limestone than over-size gravel.[123] Igneous rocks, on the other hand, usually require from three to five crushing processes. In exceptional cases limestone may even be ripped rather than blasted in the quarry, as happens with the softer chalk. Limestone is particularly easily coated with tar and bitumen in the production of coated macadams. Its ease of handling and fire resistance make it the preferred mineral of all the hard rocks in the major concrete market. Furthermore this mineral, which occurs in every region of Britain, although only in small quantities in the South-East, is more widely available than igneous rocks, though not more than sandstone. The average price of limestone for aggregates tends to be closer to that of sand and gravel than to that of either igneous rocks or sandstone. Although it is difficult to establish average prices for such localized products, the *1968 Census of Production* quoted an ex-works price of 74 pence per tonne for limestone for roadstone compared with 63 pence for sand and gravel, 95 pence for sandstone and £1·20 for igneous rocks.[124] The price disadvantage of igneous rocks and sandstone is not outweighed by their wider use for wearing course roadstone, since the markets where they are not in competition with limestone are comparatively small[125] and may diminish further since limestone's present unsuitability for surfacing major roads may well be overcome by current research into processing techniques. Since igneous rocks and sandstone are competing with the substantially cheaper limestone in the mass aggregates market, and supply smaller quantities for non-aggregate purposes, their quarries are generally on a smaller scale: the estimated average output per quarry in Britain in 1969 was 154 854 tonnes for limestone, 77 519 tonnes for igneous rocks, and 61 839 for sandstone.[125]

During the 1960s, however, output of limestone was growing less rapidly than that of igneous rocks and sandstone: limestone output increased by 115 per cent over the decade compared with a 122 per cent increase in igneous rock output and a 230 per cent increase in sandstone output.[127] Sandstone, the most widely distributed of the hard rocks in question, was extracted on only a minor scale in 1960. Consequently, the scope for expansion in such hitherto unexploited areas as Rossendale in Lancashire, close to the large Merseyside markets, was very great, as aggregate demand rose rapidly and increasing research established the suitability of certain types of sandstone for particular aggregate uses. The scope for productivity advances in this comparatively undeveloped field was also great: while productivity at limestone quarries more than quadrupled in the period 1950–70 and that at igneous rock quarries more than quintupled, that at sandstone quarries increased by more than seven times.[128]

In summary, the hard rocks as a whole take an increasing share of the aggregates market, but the share of igneous rocks and sandstone is increasing more rapidly than that of limestone (even allowing for the different percentages of consumption for aggregates). The aggregates market is certainly taking a growing percentage of limestone. Precise statistics on the relative importance of the numerous and complex end-uses of limestone do not exist, but the general pattern may be deduced from the broad categories of market served by members of the former Limestone Federation (now part of the British Quarrying and Slag Federation) which comprised some 60 per cent of the industry, excluding cement, and which published figures until 1967. As can be seen from Table 2.2, the percentage of total output

Table 2.2. Markets served by members of the Limestone Federation, 1961–7 (expressed as carbonate in thousands of tonnes)

	1961	1962	1963	1964	1965	1966	1967
Schedule 1 (Roadstone)	12 335	13 464	14 966	18 115	20 035	24 683	30 214
Schedule 2 (Industrial, etc.)	6 875	7 287	7 624	9 333	8 387	8 776	9 525
Schedule 3 (Agriculture)	2 301	3 040	2 893	3 439	2 697	2 573	2 257
Totals	21 511	23 791	25 482	30 887	31 119	36 031	41 996

Source: Limestone Federation, *23rd Annual Report*, 1968–9 (now incorporated in the British Quarrying and Slag Federation).

marketed for aggregates (roadstone) rose from 57·3 in 1961 to 71·9 in 1967. A similar indication of the importance of aggregates was given by a marketing survey of limestone quarries in the Mendips and Bristol fringe areas of Somerset (see Table 2.3). The *Census of Production* recorded a rise in consumption of limestone for aggregates from 63·6 per cent in 1963 to 71·7 per cent in 1968 (based on larger establishments in the industry only).[129] The reason for the increased

Table 2.3. Consumption of marketable stone produced by limestone quarries in the Mendips and Bristol fringe areas of Somerset, 1970 (percentages)

	Dry aggre-gates	Coated aggre-gates	Fluxing	Lime	Con-crete	Building	Agri-culture	Other
East Mendips	39	46	—	—	12	upwards of 0·5	0·5	2·5
Central Mendips	28	35	—	0·25	14	17	1	5
West Mendips	34	17	0·5 less than	3·5	31	0·5	2	11 less than
Bristol fringe	42	16	1	4	29	6	1	2

Source: Somerset County Council, *Quarrying in the Mendips*, 1971, pp. 74–8.

relative importance of aggregates is not only their high growth rate but the static or near static consumption of other major markets. The consumption of limestone for agriculture fell slightly over the period 1961–7, according to the Limestone Federation figures, and this is confirmed by data given by the Ministry of Agriculture.[130] The use of lime to promote fertility and workability of the soil is one of the earliest known commercial applications of limestone. Consumption rose sharply after the institution of a lime subsidy to farmers in 1937, but since 1955 the overall level of consumption has not fluctuated greatly, and it appears that a consistent or slightly declining mainten-ance level has been reached. Similarly, the total quantities taken by the iron and steel industry, as published by the Iron and Steel Feder-ation (see Table 2.4) fell slightly during the 1960s. The industry uses

Table 2.4. Consumption of dolomite, limestone and lime in the iron and steel industry, 1960–70 (thousand tonnes)

	Dolomite	Limestone	Lime
1960	971·3	4 146·0	1 043·4
1961	739·6	3 842·9	995·7
1962	588·9	3 439·1	919·1
1963	616·9	3 335·8	1 080·9
1964	816·2	3 643·4	1 273·7
1965	850·9	3 395·7	1 419·6
1966	676·4	3 105·7	1 336·9
1967	607·0	3 052·2	1 319·7
1968	736·9	3 194·2	1 452·2
1969	737·6	2 997·5	1 422·1
1970	782·6	3 377·3	1 510·4

Source: Iron and Steel Statistics Bureau.

lump limestone as a flux in blast furnaces and burnt lime to treat molten steel to further reduce silica and alumina content and remove sulphur and phosphorus. The marginally smaller consumption of limestone reflects mainly changes in steelmaking technology which tended to make more economical use of high quality material. The Linz Donawitz steelmaking process, for instance, required limestone whose quality is rigidly specified. The general industries market, although growing during this period, according to the Limestone Federation figures, was not growing at anything approaching the rate of aggregates. Prominent among industrial users other than the iron and steel industry is the chemical industry, which utilizes burnt and hydrated lime as essential raw materials in the manufacture of a wide range of important chemicals such as soda ash, caustic soda, organic acids and solvents, dyestuffs and bleaching powders. Limestone is also used in the glass, textiles, paper, leather, plastics, rubber, sugar and ceramic industries, for water and sewage purification and as stone dust for mines. The growth rate in this wide range of industries approximated to that of the Gross National Product, while that of aggregates considerably exceeded it. The cement industry, which uses a far higher percentage of the total output of chalk than of limestone, was actually increasing its consumption of limestone during the 1960s as a result of the policy of establishing new works away from the traditional locations in the South-East: as a result, only one of the four new works built in the period 1960–8 was based on chalk, the others on limestone. However, the impact of this was less than it might have been on cement's consumption of limestone since the growth rate of cement was comparatively slow, an increase of only 26·3 per cent over the decade.[131] The consumption for cement as a percentage of total limestone output is therefore small but growing: it rose from 0·6 in 1963 to 2·0 in 1968, according to the *Census of Production* (larger establishments only).[132] The use of limestone for building stone has contracted sharply during this century. A variety of different formations, notably the Carboniferous, the Magnesian and the Jurassic, were traditionally local sources of building stone. The Carboniferous and Magnesian are now very little worked for this purpose, largely because of the high costs of production, the competition of newer, cheaper building materials, and the lack of resistance of these limestones to atmospheric impurities. The Jurassic limestone of the Cotswolds and the Bath, Portland and Purbeck types are, however, still worked on a small-scale for building, especially for use in areas where the traditional building material is insisted upon by planning consents for building. Limestone is now used more extensively than any other type of block natural rock, and it is likely that aesthetic considerations are relevant here: building and monumental stone comprised 3·3 per cent of the total limestone output of larger establishments compared with less than 1 per cent of total igneous rock output.[133]

Although the various formations and types of limestone are an important factor in determining the suitability of limestone for particular purposes, there are a great variety of chemical and physical properties within each formation which complicate the picture. Limestone is mainly a sedimentary rock consisting primarily of calcium carbonate associated with varying proportions of impurities. Geologically, the term limestone applies to those of which calcite and dolomite (calcium carbonate plus magnesium carbonate) make up at least 50 per cent and which include more calcite than dolomite. If the dolomite content exceeds that of calcite the rock is technically dolomite. Although limestone and dolomite may be quarried together for aggregates, sometimes undistinguished by their operators for record purposes, and are often added together in statistical tables, they are separate minerals and dolomite is not dealt with here. Although there are a few thin fresh-water deposits, most limestone formations are built up of fragments of shells of marine origin. There are also some chemically precipitated deposits and vein deposits of crystalline calcium carbonate (calcite).

The purest types of limestone originated where very little contaminating silt or sand was deposited, i.e. in ocean beds furthest removed from the land masses. The purest British formation is the Carboniferous limestone, deposited with or just before the laying down of the Coal Measures. This is the formation of the greatest economic importance, but even here the degree of concentration of quarry workings within the formation reflects their respective levels of purity. Equally important, this is also a product of proximity to large markets, for even the highest quality limestone, selling in 1971 at some £4·92 per tonne,[134] is a relatively cheap commodity unable to bear heavy transport costs. The chief concentrations of Carboniferous workings, in order of volume of output in 1969, are: the South Pennine area of Derbyshire and Staffordshire (the Peak District); the Mendips, south Gloucestershire and Forest of Dean; the Northern Pennines and fringes of the Lake District; South Wales, principally Glamorgan; North Wales, principally east Denbighshire and Flintshire; and the Central Lowlands of Scotland, principally Fife and West Lothian (see Fig. 2.3). The Peak District, the most important producing area of any type of limestone, accounted for some 25 per cent of the total output for England: Derbyshire and Staffordshire produced 17 760 000 tonnes out of an English total of 65 366 000 tonnes in 1969.[135] (This

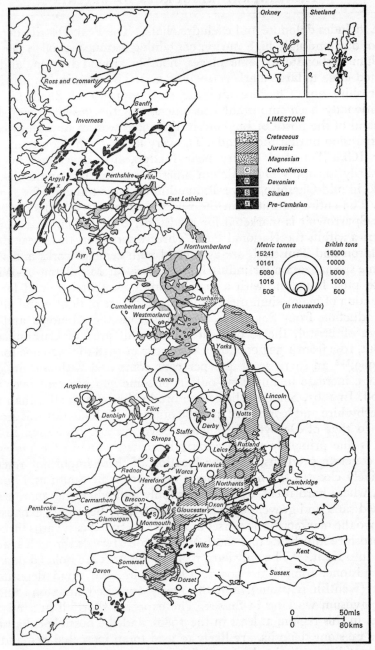

Fig. 2.3 *Limestone:* output by county, 1969
Arrows indicate location of counties whose totals are grouped
Source: Department of the Environment

data includes dolomite and excludes chalk.) The Peak District deposits are of outstandingly high purity, containing as much as 98–9 per cent calcium carbonate in some places, notably around Buxton, and are located close to large markets (see Fig. 2.4). The chemical industries of Lancashire and Cheshire and the steel industry of Sheffield have traditionally been important consumers, but the growing aggregates demand of the north of England in the 1960s was an important cause of expansion during the decade. The very large, 5·1 million tonnes per year ICI's Tunstead quarry near Buxton, first developed in 1929 primarily to supply high calcium limestone to the ICI ammonia-soda works in mid-Cheshire, now sells in addition large tonnages for aggregates. The entire output from the relatively new (1953) Eldon quarry near Sparrowpit is marketed for roadstone, the chief end-use of most quarries within the National Park. Three quarries in this area, Hope, Cauldron and Tunstead, are associated with cement works and there is some specialization for industrial purposes—at Middleton-by-Wirksworth pure limestone with a high dolomite content is mined for the extraction of magnesium used in the manufacture of light metal alloys.

Production from Somerset, primarily from the Mendips and the fringes of Bristol, the second most important area of Carboniferous output, rose from 1 524 000 tonnes per year in 1948 to 7 620 000 tonnes in 1969,[136] an increase of 400 per cent compared with the national average increase in limestone output of some 300 per cent over that period. In 1961, Somerset limestone production was smaller than that of Derbyshire and Yorkshire: by 1969 output from Somerset was second only to that of Derbyshire.[137] The above average expansion in this area is due primarily to the greatly increased demand for aggregate and concrete products, and the location of these important reserves relatively close to the high demand markets of the South and South-East, where hard rocks are in short supply and where the more easily worked sand and gravel deposits are increasingly becoming exhausted. In 1970 the markets for Somerset limestone extended eastwards through Oxfordshire into Essex and south and south-eastwards through Hampshire into Kent.[138] The only hard rocks in this area are isolated deposits of sandstone, some limestone in Oxfordshire, the small deposits in Kent (Kentish ragstone), and the newly exploited limestone underlying gypsum working in Sussex. The expected shortfall in sand and gravel in this region, at least in the 1980s, and the possible exhaustion of the ragstone deposits, are likely to lead to an increased demand for Somerset limestone in the South-Eastern aggregate market. Pressure of demand from this market has also affected the growth of limestone production from Gloucestershire which has risen from 1 million tonnes

Fig. 2.4 *Limestone quarries in the Peak District*
Source: Yorkshire Geological Society

in 1948 to about 3 960 000 tonnes in 1968, mainly from a complex of Carboniferous workings in the Forest of Dean and the area on the northern fringe of Bristol.[139] The Gloucestershire deposits supply Bristol, parts of the Welsh border, and counties immediately north and east of the A4.

The extent of Carboniferous workings in the Northern Pennine counties is difficult to determine since Magnesian limestone is also worked on the eastern flank. However, the chief stimulus to expansion here in the 1960s was the heavy aggregate demands of the North of England, although industrial and agricultural lime is also an important product. The Carboniferous deposits of Wales made up the largest part of total Welsh production in 1969 of 15 075 000 tonnes. The percentage of UK output contributed by Wales in that year was a substantial 18·3 per cent,[140] although this figure had fallen from 20·3 per cent in 1958 (including dolomite).[141] Glamorgan, which had in 1958 an output second only to Derbyshire, had by 1969 been overtaken by both Somerset and Yorkshire (see Fig. 2.3). The slightly diminishing output percentage of Wales probably reflects a comparatively low level of demand for the increasingly important aggregates market: in terms of road aggregates, the intensity of demand in Wales in 1967 was lower than that of the South-East, Northern and Midlands regions of England.[142] However, total limestone output grew from 6 604 000 tonnes in 1958 to 15 075 000 tonnes in 1969. Both North and South Wales have immense Carboniferous limestone resources, with areas of very high quality. The greater importance of South Wales production has historically been due to the much larger scale of the South Wales iron and steel industry. Although South Wales remains the largest output area, with the county of Glamorgan producing more than twice as much as any other Welsh county (mainly Carboniferous but also some Jurassic), the percentage of the Welsh total contributed by North Wales rose from 23·0 per cent in 1958 to 37·6 per cent in 1969.[143] (North Wales here comprises Anglesey and Caernarvonshire, Flintshire and Denbighshire.) The proportionally greater growth of North Wales, deriving principally from Flintshire and Denbighshire, reflects the increasing quantities of limestone aggregates being marketed in North-West England, principally Cheshire and Lancashire, although chemically pure limestone for industrial purposes is also of growing importance. Two large Denbighshire quarries, the Raynes quarry of ICI and Llysfaen quarry, have coastal locations and are able to discharge their output straight into ships, while there are no similar facilities serving coastally sited quarries in South Wales. These two quarries also benefit from good rail and road links to Merseyside, which are likely to have been of increasing importance in the 1960s. In addition, the one new cement works in Wales, that at Padeswood, started in 1950 and subsequently upgraded, is served with limestone from the Cefn Mawr quarry in Flintshire.

The major Scottish Carboniferous output, from Fife and West Lothian, derives from the deposits closest to urban concentrations in the Central Lowlands. In 1963 a new limestone based cement works was started at Dunbar in East Lothian, the only Scottish cement works apart from those grinding clinker. Scottish limestone resources of any type are, however, comparatively scarce, in contrast to Scottish reserves of igneous rocks, and total output in 1969 constituted only 2·2 per cent of British output[144] (including dolomite). There are, in spite of small, older deposits further north, shortages of agricultural lime in parts of Scotland, including most of the islands, although in some places, such as the beaches of Lewis,[145] calcium carbonate is extracted from shell sand or shingle.

The other limestone formations are economically much less important than the Carboniferous. Magnesian limestone, which in Britain is mainly identified with the Permian period, consists of more than 3 per cent of magnesium with a dolomite content of 5 to 10 per cent, and outcrops from South Shields in County Durham to Nottingham. Contained within this formation are reserves of dolomite used for both specialized refractory and industrial use, and for aggregates—dealt with in Chapter 4. The Magnesian limestone is also worked for aggregates, notably in the West Riding where there are four major quarries serving this market, for agricultural lime, and for the few manufacturing processes in which magnesium oxide is either not harmful or is definitely required.[147] It cannot be used as flux.

The Jurassic limestones which outcrop from the North Yorkshire Moors south-westwards through the Midlands to Dorset vary greatly in character and purity but are mainly too soft to be used as roadstone, a factor which greatly limits their growth potential. The Lias limestones of the Midlands are used for lime-burning and cement manufacture; the cement works at Kirton-in-Lindsey uses the Inferior Oolite ('Lincolnshire limestone'), and that at Branstone in the Vale of Belvoir the Lower Lias ('hydraulic limestone'), a formation which is also exploited for three cement works in the Vale of Glamorgan. In north Northamptonshire, the deposits are sufficiently cleaved to be worked for natural stone slates; they are mined at Collyweston and split with the aid of frost action. Apart from the Clipsham stone of Rutland, the Jurassic deposits of the South of England are now the only limestone worked on a significant scale for building stone, notably the Doulting stone in Somerset, Painswick stone in Gloucestershire, and Bath stone which is extracted in Gloucestershire and Wiltshire though not now in Somerset. The concentrations of mainly small workings in the Portland (Oolite) and Purbeck beds of Dorset still supply chiefly building stone, although here, as in the Cotswolds, the percentage of output marketed for aggregates is growing. The old Pre-Cambrian Dalradian limestones of Scotland are worked for local markets (mainly agricultural) in central Banffshire, southern Inverness-shire and Perthshire. The Silurian limestone of Wenlock Edge in Shropshire and other parts of the Welsh border supply primarily the aggregate and agricultural markets. In 1971 there were two small quarries in Radnorshire working the Silurian deposits for agricultural lime, of which there is a shortage in Mid-Wales. Probably the most important of the older formations is the Devonian limestone of the Plymouth, Newton Abbot and Torquay areas. Seven quarries are located in this deposit, one, at Plymstock, associated with a cement works and the others producing, in descending order of importance, stone for aggregates, agricultural and industrial lime, and very minor quantities of ornamental stone. Prominent among these is the Moorcroft quarry of English China Clays Ltd., an aggregates producer with a capacity of more than 1 million tonnes per year. Some of the output of Moorcroft is transported to South-Eastern markets by sea from Plymouth. The quarries in the Devonian deposits, together with two other quarries in the Carboniferous limestone of east Devon, produced 4 per cent of the national output of limestone in 1968.[147] Both deposits, reinforced by the igneous rock reserves of Devon and more particularly Cornwall, mean that the South-West is a net 'exporter' of stone for aggregates.

The Lower Cretaceous limestone known as Kentish ragstone, a sandy limestone of a type intermediate between a limestone and a sandstone, is the only hard limestone which occurs in the South-East apart from that underlying gypsum workings at Robertsbridge in Sussex. The ragstone is quarried from the Hythe beds of the Lower Greensand from quarries scattered along the outcrop of the beds from a narrow belt across the county from Westerham to Newington near Folkestone.[148] Output increased steadily during the 1960s, and in 1970 the six active quarries in the neighbourhood of Maidstone, the widest part of the outcrop, had an estimated combined output of 254 000 tonnes.[149] These quarries are small units: in the previous year the total of nine quarries in the Kentish ragstone had a total output of 609 600 tonnes.[150] Although very minor quantities are still used for walls or for building in the few areas where planning considerations dictate the use of this, the traditional building stone, the material is used preponderantly for roadmaking, particularly in the form of tar macadam. As this is almost the only hard limestone found in commercial quantities in the South-East, the markets for ragstone extend outside Kent to the southern Greater London areas (south of the Thames), east Sussex and parts of Surrey and Essex.[151] However, unworked reserves within areas for which planning consents have been given are believed to be less than 8 million tonnes; consultants estimate the mineral bearing land, with workable deposits, would provide an additional 14·2 million tonnes of stone, but there is some doubt about these being given permission to be worked. Consequently, production from this area is unlikely to continue to expand at the same rate in the 1970s and could well contract.[152]

The great majority of limestones occur as thick deposits and are worked by quarrying in areas where they are covered by little or no overburden. Explosives are principally used at the face to break down the mineral into boulders—this primary blasting is now usually large-scale or 'full face' blasting, because of increasing mechanization at the quarry. Secondary blasting at the face, to break the material into sizes small enough for transport to the primary crushers, is now being increasingly replaced by the use of a drop ball, both a cheaper and a quieter process. Transport from the face to the crushers is usually by dumpers, whose manoeuvrability and bucket capacity are critical factors in productivity. Limestone for aggregates is crushed, cleaned and screened, with processes becoming more complicated as specifications for some grades tighten. The crushed material may be coated with tar or bitumen on-site, which increases its value and consequently its market radius. Lime for the chemical industry is usually burnt on-site in lime kilns, a process which reduces bulk and hence transport costs. Some very high grade limestones are selected by flotation and optical sorting. It follows therefore that large quarries for aggregates and for lime for the chemical industry are likely to have considerable quantities of plant on-site, as of course do quarries for cement. Limestone for steelmaking flux, but not ironmaking flux, requires grinding and calcining. Most of that for agriculture and certain other uses such as stone dust for mines and some fillers is ground—this involves substantially smaller quantities of plant. The limited amounts of limestone used for building stone require very little treatment before delivery to the stonemason's yard.

In a very few instances limestone, of particular value perhaps because of its quality or location, occurs at a depth or in a situation only accessible by deep-mining. The largest British limestone mine, and the only one on any substantial scale, works the Carboniferous deposit at Middleton by Wirksworth in the Peak District. Mining here

D

is justified by the presence of very pure material, 98–9 per cent calcium carbonate, covered by 55 metres of overburden consisting of lower quality limestone.[153] The extraction method is pillar-and-stall and the primary crusher is located underground. In 1965 some 254 000 tonnes per year were produced, mainly for the Lancashire glass industry and sugar beet refining, with some quantities for aggregates and other uses such as water-repellent dust and fillers. Other smaller English mines include the working at Collyweston in Northamptonshire for well-cleaved material used as roofing slates. In west Wiltshire only one underground working remained operative in 1969 in an area formerly heavily mined for building stone and containing some 97 kilometres of tunnels. Mining here is justified by the quality of the stone, overlain by Forest Marble.[154] Medium-hard limestone underlying gypsum workings at Robertsbridge in Sussex at some 153 metres is being exploited after the extraction of the gypsum: the working at this depth is justified by the great scarcity of hard stone in this area, and economies resulting from the coincidence of the two minerals at this site. A roadstone plant on-site produces bitumen coated macadam. Two small mines in Scotland, in Midlothian and Fife, were in operation in 1969. In each case the quality required is overlain by overburden which has made opencast working uneconomic. Calcite, the crystalline form of calcium carbonate, is mined on a very limited scale at the Long Rake near Youlgreave in Derbyshire where it occurs as a gangue mineral and is produced as a by-product of fluorspar, and in Flintshire in North Wales. The Hendre mine in Flintshire was in 1971 producing 2540–3050 tonnes per year,[155] mainly for decorative uses within the building industry, such as mosaics or terrazzo. A new crushing and drying plant was being commissioned, and proved reserves provided for approximately 15 years' working at the existing level of output. Mining here is justified by the quality of the material and made necessary by the depth of overburden.

At the present time, limestone mining is an exceptional operation, only economic is unusual circumstances. The balance of economic advantage could however alter in favour of mining in the future, for instance if planning permission for surface working became more difficult to obtain, or more onerous conditions were imposed on such workings, or if rapid advances were made in techniques of underground working of bulk minerals. At present, however, the overwhelming bulk of limestone output is quarried.

The average size of limestone quarries is partially related to the markets they serve and the extent of plant required on-site. Quarries for cement and often those for aggregates tend to be large. Those for agricultural lime and building stone, historically extremely localized to serve nearby settlements, are often small. However, the overall trend in limestone extraction, as in other types of quarrying, is towards an increasing unit size. The increasing size of quarries is part of a complex of interrelated phenomenon including the growth of large public companies at the expense of small family firms and an average increase in the market radius served. The chief factor influencing larger quarry size for limestone as for other types of stone is the high level of capital investment needed for modern equipment and plant which, to be justified, requires a large, long-term producing area. The maximization of quarry efficiency depends on the proper integration of blasting, loading and primary crushing. The most sophisticated techniques utilize mobile primary crushers which reduce the rock at the blasting site sufficiently for it to be fed on to the conveyor belts to the main plant, a technique first developed in Germany and which can substantially lower the very expensive transport of material from face to crusher. Some sand and gravel pits can advantageously utilize conveyor belts for internal transport, without of course the heavy additional costs of crushing being incurred. This technique does, however, at limestone quarries, involve both substantial operating costs, which are only economic at the largest quarries, and very high investment levels, some £250 000 per mobile crusher at 1971 prices, only forthcoming from the largest firms. The continuing search for economies of scale in what is a very competitive industry is expected to mean that the trend towards larger quarries will continue in the 1970s. The director of the Institute of Quarrying has said of the quarrying industry as a whole that

there seems to be a good case for units up to the size of 1 million tonnes of annual output. This will involve an investment of something over £1 million for the plant and basic mobile equipment. There seems little point in designing for much less than this size in the '70s if the real economies of large-scale production are to be realized.[156]

Apart from the heavy investment in plant, other factors which have favoured the growth of large companies, especially in the aggregates sector, are the development of research programmes both into processing techniques and market forecasting; and the need for major aggregates firms to operate computerized predictions of regional supply and demand and to have their own laboratories, geologists and chemists. A further factor has been the much greater vulnerability of the small firm to regional or national depressions, a particularly significant matter in the aggregates industry where fluctuations in the market tend to be more pronounced than in the economy as a whole. The 1968 Road

Transport Act, which raised transport costs by up to 25 per cent as a result of insistence on high safety standards, bore more heavily not only on the small haulage contractor but also on the small quarry operator in competition with the large company-owned fleets. Although the costs of acquiring reserves of hard rock were, in 1971, only some 25 per cent of those of acquiring sand and gravel reserves, the widespread practice of relating the period of security conferred by planning permissions to the amount of capital investment in plant, equipment, transport and preliminary works[147] greatly favoured the large company. These factors, operating particularly in the aggregates sector, have tended to outweigh the advantages which a small firm, with local associations, might be expected to enjoy in what are still primarily local markets.

Some small companies, producing in some cases less than 1000 tonnes per year, do survive, and help to make up the comparatively large estimated total of some 440 firms operating approximately 542 active limestone quarries in Britain in 1969.[158] The large public companies, producing as much as 2 million tonnes per year or in the case of ICI's Tunstead quarry about 5 million tonnes per year, tend to operate in the main production areas of the Carboniferous sequence such as the Peak District (dominated by ICI and Tarmac Roadstone Holdings) and to have interest in all the main kinds of limestone market. Smaller firms on the other hand tend to be more specialized. The dominance of the large companies particularly in the aggregates sector was greatly strengthened in the 1960s as a result of the large number of mergers, both vertical and horizontal, already mentioned; many of these overlapped with sand and gravel, although limestone operators have on average less diverse interests than sand and gravel operators. The large companies produce other types of aggregates apart from limestone and almost always have interests in processing. The formation of vertical mergers between related industries has in some cases included a complete series of links between limestone extraction for aggregates, aggregate coating, ready mixed concrete, transport and civil engineering.[159] The English China Clays Group is a case in point. Horizontal and vertical amalgamation is of course no new phenomenon in the limestone extraction industry. As long ago as 1891 several Derbyshire producers combined to form Buxton Lime Firms Ltd., from which ICI Lime Division was formed in 1926, and the links between limestone extraction and steel companies, cement companies and chemical manufacturers are also of long standing. However, the pace of amalgamation in the aggregates sector in the 1960s was much faster than anything previously experienced. Indeed, it is widely predicted that the process of amalgamation, and hence the domination of limestone and other aggregates by the large producers, will continue.[160]

The continuing importance of serving local markets for this high bulk/low value commodity ensures that these large companies have a multiplicity of production units, in spite of increasing quarry size. The traditional market radius of limestone quarries is 72–81 kilometres.[161] Generally speaking, the ex-quarry price of limestone aggregate doubles at a distance of about 48 kilometres from the pit by road, which makes the cost of its transport component comparable to that of sand and gravel. (Although transport costs do vary according to the type of road and vehicle used, and are greater for urban rather than rural areas.) Traditionally, the limited market radius for the product has been a strong deterrent to large-scale quarrying operations. However, transport and other changes in the 1960s have tended to extend market radii, especially for aggregates, making the industry, in market terms, regional rather than local or, in the case of very large quarries, interregional. Since the main cause of lengthening hauls has been the shortage of certain categories of material, particularly hard aggregates, in particular areas, especially the South-East, transport costs on longer hauls have been partially contained by further on-site processing. Thus the price of coated limestone only doubles at 64 kilometres from the pit rather than the 48 kilometres of uncoated limestone aggregates. More than this, the use of larger vehicles has effected transport economies. Until recently the majority of vehicles were 4- or 6-wheeled types of between 7 and 15 tonnes gross weight. Since many vehicles had to be replaced as a result of the 1968 Road Transport Act, it is more common to find 6- or 8-wheeled tipper type lorries, or, most recently, 10-wheeled articulated hoppers or tippers of 32 tonnes gross weight.[162] The period of time in transit on the road has also been reduced as the motorway network has expanded, again leading to cost reductions.

Rail transport is by no means in general use, though there is a tendency towards its increasing employment for distances in excess of 56 kilometres, beyond which lorry transport may become uneconomic. However, rail transport is only economic when the producing quarry has its own rail link and is supplying a consumer or depot at or near the line. The chief improvement in this sphere in the 1960s was the partial replacement of British Rail short-wheelbase, non-fitted vacuum wagons with restricted speed capability by special 45 tonne bogie-hoppers capable of maintaining passenger train speeds. In a few cases large 102 tonne gross loading wagons, generally privately owned, with permitted speeds of up to 121 kilometres per hour, have been introduced.[163] Limestone from both Derbyshire and the Mendips is transported by rail to South-Eastern markets. Two quarries in Somerset send uncoated stone by rail. Amey Roadstone Corporation's New Frome quarry, which has a privately owned rail link, despatches dry aggregate to their depots at Ardingley in Kent, West Drayton in Middlesex and Totton near Southampton. The other company, Messrs Foster, Yeoman Ltd., use rail on a limited scale for the transport of uncoated aggregate from their Dulcote quarry in the central Mendips to temporary depots in the home counties and near Southampton.[164] It is expected that there will be increased use of rail transport in the 1970s, based on bulk haulage contracts utilizing liner type trains and specially designed mineral wagons. Transport by sea, which can offer substantial savings if wharf capacity is large, has a limited value because of the inland location of many major producing areas, but is used for the transport of limestone from Denbighshire to Lancashire and Cheshire, and from south Devon to the Thames wharves. A possible development which could cut transport costs is the use of pipelines. These are not yet in operation for transporting limestone, although a 92 kilometre pipeline has, since 1965, carried slurried chalk from the Chilterns to Rugby. Whatever transport medium may be used, it is likely that the necessarily increasing market radii will of themselves promote greater efficiencies is transport.

The complex of interrelated factors examined above relate broadly to all the hard rock aggregates. The improvements in productivity which result from massive investment programmes and increasing economies of scale, dependent on widening markets, are also reflected in quarrying as a whole. Over the period 1950–70 output per wage-earner at limestone quarries increased from 1921 tonnes to 9351 tonnes,[165] that is productivity more than quadrupled. This productivity increase was exceeded amongst quarrying industries only by igneous rock and sandstone. These improvements in productivity were accompanied by a reduction in the size of the limestone quarrying labour-force, which fell from 13 450 in 1950 to 9414 in 1970.[166] According to the Institute of Quarrying, a completely mechanized crushed stone quarry with an output of 1 million tonnes per year requires a labourforce of 20 to 30 men. In the immediately pre- and post-war period, this same labourforce would have had an output of only 25 400 to 30 500 tonnes.[167] This has meant that quarrying has been relatively unaffected by the great increases in labour costs during the 1960s, and the price of raw stone was held relatively stable over the decade 1960–70. However, the striking increases in overall productivity have not compared with opencast mining, where operations are conceived and operated on an even bigger scale: the average output from aggregate excavators is only about half what would be regarded as acceptable in opencast mining.[168] Rapid productivity advances on the quarry floor itself are predicted for the 1970s;[169] these are more likely to be achieved at the large quarries, whose growth seems an inescapable feature of quarrying in this decade.

Limestone extraction, in common with that of other hard rocks and chalk, is not a large consumer of land. Quarry faces usually range in depth from 18 metres up to 61 metres, and the average yield per hectare is 250 900 tonnes,[170] although this varies according to the depth of the overburden. This compares with an average of only 62 700 tonnes per hectare from most types of gravel deposits. There may be the option of vertical rather than horizontal expansion. The high output from ICI's Tunstead quarry in the Peak District is to be sustained by extending the depth rather than the area of the working, and in 1969 operations were started to open up a second working bench below floor level.[171] Operations beneath the water-table, which can further increase the tonnage extracted per hectare, are technically feasible, although these involve special problems of water pollution to be discussed later. Because of the average high tonnage extracted per hectare in hard rock quarries, the annual take for limestone or chalk extraction at cement works is generally much lower than that for the argillaceous raw material, clay or shale, although the quantities required are much larger. At Associated Portland Cement Manufacturers' Hope works in Derbyshire the annual land takes in 1953 were 0·41 hectares per year for limestone compared with 2·4 hectares per year for shale.[172] The total annual take for limestone in England and Wales is probably some 203 hectares,[173] compared with 1620 hectares per year for sand and gravel.

Limestone extraction conflicts with agricultural interest much less often than sand and gravel. Whereas alluvial gravels may underlie land classified by the Ministry of Agriculture as being grade one, deposits of limestone are usually at most covered with land in grade three; that is agricultural land with some limitations on cropping, and which may be of inferior agricultural quality. Only in exceptional circumstances is the overburden of high value—at Dunbar the limestone workings attached to the cement works underlie some of Scotland's finest red soils. The limestone deposits in the Vale of Glamorgan, the Cotswolds, and the most heavily worked parts of the Mendips between Shepton Mallet and Frome are covered by land of medium agricultural productivity. The agricultural value of most of the major limestone extracting district of Derbyshire is lower: at the Hope cement works the agricultural value of the land taken for limestone extraction is negligible compared with that consumed for shale extraction.[174] Similarly, the upland location of the majority of the workings have reduced the likelihood of conflict with areas of urban concentration. The main exception to this general rule is Glamorgan, where the limestone quarries encircling Cardiff to the north and west partially restrict residential development, although the steep slopes involved do to some extent limit urban expansion anyway. There are also instances where the spread of rural dormitory villages, especially of executive-type houses, may conflict with limestone extraction—e.g. the Wharfe valley in the West Riding which may be described as the stockbroker belt of Leeds, and the growth of 'executive housing' in the Peak Park, especially for commuters from Sheffield. Although this type of conflict is growing, it is still the exception rather than the rule. Limestone extraction and on-site processing does not, moreover, produce waste in any large quantity. Any overburden which may be present can be used for backfilling, while waste from former extraction plants or from lime-kilns can often be marketed, for instance for agricultural liming. Some waste dumps which survive from the past, for instance in South Wales, have, without any treatment, improved the quality of the grazing land on which they were deposited.

However, limestone quarrying does pose very severe problems in terms of amenity and landscape conservation, the very areas where objective judgement and quantification are most difficult. Extraction necessarily takes place mainly in upland areas valued for their scenery. The hard limestone of the Carboniferous, Devonian and Silurian deposits give rise naturally to bare rock outcrops, weathered crags of interesting colour effects and almost vertical walls and gorges where rivers have eaten into the soluble rock. This is not however a barren landscape, since the well-distributed rainfall produces more vegetation than in the typical 'karst' country of Yugoslavia and Istra. This type of country has great appeal to walkers and sightseers, apart from the special interest it may offer to naturalists, archaeologists and, in particular, spelaeologists. Limestone is one of the minerals most widely quarried within national parks. There are seven productive limestone quarries within the Brecon Beacons, six of them within the National Park and one just outside with reserves straddling the park boundary.[175] The combined output of these quarries in 1970 was 1 447 800 tonnes, and all may be said to pose amenity problems in areas of high scenic quality. Most limestone quarries in the Yorkshire Dales National Park are located in the West Riding section, near Bolton Abbey, Cracoe, Threshfield, Kilnsey in upper Wharfedale and Horton in Ribblesdale. High output in this area is related to demand from the populous conurbations of Leeds and Bradford, and land use conflicts are particularly severe in Wharfedale. Further north, limestone quarries are located close to Wensleydale, and just beyond the southern edge of the North York Moors National Park. In the Lake District National Park limestone quarries at Kendal Fell, Shap Beck and Whitborrow in Westmorland and Faulds Brow near Caldbeck in Cumberland add to the the pressure on this area which, with the Peak Park, receives the largest number of visitors annually. There were in 1970 a total of 35 active quarries in the Peak District as a whole, with four main concentrations in the neighbourhoods of Buxton, Matlock/Wirksworth, Stoney Middleton and Dale in Derbyshire, and Cauldon Low in Staffordshire. The Peak Park boundary was drawn in 1950 specifically to exclude all but the very centrally situated Stoney Middleton complex and other scattered quarries. However, the bulk of the limestone outcrop is contained within the Park, and in 1953 the Minister approved the application for a new working at Eldon Hill, within its boundaries, in the face of opposition from the Peak Park Planning Board, based on what they claim is 'the very obtrusive nature of the workings in an area of high landscape quality'.[176] As a result of the creation of the Eldon Hill quarry and the expansion of others, the proportion of total Peak District output derived from quarries within the park has risen since the boundaries were drawn. In 1970 this contribution constituted about 25 per cent.[177] As a result of this growing pressure on the Park, the Peak Park Planning Board have urged the Department of the Environment to reappraise limestone extraction policy. In the future the Board would like to see as much limestone extraction as possible carried out beyond the Park. However, the Department of the Environment have stated that there can be no policy reappraisal while the Institute of Geological Sciences are carrying out research into the quality of limestone in the Peak District. The pressures of limestone extraction in the Peak District are reinforced by the demands of other extractive industries in this area, notably fluorspar and sandstone. Apart from the National Parks, large quantities of limestone are derived from areas designated as being of Outstanding Natural Beauty or of Great Landscape Value, such as much of the Somerset Mendips, or Wenlock Edge in Shropshire.

The most obvious problem caused by limestone extraction in such areas is its impact on the landscape, in which the mineral is both an amenity and a resource. The workings may permanently change the topography. Some extraction may even involve the removal of entire small hills, leaving only grassed-over stumps, although modern planning stipulations usually insist on the preservation of hill profiles. Many more workings are bluff (perpendicular) sites which it would be impossible to restore. In the Peak District many quarries are sited on high slopes such as the outer bluffs of limestone outcrops and the sides of the dales, particularly prominent and attractive features of the landscape. The great bulk of workings are not restored since, even where pits exist and filling would be technically possible, their location is in rural areas remote from the vast quantities of fill required. A few worked-out quarries near centres of population may provide valuable tipping space for domestic refuse: Pickering Urban District Council is filling a disused quarry in the North Riding, whilst this practice is increasingly being followed in the West Riding of Yorkshire. Similarly a disused ragstone quarry near Maidstone is being filled with refuse. In a few areas deposits occur as horizontal strata covered by overburden and restoration at lower levels may be possible. At Associated Portland Cement Manufacturers' Dunbar cement works, opened in 1963, where limestone and shale are found together in parallel strata (upper shale and upper limestone, lower shale and lower limestone, separated by a band of sandstone), a cyclical method of extraction and restoration is operated. As each new strip of arable land is taken, another is restored at some 12 metres below the original level. This method of working is possible at Dunbar because the proportions of limestone and shale required are fortunately in balance, and some 18 metres of reject material, consisting of topsoil, drift and sandstone, provide fill.[178] What is being achieved at this location is probably comparable with the best of ironstone and opencast coal extraction after treatment, but the particular circumstances of the area to be restored can be crucial. In Nottinghamshire, where extraction of bedded Jurassic strata has also been followed by restoration to agriculture at lower levels, this method has not been found to be entirely satisfactory, and the practice of backfilling with refuse before replacing topsoil is now followed.[179]

The restoration of limestone quarries remains very exceptional. Only about 14 hectares per year of worked-out chalk and limestone quarries are reclaimed compared with a total annual take of about 284 hectares.[180] The main hope of ameliorating the impact of worked-out areas in the majority of quarries lies in the natural mellowing of the face. This occurs in Magnesian limestone in 2 to 3 years and in Carboniferous limestone in 3 to 4 years. However, the limestone does not begin to weather substantially until after 20 to 30 years.

The natural regeneration of flora may be helped by artificially creating screes at the foot of faces so that the slope is not too abrupt, or by layering the final working face to promote vegetational growth. These measures may help disused quarries to merge into the landscape, especially as most such quarries have up to now been small in scale. But possibly of more significance is the question of mitigating the impact of active quarries, most of which now have working lives of some 30 years and some working lives of more than 60 years. A quarried rock face does not necessarily, in everyone's view, 'spoil' a landscape, but the association of active quarrying with large quantities of plant does constitute an undeniable intrusion in otherwise rural surroundings.

The problem of the visual impact of machinery at limestone quarries is a serious and in some respects a growing one. The increase in numbers of very large quarries does have the merit of permitting the closure of more smaller works elsewhere—the expansion at Tunstead has permitted the closure of 17 of ICI's smaller quarries[181] — but these larger workings are correspondingly much more difficult to screen. A large quarry supplying aggregates is likely to have an on-site complex of crushing, asphalt, concrete batching and mixing plants. A modern, high output lime burning kiln will probably be nearly 31 metres high. A modern cement works may contain a large kiln complex, preheater tower and chimney, limestone crushers, clinker stores, cement silos, laboratory and control rooms. The growing size and complexity of plant of all types may be partially offset by the improvements in landscaping techniques, especially if tree planting, the construction of banks on which these may grow and other screening operations are carried out in advance. Large companies sometimes employ their own landscape architects and new plant complexes, although much larger than older ones, may well be better designed. The optimum choice of site from both an economic and environmental point of view is however only possible in the very rare case of an entirely new quarry; in most instances, new plant is added to an existing site where scope for concealment or landscaping can be limited.

The problems associated with the day-to-day working of limestone quarries are common to all types of hard rock extraction, and are primarily noise, vibration, dust and traffic generation. One reason why some of these problems appear to have increased recently is that, apart from the greater consciousness of such questions, more people are living in close proximity to quarries as commuter villages in rural areas are expanded.[181] The most frequent cause of complaint, as far as local residents are concerned, is the noise and vibration of explosive charges which, apart from disturbance, may very occasionally result in ground movements and even damage to property. From the planning authority's point of view, these levels are difficult to control or alter. However, there is room for technical improvement in blasting procedures within the industry to ensure the maximum of fragmentation from the minimum of explosives; this must be desirable from both an economic and amenity standpoint. In some cases it may be possible to delay blasting until there is a favourable wind to carry the noise away from local settlements.[182] However, the effects of explosives, especially in terms of ground movement, may be considerably reduced by the practice of 'interval blasting': here an interval of 1/50th of a second between the detonation of each charge in a number of shotholes is sufficient to reduce vibrations. More continuous noise is generally the product of plant operations and internal transport within the quarry. Plant noise may be substantially reduced by the installation of proper cladding equipment. In the case of recent quarries, planning stipulations may be imposed on plant noise, but the enforcement of specific standards is not easy as sound levels are difficult to monitor, especially where differences between day and night are concerned. In the long term, care will have to be taken in the siting of new housing in quarrying areas to take advantage of the prevailing winds to carry noise away.

The hard rock quarrying industry, and in particular limestone, is one of the largest producers of dust in the country. Dust may be produced at the workface, by the crushers, drying plant, screens and elevators, by stockpiles and by dumpers operating on unmetalled internal roads. The trend towards finer and finer crushing requirements in the 1960s involved a steadily increasing production of dust, which took the industry unawares and brought considerable operational and public relations difficulties.[183] Large crushers, dealing with 1000 tonnes of material an hour, can create clouds of dust visible for miles, which may settle heavily on fields and trees close to the quarry and be carried in small quantities as far as 1000 metres by the prevailing winds.[184] With efficient modern dust-suppression equipment at all points in the processing cycle, it is possible to reduce this nuisance to a minimum. Very substantial improvements can be brought about very cheaply by such measures as metalling internal roads, washing wheels, covering stockpiles of all but the coarsest material and sheeting lorries. Recently standards have improved as a result of concerted efforts by some local authorities and operators and by the Alkali Inspectorate but legitimate complaints about high dust levels continue. These may result from the overloading or imperfect maintenance of dust suppressors at modern quarries or from lack of adequate facilities at older units which may pre-date effective planning controls.

Certainly, although the disturbance caused by quarrying operations in terms of noise, dust and visual intrusion can be greatly reduced by careful planning stipulations or the voluntary efforts of the extractor, many current workings do, in fact, date from a period when planning constraints were few. In the Peak Park a number of limestone quarries still operate under permissions granted by the Minister during the 1950s which, in the main, only contained conditions about waste disposal,[185] not the most serious problem. In some cases backfilling was required on completion of the workings but nothing was done to mitigate impact during a very long working life. Because of the long-term permissions granted at that time, the planning board, which does impose controls, has only had occasion to approve comparatively minor extensions to workings. Many limestone extractors in Somerset are operating on land for which planning consent was obtained in the period 1946–8 from district councils exercising planning powers under the Town and Country Planning Act of 1932. These approvals were easily obtained for wide areas, without requiring proof of workable reserves, and without the imposition of satisfactory conditions of working.[186] By 1 July 1948, when the Planning Act of that year came into force, permission had been given for 70 quarries in the Mendips, nearly all limestone, covering an area of more than 1215 hectares.[187] In every major limestone working area quarries operating under modern planning stipulations are likely to be in the minority. However, the British Quarrying and Slag Federation repeatedly urge their members voluntarily to adopt acceptable modern practices in respect of noise, dust and other disturbance, whilst the director has asked operators working quarries pre-dating planning consents to 'realize their obligations to the public'.[188] Much has been done voluntarily and in addition some operators understand the importance of their present record when applying for new permissions. However, a great deal more remains to be done.

The problems of traffic generation cannot readily be eased by the planning stipulations even where they apply. The bulk of movements in and out of quarries are by road and involve increasingly large capacity lorries. The development of fewer, larger quarries inevitably creates heightened congestion in some localities. Somerset County Council's survey of quarrying in the Mendips, involving mainly limestone workings, found an average daily movement of 2200 loads out of the production area, as measured over a nine-month period.[189] There is in addition a heavy inward traffic or lorries carrying bitumen and other coatings, and cement, to the aggregates quarries. It was calculated that about 150 firms operating over 1000 tipper lorries were based within the production areas and nearly every village on the principal traffic routes in and out had operators located within the settlement limits connected with the haulage of stone. The chief problem in Somerset, as in the Peak District and elsewhere, is created by the concentration of heavy traffic on roads which are unsuitable by reason of their width, gradient, or route through settlements. Some planning consents stipulate the use of specific approach roads and attempt to steer traffic away from unsuitable routes, but the scope for this is clearly limited. Significant long-term improvements can only result from the creation of new road links or the improvement of existing ones to serve quarry traffic, or if widening market radii and technical improvements encourage a more extensive use of rail transport. Of particular interest in this connection is the work of Somerset County Council, who have explored with British Rail the possible retention of certain otherwise threatened branch lines for the benefit of the quarrying industry in the Mendips and Bristol fringe areas.

Clearly many far-reaching planning decisions are affected by the future output levels of quarries in particular areas. These include the creation or improvement of road links, the retention of branch lines, the siting of new settlements and the possible phasing out of some old but small ones. The adequacy of such decision-making clearly depends on detailed estimates being available of likely expansion or contraction from each area. The chief factors in these estimates must be the extent to which limestone may increasingly sustain an anticipated heavily increasing demand for aggregates. The making of such estimates involves the collation of information on the extent of future aggregates markets served by the area in question, of demand within these markets and alternative sources of supply available there, as well as an evaluation of the multitude of factors which might affect output in any given area. These questions concern different government departments and there remains no one single collecting agency at national level which could give detailed estimates of future demand and output, region by region.[190] The most advanced research into future needs is that of individual large firms, some of whom spend large sums annually on computerized assessments of the market for particular products within their markets. These are of course likely to be both specialized and private. However, Somerset, the first county planning authority which attempted such an exercise in depth for the quarrying industry of the county as a whole, found such research of value in an operation of great scope and complexity, extending far beyond the county boundaries.

The Somerset County Council report, *Quarrying in the Mendips*, attempted to analyse both demand and output of all alternative sources of aggregate within the South and South-East markets served by the quarrying industry in the Mendips and Bristol fringe areas. The report calculated that by the year 2010 quarries in the county, mainly working limestone, would need to have a combined annual output of 61 million tonnes, compared with the estimated 1970 output of 10 million tonnes.[191] This predicted six-fold increase reflects both the expected rise in consumption of aggregates as a whole and of crushed limestone aggregate in particular. Although predictions this far ahead contain a large potentiality for error, similar figures were obtained using three different methods of calculation, based on correlation of output and estimated population growth in the market area, extrapolation of the county's contribution to the England and Wales total since 1962, and by planned output of existing operating companies. The six-fold increase anticipated in Somerset by the year 2010 cannot of course be projected on a uniform scale throughout the limestone producing districts. The county had a rate of growth in limestone output second only to Derbyshire in the 1960s, and is likely to experience above average rates of growth in the period under review as a result of proximity to the large South-East aggregates market. However, other limestone producing counties within range, such as Gloucestershire and more particularly Derbyshire, could have similar rates of growth. On an extrapolation of recent trends, Derbyshire's growth rate could be even larger. There is no great problem of reserves to meet a six-fold increase in limestone output. However, the land use and amenity conflicts likely to be caused by such increase in output over 40 years in selected areas can only be described as formidable. Fig. 2.5 indicates the competition in the Mendips arising from the needs of water conservation, nature reserves, special quality landscape, caving, scientific sites, and quarrying at existing levels. A 6-fold increase in output over 40 years would greatly exacerbate the conflict with all these competing land users. The pressures on the Peak Park area of Derbyshire from other competing uses makes the problem no less difficult there.

Clearly a variety of measures will be needed to reduce these conflicts to manageable proportions. One possible line of development which could, among the many which will be needed, make a contribution to easing these difficulties is the introduction of sub-water-table workings. W. I. Stanton, the chief exponent of this policy in the Mendips,[192] has argued that this would have the advantage of greatly extending the lives of existing concessions, and greatly reducing the loss of amenity and agricultural land. He claims that 'sub-water-table working could be the last word in constructive quarrying, protecting the Mendips for at least a further century and ultimately enriching the natural

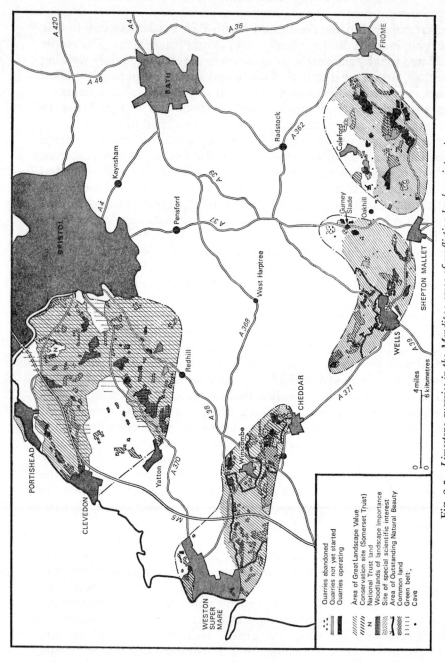

Fig. 2.5 *Limestone quarries in the Mendips: areas of conflicting land use interest*

Source: Somerset County Council

scene with vast reservoirs and attractive boating lakes, positive assets for the countryside'.[193] The slightly increased production costs due to extra haulage and pumping could, he argues, be offset by access to very great reserves at existing sites. In some cases these reserves may be of higher quality than those above the water-table.

The chief problem associated with this policy is possible contamination of water supplies which could result. Water consumption per head, as well as aggregates consumption per head, is increasing rapidly. The Bristol Waterworks Company estimated that water consumption per day/per head will rise from 286 litres in 1969 to about 409 litres by the end of the century,[194] apart from any increased demand resulting from population growth. Even quarrying above water-table can interfere with water supplies, either by interrupting the passage of water or destroying fissures or spaces in the rock valuable as natural storage in periods of heavy rainfall, or by contaminating the water supplies especially by oily residues such as phenols, commonly used at quarries. The possible damage to water supplies which could result from sub-water-table workings is correspondingly greater. The plotting of subterranean water catchment areas is a complex matter since surface and subterranean catchments bear no obvious relation to one another. Research in this field is pressing if sub-water-table working is to be seriously contemplated.

The possibility of extracting much larger quantities of limestone and other bulk industrial minerals by deep-mining* has been discussed by the director of the Institute of Quarrying.[195] There is a possibility that the additional cost involved in this method of working could be partially offset, and the site rehabilitated, by subsequent use of the hole. The director pointed out that in the United States impetus to such thinking had been given by rapid urban sprawl, shortage of space in areas where it is most needed, and pressure to preserve the surface environment. All these increase the cost and difficulty of surface extraction. One such underground working is being planned in Chicago, a city located on good limestone deposits and the centre of a very large market for the mineral. The space resulting from the sub-surface working is planned to provide a flood catchment area. Other possible after-use for such projects could be transport facilities, oil, gas and water storage, and factory space. Apart from use as reservoirs, such after-uses would not generally be practicable in Britain because of the rural location of most limestone deposits. A further difficulty is the higher cost of underground mining. The twentieth century has seen a pronounced swing away from underground to opencast operations, and surface extraction

* Modern limestone mines present few serious subsidence problems.

of industrial minerals is able to achieve a productivity rate of 510 tonnes per manshift, while that from underground mining may be only 51 tonnes per manshift.[196] If this trend is to be reversed, very substantial improvements would have to be made in the productivity of underground operations. In the United States a national committee has been set up to study rapid underground excavation and has recommended a major research effort to try to reduce the cost and sustain the rate of advance of underground excavation.[197]

Unless rapid advances are made in overcoming the problems of sub-water excavations or deep-mining, the conflicts arising from continued surface workings of limestone to meet estimated demand by the end of the century are likely to be of the utmost gravity.

IGNEOUS AND METAMORPHIC ROCKS*

An igneous rock is any rock which has formed from molten magma or lava. Metamorphic rocks which are, with the notable exception of slate, grouped with igneous rocks for trade purposes and included with them in the official statistics of production,[198] are rocks whose appearance, mineral composition or sometimes chemical composition have been changed by intense heat or pressure or both. The chief types of metamorphic rocks considered here and used mainly for aggregate purposes are the hard shales, schists (in which the minerals are arranged in sub-parallel bands or streaks) and gneisses (banded or foliated rocks of metamorphic origin having the mineral composition of granite). Igneous rocks may be differentiated according to chemical composition, mineral composition, texture, structure, mode of occurrence and age of deposit.[199] The most important of these attributes are texture, chemical composition and mineral composition, and of these, texture, which is intimately connected with mode of occurrence, may be considered of foremost significance. The chief characteristics of texture are coarseness of grain, broadly associated with plutonic (intrusive) rocks, which cooled slowly at depth; fineness of grain associated with volcanic (extrusive) rocks, which cooled rapidly at the surface; and an intermediate texture to be found in hypabyssal rocks, such as those forming dykes (intrusions into the earth's crust in the form of vertical fissures) and sills (intrusions in the form of sheets). Within this broad textural classification rocks may be subdivided according to chemical composition, based initially on silica and alkali content. The chief groupings

---

* This chapter excludes certain metamorphic rocks, notably slate, which are not used primarily for aggregate purposes, and recrystallized quartzite, normally classified with sandstone.

by silica content are: acid (more than 66 per cent silica); intermediate (52–66 per cent silica); basic (45–52 per cent silica) and ultrabasic (less than 45 per cent silica). Acid rocks contain a predominance of felspar rich in alkali. Felspars are in fact the most abundant minerals in igneous rocks—with the exception of ultrabasic rocks where felspathic constituents are absent or unimportant—and the rocks may thus be classified mineralogically according to the dominant type of felspar present, as well as by the presence of other minerals such as nepheline, leucite, quartz, mica, apatite, augite, amphibole, olivine and biotite.[200] Thus a broad comprehensive definition may be given in the terms mentioned above; e.g. granite is a coarse-grained rock, acid in chemical composition, composed mineralogically of quartz and felspars with some mica. Syenite, a coarse-grained intermediate rock, has much the same composition as granite but not as much quartz and more amphibole. A fine textured rock with the same composition as granite is termed a rhyolite; a medium-grained rock with the same composition as syenite is termed trachyte. Most widespread amongst the basic igneous rocks is the fine-grained basalt—dark grey, heavy, compact and very resistant, of which the main mineral constituents are pyroxene, plagioclase, felspars and olivine (with only some 46 per cent silica). The coarse-grained equivalent of basalt is gabbro. The scientific classification of igneous rocks includes about one thousand different names with several thousand sub-varieties.[201] However, for trade purposes, these precise distinctions are greatly simplified; syenite and other rocks with similar properties are marketed as granite. The British Standard classification for igneous and metamorphic rocks contains only six groups, namely basalt, gabbro, granite, hornfels (contact altered metamorphic rocks of all types except marble), porphyry and schist.

In Britain, igneous and metamorphic rocks are really less dispersed than either limestone or sandstone and are heavily concentrated in the highland zones of North and West Britain. Like the sedimentary rock sandstone, they date from a variety of geological periods. The chief deposits can be considered in descending order of age. Thus, starting with the Pre-Cambrian metamorphic rocks, these occur mainly in North-West Scotland, notably the Lewisian gneiss, the Moine schists and the Dalradian schists, which cover the larger part of the Scottish Highlands (see Fig. 2.6). In England and Wales Pre-Cambrian metamorphic rocks occur in Anglesey, Shropshire, the Malvern Hills, Charnwood Forest and the Lizard peninsula. Many instances of intrusive igneous rocks occur within these Pre-Cambrian metamorphic rocks, notably the Mountsorrel granite in Charnwood Forest. During the Ordovician period, lavas or sub-volcanic intrusive sheets were

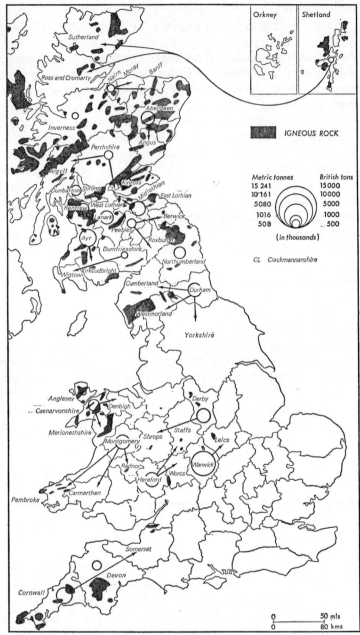

Fig. 2.6 *Igneous rock:* output by county, 1969
Arrows indicate location of counties whose totals are grouped
Source: Department of the Environment

emitted in the Lake District (notably the Borrowdale lavas, extending across the Cumbrian mountains from east to west) and in Wales (particularly the Snowdon region). The Devonian period was an active period of igneous rock formation; volcanic lavas were emitted in Devon and Cornwall and in Scotland (Lorne, Glen Coe, Ben Nevis, Ochil and Sidlaw Hills, Pentland Hills, Cheviot Hills).[202] Intrusive rocks of this period were formed in Scotland (Glen Coe and Ballachulish, the Eastern Highlands between Aberdeen, Peterhead and Inverness and the South-West Scottish Uplands) and the Lake District (the Ennerdale and Eskdale granites, the Skiddaw granite, the Threlkeld microgranite and the Shap granite). During the Carboniferous period, lavas were emitted in the Midland Valley of Scotland, Derbyshire, the Bristol area of Somerset and Devon. In the Upper Carboniferous/Permian period, igneous activity resulted mainly in the formation of dykes and sills, notably in the Midland Valley of Scotland and the Whin Sill in the north of England; in Devon and Cornwall the intrusive granite masses of the Scilly Isles, Land's End, Carnmenellis, St Austell (Hensbarrow), Bodmin Moor and Dartmoor were formed. During the early Tertiary period, the last geological epoch of igneous activity, isolated lavas were created in North-West Scotland (Skye, Canna, Rum, Eigg, Ardamurchan, Mull and Arran) followed by major plutonic complexes. Igneous activity ended with the formation of basaltic dykes, present from Mull to Yorkshire.[203]

Amongst the economic usage of igneous and metamorphic rocks, the aggregates market is of supreme importance. The 1968 *Census of Production* recorded that 91·8 per cent of sales (by tonnage) of the larger extractive enterprises consisted of aggregate material.[204] This compared with 66 per cent of sandstone and quartzite and 73·8 per cent of limestone.[205] In the case of the other hard rocks, building stone is now of very minor significance; the *Census of Production* recorded that less than 1 per cent (by tonnage) of igneous and metamorphic rocks consisted of building stone.[206] Stone for this purpose is normally of the coarser-grained type such as granite or dolerite, but not gabbro which tends to have a somewhat sombre appearance. Such materials, which are durable and weather-resistant, are now used almost exclusively for cladding rather than as structural building components. The specifically chemical properties of igneous rocks are currently of little importance, although research is being conducted into the use of basalt for refractory purposes.[207] 'Cast basalt' of the alkali type can be used for the manufacture of bottles, acid-resistant vessels, pipes, rollers, and foundations for machinery. Certain types of igneous rocks may be used for filter media.

Within the main aggregate market, igneous and metamorphic rocks are of course in competition with sandstone, limestone and sand and gravel. Igneous and metamorphic rocks are concentrated to a greater extent than any competing aggregate material in the highland areas of north and west Britain. They are absent entirely in the South-East, the area of highest aggregate demand, and are of rare occurrence even in proximity to the South-East, i.e. south-east of a line from Teesmouth to Exmouth. Scotland, Wales and South-West England, the major producing areas apart from Leicestershire, all have a relatively low demand for road aggregates and probably other aggregates as well; as a percentage of total roadstone demand, Scotland utilizes only 11, Wales 9 and the South-West 8.[208] Furthermore, igneous and metamorphic rocks tend to be more costly both to extract and to crush than the other hard rocks: their abrasiveness results in a high degree of wear and tear on machinery whilst up to five stages of crushing may be required. Higher production costs are reflected in the higher average price of igneous and metamorphic rock in the roadstone market: igneous rocks for roadstone averaged £1·20 per tonne in 1968 compared with 95·5 pence for sandstone and 73·8 pence for limestone.[209] However, both the high extraction and processing costs of igneous rocks and the cost of their long-distance transport (e.g. from Leicestershire or Cornwall to areas of high demand like London) may be justified by the special suitability of these rocks for wearing-course roadstone. The fine- or medium-grained rocks such as basalt, dolerite, porphyrite and andesite, consisting of a dense interlaced meshwork of hard minerals, are particularly tough and durable, and thus suited to providing wearing courses able to withstand the pressure of modern traffic densities. The durability of many igneous and metamorphic rocks outweighs the fact that these formations provide fewer sources of road aggregates resistant to polishing than the gritstone group of sandstones.[210] Basalts with a low propensity to become polished through wear are restricted to a limited area of Scotland though certain microgranites, a finer-grained material than granite which is for trade purposes grouped with porphyry, have similarly valuable properties, e.g. the microgranite of Castle-an-Dinas in Cornwall. Very few igneous rocks are thus suitable for road surfacing on roundabouts or on hills. For such places the most satisfactory surfacing material so far known is a calcined bauxite set in a cement matrix, a material which in 1970 cost about £39·37 per tonne, excluding delivery charges.[211] However, the estimated total market for roadstone for sites where a high degree of adhesion is essential was in 1970 only 250 000 tonnes per annum,[212] i.e. only a small fraction of the wearing-course market. In most of this market, igneous rocks are more widely used than any other aggregate material. This market too, although substantially larger than that for difficult sites alone, is in its turn a comparatively specialized section of road construction, and the tonnages required are small in relation to the total road building materials required. The wearing course of a major road may consist of only 10 cm of material out of a total thickness of aggregate of 69 cm,[213] though in some cases the entire road structure may extend to as much as 102 centimetres. In the bulk roadstone market, igneous and metamorphic rocks will be in competition with other materials and price will normally be the determining factor.

In the comparatively minor railway ballast market, igneous rock will be in competition with only the hardest of the other crushed rocks: in 1968 a higher percentage of igneous rocks was used for ballast than that of the softer limestone (7·1 per cent and 4·1 per cent, by tonnage of sales of largest establishments within the industry, respectively).[214] In the substantially larger concrete market, any of the main aggregate raw materials may be used but except in special cases—such as where concrete of high resistance to impact, wear or weathering, or of special colour or texture is required—limestone is preferred to igneous rock. This preference follows from limestone's greater ease of handling and its resistance to fire. The consumption of igneous rock in the concrete market is also, of course, affected by its substantially higher extractive costs than either limestone or sand and gravel. The disadvantages of igneous rock in both the concrete market, and in the bulk of the roadstone market referred to earlier, are reflected in substantially lower overall output figures for the UK than those of limestone or sand and gravel (36 684 000 tonnes of igneous rock, 87 822 000 tonnes of limestone, 105 168 000 tonnes of sand and gravel, in 1970).[215]

The overall resources of igneous and metamorphic rocks are very large. Since these resources are concentrated in the less populated and developed areas of Highland Britain, accessibility is a factor of great importance in the choice of working sites. The more accessible outcrops may be exploited for wearing course roadstone and for bulk road fill or other general aggregate purposes where there are few alternative sources of aggregate. Igneous and metamorphic rocks from such areas may also be used for bulk fill or embankments especially where inferior grades, such as those from fault zones or surface contaminated areas, are marketed substantially below the average prices for igneous rock. The lack of availability of competing aggregate materials is most commonly encountered in Scotland where the most extreme example of this is the Shetland Islands. There, with few other sources of aggregate material apart from two sand pits, eleven igneous rock quarries were in

1969 in operation.[216] Igneous and metamorphic rocks constitute most of the surface structure of the Highlands and even in the more highly populated Central Valley the deposits of other kinds of hard rock are of limited extent. This is the prime factor in the high percentage of British output of igneous rocks derived from Scotland (totalling 33·5 per cent of UK output in 1969).[217]

Scarcity of alternative sources of aggregate is however essentially a local or regional factor affecting market conditions at that level. The extraction of igneous and metamorphic rock for long-distance transport will be affected by other factors: clearly rocks that have a high resistance to polishing will have wider market radii than other types. Deposits in proximity to the South-East, where igneous rocks are absent and deposits of other hard rocks are very limited, will have an enhanced importance. Deposits of igneous rocks close to lines of communication to other areas of high demand where hard rocks are in short supply are also likely to be exploited. In areas serving relatively distant markets quarrying is likely to be concentrated on the coast, not only for the ease of transport by sea but also because of the generally superior road and rail links in such locations.

The largest outcrop of igneous or metamorphic rocks in proximity to the South-East occurs in Leicestershire, which in 1969 produced (together with a very small amount from Warwickshire) 4 765 000 tonnes of igneous and metamorphic rocks, or 37 per cent of English output (see Fig. 2.6). The chief producing area, Charnwood Forest in north-west Leicestershire, consists of metamorphic rocks with intrusive igneous formations such as the Mountsorrel granite. The trade classification of rocks worked here falls within the granite and porphyry groups (monzonite, diorite, syenite and soda granite: porphyry or tuff, and quartz diorite respectively). Quarrying began in this area in the period 1850–80 and the bulk of the quarries working these deposits are located on the perimeter of the forest, the more easily accessible part. Rock formations of more varied structure resulting from complicated faulting and for the most part underlying boulder clay also occur south-west of Leicester. Quarrying activity in the 1960s was however more heavily concentrated in the Charnwood Forest area where extractive costs are lower as less overburden removal is involved.[218] The number of quarries working south of Leicester, which were for the most part small enterprises, has greatly decreased although one large quarrying enterprise remains at Enderby. The prime importance of Leicestershire among igneous rock-producing areas of Britain relates however almost entirely to its geographical proximity to areas of high aggregate demand. These quarries are uniquely advantageously placed. Not only is the Charnwood Forest area some only thirty-two kilometres from Nottingham and forty-eight kilometres from Birmingham, but of additional and very great importance is their advantageous position in relation to markets in the South-East, the area of highest roadstone demand.[219] Charnwood Forest is approximately 160 kilometres from London and represents the nearest source of igneous or metamorphic rocks. Better rail transport in the 1960s, and improvements in the road network, have helped effect increased sales of crushed rock from this area to the South-East: indeed a small number of the larger national companies operating in Leicestershire have rail links into the quarries themselves and it was in 1971 estimated that deliveries from such quarries to East Anglia, London and the South-East made up between 20–50 per cent of production.[220] One company, operating in the Enderby area, delivers stone to a private hopper at St Pancras station and makes deliveries elsewhere up to a distance of 320 kilometres. Only economies of scale in production and the most advanced techniques of transport make possible the marketing of this essentially low value commodity such exceptionally large distances by land. The achievement of production economies through amalgamation and scale of operation, as well as improved transport by rail to South-Eastern markets, are important aspects of limestone production in the Mendips, an area broadly the same distance as Charnwood Forest from Greater London. This material is a strong competitor for Charnwood Forest igneous rock in London markets, where demand is especially high for concrete aggregates, a market in which limestone is the preferred material. Without the increasing quantities of Mendips limestone made available in Greater London at competitive prices which reflect both lower extraction and transport costs, it may be postulated that output of igneous rock from Leicestershire would have grown even more rapidly. As it is, output of igneous and metamorphic rock from the county grew proportionally to English and Welsh output during the 1960s. In 1963 igneous rock from Leicestershire constituted 30 per cent of demand from England and Wales.[221] In 1969 it provided almost all of the 4 766 000 tonnes classified by the Ministry as output from Leicestershire and Warwickshire—30 per cent of the England and Wales total.[222]

Although increases in output have been strictly in line with national trends, the concentration of output on a few very large quarries has been particularly marked in Leicestershire. In 1969 a total of only nine quarries[223] produced almost all of the 4 766 000 tonnes of igneous and metamorphic rocks quoted for Leicestershire and Warwickshire by the Ministry, giving a broad estimate of more than half a million tonnes of output per quarry. This compared with an estimated average output per igneous rock quarry in Britain of 77 519 tonnes per year in 1969.[224] The exceptionally large scale of quarries in the county is primarily related to the exceptionally large market available for igneous and metamorphic rock from this area, since quarry size is principally a product of market size. However, the development of such large producing units in Leicestershire has also been facilitated by the general planning framework. The bulk of the original planning permissions were, even by current standards, for very large areas and in some cases for as much as 41 hectares. This was generous considering that the quarries were often 60–120 metres deep.[225] In consequence, greatly expanded output from within the existing permitted area was possible during the 1960s. The capital investment required for quarries of this scale presupposes an operating company of some magnitude. In fact, the Leicestershire quarries were in 1969 controlled almost entirely by big national aggregates firms, namely Redland Roadstone Ltd. (three quarries), Amey Roadstone Corporation (three quarries), Tarmac Road Holdings (one quarry) and English China Clays (one quarry).[226]

The structure of the igneous rock quarrying industry in Leicestershire however is in marked contrast to that of Cornwall, which probably ranks second to it amongst English producing areas.[227] The distribution of igneous and metamorphic formations is much more dispersed in the Duchy which contains large granite outcrops at Bodmin Moor, Hensbarrow, Carnmenellis and Land's End, and smaller outcrops at Belowda, Carn Brea and Godolphin, Kit Hill and Hingston Down. In each case, coarse-grained granite is intruded with finer-grained material. The county also contains acid dykes of 'elvan' (quartz porphyry) and some intrusions of 'greenstone' (dolorite). The Lizard peninsula consists of metamorphic schists surrounding igneous rocks, mainly ultrabasic serpentine, with a large output of gabbro near St Keverne. In 1969 the Ministry recorded an outcrop of 1 911 000 tonnes of igneous and metamorphic rock from Cornwall and Somerset. Since output of this material from Somerset (basalt from the east Mendips) averaged 508 000 tonnes per year from 1964–8,[228] it is reasonable to assume a total output of some 1 403 000 tonnes from Cornwall in 1969. The extent of igneous and metamorphic rock quarrying in Cornwall must be related in the first instance to the predominance of this material in the geological structure of the county and the paucity of competing aggregate materials. Cornwall, in contrast to Devon, has virtually no resources of limestone or of sand and gravel. The china clay sand which exists in abundance on the St Austell tips has, as indicated in Chapter 4, limited commercial usage on its own. The second major factor affecting output level of igneous and metamorphic material from Cornwall is the juxtaposition of some of the outcrops with the sea. This makes possible the marketing of Cornish igneous and metamorphic rocks in both the London/South-East area and in Northern Europe. The deposits of the west Cornwall coast are more than twice as far from Greater London as the Charnwood Forest igneous rock or Mendips limestone. Igneous material could however in 1972 be transported the 374 sea miles from Newlyn to London by a 1000–3000 tonne vessel at a quoted freight rate of 100 new pence per tonne (0·267 new pence per tonne/mile).[229] Nonetheless, the competitive position of Cornish igneous rock relative to land-hauled supplies of hard rock in London markets had deteriorated during the previous ten years, as cost economies effected by improvements in rail and road transport had not been paralleled by cost economies in sea transport on this route. The maximum size of coaster on the Newlyn/London route remained at a steady 2950 tonnes. Consequently, the three west Cornwall quarries of Amey Roadstone Corporation Ltd. found that growth of output in the London/South-East market was not in line with overall output trends.[230] The North European market, on the other hand, was growing at a faster rate than the London/South-Eastern market and was chiefly responsible for the rising percentage of output being shipped by these quarries. A study of the geological map of Northern Europe indicates a lack of good hard rock from Cherbourg to the Baltic peninsula. Within this zone North Germany, whose igneous rock supplies derive principally from South German deposits some 320 kilometres away, was during the 1960s, and early 1970s, the major market for Cornish igneous rock. A study of future trends indicates the likely increasing importance of France and Holland as markets.[231] Vessels of 3650 tonnes maximum can be accommodated at Newlyn for continental ports, compared with 2950 tonnes maximum for UK ports, owing to the shallow draft broad beam of continental vessels. The larger size of vessel on the continental routes is reflected in freight quotations; the rate for igneous material from Newlyn to Lübeck (some 900 sea miles) was quoted in 1972 at as little as 7 Deutsche Mark per tonne (just under £1 per tonne at July 1972 rate of exchange) compared with £1 per tonne Newlyn/London (374 sea miles).[232] However, it must be remembered that the loading and unloading costs of sea freight represent a much larger element of costs than additional distance carried. The predicted expansion of aggregate demand in North Europe indicates a continuation of the growing relative importance of these markets for west Cornwall igneous rock: this trend could be further intensified with British membership of the European Economic Community.

Whilst the structure of the quarrying industry in Cornwall relates closely to the geological and marketing factors indicated above, the great diversity and location of deposits in the county tends towards fragmentation of quarrying activity. The elongated shape of the county, with its attendant long hauls for the transportation of material even within the Duchy itself, favours the development in inland areas of small quarries serving local markets. Since these markets are small, in view of the relatively sparsely populated nature of the area, the quarries also tend to be small, as quarry size is primarily a product of market size. Only in the extreme east of the county are igneous deposits such as that of Hingston Down in close proximity to a large market, that of Plymouth, where they are in any case in competition with south Devon limestone. Consequently, the structure of quarrying in Cornwall is highly dispersed: in 1969 there were some 49 igneous and metamorphic rock quarries operating there, with an average annual output of only some 28 634 tonnes each.[233] This compared with the national average size of igneous and metamorphic rock quarries in the year of 77 519 tonnes per annum. The great majority of these quarries are worked by small operators. However, those quarries with a coastal location offering access to larger, more distant markets have an average output much above the county average. The chief deposits adjacent to the sea are in west Cornwall, and coastal quarries are concentrated in the Land's End granite (where the Castle-an-Dinas microgranite has the added advantage of a fairly high resistance to polishing) and on the gabbro deposit near St Keverne on the Lizard peninsula. Not surprisingly, the larger operators are more in evidence in these areas than at inland locations. Three of the largest coastal quarries are those of Amey Roadstone Corporation, referred to above, of which two are at Newlyn and one at St Keverne.

The dominant effect of accessibility on output size and the structure of the industry is also manifest in the case of Welsh igneous/metamorphic rock production. Poor accessibility plays a major part in accounting for the fact that, while the extent of igneous and metamorphic rock reserves in Wales is at least as great as those in England, these resources are comparatively little exploited. Total igneous/metamorphic rock output from Wales in 1969 was 2 629 000 tonnes compared with 12 874 000 tonnes from England.[234] The abundance of the limestone and dolomite resources of South Wales, with their advantages in terms of lower extractive costs, greater suitability for the bulk of construction purposes and greater proximity to the major South Wales industrial areas, was also of significance. Competition from limestone affects not only output from the large North Pembrokeshire/Carmarthenshire outcrop but also restricts the amount of igneous rock sent from north Caernarvonshire coastal quarries by sea to Cardiff and Swansea. Total Welsh output of limestone and dolomite was 15 075 000 tonnes in 1969 compared with 2 629 000 tonnes of igneous/metamorphic rocks,[235] and there is evidence to suggest that local resources of dolomite with a known high crushing strength were displacing some igneous rock in South Wales markets during the late 1960s.[236]

The most extensive igneous/metamorphic rock outcrops of Caernarvonshire, Anglesey and Merioneth suffer for the most part from poor accessibility and are remote from the more densely populated area of South Wales. The inland quarries of this region are mainly moderate sized operations of 20 000–50 000 tonnes annual output,[237] serving purely local markets. Only the small number of quarries of north Caernarvonshire and the Lleyn peninsula, where parts of the outcrop abut the coast, have access to larger, more distant markets. The advantages of a coastal location are particularly pronounced in those cases where it affords access to good road and rail links, which have become of increasing importance. It may be deduced that the balance of advantage now lies with rail transport to such major markets as Merseyside, rather than with small coaster transport, which does not permit economies of scale. In 1958 the Caernarvonshire quarries as a whole, of which four were coastal, marketed more than two thirds of their output by sea.[238] Sea transport is still of paramount importance for the quarries of the Lleyn peninsula, and particularly for Trevor quarry on the north coast of the peninsula which has no rail connection. In the case of Penmaenmawr quarry, however, situated on the north Caernarvonshire coast between Bangor and Conway where an igneous intrusion of about 3·9 square kilometres (chiefly diorite porphyry) rises steeply from the sea, the chief locational advantages now consist of access to the main Holyhead/Chester railway line and to the Telford-built coast road, both of which follow the shoreline at this point. In 1972 Penmaenmawr despatched as much as 50 per cent of its output by rail, compared with 30 per cent by road and only 20 per cent by ship.[239] The locational advantages of this quarry compared with others in Caernarvonshire are reflected in its exceptionally large output, 585 200 tonnes in 1971,[240] comparable in size with the large Leicestershire quarries. The quarry is owned by Kingston Minerals Ltd., a large national aggregates operator. Of prime importance amongst the markets served by the Caernarvonshire coastal quarries is that of Cheshire/south Lancashire, which suffers from a scarcity of both hard rocks (except sandstone) and of gravel. About 53 per cent of Caernarvonshire output of igneous/metamorphic rocks was sent to redistribution centres on Merseyside in 1958.[241] This market is still of great importance: Penmaenmawr sends stone by road, rail and sea into the area and in 1971 20·8 per cent of total output was dispatched by rail to Liverpool and Manchester.[242] However, the Cheshire/south Lancashire market was during the 1960s an increasingly competitive field of operations. The prime factors involved were the establishment of very large, capital-intensive quarries in the Carboniferous limestone of the Peak District and north-east Wales, and the very rapid expansion of sandstone output from the Rossendale area of Lancashire (with low transport costs to Merseyside markets). Igneous rock from Northern Ireland also undercuts that from Caernarvonshire on Merseyside. Increasing competition in the major Merseyside markets is likely to have been the main factor in the low growth rate of Penmaenmawr during the 1960s, when output rose from 508 000 tonnes in 1962 to only 585 000 tonnes in 1971,[243] a period when UK output of igneous rocks as a whole virtually doubled. (These factors of competition could also have affected the growth rate of quarries operating on the smaller igneous deposits of the Welsh border, notably that running from Llandrindod Wells to Builth Wells, where larger than average extractive units serve among other markets that of south Lancashire.

The Caernarvonshire quarries have not, furthermore, been able to participate in the very great expansion of the London/South-Eastern aggregates market which took place in the 1960s. This possibility was ruled out by the limitations imposed on transport economies by the low maximum size of vessel which can be accommodated at the quarry piers: only 1320 tonnes in the case of Penmaenmawr and 1220 tonnes in the case of Trevor.* Clearly, this prevented cost economics sufficient to retain a competitive stance in London markets *vis-à-vis* land-hauled hard rock aggregate from the Mendips or Charnwood Forest, or even sea-hauled material from Cornwall by larger vessels covering a shorter route. Trade to the London/South-East area accounted for some 3·3 per cent of Caernarvonshire igneous rock output in 1958,[244] much of that inter-company trading from Penmaenmawr. By the early 1970s this trade had virtually disappeared.

However, important new markets have been secured in Northern Europe, notably Germany. Penmaenmawr exported 101 600 tonnes, or 17·3 per cent of output, via Hamburg, in 1971,[245] involving a sea journey of some 1770 kilometres. Here again, as in the case of Cornwall, freight rates are relatively low compared with those applying on British sea

* The trade between Penmaenmawr and the London area was principally inter-company trading, which came to an end when the company's precast works in that area closed.

routes: Penmaenmawr employs return load vessels to Hamburg at tonne/mile rates below those normally operative to British ports.

In spite of these new markets in Europe, the overall percentage of UK igneous rock output contributed by Wales has fallen markedly since the late 1950s. From 1938–58 Welsh output constituted 10–15 per cent of the UK total.[246] In 1969 it constituted only 7·3 per cent.[247] The prime factors operative here must be the disproportionate growth of competing hard rocks on Merseyside, and the limitations imposed on competitive marketing to more distant British ports by the small size of coasters accommodated at the Caernarvonshire coastal quarries.

The overall level of igneous/metamorphic rock output from Scotland, as from Wales, is related more closely to the availability of competing aggregate material, and particularly limestone, than to the extent of resources. The igneous and metamorphic rock resources of Scotland are indeed vast, but the high level of output from Scotland—12 015 000 tonnes in 1969 or 33·5 per cent of UK output[248]—is determined primarily by the lack of competing hard rocks, and specifically limestone. The limestone resources of Scotland are small, being limited to the minor Carboniferous outcrop of Fife and West Lothian and the Pre-Cambrian Dalradian limestones of Banff, Inverness and Perth. Total limestone output from Scotland in 1969 was only 1 892 000 tonnes.[249] In much of the Highlands and Islands there is a shortage of agricultural lime, an outlet in which, of course, igneous rocks cannot substitute for limestone. Since limestone has particular competitive strength as an aggregate material over igneous or metamorphic rocks, consisting essentially in its lower extractive costs and greater suitability for concrete, the scarcity of limestone reserves in Scotland is a factor of major importance. Sandstone reserves are more widespread than those of limestone in Scotland—and were exploited in 14 Scottish counties in 1969,[250] but these reserves are very variable both in physical characteristics and in depth of deposit: some are unsuitable for heavy duty aggregate and few have the strength or toughness of basalt. This is the dominant type of igneous rock exploited in Scotland, some of which has the additional advantage of high polished stone values. Some of the Scottish sandstone deposits, notably the Pre-Cambrian Torridonian sandstone of North-West Scotland or the Old Red Sandstone of the north-eastern border of the Highlands, are remote from the main aggregates markets. Although Old Red Sandstone occurs in north Aberdeenshire, it is less well placed than the granite deposits to serve the main markets of this country, the most densely populated area of the Highlands. As a result of all these factors, only 410 500 tonnes of sandstone were extracted in Scotland in 1969.[251]

In Scotland as in Wales, accessibility and proximity to markets play a more important part in determining distribution of output and the structure of the industry than any other factors. The Scottish Highlands are almost covered by an immense tract of metamorphic rock with igneous intrusions, the largest such formation in Britain. Within the greater part of this area, however, markets are small and fragmented, distances are great and transport facilities small-scale; consequently, a large number of small quarries are operated for local markets. The predominance of small quarries in the Highlands (and in some of the Islands, notably the Shetlands) contributes largely to the dispersed overall structure of igneous rock quarrying in Scotland. Average output per quarry for Scotland as a whole in 1969 was 63 572 tonnes[252] compared with the British average of 77 519 tonnes. The only high output area within the Highland zone is Aberdeen and Angus, where intrusive igneous rocks of the Eastern Highlands, predominantly granite, are worked. High output in this area is now related essentially to population density and corresponding aggregate demand, Aberdeenshire having at the 1971 census a higher density of population than any Scottish county outside the Central Valley. Both the marketing pattern and the type of product from this area have changed markedly since the Second World War. The near coastal quarries of this area no longer market their products to the south of England. During the pre-war period, most of the granite produced by John Fyfe Ltd., operator of three quarries in Aberdeenshire, was shipped from Aberdeen harbour to the south of England. In 1972 less than 1 per cent of output was despatched by sea, and that to the Hebrides.[253] The main markets now served from these quarries are local ones supplied by road; an estimated 75–80 per cent of output was in 1972 marketed within a 40 kilometre radius.[254] The decline in market radius (an exception to the general widening market radius for hard stone in Britain) is in this case fundamentally connected with a change in the type of product.

The granites of the Aberdeen and Peterhead areas were formerly widely used for building and ornamental stone, a speciality trade which has now been virtually discontinued. Aggregate, the chief current product, is clearly a lower value commodity; indeed, some crushed rock is produced from the spoil of old stone quarries, a cheaper method of extraction than that of virgin rock. The Aberdeenshire aggregate quarries, which are not situated directly on the coast, cannot compete in South-Eastern markets if only in view of the double handling charges involved.

The changeover of production from block stone, primarily an activity of small quarries, to that of aggregates serving the largest market in the Highlands, has produced a few large quarries near the City of Aberdeen, in addition to the considerable number of smaller ones, including eight operated by the county council, scattered elsewhere in the county. Average quarry size in the county remains small—64 926 tonnes for Aberdeen and Angus in 1969[255]—and the large national aggregates firms have not moved into the area.

Although deposits outside the Highland zone do not compare with them in extent, the smaller deposits of the Central Valley and neighbouring counties, in proximity to the major Scottish aggregates market, constitute the chief Scottish producing area. Such deposits include the Pentland Hills of Lanarkshire and Midlothian, the Ochil Hills of Perthshire and Kinross, the Lomond Hills of Fife, the Lammermuir Hills of East Lothian, the relics of plateau lavas in the Clyde area (the Kilpatrick Hills, Campsie Fells and Renfrewshire Hills) and in the sills and dykes of quartz dolerite (an exceptionally hard rock) which are abundant in the Central Valley. 6 316 000 tonnes, or more than half the Scottish output, of igneous/metamorphic rock was in 1969 derived from the counties falling within this belt (Stirlingshire, Kinross and Fife, Dunbartonshire, Renfrewshire, Lanarkshire, Midlothian and East and West Lothian).[256] Here, as is to be expected, proximity to the markets of the Central Valley has led to relatively large quarries. Within these counties, average output per quarry in 1969 was an estimated 87 820 tonnes, well above the British average for igneous rock quarries.[257] In a small part of this area deposits directly abut the coast, i.e. in southern Fife where small igneous formations adjoin the Firth of Forth, notably at Inverkeithing and Burntisland, and in northern Fife, where a large formation adjoins the Firth of Tay. Consequently, from here, unlike Aberdeenshire, it is economic to market a small percentage of output by sea to the London area.[258] It is noteworthy that some large aggregate firms have become operative in this area, notably Tarmac Roadstone Holdings Ltd. at Inverkeithing and Wimpey Asphalt Ltd. at Burntisland.

Output from the more distant parts of the Southern Uplands and the border region is however small, largely as a result of the low density of population in this area, comparable at the time of the 1971 census to all but the most depopulated parts of the Highlands. Output of igneous rock from the five border counties of Dumfries, Wigtown, Peebles, Berwick and Roxburgh was only 886 000 tonnes in 1969.[259] The Cheviot Hills, formed by lavas during the Devonian period, are largely untouched by quarrying, at least on the Scottish side of the border.

The land use and environmental aspects of igneous rock quarrying have strong affinities with those of the other hard rocks. The estimated annual take of land in Britain for igneous rock quarrying at 1969 output levels would be 124 hectares, allowing for an estimated 221 300 tonnes per hectare.[260] Some types of deposits, however, such as sills, are of limited depth and yield per hectare from such formations would probably be below the average figure. A small amount of basalt is mined from the Cleveland Dyke at Great Ayton, Yorkshire, where clearly output would be high in relation to the take of land at the surface. In most types of deposit, the chief factor inhibiting development of very deep workings is the higher costs involved in haulage charges from work face to plant, always a crucial element in quarrying costs. But on the whole, the yield per hectare from igneous rock workings may be up to ten times that of sand and gravel deposits (except for the Bunter beds). However, areas required for plant are additional to this estimated figure, and, in view of the hardness of igneous and metamorphic rocks, the size of crushing plant is likely to be more extensive than that of limestone or the softer sandstones.[261] (The comparative hardness of the rock may also have implications for noise and vibration from blasting and crushing processes.)

The land involved in igneous and metamorphic rock quarrying is, with few exceptions, remote from urban or residential areas. The few large quarries near the City of Aberdeen, an exception to this general rule, have already been mentioned. At Penmaenmawr, too, igneous rock quarrying untypically occurs in proximity to the town, but here planning consent provides for the exclusion of land which may be required for general development without seriously reducing the resources available for quarrying.[262] Furthermore, the land involved in igneous and metamorphic rock extraction is rarely of even moderate agricultural value, usually consisting of rough pasture, scrub or open moorland. The chief environmental costs of quarrying lie in the field of amenity. This term may at its broadest include conflict with archaeological interests which occurs in parts of Scotland, notably East Lothian and Dunbartonshire (the Antonine Wall).[263] Because of their exceptional resistance to weathering, igneous and metamorphic rocks tend to form upland areas which are likely to be scenically attractive and of importance for recreation. Notable examples are the Highlands of Scotland, where igneous and metamorphic rocks are the main determinants of the landscape; Wales, where the main quarrying areas are in or close to Snowdonia or Pembrokeshire coast National Parks; the west Cornish coast; and the Lake District National Park. In this last area, where the Threlkeld microgranite and Shap pink and blue igneous rocks are worked, it is interesting to note that Westmorland County Council encourage, within the National Park, excavation of these rocks at one large site rather than at a number of scattered small sites.[264] In the case of Scotland, at least, the view is sometimes held by planners that quarry faces are not an unacceptable feature of the landscape and, if disused, become re-assimilated into the scenery very quickly.[265] Where quarrying occurs in lowland Britain, however, there may well be a greater degree of concern about its visual impact. The most notable instance of this is the Malvern Hills, which consist predominantly of Pre-Cambrian metamorphic gneisses. These hills are generally considered to be of special scenic quality, and are very narrow in formation so that quarrying activity on any scale could easily damage their profile. The special factors operating in this case were recognized as long ago as 1952, when the Minister of Housing and Local Government ruled that quarrying in the Malvern Hills should be brought to an end as speedily as possible. Consequently there have been many refusals of planning permission for extensions to existing quarries and many which were operative immediately after 1947 have been closed down and compensation paid. In 1971 only two quarries remained in the Malverns, each of which had a limited life, probably not exceeding five years; at the end of this period, it is anticipated that all quarrying in the Malverns will cease.[266]

The most important area of quarrying activity within an isolated upland area occurs at Charnwood Forest, the only high point in the county of Leicestershire. Charnwood Forest is designated in the County Development Plan as an Area of Special Scientific interest; although such areas are not specifically excluded from mineral working, the county attempts to prevent new planning permission being obtained for workings within the forest.[267] Appeals have been won against such county decisions, however, and the chief arguments used have been the exceptional economic importance derived from the location of these deposits. Fortunately, the bulk of the quarries occur on the perimeter. The bulk of planning permissions now operative in this area date from 1947 and 1948, the early days of post-war planning, when the kind of stipulations now considered normal in such matters as camouflage of plant and soundproofing of machinery, embankment building and tree planting were not usual. The chief facet of these permissions, subsequently regretted by the county planners,[268] however, is the large extent of individual permissions which may, as already indicated, extend to as much as 41 hectares for one quarry. These early permissions, which have facilitated a rapid expansion of quarrying from Charnwood, unrestricted by the provisions of modern planning practice, have led the county planning office to the view that some ratifying or modification procedure should be built into such long-term planning consents, to enable working stipulations to be brought into line with modern planning practice.[269] This point is taken up in Chapter 7.

SANDSTONE

The term 'sandstone' at its broadest denotes rocks consisting largely of quartz sand, welded into solid form. Such rocks, which are normally of sedimentary type, differ widely in chemical composition, particle size and shape, degree of compaction and the geological period of their formation. The principal chemical distinctions relate to the nature of the cementing material, which may be either derived from solution of the grains, i.e. silica, or be a deposited material different from that of the grains. If different from that of the grains, which is more usual, the cement may be calcite, dolomite or ankerite; siderite or limonite; clay or clay minerals; glauconite; mica; copper; gypsum or phosphate.[270] Although the grain size of sandstone, strictly speaking, ranges between 1/16 of a millimetre and 2 millimetres, the broad term may, as in the official statistical sources,[271] include material of comparable formation but larger particle size. Similarly, the British Standard classification for roadmaking rocks includes sandstone in the gritstone group, along with conglomerate (a consolidated smooth gravel), breccia (consolidated angular rock fragments), agglomerate (an unstratified mass of fragments of volcanic debris), arkose (a coarse-grained material rich in felspar), greywacke (the product of rapid erosion of a basic igneous rock consisting of large, angular detrital quartz and felspar grains in a clay matrix) and tuff (a consolidated volcanic ash).

The degree of compaction of these rocks relates to the age of the deposit and the degree of pressure to which they have been subjected. The hardest and most compact are the quartzites; these silica-cemented sandstones include a metamorphic type in which the grains have recrystallized under extreme pressure. Other categories, in diminishing order of compaction, are quartzitic and quartzose sandstones. Loosely consolidated material which crumbles easily, such as the Bunter sandstones of north and south Staffordshire, is usually categorized with sand and gravel and the working of this type of material was therefore discussed in an earlier section of this chapter.

In general, the degree of compaction of sandstones increases with the age of the deposit. Sandstones, from a variety of geological epochs, occur extensively throughout the stratified rocks of Britain. The main deposits, in chronological order of formation, are as follows. First, the numerous gritstones and quartzites occur in the Pre-Cambrian strata, notably in Anglesey, the Welsh border, a small part of Yorkshire, and North-West Scotland (Torridonian sandstone). Then Cambrian sandstone, mainly quartzites, which occur in the Lickey Hills and near Nuneaton in the Midlands, and on the Welsh border, and other Lower Palaeozoic sandstones, mainly greywackes, which occur in Mid- and North Wales, the Lake District and the Southern Uplands of Scotland. Sandstones in the Devonian series occur in north and south Devon and much of Cornwall; these are paralleled by the Old Red Sandstones of the Welsh border and Brecon Beacons and the Midlands Valley of Scotland. Old Red Sandstones also extend along the eastern border of the Highlands from north Aberdeenshire to Caithness and recur in the Orkneys. The most abundant source of sandstone is the Carboniferous system. Sandstones in this system (which include the widespread Millstone Grit) are found in South Wales, the Bristol area, Lancashire, Derbyshire, Yorkshire, Durham, Northumberland and the Midland Valley of Scotland.[272] Apart from the Millstone Grits, other Carboniferous deposits occur in the Coal Measures where sandstones and hard clays are interspersed with coal seams. Permian and Triassic New Red Sandstone, on the whole softer than the older formations, occur in Cheshire and south Lancashire, Ayrshire, parts of the West Midlands, Cumberland, Nottinghamshire and, perhaps most typically, east Devon. Finally a Jurassic sandstone occurs in north Yorkshire.

Since the term sandstone, as used here, includes rocks with a very wide range of physical and chemical properties, the commercial uses of the various deposits vary considerably, as does the interchangeability of the mineral with other materials. Sandstones of the Permian period or older were in the past used extensively for building stone; the use of load-bearing sandstone has now diminished greatly, as cheaper steel or concrete frames, easier to handle and use, have become widely adopted, while natural stone of all types has also lost ground to bricks. Although the traditional sandstone building material is still used on a small scale in some areas, some varieties such as the dark Millstone Grit tend to be less aesthetically acceptable to modern taste than limestone. Hard sandstones are still marketed in small quantities for building work such as jetties and reservoirs, and the amount used for cladding and decorative work is actually increasing.[273] Sandstone of particular colour and texture is utilized in this market; the type known as 'York stone' is in particular demand for fireplaces. The residual materials left over from the working of stone for these purposes are sometimes used for rock gardens and crazy paving. Those fissile sandstones known as flagstones, which have bedding planes along which the rock can easily be split, were formerly widely used for paving stones, roofing slabs and kerbs; this outlet has now been greatly curtailed as a result of the manufacture of cheaper concrete products, but smaller quantities of natural sandstone sills, slabs, steps and paving are still sold, mainly now in speciality markets. Some quartzites, notably those with a low alkali content, are exploited for refractory purposes, although in diminishing quantities (see Chapter 4). A variety of types of gritstone, such as the Kinderscout Grit of Derbyshire, are used for grindstones for tool and glass grinding and as pulpstones for the pulp, paper and linoleum industries.

The aggregates market is now the major consumer of sandstones. In 1968 aggregates made up 66 per cent of sales of sandstones and quartzite by larger establishments in the industry.[274] In this market, as in others, the commercial applicability of the mineral varies according to its properties. Hard varieties with high crushing strengths may be used for concrete aggregates, railway ballast and road fill. Higher quality materials may be used for wearing course and base course bituminous mixtures. Some gritstones can have very high polished stone values which are needed for specially difficult road sites such as roundabouts and hills; indeed, the Transport and Road Research Laboratory has established that gritstones have the highest average polished stone values of any source of natural roadstone.[275] Many of these gritstones are, however, lacking in sufficient resistance to abrasion, and only a few deposits of those so far analysed are suitable for use in this specialized market. Lesser grades of sandstone are used for hardcore, fill and embankments. In every aggregates outlet, sandstone is theoretically in competition with other materials. The hard quartzites are interchangeable in the wearing-course market with many types of igneous rocks. Other grades of sandstone, suitable for concrete aggregate or base courses, may be in competition with limestone and sand and gravel. The very lowest grades compete in the bulk/fill market with such commodities as pulverized fuel ash or colliery shale. Those few sandstones with both high polished stone values and resistance to abrasion are only at present in competition with a very few sources of igneous rocks and the expensive artificial aggregates such as calcined bauxite, but research to produce a cheaper artificial aggregate suitable for surfacing the difficult sites in question is in progress.[276]

Sandstone suffers general disadvantages in the aggregates market in relation to the other main raw materials. The properties and quality of sandstone deposits are more variable than those of igneous rocks, limestone or sand and gravel and consequently there is more difficulty in finding deposits to meet British Standard specifications for the varying grades of aggregate. Many deposits are too thin to be of economic value while others may be flaggy with poor crushing strengths. In view of the wide variations in chemical and physical properties, more research is required to define the characteristics required of sandstones for specific purposes such as concrete. The chief specific disadvantages of most sandstones (excluding quartzite) *vis-à-vis* igneous rocks is their lower resistance to abrasion, and hence shorter life as a road surfacing material. The greater durability of many igneous rocks for road surfacing largely accounted for their higher average value per tonne than sandstone in the roadstone market. Igneous rocks for roadstone averaged £1·20 per tonne in 1968 compared with 95·5 pence per tonne for sandstone.[277] Although limestone is not suitable for the wearing courses of major roads, it does have specific advantages over sandstone in other important aggregate outlets where the two minerals are in competition. Limestone has a much wider range of commercial applications, including some in which it is an irreplaceable raw material. The comparatively restricted outlets for sandstone *vis-à-vis* limestone are reflected in the smaller average size of sandstone than of limestone quarries. In 1969 output per limestone quarry is estimated to have averaged 154 854 tonnes, while output per sandstone quarry was an estimated 61 839 tonnes.[278] Lower average quarry size, with correspondingly higher overheads and per unit operating costs, produces higher costs per tonne for sandstone than limestone in the roadstone market where, in most cases, the two materials are interchangeable. Limestone averaged 73·8 pence per tonne in this market in 1968[279] which significantly undercut sandstone at an average of 95·5 pence per tonne. Limestone probably has a similar price differential in the concrete market. Sand and gravel, with relatively low average production costs since crushing is not generally required, is usually comparable in price to limestone aggregate, and consequently this material too undercuts sandstone. Although sand and gravel is unlikely to be in competition with the hard quartzites or those few deposits with both high polished stone values and resistance to abrasion, for the broad spectrum of aggregate purposes it may, if available, be expected to undercut sandstone.

A general pattern of sandstone exploitation emerges from the above analysis. Quartzites—except those in very remote locations—and sandstones with high polished stone values and abrasion resistance are likely to be worked wherever they occur. Those in proximity to the South-East, where hard rocks suitable for road surfacing are very rare, will have a premium value. Other grades of sandstone suitable for general aggregate purposes are unlikely to be worked on a large scale where there are abundant reserves of either limestone or sand and gravel.

The complex of factors outlined above do much to explain the much smaller consumption of sandstone for aggregates than of igneous rocks, limestone or sand and gravel. Since aggregates is the main market in each case, the overall output of sandstone is, as would be expected, lower than that of the other three materials. Total UK output in 1970 was: 16 648 000 tonnes of sandstone, 36 684 000 tonnes of igneous rocks, 87 822 000 tonnes of limestone and 105 168 000 tonnes of sand and gravel.[280] However, sandstone, the production of which had been relatively constant from the beginning of this century until about 1963, had a faster rate of growth during the 1960s as a whole than any of the other three minerals in question. Sandstone output increased by 230·4 per cent in the period 1960–70, compared with a 115·6 per cent increase for limestone, a 121·9 per cent increase for igneous rocks and a 41 per cent increase for sand and gravel.[281] One factor in the faster growth rate of sandstone in the 1960s was the exceptionally widespread nature of sandstone deposits, covering an estimated 30 per cent of the total surface area of Britain. The rapidly growing aggregate demands of the 1960s stimulated the expansion of output from areas such as Lancashire or north Devon where unexploited potential was great and alternative sources of aggregates were scarce. Growing demand also encouraged the investigation and exploitation of sandstone with special qualities such as high polished stone values and abrasion resistance, a process which is still going on.

The pressures for expanded output of sandstone in the 1960s made themselves felt primarily in England, by far the largest aggregates market in Britain. Between 1961 and 1969 production from Scotland and Wales slightly less than doubled, while that of England more than quadrupled.[282] In general, proximity to markets was of greater significance than the quality of the deposits. By far the largest county total, 6 416 000 tonnes in 1969 or 44·1 per cent of the British total,[283] came from Lancashire. The factors involved in the very high output from Lancashire relate closely to the general principles outlined earlier. The county, and particularly the conurbations of the South-East and Merseyside, has a high aggregate demand. This area, which has been heavily glaciated several times,[284] is very deficient in gravel (especially the south of the county) although it has an abundance of sand. Since both fine and coarse particles are required for many important aggregate purposes such as concrete, the county 'imports' sand and gravel from the Bunter Pebble beds of north Staffordshire and from the glacial gravels of north-east Wales. Marine-dredged gravel is derived from Liverpool Bay. The nearest sources of limestone and igneous rock also lie for the most part outside the county; the former is derived from the Carboniferous limestone of the Pennines, chiefly Derbyshire, from North-East Wales and from the fringe of the Lake District, and the latter is brought in by sea from North-West Wales. Clearly, the transport costs involved in bringing in limestone and land-won sand and gravel, the chief competitors in the bulk aggregates market, may cancel out the advantage of their lower average production costs. Marine-dredged sand and gravel has substantially higher production costs than its land-won counterpart. Sandstone, on the other hand, is abundant within the county itself. Millstone Grit occurs extensively in west Lancashire and Permian and Triassic sandstones are found in the south. The chief concentration of sandstone workings is in the Rossendale area of the centre of the county between Burnley and Manchester and close to other conurbations with high aggregate demands. The thick deposits of the Rossendale area, the heavy demand and the competitive advantages of sandstone over 'imported' competitors have given rise to a complex of exceptionally large workings: a total of only approximately 27 quarries in the county had an average output of 237 630 tonnes in 1969,[285] far above the national average for sandstone workings. Sandstone output from Cheshire, totalling 1 273 000 tonnes in 1969 (see Fig. 2.7), was substantially less than Lancashire in view of the smaller population and aggregate demand of the county, but relatively high in comparison with most other counties. This reflected a scarcity of alternative sources of local-won aggregates: sand, much of it used for metallurgical purposes, is abundant in Cheshire but gravel and hard rock (other than sandstone) are as scarce as in Lancashire. Sandstone is derived mainly from the Carboniferous deposits of the east of the county and to a lesser extent from the Permian and Triassic New Red Sandstones.

In north Devon and Cornwall the output of sandstone, although still comparatively small because of the low aggregate demand of this relatively sparsely populated region, increased rapidly in the 1960s. The South-West has few sources of gravel, concentrated in south Devon, and a large proportion of consumption is supplied from higher cost marine operations in the Bristol Channel. Limestone deposits are also mainly in south Devon. The abundant igneous rock resources of Cornwall provide high quality roadstone but these may be expensive to use in the general aggregates market, and are remote from many South-Western markets. As is to be expected, most sandstone quarries in Devon, apart from Wembury, occur in the north of the county: sandstone output from this area doubled between 1963 and 1968.[286] Sandstone output from Yorkshire, totalling 1 218 000 tonnes in 1969, only partially reflected the high aggregate demand of this area, as

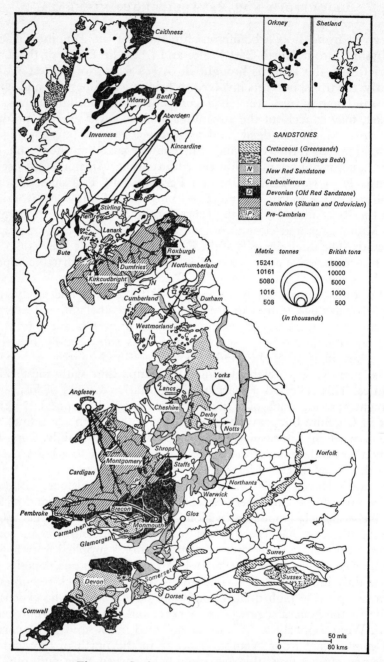

Fig. 2.7 *Sandstones:* output by county, 1969
Arrows indicate location of counties whose totals are grouped
Source: Department of the Environment

alternative sources of aggregates, notably sand and gravel and Carboniferous and Magnesian limestones, occur extensively in the county. Indeed, from 1954 to 1968, Yorkshire produced twice as much sand and gravel as any other county in Northern England.[287] This is the main factor in the much lower output of sandstone from Yorkshire than Lancashire. Sandstones are in fact widespread in Yorkshire: these are the Carboniferous Millstone Grit, Pre-Cambrian sandstones, mainly quartzites, greywackes (Ingletonian 'granite') and Jurassic sandstone. These resources are exploited in part for markets which are not in competition with either sand and gravel or limestone. The Pre-Cambrian quartzites, which are of particularly high quality in the Doncaster area, produce roadstone suitable for wearing courses of which there is a shortage in the county. Quarries producing cut decorative stone (York stone), used for fireplaces and high quality paving, also serve a specialized market. These quarries, which tend to be very small units producing a few hundred tonnes a year or less, partially account for the extremely fragmented nature of the sandstone extraction industry in the county: in 1969 there were approximately 70 sandstone quarries in the county with an average annual output of only 15 869 tonnes each.[288] Apart from the small specialized quarries, however, there are a considerable number of small quarries producing poor quality material for road bases, especially in the west and centre of the West Riding. The output from these quarries could be in direct competition with other aggregates but the fluvio-glacial sand and gravel deposits of the Pennine valleys of this area are neither extensive nor easily worked by the cheap suction dredging methods used in the South of England.[289]

Derbyshire, which has extensive areas of Millstone Grit, had only a small quantity of this material won in 1969: the combined output of Derbyshire and Nottinghamshire (only one quarry) was 85 340 tonnes. The presence of extensive limestone deposits in Derbyshire is probably the main reason for the low sandstone output of the county. The 13 quarries in Derbyshire,[290] mainly small units, are chiefly in the Matlock district, such as Stanton Moor, Tansley and Darley Dale. Throughout the Millstone Grit areas of Derbyshire abandoned quarries, formerly worked for building stone, far outnumber those still in operation,[291] mainly for aggregates.

In the South-East, the area of highest aggregate demand, sandstone is of rare occurrence. Although the general aggregate market in this region has traditionally been supplied from local sand and gravel resources, those few sandstone deposits which occur may justify exploitation in spite of higher production costs imposed by the need for crushing. Accelerating aggregate demand in the South-East has exhausted many of the more easily worked gravels, of those closest to markets and of those which most readily obtain planning permission for working. Furthermore, the isolated sandstone deposits which occur can usually be exploited in association with sand and gravel. In Norfolk a small deposit of Carstone, a nodular ferruginous sandstone, is worked jointly with sand and gravel, and two quarries in the Upper Greensand in Surrey are also joint sandstone/sand and gravel workings. The very hard Cambrian quartzites worked in the Lickey Hills and at Hartshill near Nuneaton in Warwickshire, on the other hand, come into quite a different category. The material produced here is suitable for high quality roadstone for wearing courses, of which there is a scarcity in the South-East. As such, it is not in competition with the abundant Bunter sandstone relatively close at hand in Staffordshire. Output of quartzite from Warwickshire formed the bulk of the output of 1 456 000 tonnes of sandstone produced by Warwickshire, Northamptonshire and Norfolk in 1969 (a Ministry grouping for reasons of confidentiality).

Output of sandstone from Wales is low by English standards, the total of 848 400 tonnes in 1969 being smaller than that from a minor English producing region such as Devon and Cornwall, in spite of the absence of resources of land-won sand and gravel in most parts of the principality. Low output from Wales reflects the abundance of limestone in the south and of both limestone and sand and gravel in Flintshire and Denbighshire, the relatively low aggregate demand of most of the country and the poor quality of many Welsh sandstones. Many deposits within the Old Red Sandstone of Breconshire and Monmouthshire are flaggy materials with low crushing strength and many of the sandstone and greywacke deposits of Mid-Wales are thin and poor quality. Such materials are however worked in Mid-Wales, especially for ballast and fill, in the absence of other local sources of aggregate. In some parts of Mid-Wales, it may be noted, sandstone is marketed under the trade name of 'granite', hence the absence of sandstone producing counties such as Radnor and Merioneth from the county statistics mapped on p. 124. Pennant sandstone, on the other hand, that is sandstone of a type found in the Upper Coal Measures of South Wales and the Bristol area, is of a higher quality, which justifies commercial exploitation in spite of the abundant limestone reserves of South Wales. A complex of five Pennant sandstone quarries is located north-west of Newport. At Gilfach in Glamorgan, the Pennant sandstone has been identified as having high polished stone values and resistance to abrasion, making it a valuable source of wearing-course roadstone.

Sandstone output from Scotland totalled only 410 500 tonnes in 1969. In the Central Valley, where the highest area of aggregate demand coexists with Old Red Sandstone and Carboniferous sandstone deposits, sand and gravel is readily available, although supplies were being brought increasing distances in the late 1960s, and igneous rocks are abundant. High quality sandstone deposits in the north of Scotland, notably the very hard Pre-Cambrian Torridonian sandstone, on the other hand, were too remote from major markets to be readily sold, even as high quality roadstone. Caithness flagstone, once marketed as far distant as London and other British cities for paving stones, is now sold for this purpose in only very limited markets, as the mass paving market has been captured by cheaper products. In the Orkneys, composed almost entirely of sandstone, this material has necessarily to provide most of the material for the islands' roadworks and, of the 13 quarries worked there in 1969, 11 were retained by local authorities.[292]

Methods of working sandstone, and the planning problems attendant on quarrying operations, are in most respects similar to those of limestone. There is, however, one notable difference: most sandstone workings, and especially those of coarse material such as gritstone, give rise to substantially less dust emission than those of limestone. The annual consumption of land for sandstone extraction, with a similar tonnage per hectare to that of limestone and igneous rocks, is correspondingly less as the total annual output of sandstone is substantially lower. Sandstone deposits, like those of the other hard rocks, do not usually coincide with high quality agricultural land, although that overlying the Coal Measures and Triassic deposits may be of medium agricultural quality. Millstone Grit gives rise to the wild country of parts of the Pennine Chain and South Wales, made up common land, pine wood and moorland, and used only for rough pasture. Close proximity of sandstone workings to urban areas is exceptional. In Warwickshire, however, where quartzite (together with diorite*) occurs in a narrow zone running north–west, south–east from Atherstone to Bedworth, for much of its length the outcrop adjoins urban development, and quarries are often necessarily close to residential areas, with the attendant problems of noise and disturbance from blasting and processing plant. More often, it is the creation of large amounts of traffic on steep or narrow country roads, as in Lancashire, or landscape intrusion, which causes difficulties.

Because of the hardness of many sandstones, especially the older formations, and their relative resistance to weathering, deposits may

* A plutonic igneous rock, consisting essentially of plagioclase, andesine and labradorite felspar, together with hornblende, augite or biotite.

form attractive and prominent upland areas, where there is likely to be amenity objection to extended working. The modification of such topography by quarrying may be unfortunate, particularly in those areas, such as the Lickey Hills, where the quartzite uplands occur in an otherwise lowland landscape, or in parts of Derbyshire, where a small number of sandstone workings are active in the north-west of the Peak Park. The small average size of sandstone quarries, compared with those of igneous rocks and limestone, often means that they are not out of scale with the landscape but an area such as the West Riding, with very large numbers of small sandstone workings, suffers from their cumulative effect.

Very little restoration of sandstone working has been carried out. In many areas, such as Mid-Wales or north Devon, quarries are remote from urban areas which could provide filling material. In Lancashire, where the approximately 690 hectares of derelict sandstone workings and 670 hectares of active workings[293] are close to large urban areas, other factors have so far prevented filling of disused quarries on any scale. Most of the worked-out quarries in the county occur within a water catchment area which precludes filling with domestic refuse unless it has been completely sterilized. However, Blackburn is now incinerating its domestic refuse and providing inert fill for nearby quarries whilst Burnley has similar plans.[294] There are, as might be expected, insufficient quantities of inert waste, such as building rubble, to make much contribution towards filling other very large sandstone excavations in the county. Here, as elsewhere, remoteness and difficulty of access to some sites adds to the costs of filling, and since most of the land concerned has only a low potential market value there is little direct economic incentive for restoration. In Warwickshire, where quarries are even closer to urban areas, the absence of filling to date is attributed to the great depth and capacity of the quarries and the continued quarrying activity at most of them.[295]

Although the overall impact of sandstone extraction on a national scale is now less widespread than that of either igneous rock or limestone quarrying, the faster growth rate of sandstone output during the 1960s will, if sustained, lead inevitably to much greater pressure on those areas where high quality or thick deposits occur, and, more particularly, those areas where alternative supplies of local-won aggregate are scarce. The impact on certain areas is, of course, already substantial. Although quarry scars below the tree line will be naturally revegetated in time, and walls of disused quarries are usually stable, it is to be hoped that such expansion will at least be accompanied by a parallel expansion of the filling and restoration programme.

3

UBIQUITOUS NON-METALLIFEROUS MINERALS (II)

CHALK

CHALK is geologically and chemically a limestone. Like the older types of limestone, it is a sedimentary rock, laid down in fairly shallow seas during the Cretaceous period, and composed mainly of microscopic particles of calcium carbonate. However, the physical properties of most chalk deposits are different from the other types of limestone; although hard chalks occur in Lincolnshire and the East Riding, and a small part of the Chilterns, most deposits have not been compacted and recrystallized to the same extent as the older formations and have a soft, earthy composition. As a result, chalk has a much more limited commercial use than Carboniferous limestone; it can be used as an alternative to limestone in those markets which utilize its chemical properties but only in much more limited quantities or after special treatment where its physical properties are required. Wherever the minerals are commercial alternatives, the chief factor determining which is used is likely to be proximity to the market. Whereas other limestones occur primarily in the North and West of Britain, chalk is found extensively and almost exclusively in South and East England. Here the chalk landscape is typified by such shallow uplands as the North and South Downs, Salisbury Plain, the Chilterns, parts of Essex and East Anglia and the Yorkshire and Lincolnshire Wolds. Chalk does not, except as a geological curiosity, occur in Wales or Scotland.

The limited value of the physical properties of chalk was the chief determinant of the very much slower market growth rate than limestone during the period 1960–70 (an increase of 2·3 per cent and 115·6 per cent respectively).[1] The chief outlet for limestone is aggregates, for which demand was growing very rapidly during the 1960s. On the other hand, the chief outlet for chalk is cement manufacture, consuming some 85 per cent of chalk output at the end of the period.[2] Cement production in the UK rose by 26·3 per cent during the decade,[3] a rise of very much smaller proportions than that of aggregates. Although demand for cement has clearly some links with that for aggregates, the correlation is only a minor one: concrete and cement-bound aggregates make up only about 30 per cent of road aggregates, for instance.[4] One factor in the relatively slow growth rate of cement during the 1950s and 1960s was the reduction in UK Portland cement exports from approximately 2 030 000 tonnes in 1952 to 203 000 tonnes in 1966,[5] resulting from increasing foreign competition, rising domestic fuel costs and the manufacture of their own supplies by previously importing countries.[6] In the much more rapidly expanding aggregates sector, chalk was only used in minor quantities. It is not suitable for either wearing-course roadstone or concrete aggregate, largely because of its softness and friability. In fact, natural chalk in the ground has considerable strength and little of this is lost after excavation and re-compaction. It is, however, highly susceptible to frost and is only used in its natural state either as fill for road embankments, or for road sub-base construction in those few areas of Britain where frost penetration is unlikely. Elsewhere, some stabilising agent is required if chalk is to be used for road sub-bases. Transport and Road Research Laboratory tests have shown that cement-bound chalk is acceptable for use for this purpose, subject to the removal of flints and a reduction of the moisture content which affects the mixture.[7] The quantities of chalk used for road fill were increasing in the 1960s and will probably increase further, in view of the abundance of its reserves in the South-East where other aggregates are in increasingly short supply. However, as cement-bound chalk requires twice the amount of cement of cement-bound gravel, its comparative costliness will probably limit its use to such areas where chalk supplies are abundant and the cost of other aggregates is high.

In markets such as that of iron and steel flux or agricultural lime, which utilize the chemical properties of calcium carbonate, chalk and limestone are interchangeable, but in both cases it is chalk which is used in smaller quantities. Most chalk deposits are remote from the great iron and steel centres of Wales, the Midlands and the North, although some chalk from the wolds of north and south Humberside is utilized as flux at Scunthorpe.[8] The use of chalk, either ground, burnt or hydrated, as a source of agricultural lime, is a substantial minor market, consuming some 1 million tonnes of the mineral per year.[9] The ex-pit price of chalk for agricultural purposes undercuts that of limestone similarly used,[10] since it is cheaper both to extract and process. However, chalk takes a smaller percentage of the agricultural market than limestone since it is of more localized occurrence, and the cost of its transport away from the South and East of England would more than cancel out its cost-advantage ex-pit.

The relative importance of chalk and limestone for cement manufacture has fluctuated since 1945. Portland cement manufacture requires lime, silica and alumina, usually supplied by the main raw materials, chalk or limestone, clay or shale, although sand, ash, marl or anhydrite may be used. The traditional centres of the Portland cement industry, founded in the nineteenth century, were based on chalk rather than limestone since chalk is easier both to extract and process. Most chalk deposits may be excavated by face shovels without preliminary blasting, and since the mineral is less abrasive than limestone it is cheaper to process, there being less wear and tear on machinery. The largest concentrations of cement workings still remain near the chalk boundary where chalk meets clay, i.e. along the Thames estuary (Kent and Essex banks); along the Medway estuary (Halling, Snodland and Rochester); the Humber estuary (especially Melton and South Ferriby); and the Sussex Downs (the Adur and Ouse valleys). The scarp foot of the Chilterns, where the chalk marl at the foot of the Lower Chalk provides alone both major raw materials for cement manufacture, has cement works at Chinnor, Pitstone and Sundon. Thamesside, the traditional home of the cement industry, is still of paramount importance and output in 1971 made up more than 25 per cent of the total cement output,[11] and accordingly Kent, followed at some distance by Essex, had in 1969 the largest county chalk outputs (see Fig. 3.1). The main area of working is the five-mile stretch from Dartford to Gravesend, where the Thames bends south of its main axis and cuts into the pure Upper Chalk of the North Downs. Here an important waterway, which may be used for transporting fuel in and exports out as required, occurs in conjunction with an outcrop of the main raw materials.[12] The good rail link and proximity to the important metropolitan market are further important factors in the dominant position of the Thamesside cement industry.

However, during the 1950s and 1960s there was a pronounced trend towards the siting of new cement works away from the traditional South-Eastern locations and nearer to major markets other than Greater London. In spite of increased efficiency resulting from the bulk handling of cement, mainly realized in the 1950s, high transport costs for this comparatively low cost product appeared to indicate that it would be cheaper to manufacture cement from harder, more costly but local limestone, than to bring in cement made from the more easily worked South-Eastern chalk. Since limestone contains less moisture than chalk (which averages 20 per cent moisture), the dry or semi-dry manufacturing processes could be employed at the new limestone based works, thus utilizing proportionately less fuel than at chalk based works.[13] As a result, of the four new Portland cement works opened in the period 1960–9, only one, at Westbury in Wiltshire (1962), serving the markets

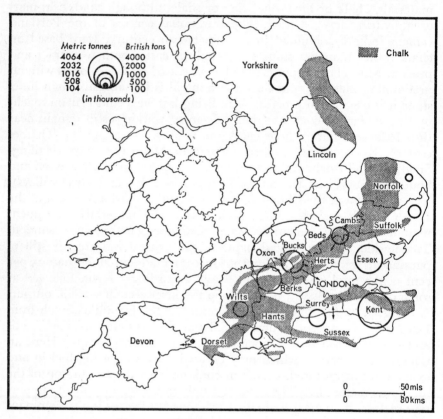

Fig. 3.1   *Chalk:* output by county, 1969
Arrows indicate location of counties whose totals are grouped
Source: Department of the Environment

of the West Country, was based on chalk, with the remainder on limestone. Most of the new sites of this period were inland ones, since access for water transport did not appear to be crucial in a period of sharply declining cement exports. The new Portland cement works at Dunbar (1962) exemplified, in everything but its coastal location, the provincial market oriented, limestone based greenfield sites of the 1950s and 1960s.

The Dunbar plant, the first complete cement works in Scotland apart from those grinding clinker, produced in the late 1960s some 75 per cent of the cement used in Scotland[14] and deliveries by rail from Kent decreased accordingly. Dunbar and the two other raw limestone based cement works of the 1960s largely account for the proportional rise in consumption of limestone compared with chalk during that period. Although no overall statistics are available, the figures of the Associated Portland Cement Manufacturers Ltd., who supplied in 1971 some 60 per cent of total cement output,[15] indicate a proportional rise in consumption of limestone for cement manufacture during the 1960s (see Table 3.1). The predominance of new limestone based works also

Table 3.1. Consumption of limestone and chalk for cement manufacture (tonnes) by the Associated Portland Cement Manufacturers Ltd., 1961, 1965 and 1970

	1961	1965	1970
Limestone	2 533 900	3 999 990	5 257 800
Marl	703 070	870 710	694 940
Chalk/marl	203 200	189 990	187 960
Chalk	9 366 500	10 048 240	9 191 750

Source: Associated Portland Cement Manufacturers Ltd.

largely accounts for the slower growth of chalk output than of cement output during the 1960s. As indicated earlier, while cement output rose by 26·3 per cent from 1960 to 1970, chalk output rose by only 2·3 per cent.

However, the trend towards proportionately greater consumption of limestone for cement manufacture is likely to be reversed during the 1970s, as a result of the creation of an exceptionally large 4·1 million tonnes per year capacity plant at Northfleet, on the north Kent chalk, by Associated Portland Cement Manufacturers.

The decision to build this new works, probably the largest and most modern cement works in Europe, taken in the late 1960s, reflects a change of policy by this company associated with the introduction of linear programming in 1965. A mathematical model was devised, incorporating among other elements raw materials sources, production and distribution costs and the areal distribution of projected demand, to establish the least cost location of new works.[16] This led to the conclusion that the cost advantages lay with extending works, to utilize fully existing facilities and staff and achieve maximum economies of scale, rather than to build on further greenfield sites. It also involved treating the market nationally and thinking in terms of larger transport distribution systems and was thus in a sense a return to pre-1945 marketing patterns. The most important decisions resulting from the operation of the model have been the planning of the New Northfleet works, complemented by the doubling of capacity at the limestone based Hope works in Derbyshire, converted to the dry manufacturing process and with a planned output of 1·22 million tonnes designed for northern markets.[17] The creation of the New Northfleet works was reinforced by the need to replace a number of older works on or near the Thames, notably Bevans, Sittingbourne, Johnsons, Wouldham, Kent and Cliffe.[18] The presence of extensive chalk reserves in north Kent relatively close at hand was clearly a major factor in the choice of this site, but by and large the importance of raw materials as a prime locating factor in cement production here has diminished, and that of other factors has increased. This is in part borne out by the fact that the clay reserves of the area capable of servicing Northfleet and Swanscombe works are now exhausted and this material will be brought by pipeline from Ockendon in south Essex 11·3 kilometres to Swanscombe quarry, where it will be mixed with chalk for transport by pipeline a further 4·8 kilometres to the works.[19] The existing facilities and personnel on Thamesside, and proximity to metropolitan markets, were important considerations in the ultimate location choice. The value of waterside facilities has been enhanced as they may enable the company to exploit a new export market for bulk cement and clinker which it believes is opening up,[20] in spite of the setbacks in overseas sales of most of the 1960s. Inasmuch, a wharf capable of berthing up to 60 960 tonnes bulk carriers has been constructed. The strategic considerations which have argued against further increasing the concentration of cement manufacture in this one vulnerable area in the past[21] no longer carry any real weight. As a result of the exceptionally large New Northfleet works, the company anticipate a net increase in the extraction of chalk of approximately 3 353 000 tonnes per year, and a decrease in the extraction of limestone of approximately 406 400 tonnes.[22] The decrease in limestone consumption will come mainly from the closure of the small Harbury works in Warwickshire, serving markets which will in future be supplied from Northfleet.[23] Some small limestone based works in the North of England have closed as a result of expanded capacity at the Hope works in Derbyshire. Clearly this policy of upgrading the capacity of a few selected works in order to achieve greater economies of scale may well lead to a rise in the average distance which raw materials are transported to cement works, although it is true that the siting of cement works must be governed by the location of the major raw materials simply because of their low value/high bulk characteristics and the substantial weight loss during processing.

The weight ratio of raw materials to final Portland cement product is 20:11.[24] However, in the future the large, high capital plants may be expected increasingly to outlive the reserves of raw material in the immediate vicinity. To a limited extent this was already happening in the 1960s at small plants. In 1969 the small cement works at Wilmington on the River Hull, utilized chalk sent by rail from Hessle and clay barged across the Humber.[25] The large modern cement works are more likely to utilize pipelines, with their cheaper unit costs, as is exemplified by New Northfleet, where both major raw materials will be transported to the works by this medium. The technique of pipelining expands considerably the radius around cement works within which it is economic to transport raw materials but it is more advantageously utilized for chalk than for limestone, since the slurried form of the delivered raw material predisposes choice of the more costly wet manufacturing process, employed in any case at chalk based works. The most striking instance of pipeline transport of raw materials to cement works is the 92 kilometre long pipeline, in operation since 1965, which carries chalk slurry from the Kensworth quarry in the pure Upper Chalk of the Chilterns dipslope to cement works at Rugby and Southam. In this case, the exceptionally long distance transport of chalk resulted not from exhaustion of reserves in the vicinity of the works, but from the unusual decision to locate works at the market on a site where only one major raw material was present, rather than away from the market on a site where the two major raw materials coincided. Such a decision would have been improbable before the advent of modern pipeline technology. It appears likely that, apart from any economic considerations which may favour further cement works locations of this type, there may be pressure in this direction from planning authorities, since quarrying alone undeniably constitutes less of an intrusion on landscape than quarrying with on-site cement works. The local authorities comprising the Chilterns Standing Conference (Bedfordshire, Buckinghamshire, Hertfordshire, Oxfordshire), for instance, have stated that 'every effort should be made to ensure that no new cement works, either in the Area of Outstanding Natural Beauty or prominently visible from it, are established, but that the raw material is removed elsewhere for processing.[26]

The policy of upgrading capacity at existing cement works is likely to lead to the increased average size of quarries serving the cement industry, which are already amongst the largest of chalk quarries. Chalk quarries of all types ranged in size in the late 1960s from approximately 1 778 000 tonnes per year to as little as 508 tonnes per year.[27] Quarries serving cement works tended to have outputs in the top half of this range. In the future, one quarry at least, that of Swanscombe in north Kent providing the entire needs of the New Northfleet plant, is likely to have an output of some 6·1 million tonnes per year. Chalk extraction for cement manufacture has always been controlled by the cement companies themselves, although in the late 1960s a limited sale of chalk to the cement industry began in south Essex. Overall, cement companies were in the 1960s quarrying an average of 1 million tonnes per year surplus to their requirements for cement manufacture,[28] and consequently several of them had an interest in whiting, flints (used as aggregate in the manufacture of pottery) and lime. Chalk quarries which serve outlets other than cement manufacture operate on average on a smaller scale and smaller firms are involved, in some cases private family businesses. These largely account for the fragmented nature of chalk extraction as a whole. There were 146 chalk quarries in Britain in 1969.[29] The quarries where chalk is extracted for agricultural lime, like those where limestone is worked for this purpose, have traditionally been on a small scale and serving only local markets. In 1969 chalk for agricultural lime and whiting was still, in the Humberside area, produced from mainly small quarries scattered throughout the wolds of Yorkshire and Lincolnshire.[30] However, the tendency in the 1960s was for quarries producing for the agricultural and industrial markets to increase both in size of operations and in the market radius served. This trend, which was of course apparent in most extractive industries during the period, is primarily a response to the greater economies to be gained by scale of working and particularly the more efficient use to be made of capital equipment. For example, in 1953 there were eight active chalk quarries along the dip and scarp slopes of the Surrey North Downs, producing chalk and lime for industry, agriculture and aggregates. By 1964 four of these quarries had closed, but production from the remaining four was greater than from twice the number of quarries in 1953.[31] The result of developments such as this, which can be discerned in most of the chalk producing areas, is the more extensive transport of the material and a more regional or even interregional marketing pattern. However, the local markets still tend to be the prime determinant of the uses to which the locally-won chalk is put: four chalk quarries in Norfolk serve only the agricultural market while the East Riding chalk quarries concentrate on the production of chalk for industrial purposes.[32]

Quarries producing for purposes other than cement manufacture tend to be scattered throughout the chalk outcrops rather than concentrated into complexes as are the cement quarries, and their existence brings the total of chalk producing counties in 1969 to twenty.

The chalk bearing land of these counties is nowhere inside a National Park, but the pleasant rolling chalk landscape is one of the most distinctive types of scenery in Britain and in South-East England the existing and proposed Areas of Outstanding Natural Beauty are closely related to the chalk outcrop. The scenic value of such areas is enhanced by their accessibility to the large population of the region. It is estimated, for instance, that at least one-fifth of the total population of England lives within easy motoring distance of the Chilterns.[33] Chalk extraction in existing Areas of Outstanding Natural Beauty occurs in Sussex, Hampshire, Oxfordshire, Bedfordshire, Buckinghamshire, Lincolnshire and in proposed Areas in Yorkshire.

The modification of the topography caused by excavation, and the visual intrusion of quarries and works, are the chief problems, although there may be chalk spillage on roads and creation of dust. Since chalk may usually be ripped from the surface without blasting, noise and vibration from chalk pits is much less than that from limestone or other hard rock quarries. Chalk-bearing land is seldom of the highest agricultural value, except perhaps in some parts of Kent. Chalk extraction does not interfere significantly with urban development, with the notable exception of parts of north Kent and the Beverley whiting works in the East Riding. Furthermore, the areas involved in chalk extraction, as in other types of rock quarries, is not large in relation to the tonnages extracted. The annual take for chalk extraction in the late 1960s was calculated to be approximately 81 hectares, of which the majority, 69 hectares, were deep-hole workings, 6 hectares bluff sites (perpendicular faces) and 6 hectares thin-seam workings.[34] In general, cement works require much smaller areas for chalk extraction than for those of clay or shale. Consequently, only in Kent do the total areas involved in chalk extraction reach large proportions. There 527 hectares were in 1971 either active chalk workings or with planning permission for workings, compared with 203 hectares in the East Riding, 122 hectares in Surrey, 55 hectares in Hampshire, 43 hectares in Wiltshire and 6 hectares on the Isle of Wight.[35] In general, there is little waste production associated with chalk quarrying; lower qualities may find a market in agriculture or aggregates, as can waste from kiln plant. Large flints, if encountered in quantity, can be marketed for ceramics manufacture. Smaller flints, which have no commercial value, are often backfilled.

The visual impact of working sites is the major planning problem in most areas. The small number of bluff sites, with an annual take of some 6 hectares per year, pose the smallest problem in this respect; disused bluff sites are naturally regenerated in time, a process which may be encouraged by leaving a layered working face to facilitate vegetation growth. Similarly, thin-seam workings, also with a small annual take, are comparatively easy to restore, since only small quantities of fill are required. Restoration of the overwhelming majority of deep-hole workings, necessarily consisting of thick strata of the mineral beneath a thin overburden, is of a much more difficult order. The quantities of material required for filling these deep holes are unlikely to be available in any but those areas closest to urban concentrations such as Kent or Surrey, where some filling with domestic refuse has occurred. Elsewhere, a small number of disused chalk pits have been put to some after-use in their unrestored state. A case in point is the recreational centre, primarily a caravan site, at South Heighton quarry in east Sussex. As it is well screened from the road, it represents an acceptable use of the modified topography.[36]

Active chalk quarries which are not associated with on-site lime burning or cement works do not necessarily intrude on the landscape. The small quarries scattered among the east Sussex Downs, for instance, are not considered to create serious problems since their pits are in scale with the landscape and, in the view of the County Planning Officer, act as points of accent within it.[37] However, the chalk working in the Dean valley beauty spot near Salisbury in Wiltshire, some 65 hectares of which are likely to be worked over 50–60 years by a subsidiary of the English China Clays group for a new paper coating process, aroused fierce objections on amenity grounds when a public inquiry was held in June 1967.[38] Other chalk quarries, although relatively small in size, are also considered to cause amenity problems in west Sussex (mainly Upper Beeding and Steyning), at Downend Chalk Pit on the Isle of Wight, in the Surrey North Downs and Hampshire Downs, and on the scarp face of the Yorkshire Wolds.[39] However, the greatest amenity problems occur where on-site lime burning or cement manufacture takes place, usually in association with large quarries. Chalk quarries on their own may add interest and variety to a landscape, but when associated with a large plant complex only the most thorough screening can mitigate their intrusive impact.

Cement works create visual problems, especially the kiln plant and chimneys, but traffic generation, noise and dust can damage the environment. All of these unfortunate manifestations can be ameliorated, and some almost totally removed, in the case of new cement works, by the imposition of planning stipulations. Noise may be modified by suppressors and soundproofing; visual damage reduced by screening, special camouflage painting of plant and landscaping; and road traffic may be partially re-routed in some cases to avoid congestion as far as possible. Dust can also be reduced by electrostatic dust precipitators. But while new cement works such as Associated Portland Cement Manufacturers' Westbury works do clearly illustrate the advances in design which have been made, these benefits have to date been felt mainly in the limestone areas, sites of the majority of post-war cement works. Apart from Westbury and the New Northfleet works, most chalk based cement works pre-date the era of planning controls and industrial landscape architects. In such cases, the creation of noise and dust may be curtailed either by the voluntary efforts of the manufacturer or by the law relating to nuisance and the powers of the Alkali Inspectorate; it is however fair to comment that the efficacy of the Alkali Inspectorate in curtailing air pollution is in some dispute.[40] The deleterious visual impact of older cement works on attractive chalk scenery is exemplified by the Chilterns, where four major cement undertakings are situated in or adjacent to the Area of Outstanding Natural Beauty. Three of the four are located in the Lower Chalk outcropping at the foot of the main scarp, and two of these, Chinnor and Pitstone, with their associated quarries, form, in the view of the Chilterns Standing Conference, 'major detractions from the landscape of significant lengths of the escarpment'.[41]

Almost every type of land use and planning problem associated with chalk workings is to be found in Kent, which contains the largest number of worked-out sites, as well as supplying 24·9 per cent of total chalk output in 1969.[42] This county has the greatest complex of associated cement works, and is likely to provide an even larger percentage of chalk output in the 1970s and 1980s. Small quarries where chalk is excavated for agricultural lime are found in the North Downs, but, as in the case of the small quarries of the South Downs of Sussex, these are not seriously out of scale with the landscape and there are no large associated plant complexes. Extraction of chalk for cement has, with the closure of the Sittingbourne cement works, become more concentrated on sites west of the River Medway, where quarries serve the two major cement complexes, and it is here that the most serious attendant problems occur. In the Medway valley, permission for chalk working at the Halling and Snodland (Holborough) cement works extended in 1971 to 203 hectares and at the Temple Marsh, Rochester works to 14 hectares.[43] These workings did not at that time seriously intrude on the North Downs Area of Outstanding Natural Beauty, but at Halling and to a lesser extent at Snodland the visual impact, dust and traffic generated did adversely affect the environment.[44] The traffic congestion was, however, likely to be reduced by the construction of by-passes for Halling and Snodland. In any event, the problems here are nothing like as acute as those on the major Dartford–Gravesend complex.

The quarrying of chalk from the steep bluffs on the river front at Gravesend dates back at least to mediaeval times, but began to expand rapidly in the nineteenth century in response to the demands of urban and industrial growth. The expansion of pits along the 8 kilometre stretch of Thamesside from Dartford to Gravesend was striking in the period 1850–1950,[45] and in this latter year aerial photographs revealed the existence of some 60 chalk pits covering 404 hectares in this locality. As chalk extraction here moved gradually away from the riverside, it was encroaching on land classified by the Land Utilization Survey as being of first-class agricultural value,[46] making up part of the great market gardening and fruit growing belt of the London Basin and dip-slope of the North Downs. There was also land use competition with industrial enterprises and settlement; in fact, the chalk workings have prevented the development of a rational and discrete land use pattern and the result remains a complicated mesh of chalk pits, industry, cement works, settlement and roads and railway. The north-west Kent complex is unique in the extent to which large-scale chalk extraction has collided with other intense pressures on space caused by cement manufacture and by industrial development in general, and the growth of its attendant housing and communications network.

The chief environmental problems created by the complex of pits up to 31 metres deep are the isolating of existing communities or curtailment of their expansion or cohesion as at Swanscombe, Knockall and Stone; the leaving of stretches of roads isolated at original levels or greatly extended in length; and the visual damage to the landscape.[47] Dust and smoke from the cement works still, in spite of compliance with the Alkali Acts, cause complaints. There is also the consumption of agricultural or horticultural land and the fragmentation of holdings caused by expansion of the quarries. The disused pits, which may be dangerously deep, create vast problems if they are to be used to any extent for other purposes, although a few are used in their unrestored state for industrial sites or, as in one case, a sports ground. Indeed, the New Northfleet cement works itself is sited in a disused quarry. The policy of the planning authority is to fill pits wherever possible. They are however highly unlikely to be able to bring the whole disused area back to its original level, partly because of these developments on some of the quarry floors and partly because filling with the only material available in sufficient quantity, i.e. domestic refuse, can give rise to the pollution of the water supplies. Restoration is concentrated on areas zoned for residential purposes and by 1971 some 5 per cent of the total area of chalk quarries in north-west Kent had been filled with domestic refuse.[48] The process of filling itself causes problems of traffic generation, dust and smell, and is a more difficult task in the west of the area where there is little or no overburden. On the other hand, the extension of settlements and communications on to chalk-bearing land in the pre-planning period has in some cases prevented the most economic and rational extension of quarries, whilst choice of direction of extended working is further restricted by the variation in the quality of the chalk, and the yield per hectare. An instance of the interference of communications with quarry extension was the northward expansion of the Cotton Lane pit in the 1950s. The operators were not allowed to remove the road at Moody's Lane, left as a spine of chalk up to 31 metres high, and an entirely new pit had to be opened up beyond it, linked to the cement works by a tunnel beneath the road.[49] Naturally, this was an extremely expensive form of pit expansion. The county council now operates a consultation area for chalk to prevent further sterilization of deposits. The backlog of problems in this area is significant because dereliction exists in very close proximity to existing working areas. The majority of derelict land in north-west Kent falls within Dartford Rural District and Swanscombe Rural District, mainly in the parishes of Stone and Swanscombe where some 194 hectares were in 1971 committed to further chalk workings.[50] The backlog of problems has been examined in some detail precisely because it greatly complicates the planning considerations of present and future chalk workings.

The bulk of the present planning consents date from 1952 when the Minister permitted such workings on 385 hectares north of the A2. In 1968, 194 of these hectares, likely to last 15–20 years,[51] remained to be excavated. The large area concerned reflects the policy, usual among cement companies, of applying for long-term planning permissions to obtain security for their heavy capital expenditure. The proposed New Northfleet works, a capital project of £50 million, which includes the creation of a new wharf, private road and rail sidings, necessitated the securing of planning permission for a further extended period. The creation of the new works releases land from active quarrying elsewhere. This has happened notably at Cliffe and Sittingbourne, but it has posed the problem of the need to allocate further substantial amounts of land for chalk quarrying in the already congested Thames-side hinterland. The planning authority was faced with two main alternatives; either the lateral extension of workings to the south of the A2 trunk road, the present boundary of the workings, or their vertical extension to below the water-table in some of the areas already carrying consents for working but only to minus 2·4 metres OD. The lateral extension of the workings would have involved encroachment into an area of metropolitan green belt, including Darenth Woods, an area of special scientific interest, the possible isolation of the A2 on a spine of chalk and visual intrusion on the motorway. The alternative, excavation to greater depths, involved the greater operating costs to the industry of works below the water-table, offset by the shorter haul from quarry to works, and the quality of chalk which would be better than that from the lateral extension. The overburden of Thanet Sand in this area is, moreover, thick enough to fill the worked-out excavations higher than the water table, above which it may be permissible to use domestic refuse for fill. Accordingly 243 hectares north of the A2, already carrying planning consent under the 1952 permission, was given additional permission by the county planning authority to be worked to minus 7·6 metres OD[52] which will, at the predicted rate of output, ensure consented reserves lasting almost until the end of the century. The method of excavation of such large areas does not, it is considered, readily lend itself to after-treatment since a number of worked-out pits will still be required to keep open internal rail and road connections from working faces to cement works. Restoration will not therefore take place until the area is fully worked-out.

This planning strategy, which arises both from the already very extensive chalk workings in the area and the intense pressures on land use, may be contrasted with that of Bedfordshire County Council in relation to chalk quarrying at Kensworth, south of Dunstable. These workings, for chalk which is slurried by pipeline to Rugby, occur in the Chilterns Area of Outstanding Natural Beauty but the pressures on land use are nothing like as great as those of north-west Kent. At Kensworth, an earlier consent for chalk working over 24 hectares with no limitations of depth was recently replaced by permission for 170 hectares of workings with a maximum face depth of 46 metres.[53] Only 105 of the 170 hectares will in fact be worked and 26 hectares of them will be afforested for screening purposes. The old workings will be restored. The preference for extensive rather than intensive workings at Kensworth—although it attracted some hostile comment at the time—in fact arises as logically from the conditions there as does the opposite preference for deep intensive workings in Kent. At Kensworth the chief concern is to preserve visual amenity in an area where pressures on space are not great. Not only does the more generous land allocation permit of extensive screening, but the depth restriction on the working face substantially reduces the problems of restoration. It is intended to operate a rolling restoration scheme, to be carried through simultaneously with extraction, whereby the topsoil will be preserved, and the land put back to agriculture within three years of excavation. The planning question is of course eased by the absence of an on-site cement works. Furthermore, the Kensworth quarry is the only one of the major Chilterns quarries serving cement works located in the Upper Chalk of the dipslope (90 per cent calcium carbonate, requiring the addition of clay for cement manufacture). Kensworth occurs entirely within the Area of Outstanding Natural Beauty, in contrast to those of the Lower Chalk which straddle the boundaries of the Area or lie just outside it, but the Chilterns Standing Committee believe that, as a general rule, there is more scope for siting workings less obtrusively in the landscape of the dipslope and the use of this zone for chalk working is to be generally preferred from the amenity aspect to the use of the Lower Chalk.[54]

The overall national planning considerations of chalk working may be considered to be less than those of Carboniferous limestone since the rate of growth in chalk output has been only minimal during the recent past and future output is unlikely to grow at anything like that of limestone. The problems of estimating future demand are probably not as complex as in the case of limestone, since the bulk of chalk output is tied to very long-term capital projects with partially predictable consumption rates. However, the Ministry of Housing and Local Government's chalk demand forecasts on a regional basis made in the early 1950s for chalk other than that for cement, were inaccurate by up to 50 per cent, and even within the highly capitalized cement industry there could be fluctuations in chalk consumption sufficient to cause serious errors in prediction. There could for instance be a fall in demand for chalk resulting from raw material substitution, and an increase in the use of such materials as blast furnace slag and clinker cement (as on Clydeside), or pulverized ash, lime and cement (as at Ferrybridge), processes which require relatively small amounts of the calcareous raw materials, chalk and limestone. There could be further alteration, other than that already mentioned, in the relative positions of chalk and limestone consumption for cement manufacture. Chalk could well be used on an increasing scale for paper coating, by means of a process similar to that patented by the English China Clays Group in which an adhesive acts as a bonding agent for ultra-fine whiting and clay. This process, utilizing 75 per cent whiting, probably undercuts normal china clay coating grades, but few chalk deposits are suitable for such a highly sophisticated process. Chalk could also be used in increasing quantities for plastics and in substantially larger tonnages for aggregates as these become scarcer and more expensive in the South-East. Conversely, there could be temporary surpluses of chalk in Kent if a Channel tunnel were constructed. All these factors argue the need for constant monitoring of planning policies in the light of a possibly changing demand situation.

The landscape quality of the chalklands, of particular amenity value in the English Lowlands, is such that the greatest care has to be taken in planning extraction. Cement works must inevitably, even with the undoubted advances that have been made, have serious social costs in their locality, and the necessarily long-term permission given for chalk extraction also makes for difficulties. New Northfleet now has permission for nearly 30 years' extraction, Kensworth for 30 years, and the East Sussex Ouse Valley complex for 50 years. The stipulations contained in current planning consents will have to offer adequate safeguards for extraction taking place at least in the 1990s, a difficult matter as the almost universal inadequacies which now appear in the consents of the late 1940s and early 1950s exemplify.

The Chilterns Standing Conference stated in 1971 that

the nationwide scale of Cement Manufacturers means that their decisions at national and regional level with important local implications cannot be anticipated by local planning authorities. Consequently, planning authorities can only make responses to particular demands, an unsatisfactory situation in which *ad hoc* decisions have to be taken without an overall view being possible.[55]

Clearly the decision-making techniques of the major companies, which may greatly affect both the type and location of raw materials quarried, are now reaching a high level of sophistication, and it is becoming correspondingly more difficult for local planning authorities to assess the validity of applications for workings within the limited context of the area under their jurisdiction. The Chilterns Standing Conference has advocated the formulation of a national plan for chalk extraction, 'worked out in the fullest cooperation with mineral undertakers so that requirement can be fully assessed against resources which would be evaluated according to their amenity value as well as their mineralogical value'[56] Some of the reasons alleged in support of such a national plan apply with even greater validity to extraction of some other minerals, notably those used primarily for aggregates. In fact both the Standing Conference on London and South-East Regional Planning and the Secretary of State for the Environment have taken the view that a national plan for chalk is not necessary, and that while an advisory committee is to be set up to advise the Secretary of State on the supply of aggregates, no such action has been taken in respect of chalk. Nevertheless, the case for greater national coordination of mineral extraction planning policies as a whole does merit serious consideration, a point which is discussed in Chapter 7.

BRICK CLAYS

The traditional pattern of brick clay extraction in Britain has strong similarities with that of aggregates for construction purposes. Brick clays, like aggregates, are found in a very varied range of deposits of widespread occurrence in every region of Britain. Brick clays, like aggregates, are a high bulk/low value commodity, and are processed in as close proximity to the working face as possible, ideally within 100 metres.[57] Although the value added by brick manufacture is higher than that added by washing and grading of aggregates, the finished product remains a bulky, comparatively low value commodity. Consequently, brick clays and their associated brickworks have traditionally had a market location, and this in turn determined the small, dispersed structure of the industry in those parts of Britain where bricks were the conventional building material. As late as 1939 there were 1316 brickworks in Britain, served by 1303 clay pits.[58] Nearly one third of these used clay and shale from the Coal Measures (in some instances worked as a by-product of coal); nearly one third recent, alluvial and brickearth materials, and the remainder Jurassic and Cretaceous clays.[59] Altogether, the Ministry of Town and Country Planning classification of brick clays distinguished 26 different types of clays and marls then being exploited.[60] Even in 1939, however, the production capacity of one particular deposit, the Oxford Clays in the Jurassic sequence, constituted more than one third of the total capacity (2606 out of 8429 million bricks per year), and the trend towards the dominance of this deposit, subsequently intensified, was already well under way. In 1971, although brickworks were to be found in every Economic Planning Region (see Table 3.2), the brickworks of the Oxford Clay, were on average exceptionally large manufacturing units, contributing a percentage of national output quite disproportionate to their local markets, and serving outlets throughout Great Britain and even exporting to the Channel Islands and to France.[61]

The total number of British brickworks at the end of 1970 was only some 360,[62] a drop of 72 per cent from the 1939 figure, with the number of claypits falling in approximate proportion. Indeed, 107 brickworks closed down in the three years ending December 1969.[63] The tendency has been towards a concentration on fewer, larger, capital-intensive producing units, utilizing mechanical aids and taking full advantage of economies of scale. These serve larger market areas by means of improved transport. This trend was a widespread and characteristic feature of extractive industries during this period. However, in the case of brick clays, the reduction in the number of producing units was probably accelerated by the overall diminishing demand for bricks during the 1960s and by one feature peculiar to the industry, namely the particular cost advantages possible at one deposit, the Oxford Clays.

Table 3.2. Deliveries of bricks from Economic Planning Regions (deliveries from brickworks situated in each region). Total bricks in millions, 1965-71.

	1965	1966	1967	1968	1969	1970	1971
Northern	371	366	415	397	352	351	390
Yorkshire and Humberside	424	384	435	405	332	317	321
East Midlands	481	324	440	382	381	414	445
East Anglia	2 458	949	1 100	1 042	914	882	959
GLC area Eastern Counties	50	1 096	233	1 167	1 016	951	1 000
Southern Counties	761	976	1 003	1 040	956	1 042	1 168
South-Eastern Counties	482	389	522	442	414	424	499
South-West	155	151	196	176	167	166	179
Wales	292	266	293	258	228	231	243
West Midlands	516	437	543	499	445	438	441
North-West	702	631	656	625	556	502	563
Scotland	731	759	767	788	720	638	618
Totals	7 424	6 729	7 700	7 221	6 481	6 356	6 825

Sources: *Annual Bulletin of Construction Statistics,* 1968-9, Ministry of Public Building and Works, Statistics Branch, Construction Economies Division; *Monthly Bulletin of Construction Statistics,* April 1972, Department of the Environment.

The raw material of the Oxford Clays possesses inherent advantages for the purposes of brickmaking. The clay, containing 18-20 per cent moisture, is eminently suitable for brick manufacture by the semi-dry process, i.e. it is sufficiently plastic in its natural state to be worked by brickmaking machines. This may be contrasted with the harder, drier Coal Measures clays which generally require preliminary crushing, the adding of water to give plasticity, and subsequent drying, before they can be processed. The Oxford Clays do not require weathering, a slow and costly process; they have a small number of impurities, and a constant and medium lime content. (An excess of lime produces quicklime and porous bricks, and a deficit produces shrinkage and cracking during processing.) They do not require mixing with other materials as do, for instance, the London Clays worked in Kent and Surrey, which shrink on firing unless mixed with sand. The Oxford Clays have the further advantage of a carbonaceous content, usually between 5 and 7 per cent, which reduces the coal requirement for firing by as much as two thirds. (Most kilns are still coal-fired.) In the West Riding brickworks, which use Coal Measures Clays, between 200 and 360 kilogrammes of coal are needed to produce one thousand bricks. In the Oxford Clays between 50 and 100 kilogrammes are needed.[64] This reduced coal consumption is vitally important in partially offsetting the disadvantage of the absence of fuel in the area of the Oxford Clays, especially when compared with the Coal Measures Clays, some of which are extracted from the collieries themselves and manufactured by the NCB, until 1972 the second largest brickmaking concern in the country. The inherent advantages of the Oxford Clays brickworks thus derive from the nature of the raw material, although the location of the major workings midway between London and the big urban areas of the Midlands may also be considered an asset. Although the major workings were between 56 and 97 kilometres from London at the beginning of this century,[65] the vast expansion and demand from the metropolis at about that time brought the deposits within the London supply area. Proximity to London is not now a major factor: the Hertfordshire brickworks, like others in the Home Counties, have in recent years been unable to compete in terms of clay quality or scale economies with the Oxford Clay brickworks, although nearer to the metropolitan market.[66] Similarly, the products of Nottinghamshire brickworks have long been undercut in the Midlands markets, and only a few works based on the Keuper Marl and the Middle Coal Measures are still in production.[67]

The particular advantages of the Oxford Clay as a raw material were first exploited by a new brickworks established at Fletton near Peterborough in 1881. The success of the methods developed there led to their adoption by many other brick manufacturers on the exposed Oxford Clay before the end of the century, and the appellation of 'fletton bricks' was given to all the products of these clays. Although the common fletton brick was used in vast quantities in the expansion of London during the first thirty years of this century, the superior qualities of the Oxford Clay for brickmaking have only been fully exploited since the 1930s. The semi-dry process used there involves low manufacturing costs but high capital investment and the potential economic advantages can only be realized at a large works. The exploitation of this potential has therefore been intimately connected with the other major scale economies already mentioned. For example, though the number of producing companies has fallen, the size of those remaining has increased. Overwhelmingly the largest current producer, the London Brick Company, results from an amalgamation in 1923 of B. J. Forder and Sons Ltd., formed in 1900, the old London Brick Company formed in 1889, with four smaller firms. In 1970, when the London Brick Company took over the Marsden Valley Brick Company, its percentage of national fletton output was approximately 85 per cent. This was in 1971 raised to approximately 95 per cent by the acquisition of the fletton interests of Redland Bricks Ltd.[68] Now the fourth and last of the major fletton brick complexes has been bought by the London Brick Company and with the sale to them by the NCB of their works near Peterborough. Parallel with the process of amalgamation has been the concentration of production in larger manufacturing units. The output of London Brick's Stewartby works near Bedford rose from 56 million bricks per year in 1923 to 575 million per year in 1936.[69] Subsequent growth has been limited by the lower national demand for bricks, but in 1971 the works produced in excess of 750 million bricks.[70] Stewartby, the largest brickworks in the world, is clearly much above the average size of brickworks in the Oxford Clay Vale but even the smallest of these works has a production capacity as great as the largest works elsewhere.

The other major factor governing the expansion of fletton output has been the widening market radii associated with transport improvement. The major centres of the fletton industry were, it has been suggested,[71] located in their respective positions on the clayfield at or very near points where the main railways from the Midlands coalfield cross the Oxford Clay. Most of the works are situated near one of these railway lines (see Fig. 3.2) and are connected with it. The earliest large-scale markets were based on rail distribution, and this is still an important means of transport for distances in excess of some 130 kilometres. The development of road haulage, used by the London Brick Company since 1936, has made possible the more economic and flexible delivery of bricks within this radius. The building of motorways, and most particularly the M1 which is no more than 10 kilometres from the major Bedford and Bletchley complexes and 30 kilometres from Calvert, together with the improvements to the Great North Road, have been significant in helping to contain transport costs. As a result, the delivered costs of fletton bricks are cheaper than those of local bricks in most parts of Britain, in spite of the extra haulage and handling costs involved. The London Brick Company prices do not reflect variations in transport costs, and consequently the more distant customers in effect benefit from cross-subsidization. Nor do the company's own prices vary according to the size of the order, and consequently the cost advantages of flettons are not necessarily confined to bulk con-

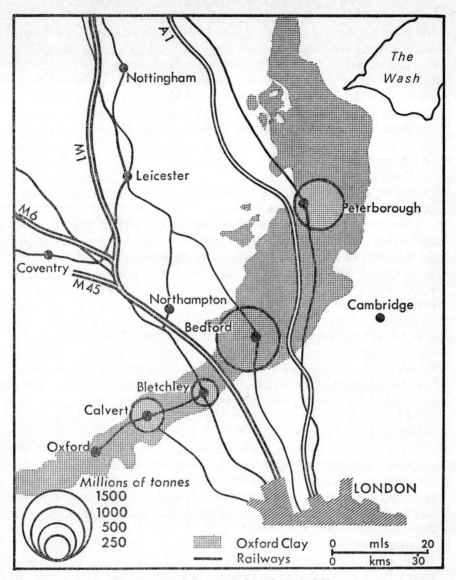

Fig. 3.2 *Brick clay output from the Oxford Clays*

tracts or big fixed orders. In general, the national outlets for fletton bricks may be contrasted with what are still the local or at most regional markets of other brickworks (although markets for special quality bricks, such as the engineering bricks, designed to withstand great pressure, which are made in the West Riding and Staffordshire, are nation-wide). The difference in market radius between facing and common bricks, which is normal at most brickworks, has been eliminated in the case of fletton brickworks of the London Brick Company, which are able to market both common and facing bricks nation wide. Market radii of most brickworks vary according to the type of brick produced, and are usually more extensive for the more costly facing bricks than for common bricks.[72]

There remains one further advantage of the Oxford Clay deposits which has only made itself felt under twentieth century conditions. In the area of the main brickworking complexes these deposits are deep, broad, and consistent in both chemical composition and geological occurrence. This makes them eminently suitable for large-scale extraction techniques, such as walking draglines, in which such great advances have been made since the 1930s. This brings a considerable cost advantage. In the clay of the West Riding Coal Measures, by contrast, the most usual method of excavation in 1965 was still hand-winning,[73] as a result of the need to mix the clay and shale found together and to remove thin seams of coal. Hand digging is now being superseded by mechanical excavation in the West Riding, but the Coal Measures deposits do not lend themselves to large-scale mechanical techniques anything like as easily as those in the Oxford Clay Vale.

The percentage of total brick output made up by flettons has been growing since the 1930s, in periods both of buoyant and of stable demand for bricks. The biggest expansion in the fletton fields, as elsewhere, occurred during the period of rapid suburban growth in the 1930s, when the annual output of all bricks doubled from 4000 to 8000 million between 1930 and 1938.[74]* The fletton percentage has continued to grow in the fluctuating markets since 1945. Although there was keen demand for bricks during the period of post-war reconstruction, uncertain economic policies led to fluctuations in demand up to 1955. The percentage of output made up by flettons rose from 31·5 in 1948 to 40 in 1960. During the 1960s national brick output has remained virtually stable, in spite of the marked expansion of building construction during that period, as a result primarily of the increased use of concrete, breeze blocks and pre-

* The annual rate of conversion of agricultural land to housing purposes was greater throughout this period than at any other time before or since in Britain.

fabricated components. The market for clay roofing tiles, a by-product manufactured at many small brickworks, continued its post-war decline because of increased use of concrete tiles.[75] Thus, this period of expansion in building construction benefited primarily the aggregates-producing industry and its derivatives, rather than the clay-producing and manufacturing industry. Nevertheless, the percentage of this virtually stable brick output contributed by the flettons continued to rise slowly, from 40 per cent in 1960 to 42·5 per cent in 1970 (see Table 3.3). Fletton output was affected to a less damaging extent by

Table 3.3. *Total annual brick production and annual fletton production, 1960–70 (millions)*

	Production, all types	Fletton production
1960	7 283	2 919
1961	7 414	3 002
1962	7 289	3 039
1963	7 139	3 021
1964	7 954	3 216
1965	7 868	3 222
1966	7 072	2 968
1967	7 208	3 031
1968	7 465	3 207
1969	7 734	2 893
1970	6 062	2 577

Source: *Annual Bulletin of Construction Statistics*, 12, Department of the Environment, 1970 table 45a.

the increased use of concrete than were, for instance, the Staffordshire blue bricks derived from the Etruria Marl formation of the north Staffordshire coalfield. Output of these special engineering bricks decreased in the 1960s in the face of increasing use of concrete, just as output of clay roofing tiles from the same formation, supplying a large percentage of national demand, fell in the face of competition from concrete tiles.[76]

The four main brick-producing centres within the Oxford Clays are complexes at Peterborough, Bedford, Bletchley and Calvert. In 1955 the two largest centres were Peterborough and Bedford, which produced 15 000 000 and 14 750 000 bricks per week respectively (London Brick Company figures only).[77] It was suggested at that time that the relative size of the workings was related to their slightly superior rail positions and the better local availability of labour at Peterborough and Bedford.[78] Since 1955, however, Bedford has overtaken Peterborough in size, and was in 1971 substantially the largest of the fletton brickwork complexes, producing 43·5 per cent of London Brick

Company fletton output.[79] The greater relative importance of the Bedford complex since 1955 probably relates to the location there of the major Stewartby works (see Fig. 3.3). This works, which is associated with a 'model village' built by the company to house labour, has achieved more in terms of scale economies than any other brick manufacturing plant. The exposure of Oxford Clay on which Stewartby and the rest of the Bedford complex is based extends 13 kilometres south-west of Bedford through the Marston valley and is one of the largest in the country. Certainly, the brickworks located there enjoy easier access to the M1 than do those located near Peterborough.

In other brick-producing areas, concentration into larger units of clay extraction and brick production is also apparent, though necessarily on a smaller scale. This process of concentration is not unrelated to the growing percentage of the national market held by flettons, since it is usually the smaller units elsewhere which are least able to compete with the mass-produced bricks of the Oxford Clays. In Surrey the digging of brick clay, mainly the London Clay, for brick and tile manufacture to serve the London market was, before 1939, an important local industry. In 1951 there were 45 clay workings in the county but by 1965 only about half of these were still active.[80] Overall production had declined, but that smaller production was coming from a smaller number of larger pits. The impact of fletton competition on the Somerset brick industry, based primarily on extraction of alluvial clays, as on that of Surrey, has been greatest since the early 1950s, when the demand created by post-war reconstruction began to slacken. The total Somerset output of 193 000 tonnes of bricks in 1953 was more than halved to 95 500 tonnes in 1961.[81] Most of the clay now worked in Somerset is used in the specialized production of handmade roofing tiles which are sold throughout Britain, although bricks and pipes are still manufactured at Bridgwater and Wellington. The pressures on small brickworks throughout the country are likely to continue. In 1965 one authority in the West Riding suggested[82] that any works in the area producing fewer than 12 500 000 bricks per year would shortly become uneconomic, and this included more than half the works for which output figures were then available. The closure of substantial numbers of brick clay pits and works away from the Oxford Clay raises a number of amenity questions. In Somerset, as elsewhere, many worked-out pits which pre-dated planning controls were left waterlogged and virtually derelict; these covered an estimated 142 hectares of the county in 1964, of which 59 hectares were in the Bridgwater area.[83] However, the long-term benefits to amenity brought about by the closure of numbers of very dispersed pits and plant may in general

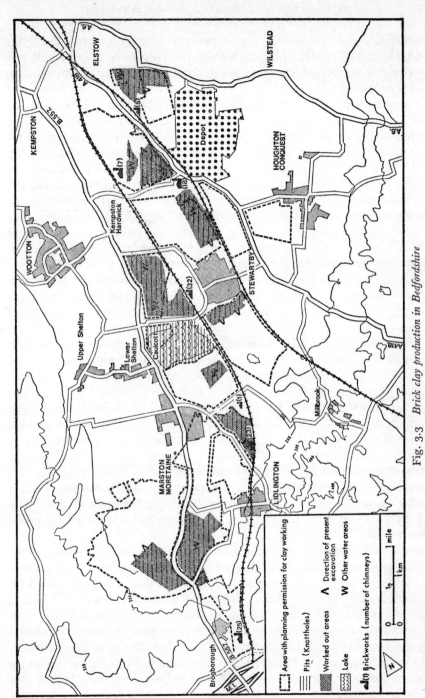

Fig. 3.3 *Brick clay production in Bedfordshire*

Source: Bedfordshire County Planning Department

outweigh the dereliction caused, especially as grants are available for clearing such derelict land. In Surrey the closure of many small pits in rural areas in or close to zones designated as being of outstanding beauty or great landscape value must be welcome. In Kent and Essex where, among other clay deposits, the brickearths are worked for brick manufacture, factors other than those of amenity are of prime importance. It has been the policy of successive Governments to set a limit of 40 years, dating from 1956, to the working of brickearth by the stock brick industry in these counties, because of the extremely high agricultural and horticultural value of the land involved, and the limited extent of the country's remaining brickearth resources. In fixing the term, the need to maintain brick supplies in the foreseeable future and to ensure that existing undertakings could reap the benefit of their investments was borne in mind.[84] Clearly the need to maintain brick supplies from these deposits is now much less pressing than was formerly the case, but brickearth extraction still continues to serve a cluster of brickmaking industries centred on Sittingbourne and extending to Faversham in Kent, as well as in the Southend area of Essex.

The most formidable planning problems are raised in connection with the Oxford Clay workings in the counties of Huntingdonshire and Peterborough, Bedfordshire and Buckinghamshire. The problems relate primarily to amenity and the restoration of worked-out pits since the agricultural value of the land is not of the highest importance. The extraction of brick clay in this area involves the working of a thick seam of mineral from beneath a comparatively thin overburden, in contrast, for example with the Kent brickearths, which are extracted from deposits averaging only 1·8 metres in depth. The 'fletton knotts', as the claypits have become known, occur in depths varying from a metre or so to more than 30 metres, although the general average is 14–15 metres.[85] The vast capacity of the knottholes is the major problem as far as restoration or after-use is concerned: the total cubic capacity of the worked-out pits in Bedfordshire in 1967, excluding three small ones, was estimated to be 69·8 million cubic metres.[86] To a lesser extent, the comparatively small quantities of waste to be disposed of, sometimes left in hill-and-dale formation at the bottom of the pits, is also an undesirable feature of the workings. In the fletton fields, both the 'callow', a clay varying in thickness from 3·1–3·7 metres produced by the weathering of the knotts, and the blue clay with low carbonaceous and high moisture content, are unsuitable for brick manufacture by the semi-dry process, although the callow was used before this process was developed. The rejection of these two materials, removed by dragline excavators and dumped in conical mounds on the pit floor—the cheapest method for the operators—has produced a depressing environment in many parts of the fletton fields. Another associated problem can be small-scale interference with drainage, although the creation of Stewartby Lake has actually had a beneficial effect by preventing the flooding of the River Ouse. Occasionally, a low hill may be removed which formerly provided welcome elevation in the comparatively flat landscape of the brickfields. The brick manufacturing plant associated with extraction may also pose difficulties: in 1967 these plants in the Bedford complex contained 111 chimneys, mostly between 30 and 60 metres high. Their prominence in the flat landscape has in places been aggravated by the diminution of trees during this century, possibly as a result of pollution from the brickworks,[87] although according to the Agriculture Research Council this is unproven. Problems similar to those indicated have occurred in all the main fletton areas.

In April 1971 the brick clay excavations in Huntingdon and Peterborough covered 810 hectares,[88] the largest area occupied by any extractive industry in the county, and land was being consumed for this purpose at the rate of something over 16 hectares per year.[89] The excavations are mainly in the fletton area to the south and the Whittlesey area to the east of Peterborough, although there are also workings to the north-east at Eye and Dogsthorpe. (The Whittlesey workings are in fact situated within the county of Cambridgeshire and the Isle of Ely and consequently are not included in the figures given above.) The excavations are worked under planning consents given by the Minister in 1953 on planning applications which he had called in. There were in 1972 approximately 690 hectares left to work under these consents.[90] The method of restoration being used here, which is in fact unrelated to any planning conditions specifically imposed, is unique in the fletton fields. Worked-out pits, amounting to one third of the London Brick Company's total excavated area, are being reclaimed over a period of more than thirty years (from 1966) with pulverized fuel ash sent by the Central Electricity Generating Board some 97 kilometres from its major Trent valley power stations. In 1972 between four and five trains per day, each containing 1020 tonnes of ash, were operating six days per week.[91] Pits were, in 1971, being filled at the rate of about 8·1 hectares per year,[92] i.e. more slowly than the creation of new pits (in excess of 16·2 hectares per year). The ash, transported in its dry form, is slurried on arrival and pumped into the pits, where it hardens sufficiently to be built on if necessary. Alternatively, topsoil may be replaced and the land restored to agriculture. The project is an expensive one: the Central Electricity Board meets virtually all the costs of the scheme, including £3·5 million for the facilities, rental for the terminal buildings and a small amount per tonne of ash pumped to the brickmakers, in addition to some 39·4 pence to 49·2 pence per tonne rail charges.[93] The scheme dates from a period when the Board had considerable fuel ash disposal problems, which is not now the case,[94] and a project of similar expense elsewhere is almost inconceivable. In fact, the availability of more economic disposal of pulverized fuel ash elsewhere has actually slowed down the rate of filling, and the scheme will now take longer than originally anticipated to complete. However, the Peterborough brick clay excavations will eventually be restored, albeit at the expense of the electricity consumer.

In Buckinghamshire there were in 1971 a total of 26 hectares of derelict land resulting from brick clay working in the Bletchley area (part excavations, part spoil heaps), 14 hectares of disused clay excavations at Newton Longville near Milton Keynes and two large worked-out brick claypits at Calvert.[95] A considerable amount of tree planting for screening purposes is needed at some of these sites, in the absence of a comprehensive landscape scheme. The larger brick claypits in this area have not been filled, primarily because of the lack of suitable filling materials. However, the London Brick Company's policy of charging for tipping, here as elsewhere, has to be taken into account. In 1971 some local tipping of refuse was being carried out at the edge of the two Calvert pits. Clearly a comprehensive after-use scheme for these workings was desirable although this had not been stipulated in the planning consents there or elsewhere in the fletton fields. In fact, more of the large pits may eventually be filled in Buckinghamshire as a result of reappraisal of the county's refuse disposal problems, whilst the possibility of bringing refuse from the Greater London area by liner train has also been raised, a scheme which would involve large quantities of waste, much larger than could ever be obtained locally, and so minimize the period of unavoidable nuisance caused by refuse dumping.[96]

The most serious problems of all occur in the major Bedford brickfield. In 1967 the total area of abandoned workings, active workings and areas with planning permission at this complex totalled 1818 hectares,[97] and land was being taken for workings at the rate of some 17·4 hectares per year. Only a small proportion of the current workings predate planning controls and these are not a serious problem. However, most of the Bedfordshire land belonging to what is now the London Brick Company was acquired, but not worked, before the Second World War and consequently, when planning controls were introduced in 1947, was subject only to the statutory reapplications. These were 'called in' by the Minister and determined at national level. These permissions granted to the London Brick Company covered most of the brickfield since worked—the local planning authority have made only minor extensions since that time—and will allow working far into the future as some 1251 hectares, more than two thirds of the total with planning consent, had, in 1967, still to be excavated.[98] The restoration and screening conditions of these Ministerial permissions, dating from the early days of post-war planning, are now considered by local planners to have been far too imprecise and undemanding. The wording of the consents relating to landscaping stated that trees and shrubs to screen the workings should be planted according to a plan to be agreed with the local planning authority or, failing that, by appeal to the Minister. No comprehensive landscaping plans were required, and although the London Brick Company has planted more than 50 000 trees since the consents were given, the plantings have not been universally successful. Some trees have died as a result of poor soil and/or pollution, exposure or insufficient after-care, and others have had to be removed for new roadworks. Other plantings are now hampering further development of the pits. Late in 1970, however, the London Brick Company and the county council agreed to provide 20·3 hectares for the experimental planting of 50 000 trees over a five-year period, to determine what types of trees are best suited to the brickfield and whether such plantations can be economic propositions. The cost is to be shared by the London Brick Company (50 per cent), the Countryside Commission and the county council.[99]

The Ministerial consents did not require that topsoil and overburden should be stored, usually an essential part of any modern planning consent, nor did they regulate the conditions in which the pit bottom should be left. In the absence of stipulations to the contrary, the industry has in some instances tipped callow and blue clay in the most economical fashion, that is in conical piles, whereas they should ideally have been concentrated at the edge of the pits, sloping inwards and covered with topsoil. The more recent local authority permissions, covering only minor additions to the working area, have been much more stringent in this respect.

The most significant part of the consents related to restoration of worked-out excavations. These planning conditions, which varied slightly from case to case, were similarly imprecise and have proved to be open to different interpretations. The following conditions, quoted by the county planning officer in his survey of the Bedfordshire brickfield in 1967 (see Fig. 3.4), is typical:

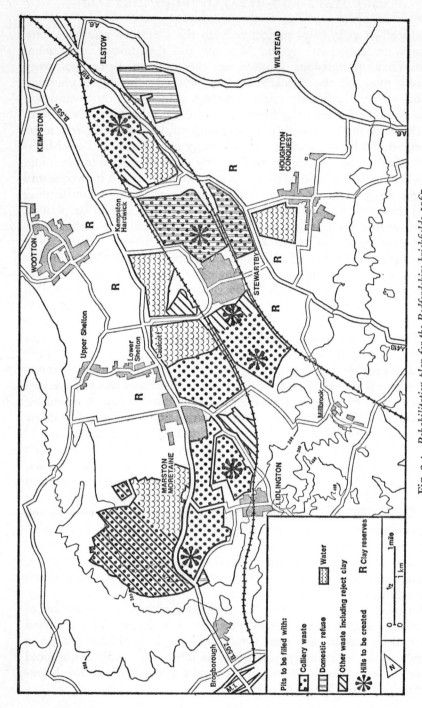

Pits to be filled with:

⬚ Colliery waste

▦ Domestic refuse

▨ Other waste including reject clay

✳ Hills to be created

▨ Water

R Clay reserves

N

0   ½   1 mile
0   1 km

Fig. 3.4 *Rehabilitation plan for the Bedfordshire brickfields 1967*

Source: Bedfordshire County Planning Department

Overburden with any other suitable filling material available at reasonable times on reasonable terms shall be deposited within the excavated areas and shall thereafter be consolidated and levelled in agreement with the local planning authority, or in default of such agreement, to the satisfaction of the Minister.[100]

The county planning office interprets the phrase 'on reasonable terms' to mean 'at reasonable cost' to the company, whereas the London Brick Company interprets it to mean 'at reasonable profit' to the company. The company policy of regarding the worked-out pits here as elsewhere as an asset to be exploited rather than as a source of dereliction which it has a duty to restore has aroused much controversy, both at the public conference on the brickfields held in 1968 and in subsequent publications.[101] It is likely that this policy, although it has not deterred the restoration scheme at Peterborough, was one factor operating against the implementation of two restoration schemes for the Bedfordshire field which were tentatively explored in the 1960s. One, the transportation of domestic refuse by rail from the Greater London area, was rejected since the cost to the local authorities concerned was found to be greater than that of incineration within London.[102] The other, the transportation of colliery waste from the Nottinghamshire coalfield by rail, a doubly attractive project which would simultaneously have reduced the amount of land sterilized by tipping in Nottinghamshire and filled Bedfordshire claypits, was also rejected on the grounds of cost. The plan envisaged the transportation of 3·25 million tonnes of coal waste per year, sufficient to fill one large pit in four years. However, the average price of 71·4 pence per tonne quoted by British Rail[103] for the 129 kilometre journey would have made an annual cost to the NCB of £2 400 000. Neither the London Brick Company nor, for that matter, the Government was prepared to contribute towards the cost of the scheme. The essence of the London Brick Company's view may be represented by a quotation from the deputy chairman's address to the 1968 Brickfield Conference:

Any suggestion that the companies should contribute to the cost of refilling can only mean an increase in the price of bricks at a time when profit margins are already being eroded by ever-increasing costs. In a trice, our highly competitive position as national distributors would be lost. How could we then compete with all the materials new and old which flood the market?[104]

It has subsequently been suggested[105] that the cost of transportation of slurried waste by pipeline could fall to as little as 12·3 pence per tonne (£460 000 per year), but there now appears little possibility of the scheme being implemented.

Consequently, the greatest part of the worked-out pits in Bedfordshire, an area totalling some 567 hectares in 1967, remains to all intents and purposes derelict. Two pits have been deliberately left unrestored in case they are needed for water storage, while, in 1967, two other pits were used by local councils for tipping and railway waste was disposed of in a third. At a large worked-out excavation at Stewartby a lake had been created, and plans for developing this area and its surroundings as a country park had been, in 1971, approved in principle by Bedfordshire County Council. The London Brick Company had offered to lease the 101 hectare lake to the council at a nominal rent.[106] This scheme, the first implemented by the county council under the 1968 Countryside Act, will involve substantial expense since there are considerable difficulties attached to making pits of this depth safe and suitable for wet recreation. Furthermore, although there is a shortage of such recreational areas in this neighbourhood, substantial improvements will be required to the immediate environment to attract potential users. There is also the possibility that worked-out pits in this area may be required for storage of power station cooling water if the Central Electricity Board, who acquired some 188 hectares of land at Elstow in 1967, go ahead with plans to build a nuclear power station at the site. In this case, the lake in question could also probably be used for angling and sailing.

The biggest restoration potential now appears to lie in the field of refuse disposal. In 1970 the London Brick Company formed a subsidiary, London Brick Land Development Ltd., to utilize the worked-out areas in a manner likely to benefit the parent company. This subsidiary is setting up a big refuse disposal organization with a collection area of some 80–97 kilometre radius of Bedford. London Brick Land Development Ltd. will set up transfer stations near main conurbations within this radius, where the refuse, delivered by councils, will be compacted before transport to pits where it will be spread in layers, with intermediate bands of soil, and the land prepared for agricultural or industrial use. The London Brick Company will essentially be operating the scheme for profit, although it must clearly also be advantageous to the local authorities adopting it. While this scheme will make possible a more rapid rate of restoration than hitherto, there is some doubt whether it will keep pace with the rate of creation of new excavations. Although some commentators[107] have appeared to take a condemnatory view of this scheme partly because it is to the profit of the company, there is no inherent reason why restoration of derelict sites should not be a process profitable to the creator of the dereliction. Indeed, it is argued elsewhere that economic incentives for land clearance or restoration would be advantageous. However, if a policy of profit maximization can clearly be seen to be inhibiting or restricting restoration, then quite a different issue arises. Should this be the case in the Bedfordshire brickfield in the future and should the extent of dereliction in fact be seen to be increasing, then some clarification of the imprecise terminology of the Ministerial consents governing these workings should be forthcoming.

There are some conclusions of a general nature relating to planning practice as it has been implemented in the fletton brickfields. The main difficulties in the Bedfordshire brickfield, apart from the unavoidable one of very large excavations in an area where source of fill is scarce, derive from the granting of very long-term consents which have subsequently emerged as insufficiently stringent. *The Control of Mineral Working*, which sets out to guide local authorities, recommends that, in the case of large-scale and highly mechanized undertakings, the allocation of planning consent for land with a life of 60 years or more may be justified.[108] The force of this argument is clear. If the raw material were prematurely exhausted, or planning permission to extend working were refused, the plant would normally have to close since the cost of transporting brick clay to the brickworks would probably be prohibitive. The policy of most large-scale brick manufacturers, as indeed of most cement manufacturers, has therefore been to seek long-term planning consents to guard against heavy losses on capital investment. However, improvements in reclamation techniques are being made all the time, and perhaps in only 20 years from now current stipulations of the most stringent kind will seem as inadequate as the Ministry's consents governing the Bedfordshire brickfield now appear. It is therefore highly desirable that, in the case of permissions covering long periods of working, some kind of review procedure should be introduced to permit stipulations on working and reclamation to be brought into line with the best modern practice. Such procedure would necessarily involve very difficult decisions about what was reasonable in each case: clearly any new stipulations imposed should not be so onerous as to put the company concerned out of business. Otherwise, the original long-term planning permission would in fact be worthless.

SLATE

Although the term 'slate' has been applied generally to any rock which can be split into thin sheets, the geological term strictly speaking refers only to fine-grained, compact rocks with the property of slaty cleavage.[109] Such rocks are formed by the action of moderately increased heat and strong lateral pressure upon certain types of sedimentary rocks such as clays, shales, mudstones and volcanic ash, when they were deeply buried under later strata. In very exceptional circumstances, slate may have been formed by the metamorphism of igneous rocks. The process of metamorphism has rendered slate highly resistant to weathering, and this characteristic, together with its fissility, gives the material its economic importance.

The four principal areas of Britain where slate has been formed are North Wales, the Lake District, Cornwall and Devon, and the Grampian Highlands of Scotland. Of the many localities in Wales where shales and mudstones have been transformed into slates, the three chief areas are central Caernarvonshire which contains slates of Cambrian age, the Tremadoc/Blaenau Ffestiniog/Betws-y-coed area of Caernarvonshire and Merioneth with slates of Ordovician age, and the Corwen/Corris area of Merioneth with slates of Ordovician and Silurian ages. There are two other areas of lesser importance, the Prescelly region of north Pembrokeshire with slates of Ordovician age and the Corwen/Llangollen (Denbighshire) area with slates of Silurian age. All these deposits form part of the old mountain chain known as the Caledonides. Another fragment of the Caledonides forms the English Lake District, where slates occur in each of the three main geological bands extending south–west north–east across the area. The oldest of these bands contains the Skiddaw 'slates', which are poorly cleaved and are only used locally for building and walling. To the south is the Borrowdale Volcanic series, forming the highest hills in the Lake District. This series contains the Lancashire green slate of Ordovician age, varying in colour from light and dark green to purple-green and consisting of metamorphosed volcanic ash. To the south of this series lies a Silurian formation which contains the Bannisdale slates, lying principally in Lancashire.[110]

Another ancient mountain chain, the Hercynides, which originated in the Carboniferous or Permian period, forms an arc stretching from southern Ireland through Devon and Cornwall, where it contains slates in the Devonian strata. These slates occur chiefly west of Camelford in Cornwall, although slates of a similar age are found near Torquay and Tavistock in Devon. In Scotland slate occurs among the metamorphic rocks of the Dalradian series which includes the Ballachulish slates of around Loch Leven in Kinross-shire, the Easdale slates extending from north of the island of Jura to Oban in Argyllshire, the Aberfoyle slates which occur along the great Highland boundary fault from north of Arran in the west to Stonehaven in the east, and the

Macduff slates of Banff and Aberdeenshire.[111] Extraction of slate from the Scottish deposits is however now only minimal.

Although the more obvious outcrops of slate were quarried for roofing during the Roman and mediaeval periods, it was not until the rapid expansion of population and housebuilding and improved transport facilities associated with the Industrial Revolution that slate roofing was adopted on a large scale in place of thatch and natural stone tiles. The industry expanded rapidly if unevenly throughout the nineteenth century and in 1898 output from Wales, the chief producing area, reached a peak figure of 493 000 tonnes.[112] Prosperity came to an abrupt end between 1900 and 1914, when a depression in the building industry produced a period of unemployment, low wages, industrial unrest and the large-scale exodus of workers from North Wales. Both output and manpower in the Welsh slate industry were, in 1914, little more than half the 1898 figures.[113] In the twentieth century, the position of the slate industry has generally been unfortunate: in periods of contraction in the building industry such as those of the First and Second World Wars, it has suffered from a reduction in demand. In periods of building expansion, most of the increased demand has been met by manufacturers of tiles. The rapid increase in both home-produced and imported tiles, which undercut slates in price, supplied almost all the growth in demand for roofing material during the inter-war period, when the building industry was buoyant. Output was also curtailed as a result of the development of overseas slate resources by countries which had previously imported British slate, notably Eire, whose tariff on the imported product severely reduced exports from Wales between the wars.[114] The industry did indeed revive during the post-war rebuilding programme, and total British output reached 165 000 tonnes in 1951, but since 1963, when 125 000 tonnes was produced, output has again declined sharply. Roofing slates, like clay tiles, have been losing ground heavily in the new housing market in the face of a rapid expansion of concrete tiles. The official British total output figure of 65 000 tonnes in 1970[115] probably includes a substantial amount of high bulk/low value slate powders and granules, making the reduction in cut slate output even sharper than the figures suggest.

Clearly, the decline in the demand for slate in the twentieth century has been caused essentially by the competition of cheaper products in the mass roofing market, where the various alternative products are sold basically on price. The slate industry, even in its most modern and highly capitalized form, has inevitably an element of labour-intensiveness. The degree of mechanization and improvement in productivity achieved at other types of hard rock quarries has consequently not been possible in the slate industry. Output per wage-earner (by tonnes) at slate quarries went up by 137 per cent in the period 1950–70 while output per wage-earner at limestone quarries went up by 386 per cent.[116] The high cost of the skilled labour needed, for instance, in splitting slabs of slate from the quarried blocks, a process which has defied mechanization, has been a major factor in the very large price increase of the product. The average price of cut slate rose from £11·81 per tonne in 1950 to £38·38 per tonne in 1971 at one of the largest modern quarries in North Wales.[117] The average value of a tonne of slate for roofing or dampcourses in 1968 was £42·22.[118] The rapid increases in production costs during the 1950s and 1960s, added to the costs of transporting the material to markets from the generally remote British deposits, has reduced sales in the bulk housing market. In 1971 slates from Caernarvonshire were facing stiff competition from tiles even within the county itself, and one English quarry reported a decline in the demand for roofing slate of 40 per cent between 1965 and 1972,[119] although in the latter year there were signs of a revival in demand based on the need for slates for repair work. Slates required for the maintenance of existing buildings now constitute a larger percentage of the roofing market than those for new houses.

Somewhat different factors are operative in certain speciality markets, where slate as an architectural feature can be sold essentially on its special qualities of colour, pattern and texture, rather than on price. Demand for slate for wall cladding and facing, flooring and paving was growing in the 1960s, especially for use for public buildings, large commercial buildings such as banks, and for the small number of individual, high budget private houses. A notable part of this demand comes from overseas markets, mainly in Western Europe and the United States. Indeed, slate exports which in 1970 totalled 9086 tonnes[120] consisted largely of such speciality products. One firm in the Lake District which has concentrated heavily on this type of slate has achieved an export figure as high as 50 per cent of total production.[121] The high value of slate for such purposes compared with most other building material means that the product can bear transport costs to the west coast of the United States or to markets as distant as Australia and Hong Kong.[122] Expansion in demand for architectural slate in both home and export markets is confidently predicted for the 1970s.[123]

Another growing market is that of slate powders or granules, prepared by crushing and screening of selected material, previously rejected as waste. Crushed slate is being used increasingly for surfacing asphaltic roofing felts, for inert fillers in a variety of products such as bitumen and bitumen compounds, coal-tar-based coating materials, insecticides, paints, thermal insulation, polyester resins, pipeline coatings, motor car underseal, paints and plastics and as a filler for concrete blocks. Crushed slate constituted much the largest part of the tonnage from several large slate quarries in 1972;[124] one of these had increased output of powder and granules by 385 per cent since 1964. However, slate for many of these applications competes with other mineral products and current usage depends to a large extent on its comparative cheapness. Consequently, the value of slate powders and granules is very much lower than that of cut slate. The price of 200-mesh powder bulk ex-Penrhyn quarry in 1971 was £4·67 per tonne.[125]

Slate used for walling and crazy paving, like that used for powder and granules, is essentially a by-product utilizing what would otherwise be waste material. The chippings and offcuts used for this purpose also retail at a low price, but the demand is growing much less rapidly than that for powders and granules.

The existence of these very different categories of slate product contributes substantially to the difficulty of interpreting the regional production figures of slate output in the case of England and Wales. The Scottish position is clear: in 1969 only three quarries were operative, two in Argyllshire and one in Bute,[126] and output had dwindled to a very small amount, not recorded separately in the Scottish mineral statistics. The Welsh slate industry, historically the most important British producing area which as late as 1918–39 contributed between 75 and 80 per cent of total output,[127] was in 1969, according to the official statistics, producing less than half the total British tonnage. The *Annual Digest of Welsh Statistics* recorded a total output of 24 400 tonnes in that year, compared with the British total of 70 100 tonnes.[128] It appears however that the figures are distorted by a differing basis of calculation. The 1969 total for England was based on output figures of 25 400 tonnes for Devon and Cornwall and 20 300 tonnes from Cumberland, Lancashire and Westmorland.[129] Both these figures appear to include tonnage of slate powders and granules and for crazy paving, which in the case of Devon and Cornwall could account for as much as 92 per cent of total output from that area.[130] The total for Cumberland, Lancashire and Westmorland also contains crushed slate and offcuts, which could amount to more than 50 per cent of the total. The statistics for Wales, however, do not include total production of slate powder and granules: the published total for Penrhyn quarry alone, 18 300 tonnes in 1970,[131] makes up 75 per cent of the total official figure for Welsh slate production in that year. The inclusion of tonnage of the high bulk/low value crushed slate does, even if included uniformly, obscures the position. The total output of cut slate for England, excluding crushed slate, in 1969 was probably 8100 to 13 200 tonnes, made up of 1000–2000 tonnes from Devon and Cornwall and approximately 7100–11 868 tonnes from the Lake District[132] (see p. 169). This would mean that Wales contributed 24 400 tonnes out of a British total of 32 500–37 600 tonnes of cut slate in 1969, or 65–75 per cent of total British output compared with 75–80 per cent between the First and Second World Wars.

The main centre of the Welsh slate industry, the Cambrian slate belt of central Caernarvonshire, is relatively narrow and ranges south-westwards for about twenty-nine square kilometres from Bethesda to Pen-y-Groes. In 1971 there were approximately five square kilometres of active and closed workings, tips and land used for ancillary purposes in the Dinorwic and Bethesda areas alone.[133] Except for eastern Caernarvonshire, the dip of the slate beds in the county is almost vertical, and individual slate beds have been followed downwards by means of deep pits, as in the Nantlle valley, or worked by a series of terraces or galleries cut into the hillside as at Penrhyn, where 21 terraces make up a total height of 366 metres.[134] Further south the beds of the Blaenau Ffestiniog area are inclined at shallower angles and since quarrying would involve removing overlying uneconomic quantities of waste rock, most of the workings have been underground. The slate mines of this area consist of a series of chambers which are in effect underground quarries. Little working now remains elsewhere in Wales: of the 5 other counties where slate has been produced in the past, only Carmarthenshire and Denbighshire were in 1969 contributing small quantities.[135] The total number of individual slate producers in Wales fell from 18 in December 1945 to 6 in 1971.[136]

A complex of factors are responsible for the disproportionate decline of the Welsh cut slate industry, relative to the English one. The Welsh industry, like slate production elsewhere, developed to serve the slate roofing market, which in 1947 consumed 97 per cent of Welsh slate output.[137] Welsh slate had however particular advantages in the roofing market since the finer grained Welsh slates can be riven to thicknesses of as little as eight to the inch (about 3·2 mm thick). This characteristic is clearly not an asset in the increasingly important cladding market, where thicknesses of an inch (about 25 mm) are normal. Many Welsh quarries are, furthermore, hampered in the architectural market by having only one colour of slate to extract. Some delayed the adaptation to new markets longer than English competitors, since the larger demand for slate roofing replacement in Wales postponed the day when this became an economic necessity. It is possible for Welsh slate quarries to adapt to new growth markets for slate, and even to expand slate roofing sales, in those instances where modernization and capital are available, and a range of colours and textures at hand. The largest Welsh quarry, that of Penrhyn, has an architectural section equipped with the special machinery, such as extra large saws, needed to produce large slate panels. Output of powder and granules more than trebled in the years 1964–72.[138] The development of new markets for Penrhyn slate has been accompanied by even more significant changes, designed to contain increases in the cost of quarry operations and particularly the transport of material from the workface to the treatment plant, a crucial element in the production costs of any quarrying operation. Modern marketing and advertising methods have also been of significance. Modernization of extraction and marketing helped to lift the sales tonnage not only of architectural slate from Penrhyn after 1964, but also that of roofing slate, which grew by more than 50 per cent in eight years, although the majority of extra sales resulted from the closure of other quarries.[139] These developments at Penrhyn, however, have been associated with the injections of capital and management expertise associated with the quarry's takeover in 1964 by Marchwiel Holdings Ltd., of which Sir Alfred McAlpine and Son Ltd. forms a major part, after nearly 200 years as a family business. Most of the Welsh slate operators in the post-1945 period continued to be small family firms, typically with a highly traditional outlook, and some of those which survived in 1969 still used quarrying methods, such as access to the working face by ropes, which were primitive in terms of modern quarry practice. Most of the small Welsh concerns suffered from a long history of insufficiently ploughed-back profits. Consequently, the adaptation to new markets, involving special machinery for the production of large architectural slates and crushing and screening plant for slate powders, and the modernization of quarrying operations, required for many of them prohibitive levels of capital investment, as well as a high degree of management, engineering and sales expertise.

The mode of occurrence of the deposits in the Merioneth area has been a further disadvantageous factor for slate operators there. Here, as indicated earlier, the inclination of the slate beds dictates the use of mainly mining methods, and in 1969 five slate mines were officially recorded for the county,[140] out of a much larger total existing earlier. The mining of slate here has the serious disadvantage that some 40–50 per cent of the good slate has to be left as pillars for support,[141] and the haulage costs from workface to cutting sheds, and even more from workface to tips, are likely to be particularly heavy, especially at a large mine. Two slate mines were in 1969 in operation in the Lake District, but it is significant that the Broughton Moor slate quarry in Lancashire, worked by one of the few companies which was expanding in the 1960s, was converted from mining to quarrying operations in 1955, when the various working levels were joined and the roof opened out.[142] This change involved both heavy capital investment and a high degree of engineering skill.

The Welsh slate industry suffers disproportionately too from the impact of diminishing returns on an old extractive industry. In slate extraction, difficulties of working increase substantially in proportion to the age of the excavation. Production in older quarries becomes more costly as excavations deepen, with the notable exception of Penrhyn where operations are currently being developed longitudinally; in some places the dumping of waste has sterilized the most conveniently placed reserves, whilst in others movement away from the plant has increased costs. Diminishing returns can be partly offset in open quarries, though not much in mines, by improved mechanical haulage. However, this, as indicated earlier, involves large capital investment not easily available especially during a period of declining markets. The slate industry of Wales has a long and extensive history of working behind it: both Conway and Caernarvon castles, built in 1282 to 1284, were originally roofed with slates. No other area has anything approaching the volume of past extraction of Wales, although the Delabole quarry in Cornwall has been worked since 1350. It is possibly significant that one at least of the expanding slate quarries in the Lake District[143] is a mere 100 years old.

The slate workings of the Lake District occur within the three counties of Lancashire, Cumberland and Westmorland. The Lancashire workings are probably the most extensive and had in 1971 planning permission for 203 hectares.[144] The chief quarries are at Broughton Moor (Coniston), Brathay, Kirkby and Bursting Stone.[145] The only operation in Cumberland in 1971 was a mine working the Cumberland green slate at Honister near Keswick, and in Westmorland the green slate at this time was quarried at three sites, notably Kirkstone, Lords quarry (Elterwater), and Spoutcrag (Langdale).[146] Although output from some of these quarries, supplying mainly roofing slates, is declining, the overall output of roofing and architectural slate may be falling less rapidly than that of Britain as a whole and, in the case of certain quarries, output is actually increasing. The official figure for English production in 1969 was based on an output of 20 320 tonnes from Cumberland, Lancashire and Westmorland. This is likely to include tonnages of crushed slate. Earlier figures derived from official statistics which exclude crushed slate showed a drop in output from the north of England (effectively these three counties) from 14 520 tonnes in 1956 to 12 274 tonnes in 1967.[147] Assuming a continuation of the trend of these last figures until 1969, an output of some 11 868 tonnes of cut slate may be postulated for this area, although the figure could conceivably be as low as 7100–8100 tonnes.[148]

In spite of the overall decline in cut slate output from the Lake District, it is clear that output from some quarries, notably that at the four quarries worked by the Broughton Moor Green Slate Company, is expanding. The company, originally working only the Broughton Moor quarry, acquired the mineral rights of Spoutcrag quarry in 1957, those at Elterwater shortly afterwards and more recently those of the Brathay quarry near Ambleside. An indication of the growing size of the company's operations is the fact that the labourforce at Elterwater, the point of most active development of the group, grew from 15 in 1968 to 50 in 1972.[149] The buoyant output of certain Lake District slate quarries is related partly to the nature of the material. The slates worked at Broughton Moor for instance are of coarser-grain than many Welsh slates: those designed for the roofing market are riven to a thickness of 2 or 3 to the inch (about 12·7 to 8·5 mm thick) compared with 8 to the inch (about 3·2 mm thick) of the finest Ffestiniog slates, which gives added strength in addition to the distinctive character of a stone tile. More important, in view of the current market trends, is the special suitability of the Lake District slates for external cladding or special architectural features. The deposits worked at Brathay, for instance, are formed in large blue/black masses from which it is possible to extract exceptionally large slates. A normal production size here is 2·44 m by 1·07 m, and altar slabs can be cut at sizes of up to 3·66 m by 1·22 m.[150] Slates of this size have particular applications in modern architectural design, and have the additional advantage in the American market that, while American firms are generally very competitive in riven slate, they cannot usually supply these very large dimensions.[151] Because of the massive formation of the deposit at Brathay, slate can be extracted in large blocks by only a small labourforce. At Broughton Moor the quarrying operation has been developed as a capital-intensive, rather than labour-intensive operation. The conversion of the working from mining to quarrying has necessitated a continuous programme of heavy blasting with a high level of shattered rock waste, but this makes possible a rapid and economical turnover at the quarry face by a small labourforce. The holding of production costs by the emphasis on high capital rather than high labour operations, in cutting sheds as well as at the quarry face, has been supported by an intensive advertising campaign, directed particularly to architects and surveyors engaged in the prestige type of building work. Vigorous sales promotion extends to export markets, which make up the high figure of 50 per cent of the company's sales.[152] The parallels in both extractive and marketing techniques between the Broughton Moor quarries and Penrhyn are clear.

Although in 1969 there were 15 quarries in Cornwall and 2 in Devon,[153] the production at most of these was very small or intermittent and much the largest part of the output from these counties derived from the large slate quarry at Delabole near Camelford, covering 16 hectares and extending to a depth of 153 metres, where fine-grained, homogeneous, smooth and well-cleaved slates have been extensively quarried.[154] Only a small percentage of current output from Delabole now supplies the roofing market and though here, as elsewhere, demand for various types of architectural and building stone is increasing, these two categories together now make up only a limited proportion of the quarry's output. Slate from this area does not have the range of colour variations found in parts of the Lake District, and the impact of diminishing returns must inevitably make itself felt in this ancient working. Consequently, much the largest percentage of output from Delabole now consists of crushed slate or slate powders, used for inert granular additives for incorporation in fertilizers, plastics, roofing felt and concrete blocks. In other words, Delabole slate makes up only a very small percentage of the national slate market by value.

The Scottish industry has contracted more completely than that of any other area of Britain. From 1870 to 1880 it is likely that the output of Scottish slates derived from all the main deposits was in the neighbourhood of 25 to 30 million slates per annum (approximately 42 270 to 50 800 tonnes), giving employment to approximately 1000 to 1500 men.[155] By 1937 output had fallen to a total of 10 410 000 slates (approximately 17 628 tonnes), employing 370 men,[156] a decrease brought about largely as a result of the competition from tiles. Since 1945, however, when all the main types of Scottish slates were still being worked, output has fallen to almost negligible proportions: two of the three quarries surviving in 1969 were small-scale units worked by the Forestry Commission.[157] The rundown of the Scottish slate industry relates partly to geological difficulties and partly to the characteristics of the material. The geological and topographical conditions of working here were often more difficult than those of the English or Welsh deposits, which added a further economic burden to be set alongside the generally unfavourable market conditions which have prevailed since 1945. In addition, certain of the slate deposits have limitations which restrict their commercial usage. In places the Ballachulish slates contain crystals of iron pyrites which are liable to weathering. Most Scottish slates are usually dark in colour, that from the chief Ballachulish and Easdale belts being the traditional blue-grey of the mass roofing market, and most Scottish quarries were lacking the special colour characteristics of part of the Lake District or Wales which readily lend themselves to speciality usage. As a result the industry's production is too small to be officially recorded, although workable reserves here, as in North Wales, are very large.

All the existing slate workings occur in high amenity areas of North and West Britain. Both the North Wales and the Lake District workings impinge on National Parks. Indeed, slate quarrying in Caernarvonshire and Merioneth presented the most formidable problem when the Snowdonia National Park was defined,[158] and the boundaries were drawn specifically to exclude the main belt of exploitation in Caernarvonshire, around Corris in the south and to avoid the Blaenau Ffestiniog working areas. Other, smaller quarries had perforce to be included within the park. Virtually all the slate beds of the Lake District occur within the Lake District National Park where there were in 1971 some active slate workings, all but two of them open quarries. Output from Devon and Cornwall derives from high amenity holiday areas. The main problem of slate workings from an amenity point of view is not so much the working faces themselves but rather the waste tips; although water-filled, abandoned quarries, too vast to be restored and usually too deep for recreational after-uses,* may constitute a public danger.

The current ratio of waste to marketable product varies from area to area. The Delabole Slate Company, which as indicated earlier markets a quite exceptionally large percentage of crushed slate, claims that its operations produce no waste.[159] In Wales and at most quarries in the Lake District the ratio is very high. Estimates of the percentage of waste to finished cut slate product vary from the 20:1 estimated of the Ministry of Works report (the Rees report) of 1945[160] to a more recent estimate of up to 50:1.[161] Similarly high ratios may apply in certain Lake District quarries such as Broughton Moor where a great deal of waste is produced by the 'high blast' method of extraction. The high waste ratios of these areas are connected with their role as the chief producers of cut slate. The amount of waste produced in connection with this operation is such that even a vigorous sales programme

* The Dorothea quarry in the Llyffni Valley, some 153 metres deep, may be developed for recreational purposes.

of powder or granules is unlikely to consume more than a fraction of the waste produced. At Penrhyn quarry, for instance, where well over 356 000 tonnes of waste had to be created to produce only 12 200 tonnes of cut slate in 1970, a greatly expanded output of slate granules and powders only disposed of 30 500 tonnes of otherwise waste material.[162] Neither the modern marketing techniques of some firms, nor the considerable amount of research and investigation into the commercial usage of waste slate by organizations such as the Department of Scientific and Industrial Research and the Rural Industries Bureau,[163] have succeeded in radically altering the relatively small percentage of waste which is used commercially.

As C. T. Crompton pointed out in 1967,[164] geological factors make a significant reduction in the amount of waste produced extremely difficult. Slate near the surface has usually been weathered to make it commercially useless. Beds of poorly cleaved material are often associated with commercial slate and have to be removed with them. Rock spoiled by closely set joints, intrusions or rock shattered by blasting is also useless, and much of the quarried material is rejected on the grounds of colour. Efforts at Penrhyn to increase selectivity at the working face and so reduce the costly transportation of such large masses of waste to the sheds have not been able to reduce the ratio of waste to finished product in any significant way. On the other hand, the deliberate adoption of a high blast, high waste technique in some Lake District quarries has resulted in reduced labour and production costs, a vital consideration in current market conditions.

Backfilling of waste into workings may be technically possible in some areas although usually additional terracing, tunnelling or deepening of mines keeps most of the working areas in continual use. Backfilling at public expense as a means of restoration of disused workings would probably be prohibitively costly in view of the vast quantities of material involved, even though such work would probably qualify for grants as clearance of derelict land. Consequently, virtually no restoration of slate working has taken place and overwhelmingly the biggest proportion of waste is surface dumped. Unquestionably, the Welsh slate areas have a backlog of waste unparalleled elsewhere. Crompton has estimated, using the Rees Committee ratio of 20:1, that from 1900 to 1966 alone some 180 340 000 million tonnes of slate waste were deposited in the North Wales slate areas,[165] apart from that produced by the intensive development of quarrying in the nineteenth century. As a result spoil heaps, from present and especially from past operations, are usually both more obtrusive and occupy more land than working faces. The slate waste is dumped as near as possible to the face, often in finger-like heaps extending hundreds of yards from the slate workings, and tips are particularly prominent because of the high altitude of the workings; in Caernarvonshire the major slate areas all lie approximately 180 metres above sea level while many of the disused quarries are much higher still. Historically, settlements have been developed very close to the quarries which provided their employment. This has resulted in villages which are blighted by waste heaps, and by present-day standards give a depressing spectacle. The urban development among the Blaenau Ffestiniog quarries is probably the worst such area. The accumulated backlog of slate waste presents a huge problem about which little has been done, partly because of its daunting size, and partly because of the low agricultural value of the land and its remote location.

The waste tips of the Lake District workings, which may be as high as 400 metres above sea level, are visible for considerable distances. Screening of working, especially waste tips, is difficult here as elsewhere because of their scale, but screening of a very limited kind has been attempted at Spoutcrag, Langdale. No tips have yet been planted within the National Park, but the planning board are not unduly worried by their existence, claiming that slate quarries were not as visually offensive as an unnatural intrusion would be.[166] It is from North Wales, where the accumulated backlog of waste is so much larger, that the main stimulus has come for research into the possibilities of vegetating slate waste heaps for amenity reasons.

Slate tips, both in Wales and the Lake District, suffer from the special problems of high altitude and the associated short growing season as well as exposure, instability and high rainfall which soon washes away the material from which soil might form. But waste slate clearly does not contain toxic elements harmful to plant life and the decreasing size of waste fragments with modern practices has helped the process of soil formation on the tips. In a few favoured places, such as Waunfawr in Caernarvonshire, natural vegetation has established itself on slate tips within 50 years.[167] In 1959 Merioneth County Council engaged the Forestry Commission, on an agency basis, to plant a 4 hectare exposed site at Fairbourne, at an altitude of 92–122 metres.[168] This and other experiments, such as these carried out at Penrhyn in conjunction with the University of Liverpool,[169] have demonstrated that both grass and trees can be grown, albeit slowly, where at least some soil is supplied, the sites are fenced off and careful after-management is provided. The vegetation also depends on excluding from these areas private individuals, often local quarrymen, who traditionally have carried out small-scale extraction to supplement their earnings. These findings seem to indicate the most likely method of reducing the impact on the landscape both of past waste tips and, for want of a better alternative, of dealing with waste from current workings. However, most slate workings pre-date modern planning controls and clearly no obligations for planting of tips attach to them. The Caernarvonshire County Planning Officer considers it highly unlikely than any new applications for slate workings will be made in the foreseeable future, since there are extensive resources sufficient for likely demand within existing consented areas.[170] (Penrhyn quarries' reserves, for example, are estimated at 711 million tonnes.)[171] In the Lake District, however, it is probable that some tips being created will be planted when they are complete,[172] and future applications for extended workings could well be made, in which case the planning consents would be highly likely to impose stipulations about planting of tips.

The working of slate for architectural and roofing stone has a waste ratio substantially larger even than that of china clay working. Although the overall output trend in slate, unlike that of china clay, is declining, it is important that slate operators, like china clay operators, should be encouraged to maximize their sales of waste products. The removal of rates payable on sales of products which consume what would otherwise be waste, such as powder, granules or offcuts, would, like the removal of rates of sales of waste china clay sand, be some incentive to this end, although the rates payable are very small. Even so, it is inconceivable that the bulk of the waste could be utilized, and the only available palliative for this appears to be tip planting, which in most cases would have to be done voluntarily by the quarry operators, or by the local authority.

4

LOCALIZED NON-METALLIFEROUS MINERALS

CHINA CLAY

CHINA clay is of very localized occurrence in Britain where deposits are found only in Cornwall and south-west Devon. The process of kaolinization affected the granite formations of southern Dartmoor, the southern half of Bodmin Moor, the whole of Hensbarrow, the northern half of Carnmenellis and a small part of the Land's End massif (see Fig. 4.1). By this process, active vapours rising from the cooling rocks altered the nature of the felspar, one of the three principal mineral constituents of granite. The resulting product was the mineral kaolinite or china clay, a hydrated silicate of alumina, which is found intermixed with the two other main mineral constituents of granite, mica and quartz. Deposits of the quality of those in Cornwall and Devon are rare in the world: this factor, and the proximity of the deposits both to ports offering cheap shipment to overseas markets and to the large consumers of continental Europe, accounts for one of several unique features of the china clay industry – that it produces Britain's one bulk raw material export (apart from the related mineral, ball clay). The remoteness of the location from the main British markets has not been of decisive importance since kaolinite is a highly specialized form of clay, and even the lowest grades are not a cheap commodity. The remoteness of the deposits from the country's major concentrations of population is, however, a decisive factor in inhibiting commercial utilization of china clay waste.

China clay extraction originated in the mid-eighteenth century to provide raw material for the pottery industry but today overwhelmingly the most important market, consuming over 75 per cent of total British output[1] is the paper industry, which utilizes china clay both as a filler and a coating pigment for high gloss products. The rapid increase in education and educational standards since 1945, leading to greatly increased demand for books and papers of all kinds, was the chief factor behind the very rapid growth in china clay output of 508 000 tonnes in 1945 to 2 795 000 tonnes in 1969,[2] of which more than 2 million tonnes were exported. Indications are that the world's china clay markets will continue to grow at an increasing rate. This future

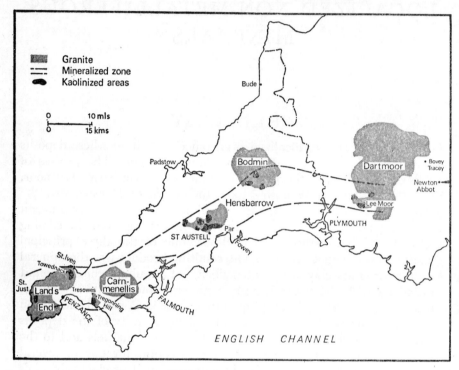

Fig. 4.1   *Kaolinized areas of Devon and Cornwall*

demand is however dependent on the rate of demand for paper, the ability of the industry to maintain both its place in the paper market, where product substitution is always a possibility, and its export percentage in the face of increasing foreign competition.

Although china clay was first identified as a product of commercial value at Tregonning Hill in west Cornwall (between 1745 and 1748), the chief producing area now is the Hensbarrow district near St Austell, which was in 1971 producing about 80 per cent of total British output.[3] The second most important area producing nearly 20 per cent of output is south-west Devon, where equally high quality deposits occurring over a smaller area have been worked since 1830. Very small workings, of less importance than hitherto, are located on Bodmin Moor and in the Land's End granite. The deposits in these areas are of lower quality, are more distant from ports of shipment, and the workings in them are unlikely to receive planning permission to expand.

The concentration of deposits in the south-west peninsula has been a contributory factor in the monopolistic character of china clay extraction in Britain. In 1969 English Clays Lovering Pochin and Company (ECLP), the clays division of English China Clays Ltd., controlled 90 per cent of total British output,[4] and dominated the main extracting areas of Hensbarrow and south-west Dartmoor. ECLP is the largest china clay producer in the world, and supplied in 1969 about 20 per cent of world china clay demand.[5] The total china clay output of the United States is larger than that of the United Kingdom, but it is divided among several companies, each smaller than ECLP. The process of amalgamation within the china clay industry dates back as far as 1843, when a group of merchants calling themselves the Cornwall China Stone and Clay Company brought under one ownership a large complex of new and established pits in the St Stephens area of Hensbarrow.[6] In the early twentieth century the most significant mergers have been related primarily to depressions in the industry. The formation of English China Clays in 1919, controlling approximately 50 per cent of the industry's total productive capacity, resulted from the damage inflicted by the First World War, when the important European export market was virtually eliminated and the labourforce severely reduced. The amalgamation of English China Clays with the two other producers in 1932, when ECLP was formed (English China Clays becoming the holding company) to represent about 75 per cent of the industry, resulted from the impact of the inter-war depression on the china clay industry when almost half the pits closed.[7]

The trend towards amalgamation has continued under somewhat different circumstances since 1945. Although the difficulties of reviving the industry after the war, during which production had fallen to approximately one third of the pre-war level, was a factor similar to those operative in earlier mergers, there were other new forces involved. Chief among these was the greater emphasis on fewer, larger pits to achieve economies of scale, one of the principal recommendations of the Board of Trade Working Party set up in 1946 to examine long-term plans for the industry[8] and the demand for more sophisticated clays, involving complex technical processing. The chief problem with china clay production is consistency, since the mineral varies greatly from pit to pit and even within a single pit. The complex blending techniques now employed by ECLP enable the company to produce standardized grades of clay from different slurry feeds by close and continuous quality control. The company has installed electronic linear programmer and analogue simulators at its Goverseth Central and Treviscoe refining plants to aid blending of the clay drawn from six different china clay pits according to formulae worked out by analogue computer in the company's laboratories. The net result is the transformation of china clay as a variable commodity into a standard industrial product.[9] The fastest growing market of the 1960s, that of speciality coating clays for paper, involves production to most detailed and stringent specifications, which are constantly tightening. Consequently, the smaller producers have been under constant pressure as a result of the increased demand for sophisticated clays and the capital-intensive technical processing which these involve. Those paper companies which had acquired china clay pits as part of a process of backwards integration to secure their raw material supplies found it increasingly costly to operate their relatively small pits. In the early 1950s there were four paper manufacturers working pits in Cornwall. In 1955 Spicer Brothers sold their Carpalla pit to ECLP, who in 1970 also agreed to purchase the Bodmin Moor china clay pit and processing plant of Bowater China Clay Company Ltd. In 1969 the Inveresk paper group sold its Bodelva-Carvear property to Engelhard Minerals Ltd., an American firm with substantial china clay interests in Georgia. This left only one paper manufacturer, Peter Dixon and Son (Holdings) Ltd., which works the Treskilling pit in the Hensbarrow area.

Similar pressures were operating against other small-scale producers of china clay so that, while 25 firms were in production in 1948,[10] there were in 1969 a total of only a dozen producers, apart from ECLP. A significant number of these were associated with large companies producing allied products. The second biggest china clay producer in 1969 was Watts Blake Bearne and Company, primarily ball clay producers, who have been operating in china clay for a century. The company extract china clay at Cornwood in Devon, where the processing plant which supplies ceramic and filler grades had recently been modernized. Until 1971 Associated Portland Cement Manufacturers controlled Anchor China Clays Ltd., owners of pits at Fal Valley and Kerrow Moor in Hensbarrow from 1948; even these pits have now come under the control of ECLP. Berk Ltd., the chemical company (now part of the Steetley group), acquired control of Greensplat China Clays Ltd., also in Hensbarrow, in 1960. Greensplat, one of the oldest china clay pits in Cornwall, has been modernized to produce 45 700 tonnes of medium to high quality filler clays, triple the former rate, of which the very high percentage of 98 is exported.[11] In a somewhat different category comes the Bodelva-Carvear pit of the American Engelhard Minerals. This property is the furthest east of all the productive pits in the Hensbarrow granite and was first worked for clay as early as 1825. Before its acquisition by Engelhard, it was producing about 20 300 tonnes of filler grade per year. Most important of the small independant china clay producers is the Goonvean and Rostowrack China Clay Company Ltd., the third largest producer and the only company other than ECLP to produce the highest grade paper clays. This company, like most of the small independent companies, operates in Hensbarrow. New Consolidated Mines of Cornwall Ltd., however, only works a pit at Lower Boztraze in the Land's End granite. The producers other than ECLP contribute 10 per cent of total output, but considerably less than 10 per cent of the highest quality clays.

The early stages of the amalgamation process were obviously beneficial to the industry. The small companies of the nineteenth century operated with inadequate capital, they usually had strictly limited areas of land and had to dump their waste sand on ground that was itself clay-bearing. Small-scale exporting was within their scope, but most small companies had insufficient knowledge of foreign markets and were too small to maintain their own overseas agents.[12] Several modern commentators have attributed the great rise in output since 1945 and the modern industry's sustained high export figures to the dominant position of ECLP. In the view of *Industrial Minerals*,[13] 'sheer size, plus the possession of excellent research and marketing facilities, have enabled ECLP to continue its growth in export markets . . . the current expansion overseas is almost entirely due to the dominant position of English China Clays'. *The Times Review of Industry and Technology* has declared that 'any reduction in its size would make it far less efficient and damage a valuable export market'.[14] In fact, the export percentage of ECLP, varying between 73 and 76 per cent of total clay turnover between 1967 and 1970,[15] was about average for the industry as a whole, and a total china clay export percentage of 75 per cent has been sustained during most of the 'normal' trading periods of this century. The rate of growth of American exports in the major European market has in fact been faster than that of British exports during the 1960s, although produced by companies each individually smaller than ECLP. However, the rising output and exports of the high value speciality coating clays is almost entirely due to ECLP and relates specifically to the resources of capital, technical expertise and research which only a very large producer can command. The market for these clays is becoming steadily more important all the time. Furthermore the company, in spite of its virtual monopoly of output in Britain, has every incentive to remain competitive since it operates largely in the context of world market prices.

In 1969 ECLP owned and operated 24 china clay pits, had a china clay production force of approximately 2500 men and an annual output running at the rate of 2·54 million tonnes.[16] The company's operations have since 1945 become increasingly concentrated on large pits, a trend which here, as in other branches of quarrying, reflects the economies of scale possible with larger producing units. This trend was initially given great impetus by the concentration scheme imposed by the Board of Trade in 1942, primarily in the interests of conserving labour, and was, as mentioned earlier, one of the principal recommendations of the Working Party on the China Clay Industry set up in 1946. Notable among the company's largest pits are Blackpool pit, near Trewoon, 3 kilometres from St Austell, and the Lee Moor pit in south-west Dartmoor. Blackpool pit was in 1969 about 85 metres deep, covered some 41 hectares at the surface and produced 7600 to 8100 tonnes of refined clay every week.[17] Lee Moor was in 1969 the largest excavation in Devon, approximately 36 hectares in area at ground level and varying between 76 and 85 metres in depth.[18] Lee Moor produced 381 000 tonnes of china clay in 1969–70,[19] mainly high quality clay for papermaking and coating and pottery. Proposals to extend operations in this area, submitted in 1970, seem to indicate the intention of merging Lee Moor with ECLP's other two pits in the locality, Whitehill Yeo and Cholwichtown. At the same time plans are afoot to re-open and rapidly work-out two other pits in the area, Wotter and Hemerdon. Plans for the future working of Hensbarrow, too, indicate a big expansion of Blackpool pit[20] (see Fig. 4.3). However, the scope for concentration of production exclusively on a few very large pits is limited by the differing physical and chemical characteristics of clay from different pits. Modern blending techniques depend precisely upon these distinctive characteristics. Furthermore, the qualities of clay from within one pit may change as working proceeds, which necessitates the keeping open of a range of sites to retain flexibility of output should the need for changes arise.

The blending techniques which draw on clay from a variety of sources are part of a technological revolution which turned the extraction of china clay into a mechanized, capital-intensive industry. The technical innovations are most clearly exemplified by ECLP, though not exclusive to them. After the removal of the overburden by mechanical excavators and scraper units, the clay matrix is broken down by hydraulic mining: remote-controlled monitors, or in some pits manually operated ones, using pressures of up to 21 kg/sq.cm,

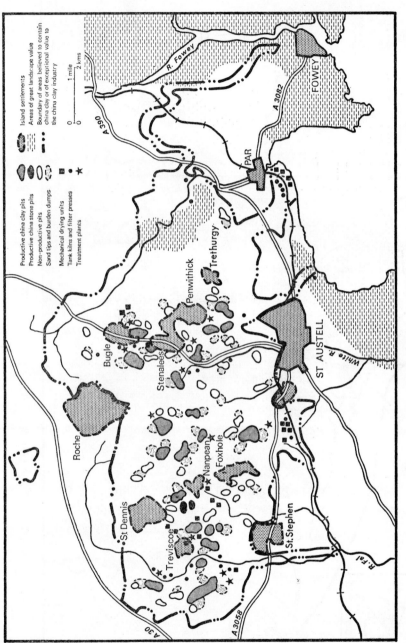

Legend:

Productive china clay pits
Productive china stone pits
Non-productive pits
Sand tips and burden dumps
Mechanical drying units
Tank kilns and filter presses
Treatment plants

Island settlements
Areas of great landscape value
Boundary of areas believed to contain china clay or of exceptional value to the china clay industry

0   1 mile
0   2 kms

Fig. 4.2   China clay and china stone pits in the St Austell area

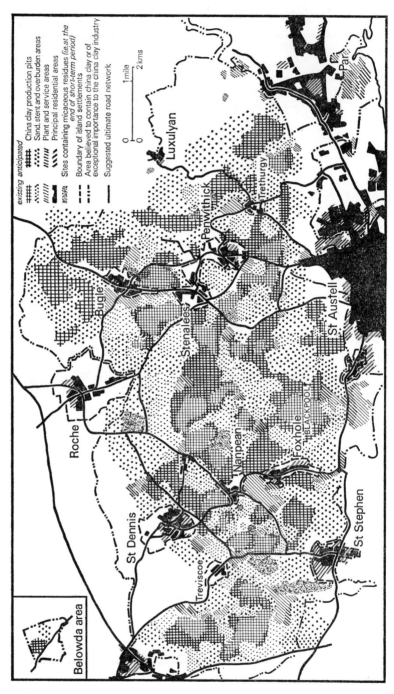

Belowda area

existing anticipated
- ▦ ▨ China clay production pits
- ⣿ ⣿ Sand, stent and overburden areas
- ▥ ▥ Plant and service areas
- ▨ ▨ Principal residential areas
- ▨ Sites containing micaceous residues (i.e. at the end of short-term period)
- ┆ ┆ Boundary of island settlements
- ┇ ┇ Area believed to contain china clay or of exceptional importance to the china clay industry
- ── Suggested ultimate road network

0 1mile
0 1 2kms

Luxulyan
Par
Penwithick
Trethurgy
Bugle
Stenalees
St Austell
Roche
Nanpean
Foxhole
BLACKPOOL
St Dennis
Treviscoe
St Stephen

Fig. 4.3   Development plan proposed by the China Clay Council for china clay working in the St Austell area

break down the matrix and wash out the clay in one operation. The clay is carried in suspension in water, together with quartz, mica and some other impurities to the 'sump' or lowest part of the pit. In some smaller pits the coarse sand is still removed by pumping the coarse slurry to the surface and settling in sandpits, but in large modern ones such as Blackpool pit, gravel pumps transport the slurry into classifiers which remove the coarse sand, subsequently taken by conveyors to the tips. The slurry is pumped to the surface for further refining in dewatering tanks when fine sand and mica are extracted. At this stage, while still in slurry form, complex blending of china clay for special purposes may take place. Filter presses reduce the water content of the clay slurry to 30 per cent, after which it is shredded and taken by conveyor belt to the driers. Cylindrical driers, introduced after the Second World War in place of the traditional and time-consuming flat-floored kilns, reduce the water content to 10 per cent; ECLP also operate a large spray drying plant, a method which is likely to be increasingly used in the future.

Technical improvements in extractive operations have been supported by heavy investment in research, again most pronounced in the case of ECLP. In the company's ceramics laboratory in St Austell, work is continually in progress to produce clays slanted to the particular and changing requirements of the different sections of the world ceramics industry, which currently consumes some 17 per cent of total British output. Earthenware contains approximately one-quarter ball clay and one-quarter china clay, bone china approximately one-half china clay. The consistency of the china clay is crucial, since the clay content is a dominant factor in determining the behaviour of the pottery body. A range of clays is produced whose fired colour, strength, particle size distribution and mineralogical composition are guaranteed within very close limits. A special method of magnetic separation is one of several processes which enable the production of clays with a wider particle size distribution range for faster firing, combined with exceptionally good fired colour.[21]

Research during the 1960s was also directed towards extending the range of minor uses of the mineral, now consuming about 10 per cent of total output. These minor outlets, which utilize china clay mainly as a filler or inert carrier, include plastics, rubber, fertilizers, insecticides, cosmetics, lubricants, fuses and accumulator cases, cleaners and polishes, inks, pencils, dyes, textiles, linoleum, soap and powdered scourers. A more specialized product, requiring rigorously specified physical and chemical properties, is an alumina silicate refractory aggregate, produced only by ECLP from specially selected china clays subjected to high temperature calcination exceeding 1500° C.[22] Clays for this purpose are selected from pits known for their low iron and alkali and high alumina content. Optimum blends are calculated by means of an analogue computer and fed into a blending plant before being piped to the processing plant at Parkandillick in Hensbarrow. 50 per cent of this refractory product is exported.

The major paper market, consuming 73 per cent of output in 1969, was in the course of the 1960s becoming increasingly more complex. Most printing paper contains up to 30 per cent of filler grade china clay—used as a paper filler for some 150 years—and there is a strong economic incentive for the paper maker to substitute as much clay as possible to fibre since, at 1969 prices, filler grade clays cost approximately £5·90 per tonne while pulp prices ranged from £34·45 to £59·05 per tonne.[23] However, in the course of the 1960s the market for high quality coating clays, existing only since about 1890, and selling in 1969 at approximately £14·76 per tonne, outstripped that for filler clays, as the percentage of glossy or coated paper increased. Speciality coating clays are produced to meet most detailed and stringent specifications. Indeed, in order to maintain their place in a field where technology is moving quickly, ECLP have expended considerable research effort in this field. Although production of paper fell in 1970–1, largely accounting for the estimated 17 per cent reduction in volume demand for ECLP's china clay during the second half of the 1970–1 trading year,[24] long-term growth of the industry is confidently expected. The underdeveloped countries will probably substantially raise their demand for paper, books and other printed educational material during the 1970s. The expansion plans of the European paper industry suggest a growth in demand from this, the most important export market. The home market could well grow as a result of increased demand for coated papers, embracing the cheaper magazines and even newspapers. Coated carton board is another expected growth area: Britain, which coated only 10 per cent of carton board in 1969, could increasingly follow the pattern in the United States where virtually all carton board is coated.[25] However, coating grade china clay is not necessarily an irreplaceable raw material in this market. There is always a possibility of product substitution, stimulated by the relatively high cost of coating clays. Research into alternative coaters during the 1960s was carried out both by paper manufacturers, and by ICI, who were experimenting on a synthetic coating material which would undercut china clay. To counter such possible developments, English China Clays' research establishment investigated a new coating material of its own, based on a mixture of chalk, substantially cheaper to produce than high quality coating clay, and china clay.[26] The process used was similar to those for which patents had been filed in Belgium, France and Holland. As early as December 1965 the company filed the first stage process at the Patent Office, by which chalk whiting was reduced to the necessary fineness; semi-matt coatings incorporating up to 75 per cent chalk whiting were produced, using an adhesive composed of casein and a special styrene/butadiene made by Dow Chemicals. To meet its chalk requirements, the company acquired a site at East Grimstead in Wiltshire, the only one of 200 sites investigated which, it was claimed, was suitable for the process.[27] In addition to the 4 hectares which the company had permission to excavate during the 5 years up to September 1973, a further 184 hectares have been acquired. This is not only to guarantee chalk reserves on a scale large enough to sustain output should this process prove to be a major innovation in paper coating, but also to ensure an adequate area of screening around the working quarry. However, rapid expansion of this process, utilizing up to 50 per cent chalk whiting, rather than that of the traditional coating clays, would clearly entail an expansion of chalk output at the expense of china clay. Nonetheless, it must be emphasized that the industry's development proposals in both Devon and Cornwall are based on the expectation that demand for china clay from world markets will continue to rise at an increasing rate.[28]

Throughout most of this century, apart from the inter-war years and the period of economic depression in the 1930s, the china clay industry has sustained an export percentage of about 75 per cent of total output. In 1971 the total volume exported exceeded 2 million tonnes and their value was £25 000 000.[29] There are some 38 other countries producing china clay, mainly of a lower quality for local markets; Britain is the world's largest exporter.[30] The quality of the English deposits, compared, for instance, with the German common and medium clays, is an important factor in the high level of British exports, as is the level of sophistication of processing techniques. However, china clay still sells essentially on price rather than quality or technical differences. For this reason, the location of the English deposits close to ports offering cheap transport to export markets by sea is a crucial factor, bearing in mind that, for all but the highest grade coating clays selling at £14·76 per tonne at 1970 prices, additional overland transport charges would add a significantly high percentage to delivered prices. Some 75 per cent of the present total productive capacity of the china clay industry lies within 16 kilometres of a port (Par, Charlestown and Fowey for the St Austell area, Plymouth for south-west Devon) and most pits are located above the 150 metre contour, facilitating cheap downhill transport first by gravity feed pipelines which are used to carry clay from the refineries to the driers, and then by road to the ports. The Board of Trade Working Party on China Clay commented in 1948 that 'in no other part of the world are important deposits of china clay so well situated for development and for distribution and shipment as are those in Cornwall and Devon'.[31]

By far the most important export markets are in the large industrialized countries of Western Europe. In 1970 the member countries of the European Economic Community (EEC) took more than 50 per cent of UK exports of china clay, and the member countries of the European Free Trade Area more than 25 per cent (these two blocks consuming together 82·3 per cent by volume and 81·8 per cent by value of all British china clay exports).[32] In the 1950s and 1960s the output of paper and board from the members of the EEC grew at a much faster rate than that of the UK. In Italy, second only to Germany in overall tonnage consumption of British china clay exports, the production of paper and board rose almost five-fold between 1953 and 1968,[33] and there are also important pottery markets. Proximity to these markets has been an asset to the British china clay industry, and their buoyant demand was a major factor in the annually increasing exports of the 1950s and 1960s, which culminated in a 9 per cent growth in exports in 1969.[34] During the period 1964–9 the value of UK exports to the countries of the EEC rose by 60 per cent. However, the value of US exports to this market during the same period rose by 140 per cent.[35] This reflects the rapid expansion of the American china clay industry of Georgia and South Carolina, stimulated by the interruption of British supplies to the American market in the inter-war period, and the economies of scale and reduced unit transport costs made possible by large bulk carriers. Such modern carriers, operating between Savannah on the Georgia coast and Genoa in Italy, means that transport costs per tonne for the Atlantic crossing are equivalent to those of clay shipped from Par in Cornwall to Genoa, although the distance is four times as great.[36] Par, which until recently shipped more than half of Britain's total china clay tonnage, including most of that bound for Europe, can only accommodate ships of up to 1170 tonnes dead weight. The port of Fowey, which has recently been developed for the shipping of china clay and is already equalling the tonnage handled by Par, can however take vessels up to 10 000 tonnes. This in itself is insufficient to counter Georgian competition since ships of this size are still small by ocean-going standards. Furthermore, the American operators have the additional advantage of working deposits with a much lower ratio of waste to saleable products than their British counterparts. The vulnerability of the British export trade was demonstrated in 1970 when the 2½-week dock strike occurred at a particularly inopportune moment for the china clay industry, coinciding as it did with increases in price of up to 20 per cent on exported clays. Several large European customers were lost to American suppliers. However, British entry into the EEC should give the British industry an important advantage *vis-à-vis* the American one, by securing access for British clays to this very important 'home' market.

Nevertheless, the operation of china clay producers principally in increasingly competitive foreign markets is undoubtedly a constraint when measures are considered to protect the environment from the very heavy demands made upon it by china clay extraction. The China Clay Council has stated that 'because of its predominant export position, it must be appreciated that the industry gives the most careful regard to any matters which may increase its production costs to the extent of weakening its ability to compete in an ever-increasingly competitive world market'.[37] Another constraint is the industry's importance as a supplier of employment, and principally male employment, in the south-west region where employment is difficult to replace. However, in spite of the physical difficulties involved, a great deal can be done to reduce the deleterious effects of workings without escalating production costs to uncompetitive levels.

The impact of china clay workings on the environment is of a unique kind among extractive industries. China clay workings are at the present time almost totally unrestored, and even with modern technical advances restoration presents particular difficulties in the case of this mineral. The chief problem relates to the depth of the deposits: no pit has yet been bottomed, and although a deterioration in the quality of the clay or its unsuitability for current production needs, or even physical restriction on the expansion of the pit, may occasionally cause operations to end, exploratory holes which have been drilled in the base of existing pits indicate the existence of reserves of clay at depth.[38] Working costs do of course increase with depth: pumping charges rise, and the inclined angle of rest which has to be maintained at the sides of the pit to ensure safety for clay workers and to prevent slides reduces the working area in the bottom of pits as they deepen.[39] At present, only clays of relatively high grades are obtained from the deepest pits. However, in view of the rarity of the deposits, the sterilization of deep reserves even in disused pits by backfilling with waste is almost entirely avoided. The tonnages of material involved are so large, that double handling of deposited waste material is very costly. A number of disused pits (or 'idle pits' as the industry prefers to call them) are used as reservoirs to help meet the large water requirements of the industry, and in the chief St Austell producing area the China Clay Council proposes that a small part of their total capacity should be utilized for mica or sand disposal.[40] But the bulk of the disused pits will remain unfilled for the foreseeable future, in spite of the superabundance of waste filling material produced by their operation.

The ratio of different types of waste to saleable clay variess patially from pit to pit and varies in time as techniques of extraction improve. In 1968 the average clay matrix in the St Austell area consisted of 15 per cent boulders, 75 per cent sand (mostly quartz), 8 per cent coarse kaolin and 7 per cent fine kaolin.[41] For each tonne of china clay produced, 0·6 tonnes of micaceous residue, in slurry form, were obtained in this area.[42] In the Lee Moor area of Devon, the sand has a higher mica content and the total ratio of waste to sand was in 1971 9·8:1.[43] At Lee Moor the ratio of waste to product during 1970 is expected to fall to 9:1 by 1974–5, because of a decreasing amount of overburden in the area of working during this period. The ratio of waste to clay is also falling in the St Austell area, due largely to improved mineral processing techniques. Clearly, however, very large quantities of waste, predominantly sand, are produced each year. In 1968 ECLP alone were handling about 20·3 million tonnes of sand and other waste materials to maintain china clay production at the existing level, and projected expansion plans will substantially increase that amount. At present, only a small percentage of the sand is marketed. In 1970 the total usage of sand at Lee Moor was approximately 8 per cent of the total[44] and in the main St Austell area 6 per cent was used commercially. Only in the comparatively very small workings of Watts Blake Bearne and Company at Cornwood in south-west Devon did waste usage rise significantly above this figure.[45] Almost all of the sand and other solid waste is deposited on surface waste tips. Extrapolation of the intended build-up of sand output during 1970–1 and 1973–4 implies rather more than doubling the size of existing waste tips in the area by the end of the century.[46] The proposals of the China Clay Council for the St Austell area indicate the possibility of more than quadrupling the area occupied by sand, stent and overburden tips during the period covering the 60 years from 1969.[47]

The combination of deep unrestored pits and high, mainly conical, waste tips has produced the unique and characteristic china clay landscape. Personal reaction to any kind of landscape, natural or man-made, is a highly subjective matter, but the response to the china clay landscape varies between wider extremes than that to most other kinds of quarrying activity. Daphne du Maurier, as a case in point, has written of 'the strange, almost fantastic beauty of the landscape, where spoil-heaps of waste matter shaped like pyramids point to the sky, great quarries formed about their base descending into pits filled with water, icy green like arctic pools'.[48] John Barr, on the other hand, finds the Hensbarrow concentration an instance of 'savage dereliction' and claims that 'the most obstinate, complex and sensational concentration of heaps and holes in the nation is the 78 square kilometres of china clay tips and pits in Cornwall'.[49]

The impact of china clay workings is likely to be confined to an even greater extent than is currently the case, on the main areas of St Austell and south-west Devon. Cornwall Planning Authority are attempting to restrict operations in the very small producing areas elsewhere in the county. In accordance with their policy of landscape conservation in areas of interest to tourists, the authority has refused requests for certain new china clay operations both on Bodmin Moor and in the Land's End granite. In the main producing areas of St Austell and Lee Moor, however, where china clay already consumes large areas for working space and tips, substantially greater areas will be required in the future. In the St Austell area much of the land required in the short-term is already in the possession of the industry and carries planning consent for working. At Lee Moor an application for planning consent for the working of a substantially larger area was approved in 1972.

Table 4.1 summarizes the land use requirements proposed by the

Table 4.1. Land requirements (in hectares) for the china clay industry in the St Austell area as proposed by the China Clay Council, 1972

	1969 (Actual)	1969–76 (Short-term development plan)	1969–2029 (Long-term development plan)
For pits*	645	787	2 491
For sand, stent and overburden disposal	830	1 560	3 776
Micaceous residue disposal	77	186	146
Plant areas	310	437	540
Total	1 862	2 970	6 953

*1969 figure includes working and idle pits.

N.B. 1. Land requirement figures are *cumulative*; e.g. the 1969 area for pits is contained within the long-term figure.

2. These proposals are both tentative and flexible, particularly the long-term figures.

Source: *Short- and Long-Term Development Plan of the China Clay Council*, published 13 January 1972.

China Clay Council in 1972. Although the short- and long-term Development Plans resulted from studies made by a Joint Working Party comprising representatives of the industry, the District Authorities and of Cornwall County Council, the proposals are those of the industry alone, but ones which the industry published with the hope that the county council would approve them and incorporate them in the county's structure plan. The figures represent therefore the industry's own estimates, and in the case of the long-term Development Plan, must, be considered as very flexible since technological changes may give rise to alterations in demand as well as changes in exploitation techniques and methods of waste disposal.

The figures for 1969 and the projected figures show that land consumption for solid waste disposal exceeds that for pits. During the period of the short-term Development Plan, eleven of the 645 hectares used in 1969 for pits will be taken for the tipping of solid waste, i.e. a very small amount of backfilling of waste is proposed, at Gaverigan, Great Treviscoe, Shilton and Singlerose pits, and part of Great Treverbyn/Carclaze. During this same period up to 1976, 56 hectares of disused pits will be used for the disposal of micaceous waste, and the remainder will be disposed of in mica dams,[50] which are shallower and have proportionately a higher land consumption than disused tips used for this purpose. During the 60 years of the long-term Development Plan, total land consumption would almost quadruple: this proposal, if approved by the planning authority and carried out in practice, would involve a very large outwards expansion within the area currently designated as being for the winning and working of china clay, and of the 'consultation area'. The existing consultation area, defined by the China Clay Standing Conference,[51] is an area containing reserves of china clay within which applications for planning permission from users other than the china clay industry are only dealt with after consultation with the industry, any disputes being referred to the Minister. The proposed plan would also involve some encroachment on minor roads and isolated dwellings.

The proposed increased consumption of land for mica disposal (previously only used to a very limited extent for this purpose) during the period of the short-term plan results from an important change of policy. Although only relatively very small quantities of mica waste are produced, the question of its disposal has in the past created disproportionately acute problems. In 1969 approximately 1·4 million tonnes of micaceous residue were produced annually in the St Austell area, of which approximately 50 per cent was discharged into the St Austell River, 25 per cent to the Luxulyan River and only the balance to inland lagoons or, rarely, disused pits.[52] Both the St Austell White River and the Luxulyan or Par River run through the area classified on the county Development Plan as being of Great Landscape Value and discharge into St Austell Bay, which is of some importance to both tourist and fishing interests. The two companies discharging mica into the St Austell River encountered in the course of the 1960s increasing opposition from tourist and riparian interests. The River Authority until recently acquiesced in the large-scale disposal of micaceous residue into these rivers, regarding them as industrial rivers under the Rivers (Prevention of Pollution) Acts 1957 and 1961. Indeed, by an agreement of 1962, only made public in February 1967, the River Authority received payment from these companies towards the maintenance of these rivers in return for their continued use. Increased public concern as the quantities of residue disposed of into the rivers and a greater awareness at local and national level of the question of pollution led the River Authority to revise their attitude, and in 1969 the authority obtained an agreement with the industry that by 1 May 1970 the quantity of residue deposited in the St Austell river should be restricted to just over 457 000 tonnes annually. Meanwhile the China Clay Association, prompted by mounting public concern and more particularly, one may suppose, by the realization that the existing arrangements were incapable of meeting long-term requirements, decided upon an initiative of its own. In 1968 it appointed a firm of consultant engineers to investigate and report on all methods of disposal available to deal with the residue expected over the ensuing 60 years, giving due consideration to questions of amenity. The first two volumes of the report, published in September 1969,[53] considered it was not possible to dispose of the waste within the existing working area. Of the several alternative methods of disposal which the report considered possible, the China Clay Association concluded that the best was a pipeline designed to carry the waste to a discharge point at sea approximately 800 metres off Maenaese Point (eliminating entirely disposal into rivers). Although an expert on sea fisheries stated that discharge in this area was unlikely to be harmful, considerable local opposition was expressed to this scheme. It seems more likely that the more vigorous championing of amenity interest and awareness of water pollution, on a local and national scale, which pre-dated the establishment of the Department of the Environment, helped to ensure that very careful surveys, costing the China Clay Association more than £200 000, were carried out into the likely effect of this scheme on sea bed and beaches, as well as the technical problems involved. The not entirely satisfactory results of these surveys fortunately coincided with the culmination of research into micro-mineral separation techniques, which has enabled the operators to recover more clay from the clay matrix and thus reduce the total amount of waste produced.[54] This development altered the calculations about on-site disposal and in May 1971 the China Clay Council announced a new scheme to dispose of micaceous residue entirely within the working area, which it hoped would be operational by 1974. This scheme, now incorporated in the short- and long-term Development Plans, will, since it has received planning consent, bring an end to the disposal of mica in rivers by January 1975.[55] The mica is being pumped from the various producing pits and refineries to the appropriate disposal pits or mica dams. On-site disposal of micaceous waste, preferably by backfilling into disused pits, and the decision to dispose of the waste in this way may be interpreted as one of the most important and significant changes in waste disposal policy from extractive industries in recent years. The land consumption for the on-site disposal of mica is comparatively a very small addition, representing 2·1 per cent of all land consumption for the long-term development period, and, since this method of disposal can be implemented without sterilizing reserves or damaging existing landscape, it is clearly preferable to disposal by rivers and thence to the sea. The new policy is an encouraging illustration of what improvements can be made in modern methods of waste disposal with the help of advanced technology, given that the necessary will exists.

The whole area of land concerned in the China Clay Council's proposals for china clay working in the short- and the long-terms lies in a very concentrated block north of St Austell (see Fig. 4.3). The block lies outside the main tourist areas and the coastal conservation belt, although the tips contained within it are visible over large stretches of Cornish countryside. The land concerned is not of high agricultural value, falling within the Ministry of Agriculture grades 3, 4 and 5, i.e. medium or poor agricultural land. Industrial pressures on the area are minimal, largely because the china clay industry itself has not given rise to on-site manufacturing processes. Apart from a very brief early experiment, no local pottery industry emerged since it was cheaper to transport china clay to the Midlands than coal to Cornwall. Similarly, it is cheaper for paper manufacturers to transport china clay, for instance, to Kent,[56] than to transport pulp to Cornwall and the end product to distant markets. Some of the older settlements within the area of china clay working house mainly china clay workers and have at present static or declining populations. In order to prevent the sterilization of clay-bearing land around these settlements the China Clay Council suggests that future housing expansion should therefore be concentrated on villages at the periphery of the area which can in any case offer a better standard of environment. An important feature of the China Clay Council's proposals is the suggestion of a comprehensive landscape plan for the whole working area. Planning permission for the new workings required would in any case stipulate landscaping of the new tips, since this has been the county planning authority's policy since 1964. What is, however, an unusual feature of the China Clay Council's proposal is the declared intention of extending the landscape treatment to older areas of working such as Foxhole and Nanpean, which received planning permission before any such stipulations were imposed. The older working areas include some land which is to all intents and purposes derelict, although not coming within the official definition of derelict land.

The object of the proposed landscape treatment is declared to be 'to produce a final result as far as possible part of the general scene. Levels, contours, and the general character of any new ground shaping should work progressively towards a viable use of the land for such an intensively worked area.' The methods used will include ground shaping to produce acceptable contours and to screen refining plants, tree planting and the seeding of waste tips. In the latter, the modern practice of mechanical conveyor tipping is of significance. The older method of skip tipping produced conical tips, which are 'alive' in the sense that more sand is deposited over sand previously laid, and thus no planting is possible until the tip is complete. Tipping by mechanical conveyors, which cannot carry the sand up at as steep an angle as skip trucks, produces lower, elongated tips, completing them stage by stage so that simultaneous planting is possible. The techniques of planting on quartz sand tips have been developed by the University of Liverpool Department of Botany and it is proposed that planting should be carried out on the first stages of tips prominent or close to settlement or public roads, thus providing some screening of later operations. Progressively, both the traditional conical tips and the newer elongated ones will become green instead of white. This, combined with contouring and tree planting, would radically change the aspect of both old and new working areas.

The China Clay Council's proposals do not of course represent an ideal solution to the planning problems of the area. The extent of backfilling or restoration of workings will necessarily continue to be very small, while the land consumption could almost quadruple within 60 years. However, the proposals have substantial merits. The first of these, as indicated earlier, is the voluntary treatment of the old working areas. In many other extractive industries, such areas now being worked under past 'loose' planning permissions constitute a major problem to which no solution is in sight. Furthermore, the advantages of a coherent overall plan for the area, which is worked by about ten different china clay operators, are very great. Whatever alterations may be necessary to the plan in detail, its proposals represent a degree of coordination, forward planning and retrospective rehabilitation which makes it unique. The china clay industry of the area has, of course, some advantages which make such a coherent plan possible. The area concerned is spatially a contained and unified one, which can readily be looked at coherently, in contrast to areas of scattered quarries such as the Peak District or the Mendips. The existence of one very large producer, dominating the extractive industry of the area, makes a coordinated plan a much easier proposition than if the industry were structurally dispersed. The concentrated resources of that one large producer, operating, unlike the NCB, in a relatively profitable field, provide access to expertise such as that of landscape consultants, engineering consultants, and research into modern extractive methods. Large extractive enterprises are, it is sometimes argued,[57] so powerful a force as local and national taxpayers and as employers, that they are unamenable to planning or conservationist pressure. Experience here and elsewhere suggests that the large profitable enterprise may offer substantial advantages where the complex planning and waste disposal problems of modern extractive industry are concerned.

The china clay workings in Devon, mainly at Lee Moor but also at Shaugh Prior and Cornwood, produced in 1971 less than 20 per cent of British china clay, but expansion plans for the main Lee Moor workings pose particularly acute problems in view of their encroachment on the Dartmoor National Park. In 1970 ECLP submitted an application to Devon County Council for further winning and workings of china clay at Lee Moor. The application was designed to make possible an initial expansion of output from 381 000 tonnes per year in 1969–70 to 634 000 tonnes per year in 1974–5,[58] output to remain at that level up to 1979–80. As in the St Austell area, the largest part of the land requirement is made up of land needed for quartz sand tips. The 1970 application involved the use of some further 328 hectares of land for tipping, 106 hectares being within the Dartmoor National Park. The planning application, which was resisted by local amenity groups such as the Dartmoor Preservation Society, was the subject of a public inquiry at Exeter in October 1971.* Undoubtedly

* In November 1972 the Secretary of State gave permission for these winning and working areas subject to modifications. One proposed 1·6 kilometre long, 90 metre high tip on a prominent moorland ridge was omitted from the permission, which was in any case for 20–25 years working, and not for 50 years as requested.

the most valuable feature of this planning inquiry was the commissioning by Devon County Council of an independent report by D. C. Corner and D. C. Stafford, of Exeter University, assessing the economic significance of prohibiting further tipping of sand at Lee Moor outside the existing permitted areas, and to consider the use of china clay sand as an alternative to the material now extracted from the sand and gravel areas around London. The detailed costing out of the economic consequences of refusing an application for mineral working, made by an independent assessor, is rare. The report concluded that the loss to exports resulting from the curtailment of china clay working on Lee Moor could amount to as much as £53 million during the 1970s alone, and could well reach £100 million by the early 1980s if existing long-term export trends continued.[59] It estimated that failure to obtain the planning permission in question could eventually lead to a loss of 1000 male jobs in the Lee Moor area, and further unemployment in and around Plymouth.[60]

The optimum solution to the problem would be to utilize a far higher percentage of the waste produced. The sand can be satisfactorily processed to produce concreting sand (except for high strength concrete), building sand and granular filling material. Some of the sand produced at Lee Moor is sold for these purposes, and some is utilized in the company's own on-site plant for the manufacture of calcium silicate bricks, but in 1970 only one-twelfth of the sand produced was utilized commercially,[61] a lower percentage than that obtaining at Watts Blake and Bearne's china clay works at Cornwood, about 5 kilometres away. The report recognized, however, serious difficulties in the way of substantially increasing the percentage of sand sold. Chief amongst these is the absence of a coarse aggregate to supply with the fine china clay sand in the concrete market, a much larger potential output than that for building sand or for fill. Normally, of course, fine and coarse aggregates are produced together in sand and gravel workings, and the report stated that 'the implication of the non-availability of a coarse aggregate at Lee Moor cannot be emphasized too much'. A further disadvantage is the high percentage of mica, particularly in sand from Lee Moor, and the particle shape of the sand, which together necessitate increased cement per unit of sand in concrete manufacture. One set of tests, using crushed quartzite as coarse aggregate, indicated an increase in costs varying from 7 pence to $21\frac{1}{2}$ pence or from 7 per cent to 21 per cent for each cubic metre of concrete[62] (depending on the mica content of the sand). Consequently, china clay sand for concrete manufacture may well sell at a considerable discount relative to conventional pit sand. The disadvantage of the china clay sand in terms of the absence of coarse aggregate and high mica content is a crucial factor in impeding its marketability. As is demonstrated elsewhere, aggregates of high quality are being transported interregionally to meet shortages in particular areas as improvements in transport produce economies. Sand and gravel was in the late 1960s being hauled some 97 kilometres to the Greater London market and limestone from south Devon was shipped there by sea. The reduced value of the china clay sand resulting from its uniform size and chemical composition meant that in 1971 it could, by contrast, only be sold commercially within a maximum radius of 32 to 42 kilometres of Lee Moor. The report concluded that the prospects of marketing the sand in the South-East where local supplies of sand and gravel are expected to be in short supply,[63] were not good. The areas of the South-East of England which were most likely to suffer from a shortage of sand and gravel at present prices were distant from the Lee Moor workings and it was considered doubtful whether they could absorb the whole of the Lee Moor output unless all local working of sand and gravel came to an end. The report found that the high transport costs involved in moving the material meant that, for many parts of the South-East, the gap between local sand and gravel price and the delivered china clay sand would be as much as £1·38 per tonne.[64] The profits of English China Clay from the Lee Moor workings were, it was concluded, nowhere near large enough to bear the costs involved in marketing the china clays and in the South-East at the prevailing market rates, and if a public subsidy were considered, it would need to be approximately £4 million per year from the mid-seventies onwards, for all the additional sand to be marketed. However, if planning policies towards sand and gravel workings in the South-East became markedly more restrictive, thus raising prices, and if a suitable synthetic coarse aggregate could be devised to market with the sand, some sales in the South-East might be possible. This was, however, by implication a distant and tentative possibility.[65]

The report could only recommend measures which might increase by a small amount the sales of sand from Lee Moor in local markets. It suggested that ECLP should pursue a policy of maximizing sales, rather than profits, within the local market, and recommended the abolition of the rates payable on sales of sand and their replacement by a low 'amenity tax' on sand dumped on the tips. The proceeds of the tax should, it suggested, be used in the first instance for research into the production of a synthetic coarse aggregate to market with china clay sand.

The problems demonstrated to exist in the commercial utilization of substantial quantities of china clay sand at Lee Moor apply equally to the larger quantities produced in the St Austell area. China clay sand from this area too is at present mainly used only in the locality of the working although the Cornish unit precast houses, manufactured by Selleck Nicholls Williams Ltd., a subsidiary of English China Clays, are marketed nationally. This much wider market radius results from the higher value of these prefabricated components than that of china clay sand. The demand of sand in the St Austell area is only able to absorb a small percentage of the tonnage available. The St Austell workings are 72 kilometres further from South-Eastern markets than those at Lee Moor, although nearer to the railway line. Clearly, for the foreseeable future, expanded china clay working is inseparable from expanded land consumption for sand tips. The particularly difficult choice at Lee Moor, where the National Park is involved, has at least the advantage of the alternatives having been costed out. However, now that a decision in favour of the expanded workings has been made, with the encroachment on the National Park which this entails,* there is at least the mitigating factor that the workings will be concentrated in one compact sector at the edge of the Park, where a comprehensive landscape plan on the lines of the one proposed for the St Austell area has been promised.

The disposal of micaceous residue on-site in Cornwall illustrates what a combination of public pressure and highly capitalized research and expertise can achieve in providing acceptable solutions to waste disposal problems. The study of the utilization of china clay sand from Lee Moor, on the other hand, indicates that, in some cases, the economic and social cost of landscape conservation may indeed be very high.

CHINA STONE

China stone is essentially a granite which contains varying amounts of accessory minerals and has sometimes been partially kaolinized.[66] The granite parent rock of china stone was changed in a different manner from that which gave rise to china clay: the geological changes producing china stone have been brought about by the action of fluorine and lithium on a rock with a higher albite content than granite normally has.[67] The main components of china stone are felspar and quartz, and the main accessory minerals are either fluorine-bearing (fluorite) or iron-bearing (chiefly potash mica or lithionite mica). Of the two main types of china stone, fluorite granite contains fluorite, potash, mica and topaz and is suitable for commercial use in its

* See footnote p. 194.

unrefined state while lithionite granite contains lithionite mica, tourmaline and topaz and requires refining before it can be marketed. The varying degrees of hardness of the stone depend on the extent to which kaolinization has occurred. There is, however, no very consistent standard applied between the various types and grades of the product.

Although a closely related mineral was until recently mined on the Isle of Man,[68] china stone occurs mainly in the St Austell area of Cornwall, where the deposits are interspersed with those of china clay. Apart from a similar formation worked at St Yrieix, south-west of Limoges in France, other deposits of China stone of commercial importance are unknown in Europe or the United States, although the latter manufacture a synthetic compound of kaolin, felspar, quartz and a little fluorspar which serves the same purpose.[69] China stone is used exclusively as a flux in the manufacture of ceramics. If a flux were not used, a much higher firing temperature would be needed, which would involve both technical problems and higher costs. The fluxing compound of china stone is felspar, while the quartz component serves as a filler: if the felspar content has been decomposed by a high degree of kaolinization, the fluxing power is lost. China stone is used in Britain in the manufacture of bone china, porcelain and glazes, and until recently it was also used in the making of vitreous sanitary ware and wall tiles. Although there are a large number of alternatives which could be used for flux in these types of ceramics, the chief alternative to china stone is felspar, which is of rare occurrence in Britain but is imported in large quantities, principally from Norway and Finland, for use in glass manufacture.

The Cornish china stone industry has been from its inception very closely identified with china clay. Both minerals, which were known to be used in the Chinese ceramics industry, were identified together at Tregonning Hill in Cornwall in the mid-eighteenth century and their extraction as raw materials for the pottery industry began simultaneously. China stone has of course always been required in smaller quantities. China stone quarries have traditionally been controlled by china clay operators; indeed, occasionally the two minerals have been worked from the same excavation. In 1807 there were seven quarries producing up to 50 800 tonnes of china stone per year for home and export markets.[70] Output grew steadily throughout the nineteenth century, and reached a peak in 1913, when 30 quarries were producing up to 71 100 tonnes per year, for both home and exports markets.[71] The First World War, with its attendant interruption to the export trade and shortage of labour in extractive industries, caused serious damage to the china stone industry. Like china clay, china stone suffered from the development of overseas mineral resources. The period of the First World War marked the growth of a felspar industry in Scandinavia which not only replaced china stone in some European markets but also began after 1918 to make gains at its expense in the home market. Unlike china clay, however, china stone never recovered its 1913 level once the war was over—this is clearly connected with its dependence solely on the pottery industry, where it is in any case not an irreplaceable raw material.

The organization of the china stone industry in the inter-war period too was ill-equipped for increasingly competitive markets. In spite of the considerable degree of company amalgamation which had taken place, output of china stone at this time was still derived from a number of small separate units which had not been merged because of the fragmented nature of the mineral leases. Little lateral extension of workings had taken place for this reason,[72] and the increasing depths being worked led to steeply increased operating costs. A committee on china stone extraction set up within English Clays Lovering Pochin and Company reported as late as the 1940s that 'the general equipment of the quarries is completely out of date and in a decayed, inefficient state . . . The general system of conveying stone from the quarries to the wharves and loading into mainline trucks can only be described as primitive . . . The loading from stockpile to truck is done by hand with wheelbarrows.'[73] This very unmechanized industry suffered badly from the labour shortages of the Second World War, and the further development of foreign deposits serving similar purposes, notably the United States felspar industry. In 1950 there were only ten china stone quarries left in Cornwall. Since that time the costs of working have increased very considerably. As the components and quality of the mineral vary very greatly within a small area, it has to be hand selected at the working face, an increasingly costly procedure as labour costs have risen. The method of working is of course very different from that of china clay, involving the normal quarrying techniques of hard rock winning, including primary and secondary blasting, crushing and screening. The product is, furthermore, a comparatively cheap commodity, selling for some £3·94–£4·92 per tonne ex-pit in 1969,[74] a price equivalent only to the very cheapest grades of china clay. Consequently, the remoteness of the deposits from the chief market in the Potteries is a disadvantage, since transport costs to the Midlands make up a high percentage of delivered prices.

The 1960 Clean Air Act had an important effect on the china stone industry since it restricted the emission of hydrofluoric acid gas, which is given off by the fluorine content of china stone when it is fired. The impact of this measure, added to the other factors outlined above, meant that the output of china stone was falling during most of the 1960s (see Table 4.2) but the particularly sharp drop in output be-

Table 4.2. Output of china stone, 1961–9 (tonnes)

1961	50 223
1962	52 488
1963	50 800
1964	57 912
1965	29 927
1966	30 105
1967	20 320
1968	30 480
1969	33 528

Source: *Annual Abstract of Statistics* for figures 1961–6 inclusive, and thereafter, Institute of Geological Sciences, Mineral Resources Division, *Statistical Summary of the Mineral Industry*, HMSO 1970, p. 60.

tween 1964 and 1965 was due to a change in the materials used in wall tile manufacture. Traditional earthenware, containing china stone as a fluxing agent, was replaced by lime based bodies to give improved craze resistance. By 1969 only four quarries were working, one owned by ECLP and the other three by the Goonvean and Rostowrack China Clay Company. The chief producing area at that time was and remains Nanpean, at the heart of the oldest china clay workings in Hensbarrow, although some output was also obtained from an island of lithionite granite on the east side of Kermick china clay pit.

The partial revival of china stone output at the end of the 1960s was mainly the result of the development of a refined, fluorine-free product. The regulations of the Clean Air Act, although initially a setback for the industry, were eventually a stimulus to this development but other contributory factors were suspicion that certain unfavourable effects on the firing properties of some earthenware might be caused by the fluorine content of china stone flux, and the need to improve quality and consistency beyond the level provided by hand selection.[75] In the late 1950s, ECLP evolved a flotation process which substantially reduced the contents of fluorine, iron, mica and tourmaline in Cornish stone, and in 1959 a pilot scale plant was put into operation. The product, defluorinated stone (DF stone), with a felspar content of about 55 per cent, was found to give whiteness and good translucency to fired bodies with the minimum of air pollution.[76] Production on a commercial scale began in 1960[77] and by 1971 sales totalled 27 000 tonnes while the productive capacity by that time was 35 000 tonnes.[78]

DF stone, which clearly has higher production costs than traditional china stone, sold in 1972 unground at approximately £8 per tonne or dry ground at £17 per tonne. The product can command these prices because of the accurately guaranteed specifications. The material is not however exported in large quantities since it contains 44 per cent quartz.[79] This is its least valuable constituent which merely acts as a filler and is widely available from other sources. Since the importance of china and DF stone lies in its property as a fluxing agent and substitute felspar is readily obtained by European markets from Scandinavian or even more localized sources, this commodity in either form finds it hard to compete in many external markets when freight charges are added to its price. Virtually the whole output is sold in bulk to consumers in the Potteries and is transported there by liner train. ECLP has since 1969 ceased marketing untreated china stone, now produced only by the Goonvean and Rostowrack China Clay Company. In the 1970s one may reasonably expect a greater percentage of total output to be in the form of defluorinated stone rather than unrefined china stone.

One other development could conceivably affect demand for DF stone. Preliminary exploration by the Highlands and Islands Development Board during the 1960s revealed what is believed to be one of Europe's largest undeveloped deposits of felspar at Durness in Sutherland, on the extreme north coast of Scotland. More recently the Development Board commissioned a report from Robertson's Research International Ltd. This analysed the properties of the deposit and the form in which it might most economically be processed and marketed. Although much more remote from the main home market in the English Potteries than the Cornish chine stone deposits, ground ceramic grade felspar, selling in 1971 at some £14·27–£17·22 per tonne,[81] would be able to bear the transport costs involved, especially since the coastal location of the deposit facilitates transport by sea. While exploitation of this might affect outlets for china stone in the home markets, the chief impact would clearly make itself felt on felspar imports. It is claimed that exploitation of the Durness deposit could save £1 million on the balance of payments.[82] Although the North of Scotland is a high amenity area, local authorities as well as the Highlands and Islands Development Board are generally anxious to encourage mineral exploitation in view of the jobs which they anticipate would be created in an area of high unemployment. Exploitation of the Durness felspar deposit could, it is reported, provide 40 jobs initially in this area.[83]

The exploitation of china stone, also from a high amenity area, does not of itself raise significant planning implications. Since china stone is derived from sites within the china clay working area, and is obtained to an increasing extent as a by-product of china clay, it forms, from a planning point of view, an integral part of china clay extraction. Land required for the future working of the mineral is included in the overall estimates given in the china clay short- and long-term development plans (see p. 189). Since the output of china stone constitutes only 1·2 per cent of combined china clay and stone output, it makes up only a tiny fraction of the overall land requirements of the industry.

BALL CLAY

Ball clay, like china clay, was formed by the decomposition and hydration of felspathic rocks, but ball clay is a secondary derivative of china clay, being formed when kaolinite was eroded and transported by water during the Tertiary Age. The parent rock of the English ball clay deposits is thought to have been the granite of the Dartmoor massif.[84] The action of the rain on the kaolinized parts of the granite washed away the fine mica and kaolinite from the heavier quartz grains. Although the quartz impurity is consequently not generally present in ball clay, other impurities, notably silica, and the iron and titanium which darken the clay, were picked up during transportation. Transportation also ground the clay to a finer particle size than china clay, making it more plastic and workable for pottery purposes.

The earliest ball clay deposit was formed when rivers flowing eastwards off the granite dropped their load in a delta in the Poole–Wareham area of Dorset, probably before an incursion of the sea formed Lyme Bay (see Fig. 4.4). Later, rivers flowing eastwards along the course of the Teign deposited their load in a lake in the Bovey Basin and others flowing off the northern slopes dropped their material in a lake near Torrington. The Dorset deposit is thus termed 'estuarine', the Devon ones 'lacustrine'. Since the heavier particles could only be carried on the steeper slopes of Dartmoor or while the rivers were in spate, the deposits nearer to the parent rock have a larger particle size than does the Dorset deposit.[85] The clay seams of all three deposits, however, are usually separated by bands of lignite, formed by wood and peat carried down by the transporting streams and varying in thickness from 0·3 to 9·2 metres, and clays of no commercial value.

Ball clays may be divided into two main categories.[86] The whiteware clays are highly plastic and, after firing, yield a white or cream coloured pottery body, while the stoneware group, containing appreciable

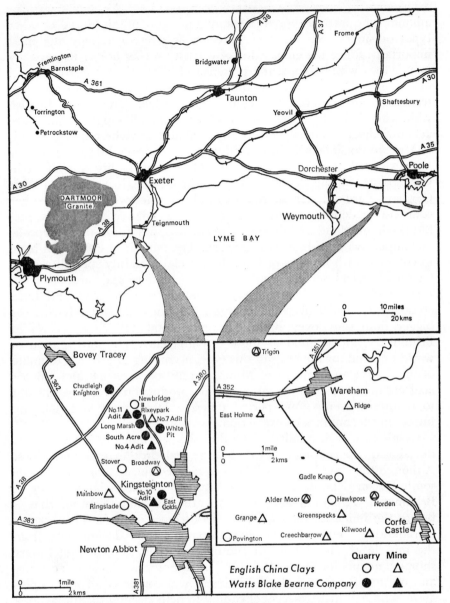

Fig. 4.4 *Ball clay workings in Devon and Dorset*

amounts of quartz, are used in the manufacture of salt-glazed or other types of stoneware. The first category is overwhelmingly the most important. Since the chief value of whiteware clay lies in its capacity to fire to a white colour, the presence of more than 1 per cent iron oxide, organic impurities or other contamination picked up during transportation reduces the commercial value. The three English whiteware ball clay deposits are of exceptionally high quality, are acknowledged to be as good as any available anywhere in the world, and make possible Britain's position as the world's leading producer and exporter of ball clay. Deposits of similar quality are found in Czechoslovakia, but deposits elsewhere in Europe, in Spain, and West Germany, are inferior in quality and consistency. The only other comparable deposits occur in Kentucky, Tennessee and Mississippi, but high overland freight rates make supplies from these deposits uncompetitive outside North America. The American clays even have to compete with imports of English ball clays, mainly speciality clays for the electrical porcelain industry, on the eastern seaboard, since the English clays are advantageously situated close to ports and have consequently small overland charges. No single deposit anywhere is bigger than the Bovey Basin. However, total ball clay reserves in Britain are not as great as those of china clay. The anticipation of world demand for minerals of this type, according to a recent estimate of the American Ministry of Mines, is only between 2·8 and 3·8 per cent cumulative: even on this estimate, production would be difficult to maintain over a long period unless a lot of work was done on improving techniques of extraction.[87]

Despite the high quality of the deposits, the industry has only produced and exported ball clay on a large scale in the 1950s and 1960s. Although the clays have possibly been worked since Roman times, the south Devon deposits were first extensively worked about 1730[88] at Bellamarsh, Knighton and, subsequently, at Kingsteignton, that is before the indentification of china clay from Cornwall. There was a considerable volume of ball clay shipments from Teignmouth from the middle of the eighteenth century; in 1820, 20 300 tonnes were shipped, mainly for Staffordshire.[89] Throughout the nineteenth century and on into the twentieth, the industry was composed of small operators, who had little reserves of capital to help cushion the impact of a prolonged depression during the 1920s and 1930s, followed by a severe wartime labour shortage. The 'lack of enterprise', said by an official inquiry in 1946 to be 'prevalent in the ball clay districts', was largely the result of this small-scale organization lacking the capital resources to invest in modern equipment. The Report of the Inquiry on the Ball Clay Industry remarked that 'it would be difficult to find any industry in this country where there has been so marked unaware-ness and lack of initiative on the part of many of the producers to modern industrial trends'.[90] Part of the recommendations of the report were based on the need to expand the home pottery industry. They included the proposal that export restrictions should be introduced to ensure adequate supplies for the home market since the export of finished ceramics was argued to be of greater national value than that of the raw material. In view of the extremely limited capacity of the ball clay industry at that time, producing 91 950 tonnes in 1945, this was probably a reasonable decision to make, although some export markets for ball clay lost at that time have never been recovered. The prolonged interruption in English ball clay supplies during and after the war encouraged the expanded development of the American deposits at Kentucky, Mississippi and Tennessee. The eventual removal of export restrictions, however, and the modernization of the industry, made possible the meeting of steadily increased demand in the 1950s and 1960s, especially from Europe. Output increased from 385 000 tonnes in 1950 to more than 609 600 tonnes in 1969, mainly as a result of buoyant export markets.

The expansion in ball clay, as in china clay, has been associated with a series of mergers, encouraged by the localization of deposits within three areas of the South and South-West. This process of amalgamation has been of great importance. It has made possible a rationalization of extractive and processing operations, the attraction of capital, invest-ment programmes in mechanization and research, and the employ-ment of high quality managerial staff, all of which have interacted with booming markets. Between 1957 and 1969 the number of ball clay producers decreased from 12 to 3, and by 1969 the two main producers, Watts Blake Bearne and Company and English China Clays Ltd., controlled approximately 95 per cent of production.[91] The largest single producer, contributing approximately 55 per cent of UK output, is Watts Blake Bearne and Company who are probably the largest producers and exporters of ball clay in the world. The earliest recorded partnership from which this company developed is that of Whiteway Watts and Company, formed in 1796 and lasting until 1860. In that year the partnership came to an end and the separate companies of Watts Blake Bearne and Company and Whiteway and Company were set up. In 1964 a re-amalgamation took place when Whiteway and Company and the Devon and Courtenay Company merged with Watts Blake Bearne and Company. More recently the North Devon Clay Company and Newton Abbot Clays have been acquired. On the

North Devon Clay Company property, a modernization programme has replaced the old, traditional and expensive mines by modern open-cast workings. Newton Abbot Clays, producing about 41 000–51 000 tonnes annually,[92] was a particularly important acquisition since the property adjoined that of Watts Blake Bearne and Company and the integration of operations brought considerable advantages.

The other large operator, English China Clays Ltd., entered the ball clay field in 1919 with the formation of the Mainbow Clay Company which had workings at Mainbow and Newbridge in south Devon. In 1938 English China Clays acquired the Rempstone property near Corfe Castle in Dorset. The company's big expansion in ball clays, however, came in the 1950s and 1960s: they acquired the south Devon workings of the London Australian and General Exploration Company in 1951, Hexter and Budge Ltd. in 1957, the Meeth North Devon Clay Company in 1966 and Pike Brothers Fayle and Company Ltd. of Dorset in 1967. Pike Brothers Fayle, itself the product of amalgamation between two older companies, controlled a large part of the Dorset ball clay output and had interests covering about 104 square kilometres of the Wareham/Corfe Castle area.[93] In 1970 English China Clays produced approximately 40 per cent of total UK ball clay production.[94] Whilst their largest operations are in Dorset, the company is the only producer extracting clay from all three of the British producing areas. The third, much smaller producer, is the Wareham Ball Clay Company which operates in Dorset and had in 1969 a productive capacity of 15 200–20 300 tonnes.[95]

The smaller ball clay industry has organizationally strong similarities with that of china clay, some four times larger. Both are now industries dominated by large producers, although ball clay is primarily dualistic whereas china clay is largely monopolistic. Both of the major ball clay producers also have interests in china clay, although English China Clays are primarily very large china clay operators producing substantial quantities of ball clay while Watts Blake Bearne and Company are primarily ball clay operators producing small amounts of china clay. The geographical proximity of the china and ball clay deposits, the overlapping of some markets and a certain similarity in processing technology make operations in both fields advantageous. In both industries the process of amalgamation has been accompanied by extensive modernization, rationalization of production, and the large expansion of export markets since the Second World War.

Ball clays, like china clays, vary from deposit to deposit and within a deposit. About 40 different seams have been identified in the Bovey Tracey Basin, the deeper ones being more siliceous than upper ones.

The mica and kaolin content of the beds is variable. However, the three chief locations have distinctive overall characteristics. The largest deposits of the Bovey Basin produce a carbonaceous type of clay which is the whitest firing of the three deposits. The north Devon deposits, which contain a quantity of very fine silica, are cream firing but are generally of greater strength than the south Devon ones. The blue Dorset clays are almost white firing and have outstanding strength and plasticity.

The largest producing area, accounting for some two thirds of production in 1969, is the Bovey Tracey Basin in south Devon, which is about 16 kilometres long by 5 kilometres wide and forms part of the River Teign valley and estuary (see Fig. 4.4). The clays outcrop within the basin, and the deposits reach a depth of 305 metres near the centre. Although the bulk of the workings in this area are opencast ones at comparatively shallow depths, some of the deepest clay mines in the world, excluding fire clay, are found here. Mines of the adit type, in operation since 1960, are of growing importance. The less important north Devon deposits, accounting for 10–15 per cent of UK output in 1969,[96] occur in a narrow basin running south-east of Petrockstow north-north-west to Marland Moor. The north Devon deposits are probably of similar age and origin to those of south Devon but the basin in which they are found is smaller and comparatively shallow, and the workings are opencast. The Dorset area accounted for 25–30 per cent of UK output in 1969. Although the lens-shaped clay seams of this area are shallower than the Devon ones, occurring at depths of up to 61 metres, the best remaining clay is found at the lower levels, and less than 20 per cent of this field was worked opencast in 1969.[97] In September 1970 the Department of Trade and Industry listed 12 ball clay mines in Dorset, all operated by English China Clays. Clearly this company, whose operations centre on Dorset, has a higher percentage of deep-mined clay than Watts Blake Bearne and Company, centred on south Devon, who in 1970 quarried 80 per cent and mined only 20 per cent of their output.[98]

Open quarrying is in general economically viable to a depth of about 31 metres and is carried out by hand- and mechanical-winning. A fully mechanized quarry is clearly capable of greater productivity than one at which the clay is hand-won; the output per manshift figures for Watts Blake Bearne and Company in 1964 were 17·2 tonnes for hand-worked and 40·6 tonnes for machine-worked pits.[99] (Later figures are not available because as part of a productivity agreement it was agreed not to publish these.) However, hand-working is indispensable in small areas where high quality clay in seams of variable thickness is combined with a high proportion of lignite waste, perhaps over 50 per cent, and where mechanical-working would contaminate the clay. In such areas, the ability of an experienced manual operator to distinguish clay and waste is irreplaceable. In 1970 some 6 per cent of Watts Blake Bearne and Company's output was handcut.[100] In the hand-worked parts of their quarries in the Bovey Basin, the labour-force is divided into gangs of three, each working a vertical section approximately 1·8 metres by 3·1 metres. Clay and waste, dug with compressed-air spades, are extracted separately from the top of the working section downwards, good clay being taken by dumper to the storage sheds and waste lignite dumped on the spoil heaps. Elsewhere, where uniformity of the clay seams and the presence of comparatively little lignite makes possible the use of mechanical equipment, power shovels and small bucket wheel excavators are used, but, even so, the services of an experienced operator, able to distinguish good clay seams, is vital. The ground is kept as dry as possible by collecting water in a sump at the deepest part of the quarry and pumping out the excess, but, even so, wet weather severely interrupts the work.

Below 30 metres, as a general rule, vertical shafts or adits are used, the clay being in some cases hauled to the surface in wagons worked by an electric winch. The underground workings of Watts Blake Bearne and Company were until recently worked by gangs of two men using compressed-air spades and in 1964 productivity was 7·6 tonnes per manshift.[101] But recent technological innovations have been introduced at the Preston Manor clay mines in south Devon which helped to win the company the Queen's Award for Industry, both for technical innovation and export achievement, in 1969. Underground clay cutting and loading machines and steel arch supports have replaced the traditional methods of compressed-air spades and wooden supports. Underground electrically operated locomotives, which discharge mechanically at the surface by remote control, have also been installed.

The chief market for ball clay remains the traditional one of ceramic whiteware, once virtually the sole outlet but in 1969 consuming approximately 60 per cent of total UK production.[102] The ceramic whitewares include earthenware, tableware, wall and floor tiles and sanitary ware. The growth in the Western European ceramics industry has been the main reason for increased sales since 1964. The ceramics market generally requires shredded clays, mixed to standard blends with guaranteed properties, and these make up the bulk of the sales, but a new development is calcined clays which, it is claimed, make possible faster and cheaper ceramic processing. In 1970 calcined clays made up 3 per cent of Watts Blake Bearne and Company's sales. The other, more recent markets mainly utilize the bonding strength of the material: ball clay is used in the manufacture of refractories for bonding pre-fired materials to produce blast furnace bricks, kiln furniture and refractory mouldables. This refractory market is an important subsidiary outlet but the prospects for growth are not great. The granulated fertilizer industry utilizes ball clay's chemical inertness and comparative cheapness as a dusting agent to prevent caking during storage and field application, and this could well be a growth market. The rubber industry utilizes the fine particle size of ball clay as a reinforcing fill for natural and synthetic rubbers.

A significant new development in marketing has been the presentation of the product in ways designed to reduce handling and transport costs. As a bulk mineral, selling at on average half the price of china clay, transport and handling costs form a large part of the delivered price, and any reduction in bulk is valuable for the export market, which faces rising transport costs at least for the overland journeys. Consequently, the proportion of pulverized clays, which save on weight, transport and storage costs, is growing and in 1970 constituted 25 per cent of Watts Blake Bearne and Company's sales. English China Clays have pioneered the development of pelletized clays, a range of ball clays supplied in the form of pellets up to 6·4 mm diameter and dried to a low and uniform moisture content which, like pulverized clays, reduced transport and storage costs. Both pelletized clays can be handled more easily than lump or shredded clay, whether by traditional methods or in modern bulk handling systems.

Proximity to ports of shipment remains, however, a crucial factor in the competitive pricing of ball clay exports which constitute the major market, since the unit costs for transhipment by sea are much lower than those by land. South Devon clays are loaded at Teignmouth, Plymouth and Fowey while occasionally a combined ball clay/china clay cargo is shipped from Par. Smaller, less regular shipments for more distant and smaller markets are also made from London, Liverpool, Newport and Avonmouth. The bulk of the continental trade is exported through Teignmouth, which is only 11 kilometres from the heart of the south Devon clay workings and in 1969 shipped 414 481 tonnes of ball clay.[103] The bulk of the Dorset clay is shipped from Poole, located in close proximity to the ball clay producing area around Wareham. The smallest of the three producing regions, north Devon, is, since 1970 when the port of Fremington was closed by British Rail, the least well served of the regions, the clay for export being transported some 45 kilometres overland to Teignmouth for shipment. The proximity to ports is not, however, an advantage in terms of the home market, which is served by rail. But in spite of the comparatively heavy, and recently increasing, rail freight rates, English ball clays make up much the largest percentage of the English pottery market, since imported material of equivalent quality is bound to be more expensive, delivered to the inland site of the English Potteries. It is largely the inland location of the chief English market, causing double handling as well as expensive overland haulage of any imported raw materials, which relieves English ball clays of the kind of competition faced by American ball clays in the markets of the eastern seaboard.

The ball clays industry had an export level in the region of 70 per cent in 1970, having increased its exports by almost 50 per cent in the years 1964–9.[104] In 1968 Watts Blake Bearne and Company exported 73 per cent of their total ball clay sales, a 21 per cent increase over exports in the previous year.[105] Until English China Clays acquired Pike Brothers Fayle and Company their ball clay exports were also about 70 per cent of total output. The output of Pike Brothers Fayle workings were however predominantly home market and only 18 per cent of output was exported at the time of acquisition. English China Clays have continued the concentration on home markets to which these particular workings were geared, and this had reduced English China Clays' overall ball clay export percentage to 40 in 1970.[106]

Although British ball clay exports are sent to more than 40 countries, drawn from North and South America, Africa and Asia as well as Western Europe, it is these last which are overwhelmingly predominant, taking approximately 90 per cent in 1968. In addition to these direct ball clay exports, it is estimated that well over half the ball clay supplied to the home market, mainly to the pottery industry, is exported in the form of finished products. Watts Blake Bearne and Company estimate that 90 per cent of all their clays are exported either directly or indirectly.[107] They are confident that the recent upward trend in exports will continue, and envisage an annual growth rate in ball clay exports of 3 to 4 per cent by tonnage, and at least 7·5 per cent by value, partly as a result of inflation but also from increasing processing of the clays in the future.[108]

English China Clays have also reported[109] increased sales and profits, but their capital return on ball clay has been substantially lower than that from china clay and has been below the mean return on capital for British industry as a whole. There are several factors which have influenced this. In the first place, the company has incurred increased costs due to a growing percentage of mined to opencast clay, a trend which is likely to continue as surface deposits of first-grade clay are exhausted. A further problem in the late 1960s was that of recruitment of labour for mining, particularly in the Dorset area, where light engineering at Poole at attractive rates of pay was an alternative form of employment. This applied to a lesser extent in the Bovey Basin, from employment competition at Newton Abbot. English China Clays also regarded the general fiscal system, whereby clay exploitation offers an unattractive return to landowners in terms of taxed income, taking into account the general disturbance involved, as a factor in the low capital return. Furthermore, they complain of delays in planning permission and general contraints on development,[110] although this is perhaps unexpected in view of the special provisions made for extraction of ball clay in both Devon and Dorset.

The three ball clay areas all lie within what may be regarded as holiday counties, although in each case the extraction takes place outside the boundaries of areas defined as being of Outstanding Natural Beauty. In Dorset, the planning authority has recognized the importance of safeguarding the deposits from sterilization by other development. The county Development Plan defined a ball clay consultation area, intended to include all locations where workable deposits of ball clay may exist. Wherever an application for development unconnected with ball clay is made here, a consultative procedure takes place between the industry and the planning authority. In 1971 the total area actually approved for the extraction of ball clay was about 757 hectares.[111] The planning problems posed here are generally less serious than those in Devon, since a very high precentage of the workings lie underground. No applications for workings were refused in the period 1968–71 and the planning stipulations for opencast workings cannot be described as rigorous. The normal stipulation is that surface areas shall be progressively worked, and, wherever practicable, back-filled and left suitable for some form of after-use such as afforestation. The exceptional physical difficulties in any specific instance are allowed for, and clearly the greatest of these is the lack of sufficient filling material, since the lignite waste is insufficient by itself. Certainly the absence of fill in sufficient quantities has been the major limiting factor in the absence of restoration in the Dorset area, although a certain amount of back-filling and afforestation has taken place.

The problem of restoration occurs in a more acute form in south Devon where the workings are more extensive and a much greater proportion of output comes from opencast workings. Here again, the absence of fill, in sufficient quantities, has been a limiting factor. A small proportion of Watts Blake Bearne and Company's workings has been restored to its original use, i.e. agriculture, while the remainder of the worked-out sites are wet areas used for various kinds of amenity. These amenities include a nature reserve, a sailing lake, and, the most frequent after-use, fishing areas, although some of the fishing ponds are only temporarily restored and may well be worked at some future date. The quality of the restoration work of Watts Blake Bearne and Company during 1960–70 was recognized by the issuing of a Countryside Award in 1970, the only such award to an industrial company for restoration planning. Nevertheless, Devon County Council argues that the whole ball clay area of the Bovey Basin is in need of a comprehensive landscape plan.[112]

In Devon as in Dorset, the county Development Plan defines consultation areas intended to protect for the future workable reserves of ball clay. This is particularly necessary for this mineral, the reserves of which are localized and limited – more limited than china clay – and where consequently the need for long-term planning is more pressing than in some kinds of quarrying operation. The timescale over which plans are made was illustrated by Watts Blake Bearne and Company's application for planning permission for a 122 hectare site in the Bovey Basin, part of their long-term reserves which they do not anticipate working until the end of the 1980s,[113] subject to satisfactory geological exploration. The proposal aroused some disquiet, and a public inquiry was held in 1971, but since the application is for underground workings the planning problems involved are not of major proportions.

Although much remains to be done, the after-use problems of ball clay as a whole do not compare in severity with those of china clay. The ball clay industry's impact on the environment is much less striking because of the much smaller scale of its operations, producing approximately one-quarter of the output of china clay in 1970, and the existence of a significant and growing percentage of underground workings. Unlike the china clay industry with its vast spoil heaps, ball clay operators have few waste disposal problems, except in connection with lignite at some of the mines – in fact, ball clay operations cause a deficit rather than a surplus of waste for filling. However, the comparatively shallow unfilled ball clay excavations have the immense advantage of suitability for after use as wet recreational areas, for which demand is growing very rapidly. The great craters of the china clay districts, in contrast, cannot be put to any comparable after-use. All the same, the location of the ball clay workings in the high amenity South-Western counties does mean that comprehensive landscape plans for the major opencast working areas at least are highly desirable.

FULLER'S EARTH

The current diverse and sophisticated markets for fuller's earth (calcium montmorillonite clay), now marketed in three main forms, natural, acid-activated and sodium-exchanged, has little in common with earlier history of the mineral which dates back, like so many British extractive industries, to the Romans who mined it from the Redhill district of Surrey and from Bedfordshire nearly two thousand years ago.[114] The mineral was extensively used during the Middle Ages for scouring raw wool and 'fulling' or bleaching woollen cloth (part of the finishing process), and was still being used by the Witney Blanket Company as late as the 1930s. In the nineteenth century fuller's earth was also used medicinally. Twentieth century research into new applications derived from the formation of the Fuller's Earth Union, an amalgamation of five works at Redhill and about the same number at Bath, in 1890. From this amalgamation came eventually the development of the processed forms of fuller's earth from which much of its present importance derives. In 1921 total UK output was only 20 566 tonnes;[115] in the 1930s, however, the Fuller's Earth Union began the production of activated earths, and subsequently started preparation of sodium-exchanged earth, from which important new applications have been developed. The Fuller's Earth Union was taken over by Laporte Industries Ltd., currently the largest producer of the mineral, in 1954. In 1970 total UK output was reported as being 121 920 to 132 080 tonnes,[116] although no official production figures for the mineral are issued. Other information leads to the view that it may well have been as high as 162 600 to 182 900 tonnes.

The chief current market for fuller's earth, as a binder for foundry sands, utilizes its bonding rather than its bleaching properties. The fuller's earth used for this purpose may be either natural, i.e. unprocessed apart from drying and milling, and/or sodium-exchanged. Sodium-exchanged earths are natural calcium montmorillonite treated with soda ash which enhances the bonding properties. In 1969 an estimated 76 200 tonnes of UK produced fuller's earth in one of these three forms was used in foundries, i.e. approximately half the total UK output.[117] The fuller's earth, as well as providing a bonding agent for foundry sands, adds plasticity to the sand, enabling it to be rammed to take up the fine detail of the pattern.

The special adsorptive qualities of fuller's earth are, however, still widely used for bleaching purposes. The adsorptive and absorptive properties of the mineral are derived from its crystal structure and are related to the very high surface area of each particle. Natural fuller's earth has the very high surface area of 80 square metres per gramme.[118] Acid-activated earths, those which have been treated with either hydrochloric or sulphuric acid, have an even greater surface area, sometimes approaching 300 square metres per gramme. In consequence, their bleaching powers are further enhanced. Acid-activated earths made up about one-fifth of total UK output in 1969.[119] The markets utilizing the bleaching properties of natural and acid-activated earths are similar: both are used in significant quantities in glyceride oil refining and soap manufacture, depending on the degree of bleaching required. A limited and declining quantity is still used for refining lubricating oil. Ten years ago this was a major outlet but the technology has changed and lubricating oils are now usually refined with hydrogen by a catalytic process. Fuller's earth is still used for refining used lubricating oil. Natural earth is also used in sugar and glucose refining.

Other comparatively minor markets utilize different combinations of properties. The civil engineering industry utilizes one grade of sodium-exchanged earth, processed to produce good swelling properties and low permeability to water, in, among other things, the building of foundations on damp sites. Other grades are used in the manufacture of animal pellets, the treatment of domestic water supplies, and as a drilling mud in oil-well drilling operations.

Fuller's earth, even in its natural form, is not a low value mineral the natural foundry grade sold at £14·76–£16·24 per tonne in 1971 while other grades rose in price to £29·53 per tonne and beyond[120]— and consequently the products of the three deposits now being worked, all in the south of England, will travel considerable distances to national markets. Not all the national demand is, however, met from UK sources and clearly it is the more expensive sodium-exchanged earth (bentonite)—selling at £25·59–£27·56 per tonne in 1971— which must justify the heavy transportation charges involved in importing the material. Imports of Bentonite totalled 47 337 tonnes in 1969.[121]

The three domestic sites now being worked are Nutfield near Redhill in Surrey, Combe Hay near Bath in Somerset and Woburn in Bedfordshire, although Laporte Industries Ltd. also own reserve deposits at Clophill in Bedfordshire and Maidstone in Kent. The Clophill deposit has been worked in the past to make certain qualities of fuller's earth which could only be made from the Redhill deposit by a system of more intensive processing. This would have used too much of its total capacity. However, the greatly increased productive ability of the Redhill plant now makes possible the production of such qualities along with other grades. It is intended to work the Maidstone deposit intensively over the next five years for the first time.[122] These were, until very recently, the only known deposits in Britain. At Nutfield near Redhill the deposits, of Lower Cretaceous age, consist of clay seams between 1·5 metres and 5·5 metres thick, overlaid by an overburden of sand and calcareous sandstone varying from 1·5 metres to 30·5 metres in thickness. The deposits cover an extensive area: in July 1954 permission was given by the Minister of Housing and Local Government for the winning and working of fuller's earth and overlaying minerals over a total area of 405 hectares. The deposits are worked opencast and mechanization at this field by Laporte Industries Ltd. has greatly increased productivity per manshift.[123] In some areas the sand overburden is also a commercial product; Laporte produce two main grades, a soft building sand and a cream coloured sand mainly for asphalt.

The Bath deposit, of Jurassic age, is located at Combe Hay within the area covered by the Bath Environs Town Map, although not in the urban area itself. It is thought to be smaller than the Redhill deposit, covering an estimated 162 hectares in 1964,[124] and planning permission has been given for the working over 107 hectares. This deposit is the only one of the three in operation in 1971 which is deep-mined. This difference of extractive methods is due to a combination of geological and environmental factors. The rock overlaying the fuller's earth provides a very good roof for deep-mining and would involve problems in opencast working. In the area concerned the depth, which is about 24 metres, could involve a very large excavation on the top of a ridge. Laporte Industries Ltd., the operators, work from drift mines, using pillar-and-stall methods which, it is claimed, achieve some 75 per cent extraction.[125] Seams, from 1·8 to 3·1 metres thick, lie under the hard overburden. The wet clay is extracted by hand, using compressed-air picks. Although this may seem a primitive method of working, it allows only the best and purest material to be worked, and is suited to the scale of the operation. In spite of faulting of the seams and problems with water, it is claimed that overall costs compare favourably with opencast working elsewhere.[126] The fact that the roof is firm means a minimum of propping and good control of roof subsidence when areas are worked out. Furthermore, selectivity at the working face is possible and this is important in the Bath mine because there is a thin layer of rock in the middle of the seam.[127] Reserves were in 1964 thought to be sufficient for a century at the then rate of extraction.

At Woburn, the deposits of Cretaceous age laid down as substantially pure calcium montmorillonite are worked by Berk Ltd. (part of the Steetley Group), the other major extractors of this mineral and the second largest suppliers of montmorillonite group clays in the UK, who also process imported material at their plant at Middlesbrough. Annual production from the Woburn site is approximately 50 800 tonnes per year.[128] The fuller's earth seam, averaging approximately 3·1 metres in thickness, is overlaid by 24 to 31 metres of red sand and is worked opencast. The area actually in course of excavation in 1969 was approximately 3·2 hectares.[129]

Each of these deposits occurs in areas which, for varying reasons, may be described in terms of amenity as sensitive ones. The Surrey deposits, being worked opencast over a considerable acreage, naturally impinge on the nearby Areas of Outstanding Natural Beauty and Areas of Great Landscape Value, and are clearly visible from the nearby North Downs. The Combe Hay deposit lying in the immediate vicinity of Bath, inside the Green Belt for the Bristol–Bath area and in a zone designated as being of Great Landscape Value, clearly causes problems even though the extraction in this case takes place underground. A good deal of traffic is generated, both here and at Redhill, since the lump earth is transported by lorry to the processing plant using company and public roads. However, the traffic is small compared with that of sand and gravel operations for which the tonnages moved are very much greater. The Woburn deposit lies in an area of great natural beauty, perhaps the most attractive part of Bedfordshire, and a tourist centre. At all three sites close attention is necessarily paid to questions of restoration, since all have involved recent applications for planning permission for new or extended workings. The planning consents in Surrey have been devised in such a way that continuous appraisal can be made of the effect of the workings on the landscape and a review of the working programme and its effects can be made approximately every five years. The Minister's permission granted in 1954 for the present working required among other conditions the submission to, and appraisal by, the local planning authority of a programme of operations for the working from time to time. A formal working programme for 40·5 hectares over a period of five years was submitted in 1958. During this period the County Planning Office was able to assess the effect of the working on the landscape and the success of the restoration programme before further working programmes were approved. Revised working programmes have been submitted and agreed at intervals since then.[130] Restoration is planned as an integral part of extractive operations. First rock, then soft overburden, is deposited in the previous cuts from which clay has been extracted, and covered with a layer of topsoil. Worked-out areas are also used as dumping grounds for the waste from the processing plant. The area to be restored is deep-ploughed to about 0·6 metre to prevent compaction, before the ground is seeded. Most of the restored areas are used for agriculture, and tree belts are retained or replanted wherever possible. Semi-mature trees have been satisfactorily transplanted here.

Near Bath the mining operations have, in the opinion of the local planning authority, no 'significant interference with agricultural use of the land concerned',[131] although the surface area may be liable to subside. There is no waste here apart from the rock in the seam which is left behind in the mine, as no wet chemical processing is carried out at the Bath works. A current restoration programme of the surface area includes a district affected by workings dating back to the nineteenth century. At Woburn, as in Surrey, restoration is carried out as part of a continuous extraction and reclamation cycle. The chief problem here is that the sand overburden is rather barren and there is little in the way of topsoil. However, all the existing topsoil is replaced, the worked-out area is graded to conform with the natural contours of the surrounding country, is treated with lime to increase fertility, and grass seed is sown. After approximately two years trees are planted.[132] Birch, larch, spruce and Scots fir have been satisfactorily established. Fortunately, both extraction area and plant are screened by extensive mature woodland.

The two opencast fuller's earth workings, both in attractive countryside, are encouraging examples from the planners' viewpoint. In both cases the continuous reclamation cycle, and care taken with aftertreatment, minimize the impact of excavation. Short-term planning permission for the working of minerals is very unpopular with operators since there is no guarantee that heavy capital investment in plant will have time to be amortized and this is particularly important in the case of fuller's earth because the processing plant represents a substantial investment. In the case of the Surrey fuller's earth deposit the mineral operator has been satisfied in this respect as the planning consent relates to the whole deposit without a final date. The Surrey Planning Authority, by the virtue of the conditions of the planning consent, are assured that a working programme shall be submitted and agreed with them at intervals enabling the authority to satisfy themselves of the success of restoration on a continuous basis. At the same time the operator has not lost the ability to plan and invest for his operations over a long period. With good will on both sides such schemes, making available an indefinitely extended period of consented working, conditional upon agreement of the details of a working programme with the planning authority, need not damage the interests of either the mineral operator or the planning authority. In default of agreement on the working programme the consent provides for a right of appeal to the Minister for his determination of the working programme.

It should be remembered that fuller's earth is a special case usually involving the removal of thin seams of the mineral from a considerable quantity of overburden thus making it comparatively easy to restore to satisfactory contour lines. Furthermore, the value of the mineral does mean that operators are prepared to accept fairly stringent planning stipulations. Equally, local planning authorities are prepared to be reasonably sympathetic in view of the rarity of the deposits in Britain. Since fuller's earth is a prime example of a mineral where virtually no choice of working exists, all efforts have been concentrated on making the few sites as acceptable as possible. The first review of the Somerset County Development Plan referred to the rarity of the mineral and explained that the importance of this factor was taken into account when planning decisions were made. Bedfordshire have taken a similar view, looking upon exploitation of the mineral as a necessary evil but an evil that can be successfully accommodated.

In the circumstances, it is perhaps not surprising that Berkshire County Planning Office view with equanimity the possibility of an entirely new fuller's earth working in that county. Important deposits near villages of Baulking and Fernham were recently located by the Institute of Geological Sciences in the Lower Greensand formation.[133] In 1970 about 42 boreholes were drilled to prove the deposit and investigations have continued to establish its extent. Although there are as yet no workings, several groups were reportedly interested and the likelihood of exploitation must be great in view of the comparative rarity of the mineral. If worked, the method would be opencast: the beds lie at a steep angle with an overburden of 24 to 27 metres, the overburden to material ratio varying between 8:1 and 14:1. This means that restoration would not be difficult. Although the deposit occurs in a pleasant rural area, the County Planning Office believe that a continuous restoration programme, on the lines of that carried out in Surrey, would overcome the main amenity objections, in view of the sophistication of present-day operators, and the techniques open to them.[134]

SALT

The extraction of salt, whether in the form of rock salt or brine, has always been heavily concentrated on Cheshire, which in 1969 produced 82 per cent of all UK salt output.[135] In that year salt was also produced in Lancashire (Fleetwood), Staffordshire (Stafford), Worcestershire (near Droitwich) and Yorkshire (near Middlesbrough). However, the relative importance of Cheshire has subsequently increased and will increase further as the result of a complex of technical, economic and environmental factors, to be explored later. Operations at Stafford and Middlesbrough have now ceased, and those at Droitwich which were the last to end terminated in 1972.

The salt beds were laid down during the semi-desert conditions of the Triassic period, at or close to the period when the other evaporites—gypsum, anhydrite and potash—were being formed. The Triassic deposit outcrops over a wide area surrounding the Southern Pennines, but an unusually large deposition occurred in the Cheshire plain. It is believed that these Cheshire saliferous beds were formed by a steady flow of sea water landwards across a wide and shallow shelf giving restricted access to the ocean.[136] The highly concentrated sea water, becoming steadily more saline as a result of evaporation as it moved across the shelf, deposited salt in solution in a sagging basin centred on Byley. The salt quickly crystallized as a result of the prevailing tropical temperatures, punctuated by sharp falls in heat levels. Other evaporites, which occur only in very small quantities in Cheshire, are believed to have been crystallized out during transportation across the shelf.

Unlike insoluble rock strata, rock salt does not outcrop: the head of each bed culminates in a natural salt solution found usually at a depth of 61–122 metres, which in Cheshire lies beneath breccia, an agglomerate of angular rock materials. This characteristic leads inevitably to considerable mapping problems.[137] In these 'wet rock head' areas, solution and natural subsidence on a geological time scale have destroyed large parts of the saliferous beds since the Triassic period. The salt beds can however be followed down the dipslope to depths unaffected by circulating ground waters where the full sequence will be present, topped by the so-called 'dry rock head' area. The stratigraphy of the saliferous beds of Cheshire was until comparatively recently imperfectly understood. But as a result of a borehole sunk in 1960 at Wilkesley, in the extreme south of the county, by the Geological Survey of Great Britain, both the nature of the beds and the extent of the reserves contained in them had to be reappraised.[138] The borehole established a sequence of nearly 610 metres of saliferous beds in two main groups, the Lower Keuper Saliferous beds and the Upper Keuper Saliferous beds. The full extent of the substantially thicker Upper Keuper beds had not previously been appreciated since in the more northerly Northwich area, near the centre of the depositional basin, they have been almost completely dissolved away by solution. The

Wilkesley borehole demonstrated that what had, in the Middlewich area, been thought to be top and bottom rock salt was in fact only the lowest deposit in a much larger formation.

The Upper Saliferous beds are best preserved at Wilkesley, where the upper formation consists of 5 salt beds ranging from between 34·5 and 106·1 metres in a total thickness of 404·7 metres. The area of the upper beds is thought to be 241 square kilometres and the estimated reserves 71 000 million tonnes.[139] This compared with about 293 square kilometres of the lower group with estimated reserves of more than 52 800 million tonnes.[140] The much thicker sequence proved as a result of the Wilkesley borehole and the existence of much greater reserves than previously thought means that continued expansion from the Cheshire saltfield can confidently be expected, to meet rising demand which has increasingly to rely on this area as a source of supply. The Geological Survey also considers that ample reserves exist to justify the establishment of a new salt-producing industry to the south of the present extractive areas, possibly in the neighbourhood of Whitchurch in Shropshire.[141] However, even if a new centre of extraction were established, only a very small fraction of the available salt is likely to be worked. If only 0·1 per cent of the estimated total was regarded as workable reserves, this could supply the needs of an expanded market for the foreseeable future.[142]

The early demand for salt, dating back to pre-historic times, derives from its value as a preservative and condiment, a market now of very minor importance compared with that of the chemical industry. Although recorded production in Cheshire can be traced only to the Domesday Survey, it is extremely likely that brine springs were worked at least in the Roman period and possibly earlier, probably in the Northwich area. These springs were formed by brine from the areas of wet rock head draining laterally into river valleys and giving rise to saline springs, which represented salt in its most accessible form. The Roman and mediaeval brine springs industry was sustained at a fairly static level, limited not only by the number of such springs but also by their output and the difficulties of transporting coal, which was needed in the evaporation process, to the saltfield, and salt away from it. It was in fact an unsucessful search for coal which led to the accidental discovery of rock salt in 1670 at Marbury near Northwich. The rock salt industry, i.e. the digging out of salt in its solid form, which began in the Northwich area, had clear advantages over the brine springs industry in that larger sources of supply were available. The rock salt industry around Northwich was stimulated by the canalization of the River Weaver as far as Winsford in 1732, which made possible the more economical marketing of this bulky material, and marked the beginning of a close association between the Cheshire salt industry and the canal system of the area. The opening of the Trent and Mersey canal in 1777 brought the benefits of this cheap form of transportation to the more southerly area of the saltfield around Nantwich, which had previously to send its salt by pack-horse to the canalized Weaver at Winsford. The stimulus to salt production provided by the building of the canals was supplemented by the removal of the salt tax in 1825. These stimuli affected not only the scale of rock salt working, but also the development of a method of extracting brine by pumping. This first form of brine pumping, now termed 'natural' or 'wild' brine pumping to distinguish it from the new controlled method developed in the twentieth century, made possible salt production in the wet rock areas, where rock salt mining was clearly impossible. Natural brine pumping, which is still practised, involves sinking wells in areas of wet rock head to tap the natural brine runs and, since these are actually in contact with rock salt underneath them, they provide a much stronger solution than that of the brine springs exploited earlier. Total salt output from Cheshire, made up of evaporated salt from natural brine pumping and crushed salt from rock salt working, stabilized at about 1·27 to 1·52 million tonnes a year by the mid-nineteenth century,[143] the bulk of it transported by water to chemical markets in Northwich and the mid-Mersey towns.

During the twentieth century, the pattern of salt extraction in Cheshire and elsewhere has been radically altered as a result of the perfection by ICI of a new method of brine pumping, which began experimentally in 1892 and was first implemented on a large scale in the Lower Saliferous beds at Holford near Northwich, discovered in the years 1906–10. The 'controlled' method of brine pumping involves the sinking of deep boreholes into the solid rock of the dry rock head area; water is inserted through these boreholes into the solid rock which is then extracted in the form of brine. The development of this method, which involves the controlled solution of large stable cavities in the salt at considerable depth, has made possible an expansion of brine pumping far in excess of rock salt mining. This expansion would not have been feasible by 'natural' brine pumping, which has to rely on the natural replacement of the brine pumped off. Furthermore, surface subsidence, although not necessarily eliminated in every case, is generally thought to be much smaller and more predictable than that resulting from natural brine pumping. The development of the controlled method has led to the much greater concentration of salt extraction operations, both within Cheshire and on a national scale.

Natural brine pumping, which has relatively few capital or technical requirements, was and is a dispersed activity within the wet rock head areas of Cheshire: controlled brine pumping in the county, on the other hand, was in 1968 carried out exclusively by ICI at the Holford estate near Northwich, where 17 700 million litres of brine, or 88 per cent of all the brine pumped in Cheshire, was extracted.[144] The controlled method has since about 1930 also been employed at Fleetwood in Lancashire, the only saltfield outside Cheshire which now has a future. As a result of the development of controlled brine pumping on a large scale, ICI has found it economic to phase out smaller natural brine pumping operations elsewhere in the country, notably at Stafford in 1957 and more recently at Saltholme near Middlesbrough. The economies of scale possible at the Holford complex have outweighed the cost of transporting increased quantities of evaporated salt to the Midlands and North-Eastern markets. Now that the full extent of the Cheshire salt beds has been established, and the geology of the formation is relatively clear, it is likely that during the next decade other firms will develop controlled systems in the county, or possibly across the county boundary in north Shropshire, to meet an increasing market demand.

Other special circumstances have also served to increase the relative importance of the Cheshire workings, notably the bringing of a court action against British Soda Ltd. for subsidence damage caused by the company's natural brine pumping in Stafford.[145] The wet rock head of the Saliferous beds of Staffordshire, within the Keuper Marl series, lies at depths of some 76–99 metres beneath the town of Stafford. Natural brine pumping began in 1893, following the discovery of brine in 1881 when a borehole for water was sunk by the corporation. In 1948 four companies, subsequently amalgamated as British Soda Ltd., were pumping brine here, apart from ICI. In 1969, after the withdrawal of ICI, about 410 million litres of brine were being pumped per year, one-seventh of national output.[146] Subsidence resulting from this pumping had been reported since 1948 and had become more severe from 1964 onwards. As a result of the action brought in the High Court in 1969 by Lotus Ltd., claiming damage to their shoe factory, British Soda Ltd. were ordered to cease pumping from August 1970, and damages were settled out of court. It was at least partly as a result of this decision, which created a precedent for natural brine pumpers' liability for subsidence damage, that prompted ICI to plan a phased withdrawal from natural brine pumping at Stoke Prior, north of Droitwich in Worcestershire. In that area both amenity and agricultural problems had been caused by this method of working:

ponds and lakes became enlarged, and poor drainage caused agricultural land to go out of production.[147]

Consequently, it is now only in Cheshire, the one county to apply the provisions of the Brine Pumping (Compensation for Subsidence) Acts, that natural brine pumping is likely to continue on any scale. These acts offer some kind of insurance against claims for damages, although not of course precluding action for damages being taken under common law. The 12 per cent of brine still obtained by natural brine pumping in Cheshire comes mainly from Middlewich, Sandbach, Northwich and Lymm, which in 1969 produced a total of 2270 million litres,[148] almost all from the Upper Keuper Saliferous beds. The total output of naturally pumped brine was slightly less than that pumped in 1951, when 19 per cent of all brine was obtained by this method in Cheshire. The closure of several pumping firms during the 1950s and 1960s, when the number of salt extraction firms in Cheshire approximately halved, and the ending of natural brine pumping by ICI at Winsford, accounted for the falling percentage of brine obtained by this method in the county. The larger companies formed mainly by mergers in the natural brine pumping sector during the 1960s did, however, greatly increase their individual outputs and these firms are expected to achieve a faster rate of growth during the 1970s. Consequently, as predicted the percentage of naturally pumped brine returned to 19–20 per cent by 1974, with output doubling to over 4540 million litres per year[149] to meet an anticipated rise in demand. This development is bound to have serious implications for subsidence, discussed on p. 227. In the long term, however, natural brine pumping in the county must contract, since workings at existing sites cannot rely indefinitely on natural replacement of the brine pumped off, and it is the planning authority's policy not to permit new natural brine pumping operations.

The chief market for salt derived from brine is the chemical industry. In 1969 a total of 7 187 000 tonnes of salt were extracted in solution in Britain;[150] of this total only 1 605 000 tonnes were made into salt[151] and most of the remainder was supplied to the chemical industry in solution form. Some 75 per cent of brine pumped in Cheshire goes directly to the chemical industry in this state.[152] The Cheshire saltfield was the prime locating factor for the important chemical complex which is based partly on the saltfield, especially at Northwich, and in the mid-Mersey towns of Widnes and Runcorn. The chemical industries of Widnes and Runcorn were located originally by their mid-way position between the salt of Cheshire and the coal of Lancashire. Now, however, water transport has been partly replaced by brine pipelines, such as that running from Holford to the huge ICI chemical works at Weston Point, Runcorn. The most important chemical processes are brine electrolysis for the production of chlorine, hydrogen and caustic soda, and the Solvay-soda process. After lengthy and complex treatment, a multitude of end-products such as the plastic PVC and anti-knock additives for petrol are produced. The most important use of brine in the chemical industry is the production of chlorine, and the rate of growth in this field will be the largest single factor in determining the rate of expansion of brine pumping in the 1970s. Chlorine output increased by at least 80 per cent during the 1960s, and it is estimated that UK output will be increased by at least 40 per cent between 1969 and 1975.[153] It is clear therefore that the chemical industry alone will ensure substantial growth in brine pumping.

Of the much smaller total of 1 605 000 tonnes of salt obtained from brine in Britain in 1969, all but 60 960 tonnes was evaporated in vacuum plant. In that year 518 644 tonnes, or 29 per cent of this total, was exported, and these exports supplied some 15 per cent of the world's markets for evaporated salt.[154] Exports of evaporated salt increased by 30 per cent in the 1960s, a large part of the shipments going to the growing chemical industries of Africa, Australia, Scandinavia and Eire. The proximity of the major Cheshire deposits to ports of shipment, notably Liverpool, is a great advantage. Evaporated salt is also transported from Cheshire to British chemical works away from the region. The growth rate in the use of evaporated salt outside the chemical industry has been comparatively slow. The most important category of consumer, taking some 66 per cent of total evaporated salt (excluding exports and chemical consumption) is industry, which uses the mineral for a wide range of products and processes, such as dyestuffs, soap manufacture and leather tanning. The growth rate in this market is likely to reflect that of the economy as a whole, i.e. 2·5–3 per cent a year.[155] The second largest category of consumer, taking about 26 per cent of this total, is the food processing industry, which uses salt for dairy products, curing bacon, baking bread and a wide range of canning and preserving functions. Only a very small proportion is used as table salt. The much smaller agriculture and fishery markets, taking 8 per cent of this total, declined steadily throughout the 1960s, consuming in 1969 less than 70 per cent of their tonnages ten years earlier.[156] It is clear that the relative importance of the chemical market as opposed to other outlets will increase still further in the 1970s.

The number of rock salt workings has been drastically reduced in this century. This form of salt extraction exploits a much coarser form of the mineral than brine pumping, since the deposits worked often contain material coloured brown, red or yellow by iron or other impurities, and the markets for it are consequently now restricted almost entirely to the de-icing of roads in winter. However, the growing demand in this one market caused in the 1960s a big expansion in the production of the only mine now in operation, and could lead to the opening of other rock salt workings in the 1970s. The Meadowbank Mine of ICI's Mond Division at Winsford in Cheshire produced in 1969 the entire British total of 1 357 000 tonnes.[157] Mining operations take place in the 24 metres thick Lower Saliferous beds, of which only the bottom 6·1–7·6 metres are worked.[158] The mine, made up of six very large interconnecting caverns, covers a total area of more than 53 hectares. The pillar-and-stall method of extraction is used and although there are some 18 metres of hard rock above the workings, large pillars of salt are left as supports. The mine, which opened on a small scale in 1844, underwent a major modernization programme in 1960, designed to treble its productive capacity. However, as demand for rock salt in the UK grew tenfold during the next decade, from 152 400 tonnes in 1960 to 1 524 000 tonnes in 1970, further expansion of the mine rock took place in 1969 in order to raise production to 1 829 000 tonnes by 1971.[159] Demand is expected to grow rapidly in the 1970s.

Although by far the largest market for rock salt is for winter road clearance, some is used as fertilizer for sugar beet and mangolds, as a fluxing agent in non-ferrous metal refining and in salt glazing for earthenware. However, there is little doubt that demand is largely governed by the severity of the winter and the extent of the road building programme. During the 1960s the motorway building programme resulted in overall greatly increased requirements, but the market varied greatly with each winter's degree of severity, sometimes by as much as 762 000 tonnes per year,[160] and ICI operated a system of building up stocks during mild winters to meet demand during hard ones. The three comparatively hard winters of 1967–8, 1968–9 and 1969–70, the latter the second hardest in twenty years, caused a shortfall of supply during 1970. During that winter, when ICI operated a rationing system for domestic consumers, local councils were forced to import inferior salt from Ireland, Germany and Sicily, at prices much inflated by the heavy transport costs of this low value mineral. Apart from the need for larger stocks to be held in reserves which this experience indicated, the large new motorway building programme announced by the Government in 1971 assures expanded demand. In that year ICI received planning permission to sink another shelf at

Meadowbank to increase the production potential of the mine to 3 million tonnes per annum.[161]

Rock salt mining does not, under present conditions, present severe planning problems. Surface developments are confined to storage areas in the locality of the winding shaft, which can be screened, and to the associated traffic which is generated. The crushing plant is located underground. With the present system of working, the chance of a collapse in the mine roof, leading to surface subsidence, is remote. In the past, however, rock salt mining has played its part in the long and severe subsidence problem which has been associated with salt extraction in Cheshire. In the eighteenth and nineteenth centuries, the collapse of rock salt mines produced flooded pit holes. The most catastrophic subsidence occurred however late in the nineteenth century, when 'bastard' brine was pumped from the flooded rock salt mine workings,[162] producing the Ashtons and Neumanns 'flashes' north of Northwich. Current planning problems are not however of this order. The presence of the underground working does act as a psychological deterrent to surface users. The 53 hectares above Meadowbank are largely confined to agricultural use, although their proximity to Winsford might otherwise have dictated their zoning for urban development. Existing planning permissions are adequate for the whole 1970s, allowing for the anticipated increase in production. It is, however, possible, in view of the expected increase in demand, that applications will be made to start new rock salt mining enterprises in other geologically suitable areas in the county. In this event, the county planning authority's policy would be to restrict such mining to areas where the surface use is confined to agriculture; to ensure that no unacceptable degree of traffic would be generated and that surface developments are acceptable within the landscape; and to stipulate that a landscape after-treatment scheme should be approved in advance.[163] It certainly seems likely that the heavy increased demand for rock salt, whether met solely from expansion at Meadowbank or from new projects elsewhere, can be supplied without significantly damaging the area above the saltfield or adding to the serious accumulated subsidence of the past. Unfortunately, the land use problems of brine pumping are of a much more difficult order.

Subsidence in the Cheshire saltfield has always presented serious problems and studies of mining subsidence nearly always draw on classic examples from this area. Many of the hollows caused by natural subsidence have been aggravated by natural brine pumping, which in the eighteenth and nineteenth centuries led to gradual sinking over wide areas and the formation of the Winsford 'flashes'. The damage here has inevitably been on a larger scale than that caused by natural brine pumping at Stafford and Droitwich; indeed it has nowhere been found possible to reduce the amount of subsidence caused by this method of extraction. The greatest problem arises from the unpredictability of the subsidence, since the course of the natural brine runs is not clearly established and the extent of the areas from which the solution is derived is unknown. In spite of the long experience of this problem in Cheshire, the occurrence of subsidence resulting from natural brine pumping still cannot be forecast and, to quote the county survey, 'the risk of gradual settlement as a result of natural brine extraction remains as a question mark over many areas in mid-Cheshire'.[164] The existing situation in the county thus compares very unfavourably with that in the deep-mined coal areas, where very great advances have been made in the accurate prediction of subsidence, and surface developments can be planned accordingly. The Cheshire county survey indicates the scale of the current problem: the total subsidence resulting from natural brine pumping in 1968 would be equivalent to a drop of 0·3 metre over 54 hectares. If the county planning department's projections of natural brine pumping for 1974 are taken as a basis for estimate, the total subsidence resulting from this activity in 1974 would be equivalent to a drop of 0·3 metre over 119 hectares, although in reality falls measured in fractions of a metre over a much greater area are more likely.[165]

The subsidence problem of brine extraction in Cheshire has, since the late nineteenth century, been recognized to be of such exceptional proportions as to justify special action at national level, as explained in Chapter 1. At the very early date of 1891 the Brine Pumping (Compensation for Subsidence) Act set up compensation boards for Northwich and district to make an annual levy on brine pumpers of three old pence per thousand gallons pumped (about 1·23p per tonne of salt), to pay compensation for certain types of damage resulting from subsidence, and to advise on and contribute to the cost of precautions in building construction. This was an advanced act for its time. The provisions of the 1891 Act were subsequently extended in the 1952 Cheshire Brine Pumping (Compensation for Subsidence) Act which set up a single compensation district for all areas of the county liable to subsidence. A two thirds rebate of the levy was to be made to controlled brine pumpers, provided that no subsidence resulted from their operations and local authorities previously excluded from claiming damages as a party benefiting from extraction through the rates could henceforward claim compensation for damage to their residential property. The Compensation Board has defined a 'yellow area' which is subsiding or liable to subside, and the local planning authority is required to consult the board about any applications for building within this area, although it has not been possible, because of the need for urban development, to avoid new building entirely in areas of doubtful stability.

ICI have usually been entitled to the two thirds rebate on the levy payable for their controlled pumping at Holford, since there has been very little evidence of subsidence caused by this method. However, Lancashire County Council, whose area does not in fact come within the scope of the compensation scheme, are not satisfied that the cavities created by this method will be stable over the long-term. The council feels that more research, such as the initiation of checks on land surface levels and seismic surveys, should be carried out. They point out that, should subsidence ever occur as a result of the controlled workings at Fleetwood, which are close to the sea, disastrous flooding could result.[166]

Cheshire County Council, on the other hand, are satisfied about the claims made for the stability of land overlying controlled workings. Their concern is for the large-scale continuance, and projected expansion, of natural brine pumping in the county. The current extent of this activity is largely the result of decisions made during the early 1950s. In 1947, when the Town and Country Planning Act came into force, each existing brine pumping concern was required to make an application to continue working. The opportunity which this provision presented was not then appreciated. The Ministry of Town and Country Planning paper on rock salt and brine, produced in 1950 to guide the local authority, concluded that it would be difficult to justify a refusal of planning permission for existing natural brine pumping undertakings, as long as that remained the normal method of extraction. Regrettable as this advice now appears, it must be conceded that the apparent advantages of the controlled method from a subsidence point of view were not as clear at that time as they now seem. Furthermore, the extent of future demand for chlorine could not then be foreseen: PVC had not been invented and the major use of natural brine was for the production of white salt to supply a completely different, and much smaller, market. Largely as a result of the Minister's advice, a substantial number of permissions to continue natural brine pumping were therefore given by the planning authority during the period 1951–3; no stipulations about subsidence were made in these consents—these being considered impractical—and no limitations were made on the amount of brine to be pumped from the approved site. In the light of subsequent events, the planning authority now regrets that no condition was imposed requiring operators to apply for planning permission to increase the quantity of brine pumped above the level obtaining in 1950.[167] The decisions of the early 1950s have had far-reaching effects: from them derive the current continuation of natural brine pumping and its projected expansion in the 1970s, in direct opposition to what is now the local planning authority's policy. Like other 'loose' planning consents given elsewhere both for salt and other extractive industries at that time, the effects have been of very long duration. Similarly, in Staffordshire, it was a ministerial decision of the early 1950s which gave natural brine pumping in this area a future. A decision by the local planning authority to restrict the life of natural brine pumping was overruled on appeal by the Minister, although he acknowledged the dangers of the operation.[168] In Cheshire, no further application for natural brine pumping was made until 1968, an application which the local planning authority refused. The county planning committee subsequently resolved that natural brine pumping in the county should be phased out as soon as possible. The county's policy now is that large expansion by a natural brine pumping concern should be resisted unless accompanied by active development of a controlled pumping system. The county council would like to restrict controlled pumping to the ICI method, since this has been tested and proved safe to their satisfaction over the past 40 years, but they recognize that the acquisition of the necessary expertise from ICI could prove expensive for other companies. Consequently, they are prepared to accept on a trial basis controlled pumping methods which are not identical with the ICI one.[169] In some circumstances the county would aid operators to obtain mineral rights in areas approved for the winning and working of salt, by the designation of such areas so as to allow appeal to the High Court in case of difficulty.[170]

There are, however, considerable difficulties in the way of implementing this policy. It is perhaps ironic that the special provisions of the Brine Pumping (Compensation for Subsidence) Acts help to cushion natural brine pumpers in the county from large claims for damages, although the acts do not pre-empt a claim for restraint of these activities in the High Court. Very substantial expense is involved in a change from natural to controlled brine pumping, which may entail a change of site as well as pumping to deeper levels by more expensive methods. However, geological surveys have shown that other areas suitable for working by the controlled method do exist, and the development of large concerns during the 1950s and 1960s has meant that more firms may be able to find the necessary capital involved. Certainly, there are, for large operators, positive economic advantages in making the change for it is not possible to expand natural brine pumping indefinitely at any one site and in some areas underground water supplies become exhausted. A controlled system of pumping does therefore facilitate the long-term production planning necessary for a major operator. There is also the incentive to convert to controlled systems inherent in the compensation scheme, with proportionally bigger incentives for a major operator. The greatest long-term problems derive from the remaining small natural brine pumpers: in their case, the county planning authority has only been able to make the policy statement that their position will be 're-examined when those large firms prepared to establish their own brinefields have done so'.[171] Meanwhile, the number of small operators may, in the 1970s, continue to decline as it did in the 1960s, a development which can only be helpful to the planning authority.

The role of increasingly more stringent planning policies as one factor in the growing average size of extractive operations, both in terms of extractive units and structure of firms, is very clear in this instance. The greater the stringency of planning constraints and the pressure of environmentalists, the greater the relative advantages of large firms over small ones because of their large capital resources, management and technical and landscape expertise. The inevitability of this process may be difficult to reconcile with the statutory duty of planning authorities to avoid creating monopolies. In the case of brine pumping in Cheshire, the long-term strategy of the planning authority does seem to ensure that, in the long run, the large-scale expansion which is likely in this field will be concentrated in the sphere of controlled brine pumping, although there seems now little hope of averting an increasing percentage of natural brine pumping in the short-term. That the long-term reduction in natural brine pumping can only be achieved by increasing the pressures on small operators is regrettable but unavoidable.

GYPSUM AND ANHYDRITE

Gypsum, hydrated sulphate of calcium, is not a rare mineral. The world reserves are enormous and the mineral is found in abundance in England, though not in Wales or Scotland. The main English deposits derive from the Permian and Triassic periods when the arid climate and the evaporation of sea waters resulted in pockets of gypsum and anhydrite being formed among the sedimentary rocks. The most extensive deposits occur in the Triassic Keuper Marl in the Midland counties of Nottinghamshire, Derbyshire, Leicestershire and Stafford-shire as well as in Gloucestershire and Somerset. Gypsum is also in the Upper Permian strata of Cumberland and Westmorland and has, within the last century, been discovered in the Purbeck beds of the Jurassic sequence in east Sussex. Although the deposits are widespread, however, production has become concentrated in three main areas: the Midlands (Nottinghamshire and Staffordshire), Cumberland and Westmorland, and Sussex; though extraction on a small scale is still carried out in Yorkshire. The chief factor determining this concentration has been transport costs. Gypsum is a very low value commodity—the average price of crude gypsum, ex-mine, in March 1971 was £1·72–£2·21 per tonne[172]—and the consequent need to minimize transport costs to processing plants is paramount. The concentration of extraction has been further stimulated by the increasing dependence on the plaster and plasterboard markets: the national output of plasterboard more than doubled and that of building plaster more than trebled during 1950–70.[173] Consequently, there has been a growing spatial association between the mines and plaster mills and plaster-board factories. A further factor of concentration has been the dominant position within the industry of British Gypsum Ltd., a member of the British Plaster Board Industries group. In 1970 British Gypsum Ltd. took over Bellrock Gypsum Ltd., the only other large gypsum producer, and that same year ICI ceased production of gypsum as a by-product of phosphoric acid manufacture. In the financial year 1970–1, British Gypsum Ltd. produced 2 970 121 tonnes of gypsum;[174] total UK production during 1970 was 4 427 160 tonnes.[175] The only other company now extracting gypsum on any scale is Associated Portland Cement Manufacturers, who use it as a retarding agent.

Anhydrite, the anhydrous form of sulphate of calcium, is heavier than gypsum, has sharp-edged fragments and a metallic ring when struck, whereas gypsum is woody and soft, forming a rock somewhat like sugar. Anhydrite is virtually absent from the main Midlands horizons but occurs in close association with gypsum in the Cumberland/Westmorland area and in Sussex. It is also found in North Yorkshire/Durham inside the eastern England Permo-Triassic basin. Anhydrite, like gypsum, tends to be extracted as close as possible to the processing plants. Apart from the anhydrite operations of British Gypsum Ltd., only two other operators, both chemical companies, were in 1971 mining anhydrite in very close proximity to their chemical works. The ICI anhydrite mine at Billingham-on-Tees, which closed in that year, was actually within the confines of the large 405 hectare chemical complex there. The Sandwith mine in Cumberland of the

Marchon division of Allbright and Wilson supplies the adjacent chemical and cement works.

Anhydrite extraction is a comparatively recent phenomenon: as late as 1918 the Geological Survey reported that it had at that time no commercial use.[176] Extraction began during the 1920s as the result of the development of a process for manufacturing ammonium sulphate from the mineral, and is now used for the manufacture of sulphuric acid, with clinker cement and fertilizer as by-products. Gypsum, on the other hand, has been worked for about four centuries in Nottinghamshire. Although in terms of overall tonnage gypsum extraction remains a small industry, demand has grown steadily in the course of the present century: output has risen from an average annual figure of 283 124 tonnes in 1912–14[177] to 2 847 000 tonnes in 1970, an increase of 905 per cent. As is clear from the post-war growth rate of plaster and plasterboard mentioned earlier, the greatest market expansion has been in the building industry. The properties of gypsum, which make it a valuable ingredient of wall plasters, are primarily its considerable mechanical strength when hard, its lack of shrinkage or expansion, its quick setting and resistance to fire. Plasterboard, first manufactured in Britain in 1917 as a prefabricated building component, is a 'sandwich' of aerated gypsum plaster between two sheets of heavy paper. Gypsum is also used for tiles, coving and partitioning, as well as a retarding agent for Portland cement, of which it makes 3–5 per cent volume. In 1966 almost 90 per cent of the gypsum output from the Midlands was used in the building trade.[178] The output of the industry has therefore in the past, and is likely in the future, to reflect the state of the building industry. In general, the lowest qualities of gypsum are consumed by the building market. The highest quality, such as that derived from the best beds of the Newark horizon in Nottinghamshire, is used for the manufacture of barium plaster, plaster of Paris and dental plaster, as a filler for bread and paint, and in the brewing of beer. Medium quality gypsum is used for moulding plaster for the pottery industry and for moulds for tyre treads.

In 1971 British Gypsum Ltd. operated ten underground mines and five open pits.[179] The main focus of their activities is Nottinghamshire and in 1966 the area covered by the East Midlands Economic Planning Council contributed about half of the total gypsum production for England and Wales (see Fig. 4.5).[108] There are three gypsum horizons in the county; of these, the Retford horizon, found discontinuously in Nottinghamshire west of the Trent, has been uneconomic to work for many years although small outcrops were worked throughout the nineteenth century for the floor-plaster and agricultural fertilizer markets. The upper of the two remaining horizons, the Newark horizon, extends from the neighbourhood of Newark southwards to Cropwell Bishop and probably as far south as Leicester. This horizon, a succession of between 15 and 18 metres in depth, contains up to 16 'seams'* of gypsum varying in thickness from a few centimetres to 1·8 metres, interspersed with bands of Keuper Marl.[181] The Newark horizon, containing two beds of very high quality, is in general superior to that of the third, Tutbury horizon, some 21 metres below it. The Tutbury horizon, extending intermittently from Gotham in Nottinghamshire to Tutbury near Burton-on-Trent in Staffordshire,

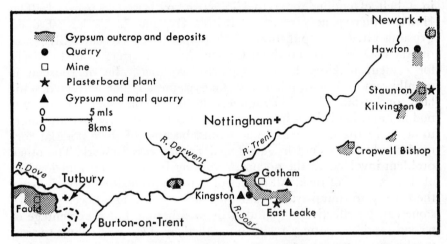

Fig. 4.5 *Gypsum workings in the East Midlands*

consists of discontinuous oval masses of gypsum, varying from a few millimetres in thickness to a metre or so, separated by gypsiferous marl. Reserves in the Midlands, although difficult to assess because of the discontinuous nature of the deposits, are believed to be considerable.

British Gypsum Ltd. both mine and work opencast for gypsum in Nottinghamshire and in 1971, 3205 hectares carried planning consents for gypsum working there.[182] The underground extraction area is located primarily between Gotham and East Leake and the mines, most of which have their own plaster mills, also serve important plasterboard factories at East Leake (which contributes a large percentage of total national production) and at Staunton near Newark. Workings in this district have moved steadily in an east-south-easterly direction and have increased in depth as the more accessible deposits

* 'Seam', the most convenient term, is not strictly speaking correct for gypsum, bearing in mind its discontinuous nature consisting of cakes or balls.

became exhausted. British Gypsum now operate mines at Gotham, Kingston, Newark, Staunton, Cropwell and East Leake, all working the Tutbury horizon. The pillar-and-stall method is used exclusively and an extraction of up to 75 per cent is often achieved,[183] even though usually half a metre or so of seam is left in the floor and roof as a precaution. Conventional methods of drilling and blasting, mechanical loading and belt conveying are employed; the nature of the deposits, and the comparatively small scale of operations, do not lend themselves to the most sophisticated processes of mechanization.

The Newark horizon is now worked exclusively by opencast methods in a belt extending some 19 kilometres south-west of Newark. The Hawton quarry at Newark is British Gypsum Ltd.'s largest open gypsum pit.[184] Output from the comparatively recent Kilvington quarry of Associated Portland Cement Manufacturers is used entirely for cement making. In the opencast workings, the overburden is usually removed by dragline and the gypsum is either extracted similarly or by face shovel. Draglines alternately pick out the gypsum nodules and load them into dumpers or trucks and remove the marl to lay bare the next seam. The seams, because of their nodular formation which does not fragment well, are not easy to work. The other problem involved in the opencast working is the sorting and loading of three grades of rock. All grades of gypsum are loaded directly from the quarry to dump trucks and then stock-piled. The lower grade of stone can be effectively upgraded by weathering, but a percentage of second grade or pottery rock is upgraded by the use of colour sorting machines—100 per cent gypsum is pure white and the degree of adulteration is reflected in the extent to which it is tinted by marls and clays.

Fauld mine, British Gypsum's most productive mine and the only working remaining in Staffordshire, has been in operation since 1868. It is located on an extension of the Tutbury seam which is here 82 metres below the top of the Trias.[185] Only about 2·4 metres of the 6·1 metre seam is worked, but production, 521 845 tonnes in 1970–1,[186] is substantial. Most of the production is mechanized, in similar fashion to the Nottinghamshire mines, but one section is worked manually for the supply of alabaster, a particularly high quality gypsum. The Yorkshire working is comparatively minor. The only mine now active in the county is British Gypsum's Sherburn no. 2, south of Tadcaster, which produced in 1970–1 only 77 234 tonnes.[187]

The Cumberland/Westmorland strata are, after Nottinghamshire, the second most important centre of gypsum/anhydrite production in the UK. In Cumberland 2933 hectares carried planning consents for the working of gypsum and anhydrite in 1971, a much larger figure than that for any other extractive industry in the county.[188] The deposits lie mainly to the east of the Lake District Dome, in the Vale of Eden, and the beds occur in the St Bees shales, lying above the Penrith sandstone and beneath the St Bees sandstone. In the neighbourhood of Penrith there are four gypsum horizons of which only the lowest two are currently being worked. The lower of the two averages 31 metres in thickness whilst the upper seam is 3·1–3·7 metres thick. British Gypsum Ltd. operate three mines in this area. Only one, the New Stamphill mine, near Kirkby Thore in Westmorland, which started production in 1937, is a large-scale gypsum producer, with an output of 255 583 tonnes in 1970–1.[189] The more recent Newbiggin mine in Cumberland, which began production of gypsum and anhydrite in 1964, works only the second lowest seam and produced in 1970 only small quantities of these minerals, 47 729 tonnes of gypsum and 29 711 tonnes of anhydrite.[190] The oldest of the three mines, Long Meg, near Langwathby in Cumberland, which has been working since 1895, is now primarily an anhydrite producer with an output of 254 900 tonnes in 1970–1,[191] second only to the Whitehaven and Billingham anhydrite mines. Minor quantities of gypsum, some 36 750 tonnes in 1970–1, are also produced from this mine.

Also in Cumberland, but to the west of the Lake District Dome, lies an anhydrite deposit at a depth of 183 metres near the base of the Permian. This is mined in the area of the St Bees headland on the coast, by the Marchon division of Allbright and Wilson Ltd. This comparatively recent mine, which began production in 1955, was in 1969 producing some 660 400 tonnes of anhydrite per year.[192] Production has risen rapidly as a result of heavy investment in improved transport of the mineral to the underground crusher and from there to the surface. In future, mining, which is by pillar-and-stall methods and achieves an extraction rate of 72 per cent, will extend under the Irish Sea at a depth of 275 metres below the sea bed. All of the current output is supplied to the adjacent sulphuric acid and cement plant of Marchon division at Whitehaven. With the close of ICI's anhydrite mine at Billingham in 1971, the Whitehaven mine became the only working producing anhydrite alone. Those of British Gypsum Ltd. also produce gypsum.

The Billingham anhydrite mine was started as a result of the development of the processing of ammonium sulphate from anhydrite, and the production of sulphuric acid. This process, which originated in Germany during the First World War, was further refined at Billingham by Brunner Mond Ltd., who in 1926 became part of ICI. That same year mining operations began with the sinking of two 3·97 metre diameter shafts to a depth of 259 metres[193] to the main anhydrite seam which lies beneath a covering of glacial drift, Bunter sandstone and Upper Permian marls. In the early years small amounts of silica, dolomite and rock salt were also produced. In 1969, when anhydrite production was reportedly 1 million tonnes per annum,[194] the pillar-and-stall method permitted an extraction rate of only 51 per cent, considerably less than that achieved at Whitehaven. The decision to close the mine, taken in 1970, reflected rising costs both in mining and processing. Although this process of ammonium sulphate manufacture enjoys certain advantages—heavy expenditure on fuel is avoided and anhydrite is a low cost commodity—the capital cost of the plant was high. In spite of the introduction of mechanized mining, the mine had become increasingly expensive to run. The closure of the mine was accompanied by the shutdown of the associated sulphuric acid, ammonium sulphate and sulphuric acid plants, and production of sulphuric acid is now from elemental sulphur.

The Billingham mine, within the chemical complex, and the Whitehaven mine, in an already industrialized part of the Cumberland coast, did not present especially difficult planning problems. The main belt of gypsum workings in Cumberland and Westmorland, located to the east of the Lake District Dome, are outside the boundaries of the National Park and do not constitute a major planning difficulty. In Nottinghamshire, considerable signs of old workings are still visible, especially in the Gotham district, where traces of old mines, adits and mineral railways remain. More important, the active plaster mills attached to current workings are somewhat obtrusive in this predominantly rural landscape and the workings themselves leave a film of white dust on the vegetation. Apart from the processing plants, however, surface developments need not be extensive. At East Leake, the first integrated works of its kind, which claims to be the largest in Western Europe, engineering and electrical workshops, offices, stores and canteens are situated underground. Furthermore, gypsum mines do not present subsidence problems. Since they work a thin seam of mineral beneath a thick overburden, it is possible to design the mines to remain virtually stable for all time.[195] The opencast operations, which in 1968 accounted for less than 10 per cent of British Gypsum's total output,[196] are unavoidably disfiguring in operation. However, they are filled as working proceeds and are restored so that evidence of previous working is difficult to detect. The gypsum and anhydrite workings of the Midlands and north do not coincide with high amenity landscape. However, the exceptionally attractive rural environment of the workings in the High Weald of Sussex, remote from any other mining activity except the Kent coalfield, means that particular planning problems have been apparent in this case.

The Sussex field was discovered in the second half of the nineteenth century as a result of the experimental boring in Sussex known as the Sub-Wealden exploration. This proved the existence of high quality gypsum, four seams in all, in the Purbeck beds of the Jurassic sequence. In the Mountfield/Heathfield district are to be found the only exposed Jurassic strata in the weald: these strata, consisting of elongated inliers of Purbeck beds, were brought to the surface by anticlinal uplift and erosion has exposed them in the dipstream tributaries of the River Rother. Gypsum and anhydrite are near enough to the surface to be worked by shallow mining, which started in 1875 at Mountfield.[197] In the early 1950s it became clear that, with rising demand and the possibility of exhaustion of reserves at Mountfield, a second mine in the area was needed. The Sussex deposits, as the only ones located close to the large markets of the South and South-East, have a greatly enhanced importance: crude gypsum is a low value commodity and the transport costs, even when made into plaster and plasterboard, are high in relation to its bulk. Similarly the limestone deposits which underlie the gypsum at about 153 metres and which are now worked for bitumen coated roadstone have enhanced value resulting from the rarity of the mineral in this area and its high unit transport costs. The Sussex gypsum deposits are the chief source of supply to the major cement industry on Thamesside. They also serve important plaster and plasterboard markets in the South and South-East. However, the gypsum used for plasterboard manufacture has to be transported to Erith and Rochester plasterboard factories since clearly this kind of development could not be sanctioned in the High Weald, and in this respect some of the cost advantages of the location of the working in Sussex are reduced.

The expansion of gypsum mining in the high amenity area of the High Weald created a considerable planning problem. The basic decision was whether to construct a new plant at the new proposed mine at Brightling, thus duplicating plant in the area and adding to the surface developments at the new site, or to transport the ore about 5 kilometres across unspoilt Wealden scenery to the Mountfield plant. The decision to move the ore was made on both economic and amenity grounds, and stringent planning conditions ensured that the method of transportation was chosen and devised to make the minimum disturbance and impact on the landscape. There were three possible means of achieving this—by light railway, by road or by aerial ropeway. As the planning authority would not allow road transport, an aerial ropeway was decided upon and opened late in 1961. The route, stipulated by the planning authority, was chosen to avoid settlements as far as possible and to take advantage of high woodland cover. The route crossed existing woodland for some 80 per cent of its length[198] and more trees were planted to provide additional cover. Tunnels were built to carry the ropeway beneath two of the three intervening roads. Since its opening in 1961, production from Brightling has over-taken that at Mountfield, output being 376 891 tonnes and 173 840 tonnes in 1970–1 respectively.[199] British Gypsum Ltd., the operating company, found the process of obtaining planning permission a protracted one, but they consider that the conditions imposed were reasonable.[200] Capital expenditure on the project was considerably increased because of planning stipulations, but these costs will be depreciated over 20 years, and the additional per unit output expen-diture brought about by this localized system of transport is minimal. In the view of P. B. Ellis and V. Turnock, 'the mines at Mountfield and Brightling prove that economic development and the protection of landscape can be reconciled, if sufficient thought and effort are employed'.[201]

CELESTITE

Britain is the world's largest producer of celestite (strontium sulphate). The most favourable geological conditions for the formation of this evaporite mineral were hot saline lagoons or shallow landlocked seas, conditions which existed in Britain in the Triassic era, similar to those which pertain today in the Red Sea. The mineral is therefore found, either as veins, nodules, irregular layers or pockets, mainly in the Keuper Marl, where it lies unconformably over the Coal Measures.[202] But it is also found in the gypsiferous Purbeck beds of Sussex; in the gypsiferous beds of the Newark area of Nottinghamshire; and in the Butcombe Sandstone, south-west of Bristol. It has also been reported in the Permian evaporites of Yorkshire.[203]

However, though its occurrence is comparatively widespread, it is rare to find a deposit which has economic value, for where celestite exists in any quantity it is often associated with gypsum, barytes, calcite and silica, and the separation of these minerals is expensive to the point of being prohibitive. For this reason, the only deposits currently worked are those in the Triassic Marl of the Yate area of Gloucester-shire which are sufficiently free from gypsum and barytes to yield a high grade strontium sulphate by relatively simple washing and crushing techniques.

Thus, though other British deposits with lower strontium sulphate values are at present being examined, their size and quality, and the costs of treatment plant needed to separate them from their associated minerals, may dictate against their extraction, since the mineral is of only medium value.

British celestite output has remained approximately stable during this century, usually at between 6100 and 10 200 tonnes per year. In 1921, total output was 6728 tonnes,[204] from 1934–8 the average was about 7625 tonnes per year, from 1947–52 about 8740 per year and from 1956–60 about 6910 per year.[205] Output for the early and late 1960s was higher than these former averages (see Table 4.3) but not

Table 4.3. UK production and exports of celestite, 1964–9 (tonnes)

	Production	Exports
1964	17 306	15 478
1965	9 702	5 528
1966	9 555	7 501
1967	6 787	3 925
1968	7 887	5 917
1969	11 721	7 667

Source: Institute of Geological Sciences, Mineral Resources Division, *Statistical Summary of the Mineral Industry, 1964-9*, 1970, p. 343.

in the main substantially so. This relatively stable output has occurred in spite of a changing pattern of outlets for its usage. Before the First World War the main usage was for conversion to strontium hydroxide, used to recover sugar from beet molasses. Strontium salts, especially strontium carbonate into which most consumers convert celestite, now find applications within a range of markets including pyrotechnics (where it provides the intense colour of distress flares, fireworks, tracer ammunition, etc.), metallurgy (especially metal purification), pharmaceuticals (especially depilatories and toothpaste), the electrical industry (notably for fluorescent lighting, and colour television screens) and ceramics (including the manufacture of several types of glass, the ceramic shells of spark plugs and high temperature kiln ware).[206] Most of these outlets use the mineral very economically. The bulk of British output is exported (see Table 4.3) and until recently Britain held a large proportion of world markets. The most important overseas importer is the United States, consuming about two thirds of British output, mainly for the chemical market. Transport costs are important too for a medium price mineral—the quoted price in March 1971 for British celestite, crushed, washed and graded, ex-works, was £15·35 per tonne[207]—and the Yate deposit, some 14–16 kilometres from

Bristol, is well placed for overseas trans-shipment through Avonmouth. The high percentage of world markets until recently held by Britain was primarily the result of the exceptionally high quality of its output. Although Spanish suppliers export the bulk of their output through the merchant Bruno SA to the United States, and Pakistan, Mexico and Argentina also publish output figures,[208] the specification for strontium sulphate supplied by the Bristol Mineral and Land Company at 95 per cent strontium sulphate has been generally superior to other suppliers, notably those from Mexico and Spain. There is, however, some evidence that Spanish sources can now be upgraded to approximately 95 per cent strontium sulphate, and a new producer (Kaiser Aluminium and Chemical Corporation) has opened a plant in Nova Scotia capable of producing 30 480 tonnes per year of strontium compounds.[209] Consequently, the overall percentage of world markets supplied from Britain has diminished.

Celestite extraction, in recent years confined to the area north of Yate, remains a small-scale, relatively unmechanized operation. In the course of this century, however, considerable changes, both in the extractive organization and in methods, have been made. Until 1912 extraction at Yate had been a sporadic, part-time activity of local farmers. In 1912 the Bristol Mineral and Land Company was formed with the object of organizing celestite extraction on a regular full-time basis.[210] In 1969 this firm was acquired by the English China Clays group, one of the country's major extractive organizations with very widespread interests. The extractive methods have also changed considerably; until the 1940s, when a modest amount of mechanization was introduced, hand-working prevailed throughout the operation. An important element of hand-selection still remains, however. After removal and stacking of topsoil from individual sites of about 0·4 hectare, celestite is removed by excavators working in small open pits to maximum depths of about 9 or, rarely, 11 metres in the Keuper Marl. The celestite-bearing material is spread thinly over the ground on either side of the track leading into the working, and the mineral is then hand-picked and thrown on to the centre track for collection. In general, a team of three men and an excavator driver are allocated to a particular field, and the output per man in 1971 was about 10·2 tonnes per week. Thus, it is a labour-intensive operation in terms of tonn ageproduced. When approximately 20 tonnes has been accumulated, it is taken by lorry to the Hall End plant for crushing and washing. Since the installation of a crushing and grading plant in 1959, the product has been sold mainly as a gravel, i.e. in lump form, although a proportion is sold ground.[211]

The extractive operation at Yate is essentially a small one, involving a maximum of 4 workings at any one time and no more than about 20 men, in spite of the labour-intensive characteristics of the operation. The disturbance to the landscape is slight; apart from the small areas involved, the mineral occurs in thin seams or nodules in shallow deposits which are essentially easy to restore. Complete restoration of the land to its original agricultural use is carried out within two years of the mineral's removal and high standards have been achieved. When a field has been worked-out, the spoil heaps are bulldozed back to their former level and topsoil is usually replaced immediately. In low-lying areas, however, it may be preferable to leave the land for several months, and only begin topsoil spreading immediately after a programme of sub-soiling to promote better drainage just before seeding takes place. The preparation of the soil, fertilizing the ground and grass sowing, is usually carried out by an agricultural contractor. Land drains, whose occurrence is mapped before extraction starts, are replaced, and it is sometimes possible to re-shape or even re-grade drainage ditches to improve surface run-off and the original land contours can be modified to suit the owner's requirements.[212] The only real damage done as a result of celestite (and this need only be short term) is the destruction of thorn hedges used as wind breaks. These are sometimes replaced by post and rail fencing but shelter is often re-established by using a post and wire fence interplanted with thorn quicks.

Celestite working in Gloucestershire does, therefore, with its small annual take, and ease of restoration, make few demands from a planning point of view. It is not perhaps surprising therefore that this mineral, of comparative rarity, is one of the very few whose extractors are given special assistance in the County Development Plan under the Mines (Working Facilities and Support) Act of 1923 (subsequently extended). The Gloucestershire County Development Plan acknowledged the importance of this mineral by allocating land for its working in such a way that its operators could apply to the High Court for extraction rights, should consent from the owner of those rights not be forthcoming.

FLUORSPAR*

Fluorspar has currently one of the fastest growing markets of any mineral found in Britain. World fluorspar consumption, which is

* In this chapter, following the practice of the Geological Survey, 'fluorspar' refers to commercial products consisting mainly of calcium fluoride, 'fluorite' to the pure mineral.

allied to the rapidly growing requirements of the steel, aluminium and fluorine chemical industries, has been increasing very quickly. Over the ten-year period ending in 1965, world crude steel production increased by about 65 per cent and, as the rate of increase has quickened since then, it is considered possible that output may double in the period 1966–75.[213] Even if consumption of fluorspar per tonne of steel were to remain static, the growth prospects for fluorspar would be good. In fact, the widespread adoption of the basic oxygen process of steel-making, accounting for approximately 30 per cent of world steel output in 1970 but expected to account for 75–85 per cent by 1985,[214] will create a vastly enhanced demand. The basic oxygen furnace requires 4·5–6·7 kg of metallurgical grade fluorspar per tonne of steel, compared with 3·6–4·5 kg per tonne for the electric furnace and 1·3–2·2 kg per tonne for the open-hearth method. At the present time there are no substitutes for fluorspar as a steelmaking flux, and the meeting of requirements for the world steel industry, estimated at 2218·3 thousand tonnes by 1975 compared with 1616·5 thousand tonnes in 1969,[215] is complicated by the simultaneously rising demand for acid grade fluorspar.

In 1970 approximately 55 per cent of the world's production of fluorspar was acid grade.[216] Acid grade fluorspar consists of 97·5 per cent calcium fluoride compared with the 70–85 per cent calcium fluoride of metallurgical grade fluorspar. At least half of total world fluorspar production is used to manufacture hydrofluoric acid, and at least three-quarters of world output of hydrofluoric acid is consumed by the fluorocarbons and aluminium industries,[217] which are both maintaining steady growth. It has been estimated[218] that world production of primary aluminium will throughout the 1970s grow at a compound annual rate of approximately 9 per cent. The quantities of cryolite (either natural or artificial manufactured partly from fluorspar) and aluminium fluoride required to produce a tonne of primary aluminium have been decreasing, and may well decrease further from the approximately 59–63 kg of acid grade fluorspar (converted to fluorides) to approximately 56 kg by 1980 for each tonne of aluminium smelted. In spite of this, the overall increase in consumption is likely to be considerable. There has similarly been a rapid world-wide growth of fluorocarbons consumption. Fluorocarbons have been used for refrigeration since the 1930s, aerosols since 1947 and urethane foams since 1960, and it has been estimated[219] that the hydrofluoric acid requirement of the fluorocarbons industry ought to increase by about 8 per cent per year during the early 1970s. *Industrial Minerals*, whose calculations of future world demand are the most detailed yet published in the UK, estimated in 1970 that world consumption of all grades of fluorspar would rise from 3·5 million to 5·5 million tonnes by 1975[220] (a 71·4 per cent rise).

Although predictions of this kind clearly contain a large element of speculation, this estimate agrees broadly with that of *The Mining Annual Review*, 1970, which, working from slightly higher world output figures, estimated a rise in consumption from 3·6 million tonnes in 1969 to 6·2 million tonnes by 1974–5[221] (a 72·2 per cent rise). A review of the world fluorspar situation issued by the Mineral Resources Branch of the Canadian Department of Energy, Mines and Resources put the increase substantially higher, predicting that world consumption would double between 1969 and 1974.[222]

Within the UK demand is likely to approximate broadly to the world trend. Demand from the UK steel industry is likely to double in 1970–5 in response to plans for expanded steel production at Port Talbot and Scunthorpe and the progressive changeover to the basic oxygen process. The aluminium industry in particular will create added demand for acid fluorspar. The three new primary aluminium smelters at Lynemouth, Holyhead and Invergordon now have a capacity of 325 100 tonnes of primary aluminium, and will have an eventual capacity of 365 800 tonnes of aluminium requiring 25 400 to 30 500 tonnes of acid grade fluorspar for aluminium fluoride and artificial cryolite.[223] There is also a likely increase in demand from the fluorine chemical manufacturers, the largest of whom are ICI, the Imperial Smelting Corporation and Laporte Industries Ltd. In 1971 an ICI subsidairy, Tangent Foams, stated that the demand for rigid urethane foam was forecast to grow at about 20 per cent per year.[224] Only the consumption of much smaller users, such as ceramics manufacturers who use fluorspar as a flux and opacifier, has remained relatively constant in recent years. The domestic market for fluorspar, of which the UK has currently an exportable surplus, is likely to increase as fast as the export market, and extraction in the Pennines is undergoing rapid development to help meet the demand.

The Pennine metalliferous suite, in which by far the most important UK deposits occur, contains, in addition to fluorite, one or more of the minerals galena (sulphide of lead), blende (sulphide of zinc), calcite, barite and other minor minerals.[225] The Southern Pennines orefield, the main centre of fluorspar production in the UK, stretches from Castleton in the north through Bakewell, Darley and Matlock as far as Wirksworth (see Fig. 4.6). Fluorspar production comes from two main districts, one at the northern end of the field around Eyam, the other in the neighbourhood of Matlock, these two districts being separated by

I

an extensive area of virtually unmineralized Millstone Grit rocks. There is also fluorspar in commercial quantities in the limestone inlier of Ashover—the inlier of Crich is now no longer worked. The crude ore from the Southern Pennine orefield varies widely in grade from 20–60 per cent fluorite content; it averages 35 per cent fluorite, 12–15 per cent barite and 1–2 per cent galena.[226] The country is a dissected upland which only occasionally reaches 458 metres above sea level and is more accessible than the Northern Pennine field. Production here has had considerable links with chemical and steel industries in Sheffield, only 24 kilometres from an important part of the field.

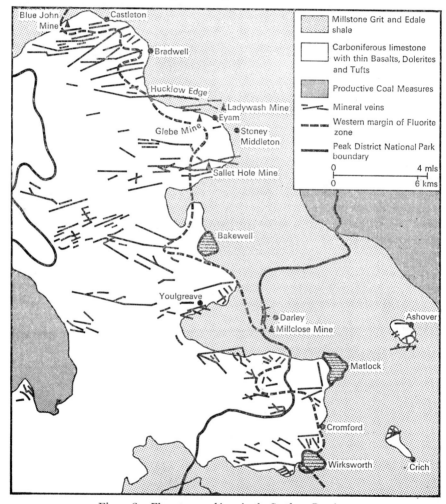

Fig. 4.6 *Fluorspar workings in the Southern Pennines*

The Northern Pennine orefield also falls into two main districts. The more important northern district extends from west Durham into south Northumberland and east Cumberland, from the headwaters of the Derwent at Hunstanworth southwards to Teesdale. The fluorite is found for the most part in the thin alternating limestones, sandstones and shales of the Yoredale facies of the Lower Carboniferous and to some extent in the intrusive sheets of quartz dolerite known as the Whin Sill. In this district the fluorite-bearing veins occur in the central parts of the orefield separated from the barium minerals which form a wide outer fringe; consequently barite is not a by-product of fluorspar production here as it is in Derbyshire. The crude ore is usually higher grade than that of the Southern Pennines, averaging 60 per cent fluorite and 2 per cent galena,[227] although the quantities of silica impurity are larger. The deposits in north-west Yorkshire are for the most part similar in general configuration although the fluorite is usually less abundant. On the extreme southern margin, however, at Greenhow Hill and Grassington Moor, the fluorite deposits occur in the massive limestone of the Lower Carboniferous and the overlying Grassington Grit of the Millstone Grit series, and the crude ore here is comparable in fluorite content with that of the Southern Pennine field.

The only area in the UK outside the Pennines where fluorspar has been produced in commercial quantities, and then only intermittently and in small amounts, is that of Devon and Cornwall. There, fluorite occurs in metalliferous veins associated with the exposed granite masses, and the main concentrations are in the Camborne–Redruth area, the St Agnes area, the Tamar valley south of Launceston and the Teign valley area north-east of Bovey Tracey. There is currently a very small amount of metallurgical grade fluorspar being obtained from old mine dumps and it was estimated[228] in 1970 that at most 10 200 tonnes have been obtained since production began.

Production in the South-West is likely to continue only on a very limited scale either from dumps or as a by-product of new mining operations for other minerals. The deposits in Devon and Cornwall, together with the other minor occurrences elsewhere in England, Wales and Scotland which are not worked commercially, are generally ignored in the calculation of fluorite reserves.

UK reserves of economically workable crude ore are conservatively estimated[229] to be 25 million tonnes, 20 million tonnes in the Southern Pennine orefield and the remainder in the Northern Pennine orefield. (The difference between the two fields in terms of fluorite is of course substantially less than these figures suggest, in view of the higher grade of the northern orefield.) The bulk of these reserves are unproven, and probable proved ore amounts to only 5 million tonnes. Further workable reserves may well be found, especially at deeper levels, since the amount of detailed information relating to deposits is in most cases incomplete, and exploration has been relatively superficial by world mining standards. Although the areas concerned have a long mining history in terms of lead, fluorspar production has only reached major proportions in the twentieth century, particularly since 1960.

Fluorspar of a particular ornamental variety suitable for vases and jewellery was first mined from about 1775 onwards at the Blue John mine, 2·4 kilometres from Castleton in Derbyshire, and adjacent mines. As far as the industrial use of fluorspar is concerned, small amounts were being worked in Derbyshire, Durham, Devon and Cornwall. Fluorite was still encountered primarily as a waste product of Pennine lead mining which, although dating back at least to Roman times, entered a particularly active phase in the eighteenth and nineteenth centuries until the slump in base metal prices virtually halted operations in the 1880s. The lead was worked by both underground and opencast methods, and the lead ore was normally dressed for the extraction of galena at the surface close to the deposit. The waste from the dressing operations consisted of material crushed to various sizes, and was made up primarily of fluorite, calcite and barite, varying in proportions according to the relative position of the deposit in the orefield. This waste material was often backfilled into the workings, especially the open-cuts, which were sometimes as much as 31 metres deep.[230] Since the ore 'bulked' on breaking, there was often too much waste material to dispose of entirely in the old workings and as a result waste dumps accumulated beside the deposits.

Substantial production of fluorspar began only in 1899–1901 as a result of the introduction of the basic open-hearth method of steel manufacture, which requires fluorspar as a fluxing agent. The pioneers were Blackwells of Derbyshire and the Weardale Lead Company in Durham. Fluorspar was largely obtained by working over the old dumps although eventually a small amount of underground and opencast mining was started. Up to 1927 the UK was the main exporter of metallurgical grade fluorspar to the United States. Output has steadily grown in the course of the century and the percentage obtained from dumps has diminished. Production in 1921 was 23 507 tonnes.[231] In the 1930s the first beneficiation process to produce acid grade fluorspar began at the British Fluorides Ltd. flotation plant in Derbyshire. By 1948 total output had risen to 64 567 tonnes, about 72 per cent of which came from mining and quarrying operations and the remainder from reworking of dumps.[232] The most striking expansion however had to wait until the 1960s: output then rose spectacularly from 99 108 tonnes to 190 297 tonnes in 1969, a rise of 92 per cent in 9 years.[233] By far the largest increase was in output of acid grade fluorspar, which increased by 212 per cent during 9 years.

The expansion of output during the 1960s was largely due to increased production in Derbyshire from the operations of Laporte Industries Ltd., whose Cavendish mill and mining operations contributed more than 60 per cent of total UK output in 1970[234] when an expansion programme at the mill was completed. Laporte Industries Ltd. has extensive holdings in the two fluorspar producing regions in Derbyshire but its main operations are located in the northern one. The original focus of activities in this area was the Glebe or Townend mine at Eyam, now used only as a ventilation shaft.

Glebe was an old lead mine, last worked as such during the nineteenth century. The lead workings produced besides galena much good quality fluorspar, the bulk of which had been removed from the dumps by 1915.[235] The mine, re-opened in 1937 as a source of fluorspar and lead, had a mill on-site and supplied among other products acid fluorspar for the manufacture of hydrofluoric acid. In 1945 Glebe Mines Ltd. was formed to operate the company and in that same year a virgin section of Old Edge Vein, 763 metres long, was discovered. The main level crosscut was subsequently extended north-westwards to link up with Ladywash Shaft and the Great Hucklow Edge Rake. In 1959 Glebe Mines Ltd. with two of the chemical companies it supplied were acquired by Laporte Industries Ltd., manufacturers of fluorine chemicals, who, a year later, also took over the nearby Cupola Mining and Milling Company. The Glebe mine, where reserves were approaching exhaustion, subsequently ceased operations and the old Eyam mill was demolished. Laporte's mining operations now centre on the Ladywash working to the north and a new project, the Sallet Hole mine, which exploits the extensive deposits of Longstone Edge to the south of Eyam. The Longstone Edge property is dominated by an east–west vein which extends for at least $4\frac{1}{2}$ kilometres, attains a maximum surface width of some 24 metres and has been described[236] as 'one of the world's largest and most spectacular fluorspar deposits'. In addition to the Sallet Hole mine, Laporte Industries have opencast workings on Longstone Edge, although these were in 1970 nearing exhaustion.[237] The company also holds a number of properties in the southern fluorspar-producing district around Matlock, and has negotiated a number of long-term contracts for material to be supplied by tributers. 'Tributers' is the term applied to individuals or small companies extracting the material mainly from dumps which they own or lease in the area. Some of them carry out small opencast or, very rarely, underground operations but they have in general little or no ore dressing facilities of their own. Tributers' ores vary greatly in physical character and composition and they receive payment per unit content of fluorspar (percentage per tonne). Dumps with less than 23–25 per cent fluorite are uneconomic to work: dumps with more than 40 per cent fluorite content are worked very profitably.[238] Milling operations, both of Laporte's own and of tributers' material is carried out at the Cavendish mill, situated in open country away from Eyam village near Stoney Middleton, well placed to receive ore from the northern district although ore from the southern district has to be transported a considerable distance. The Cavendish mill, completed in 1965, was in 1971 the only large-scale beneficiation unit in operation in the UK, and is generally recognized as being one of the most sophisticated of its kind. The operations here are necessarily complex since the chief mineral components of the crude ore, fluorite, calcite, barite and galena, are in general closely banded with each other, while the main product is acid grade fluorspar for which rigid specifications apply. There are five main processes: crushing, washing and sizing; dense medium separation; grinding and classification; flotation and filtration; drying and storage. The flotation process involves the selective separation of a lead mineral concentrate, fluorspar and barytes[239] (barium sulphate). Barytes is now sold mainly as a filter cake and the lead concentrates are shipped as filter cake to smelters on the continent of Europe. Clean tailings from the dense medium separation plant, similar in character to Thames' washed gravel, are graded and sold for road metal or concrete aggregate. There are also tailings of fine particles which are pumped out as waste slurry, the disposal of which presents considerable problems to be discussed later. The dried fluorspar itself is conveyed to silos, either for packaging or for despatch in bulk by road tanker. Alternatively it may be left as filter-cake and stored to await export.

Laporte's production of acid grade fluorspar increased from 25 400 tonnes in 1960 to 142 200 tonnes in 1970, considerably in excess of the original stated capacity of the plant.[240] In 1969 Laporte produced more than 90 per cent of UK acid grade fluorspar and clearly made by far the largest contribution to the nearly 43 000 tonnes of acid grade fluorspar exported in that year, the largest shipments being, in order of size, to the USA, Japan, Canada, Australia, Sweden, Germany, Finland, Norway and India.[241] Clearly, acid grade fluorspar, selling in March 1971 at £19·68 to £23·62 per tonne, can economically be transported to world markets. Laporte's operations are now being substantially expanded in view of the increased home and export demand; their widespead holdings, and contracts with tributers, place them in a strong position for an extended period of production and expansion. The company's policy is always to maintain at least 15 years' proved reserves, although new mining operations will be necessary to exploit all these.

The first significant addition to UK beneficiation capacity since the Cavendish mill is the new 80 000 tonnes per year capacity milling plant of the C. E. Guilini Group, which began commissioning in mid-summer 1971. The plant is housed in the Hopton works, formerly owned by Magnesium Elektron Ltd., 6·4 kilometres south-west of Matlock in the southern district of the orefield. The C. E. Guilini Group has been the main force behind the recent rapid expansion of the Italian fluorspar producing industry, and controls Mineraria Silius Spa, Europe's largest producer of acid grade fluorspar. The Group's interest in Derbyshire is a significant indication of the potential of the area, and a possible trend in the UK as elsewhere towards larger-scale fluorspar mining and milling operations. However, securing adequate long-term supplies for a mill of this size was not easy, in view of Laporte's extensive holdings throughout the orefield and supply contracts with the majority of tributers. Feed for the Guilini mill was obtained in the first instance from dumps leased or acquired by the company, and contracts of supply were also negotiated with available tributers. It is possible that the company may also begin its own mining operations. Meanwhile it is reworking the failings of the famous Mill Close mine, a former lead working some 5·6 kilometres north-west of Matlock. The Hopton mill, producing solely acid grade fluorspar for export, should add considerably to UK acid grade capacity, bringing the total output of acid grade to an annual rate of 203 200 tonnes,[242] of which up to an estimated two-thirds could be exported. This would make the UK one of the world's major acid grade fluorspar producers and put her in second place among European producers of acid grade fluorspar, behind Italy. By-product barytes, lead and zinc concentrates, mainly for export, will also be produced from the Hopton mill, the first by-product zinc to be obtained from fluorspar operations in the UK.

The problem which faces the Guilini Group—that of securing sufficient supplies of crude ore to support a large-scale milling oper-ation—is likely to be even more acute for the other large mining houses, including, it is reported,[243] RTZ, which have or have recently had exploration teams attempting to locate commercially exploitable reserves in Derbyshire. A third processing plants, however, could mean underutilization of capacity at all three plants in this area. There are, on the other hand, possibilities of expanded mining output from two medium-sized companies. One of these, Deepwood Mining, claims to have recently located new reserves. The company produced in 1970 20 300–30 500 tonnes per year from four deposits in the area around Bakewell, about 19 kilometres from Buxton. In that year they were reported[244] to have discovered a new deposit of significant size, the surface samples of which averaged 60–80 per cent fluorite and contained in addition barite and lead. The deposit outcrops in a dale and could be worked opencast. The other company, Spar Mining Ltd., is a new one formed to begin mining at Cromford Court near Matlock. The company hopes initially to produce about 100 tonnes per week which it might be able to increase to 1000 tonnes per week. If this target were reached, the company would be among the few largest extractive operators in the country, and a beneficiation plant might be installed.

Apart from these large- and medium-sized extractors, Derbyshire also contains a number of small fluorspar operators, whose total output in 1970 was estimated to be at most 25 400 tonnes.[245] Some of these had sufficient plant of the comparatively simple type such as jigs or sink/float processes needed to produce metallurgical grade fluorspar, and a few have concentrated on particular outlets. Two of the more important small operators are the Bleaklow Mining Company, who principally supply the Sheffield steel industry, and the Clay Cross Company, working the limestone inlier in the Ashover district, which supply the Ford Motor Company with fluorspar briquettes for foundry use. Other small operators had extremely limited plant and consequently came into the category of tributers. Certainly, small operators are very numerous in this area: in 1971 there were approximately 100 small fluorspar workings within the boundaries of the Peak Park alone.[246] The survival of such a multitude of small operations defies recent trends in most extractive industries where concentration into larger units has been the rule. The prime reasons for their survival are clearly the existence of fluorspar in the dumps left over from lead mining, which can be readily worked by small, mobile operators with the minimum of capital overheads, and the long-term markets assured by the tributer system. The future position of the small operator is in one way being helped by the creation of a second large milling operation and the increasing competition for feed for mills. However, it is not likely that any of the small companies will on their own substantially increase output here, and future growth on the extractive side will more likely come either from medium-sized operators such as Deepwood Mining or from new mining or opencast operations directly controlled by the big companies, either those already owning mills here or conceivably one of the other companies now prospecting. Furthermore, if the very strong market demand situation which prevailed at the beginning of 1971 continues, as seems likely, some small operators may be tempted to sell out to a large mining house or foreign company. The Derbyshire fluorspar industry will probably not entirely escape the national trend in the extractive industries of concentration into bigger operating units.

Major expansion of output is also planned in the somewhat less important Northern Pennine orefield (see Fig. 4.7). The three main extractive operations, one controlled by the Weardale Lead Company and two by the BSC, are concentrated in a relatively small area between Weardale and the River Derwent, in the northern district of the field. The largest single operator in this orefield in 1971 was Weardale Lead Company, since 1962 a subsidiary of ICI, which in 1969 produced approximately 20 300 tonnes per year (12 700 acid grade and 8100 metallurgical grade), with lead concentrates as a by-product.[247] The company operates a combined heavy media, separation jig and flotation plant in the village of Rookhope north of Weardale near the Northumberland border, which until recently obtained its feed from nearby Stotfieldburn mine, a former lead working. This mine, now exhausted, is being replaced by a new mine, the Red Burn mine, on a completely virgin section of the vein between Stotfieldburn and the BSC's neighbouring Groverake mine. This development was expected to add substantially to Weardale Lead's reserves but has to date not entirely lived up to expectations and there are no immediate plans for enlarging the existing mill or building a new plant.

The major scheduled expansion in the Northern Pennines is likely to come from the properties owned by the BSC and devoted primarily to the production of metallurgical grade fluorspar. UK metallurgical grade fluorspar met only domestic requirements in 1969, with the addition of very small imports from Spain. It is estimated[248] that by 1977 the BSC alone will need about 101 600 tonnes per year of metallurgical grade fluorspar, about half the current total output of all grades, while developments in Derbyshire will principally expand the supply of acid grade. In an attempt to build up much larger 'captive' supplies of their own, the BSC General Steels Division at Scunthorpe plans to spend about £2 million developing old lead mines inherited from steel companies on nationalization. Two of these operations are currently in production. The smaller of these is the Blackdene mine near the hamlet of St John's Chapel on the north bank of the Wear, which had in 1971 an annual output of 8100 tonnes of fluorspar.[249]

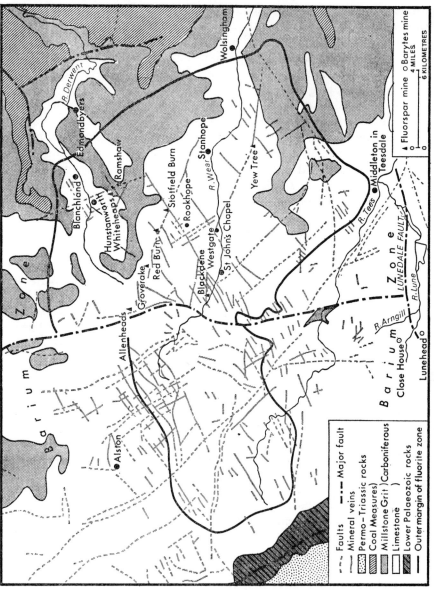

Fig. 4.7 *Fluorspar workings in the Northern Pennines*

The mine, originally developed for lead, yielded 5207 tonnes of concentrates between 1832 and 1845;[250] lead mining ceased in 1862. It was clear from the records of the Beaumont Company, who at one time worked the mine for lead, that the Blackdene vein was mainly a fluorspar vein, the width varying from 0·9 to 4·2 metres, and in 1948 the Geological Survey[251] reported that 'Blackdene vein probably contains substantial reserves of fluorspar, both in ground previously worked for lead ore, and also in virgin ground beneath Blackdene level'. Large quantities have not yet been extracted—in 1952 the United Steel Companies of Sheffield, from whom BSC acquired the mine, produced only 4697 tonnes—and the potential of the mine, at which BSC has a crushing and separating plant, appears to be good.

A few kilometres further north, in the area of Blanchland on the Northumberland/Durham border, BSC has a larger operation based on a group of mines including West Whiteheaps, Sikehead or East Whiteheaps and Groverake, formerly owned by the Consett Iron Company. West Whiteheaps and Sikehead form part of an extensive complex of old lead mines to the south of Hunstanworth village. The mines were operated by the London Lead Company from 1725 to 1807, when they were taken over by Easterby, Hall and Company; in 1810 they passed to the Derwent Mining Company who continued operations until 1883. West Whiteheaps mine has been exploited intermittently for fluorspar since 1924, when Hunstanworth Mines Ltd. was formed to work for fluorspar and lead. Until 1931, when operations by this company ceased, it is estimated that fluorspar output was of the order of 15 240 tonnes.[252] Blanchland Fluor Mines produced 5119 tonnes of fluorspar from 1938 to 1940 and resumed production in 1956–60 before handing over to the Consett Iron Company. In 1970 Whiteheaps produced 10 160 tonnes of fluorspar for BSC, the bulk of it metallurgical grade.[253]

Groverake mine, situated next to the Allanheads–Rookhope road, has an even longer history of fluorspar extraction than West Whiteheaps. A former lead mine, producing 25 120 tonnes of lead concentrates from 1832 to 1903, it began to produce fluorspar as early as 1897 and under five different operators a total of 32 326 tonnes had been obtained by 1940.[254] In 1952, when the mine was being worked by Blanchland Fluor Mines, the Geological Survey reported that 'a potential reserve of fluorspar clearly remains to be worked'. The reserve still remaining is likely to be at lower levels. At present the extracted ore is moved by lorry to the recently modernized plant 4 kilometres south-west of Blanchland. BSC produced in 1970 an annual output of approximately 20 300 tonnes from Groverake,[255] and sub-stantial expansion is planned. Both Whiteheaps and Groverake have shafts about 183 metres deep, but it is likely that BSC will put down drift mines for the extraction of fluorspar on a larger scale.

Slightly west of these mines is the site of BSC's third and newest development, Allenheads mine in south Northumberland which the Corporation plan to re-open after a long period of disuse. Allenheads, 11 kilometres south of Allendale Town, was the most productive single lead mine in the Northern Pennines. In the period 1729–1896 the total amount of lead concentrates amounted to 264 200 tonnes.[256] According-ing to old records there should be potential here for a fairly large out-put of fluorspar which has hardly been tapped. Fluorspar is said to have been extracted from the dumps only during the First World War and in 1943–4 when the Weardale Lead Company milled some of the material from this source. At least some of the waste from the lead operations was backfilled into the stopes and is presumably intact, quite apart from the hoped-for virgin fluorite deposits. BSC has pumped out the flooded workings to examine the possibility of re-opening the mine, and in 1971 embarked on driving a drift to avoid use of the lead mine's old shaft. The Corporation, who plan to spend about £630 000 on the first phase of the Allenheads development, expect the mine to be in full production by 1975 when it is expected to employ 50 men.[257] The mine will exploit both fluorite veins and backfill from the old workings, but it is obviously difficult at this stage to predict what the output will be. It is hoped that the Allenheads mine, together with the expansion at Blackdene and Blanchland, could take BSC production of fluorspar to some 142 200 tonnes by 1980, a figure which is clearly speculative. If the actual production figure in any way approximates to this target, the expansion will be very large, from 38 600 tonnes to 142 200 tonnes in 10 years.

It may well be that, in spite of these new developments, the demand for metallurgical grade fluorspar of the conventional type will still outrun supply. The traditional metallurgical grade of fluorspar is bought in lump form, with widely varying fluorite content, and metallurgical grade producers usually carry out gravity separation using the compar-atively unsophisticated methods of jigs and sink/float processes. The specifications for metallurgical grade are not normally met by flotation processes, on which the major Derbyshire expansion will be based. Flotation processes are increasingly attractive to present and potential large-scale producers: they can utilize a lower grade of ore, make more efficient recovery from that ore, and produce principally acid grade fluorspar which sells at twice the price of conventional metallurgical grade. It may well be that steelmakers in the UK, following the trend in the United States and Europe, may be forced to use some quantities of the more expensive pelletized metallurgical grade fluorspar, which can be produced from flotation plants if special techniques are employed. Increased costs need, however, only be small as a percentage of all steel costs, and could be offset by the advantages of a high specified fluorite content to meet the more stringent needs of basic oxygen furnaces.

The BSC projects are likely to be the largest in the Northern Pennines orefield in the foreseeable future. However, there is the possibility of another development there of fluorspar for a captive market within the aluminium industry. Anglo-Swiss, an associate company of Star Aluminium, were in 1971 reported to be undertaking a survey of a Weardale mine at Whitfield Brow costing about £200 000.[258] In the southern district of this field, near Pateley Bridge in the West Riding, an American company, Weardale Mining, is re-working Greenhow Mines. Some fluorspar is also obtained from dumps on Greenhow Hill, and the small production from the nearby Grassington Moor area is obtained entirely from dumps. The small operators in the Northern orefield, mostly in the Weardale area, produce altogether approximately 2030 tonnes of metallurgical grade fluorspar. The output from small operators in the Northern Pennines orefield is disproportionately lower than that from small operators in the southern field, even allowing for the much smaller deposits in the former. The probable reasons for this are a combination of the following factors. Extraction of fluorspar in the northern field is more likely to be by deep-mining, with its attendant higher capital and running costs, whereas the overwhelming majority of small operators in Derbyshire work the dumps or use opencast methods. Only four small operators out of the very large number extracting fluorspar in Derbyshire were listed as mine owners in 1970, according to the records of the Mines Inspectorate Division.[259] Of the very much lower total of small operators in the northern orefield, five were listed as mine owners, four of them in the northern district. Mine dumps are not as extensive in the northern field as in Derbyshire. There has also been less scope for a tributer system in the North Pennines in the 1960s, where there has been no beneficiation plant comparable in size with the Cavendish mill in Derbyshire. The comparatively small occurrence in the North Pennines has had a circular effect: two small mining and milling operations, each with less than 7100 tonnes per year, were closed down during the 1960s following takeover by Laporte Industries because their size and potential were considered to be uneconomic.[260] The comparative

255

inaccessibility of the northern orefield may also have been a factor: the cost of processed fluorspar is small in relation to the cost of such end-products as steel or aluminium and transport costs can constitute as much as 30 per cent of the delivered price of metallurgical grade fluorspar.

It is unfortunate from a planning point of view that, of the producing areas, the northern district of Derbyshire, falling substantially within the Peak District National Park, should be of prime importance. Not only is the Peak Park under pressure from the heavy demands of other extractive industries, notably limestone, but is of all the National Parks the one nearest to large urban areas and thus of paramount value as a recreational area.[261] However, the Planning Board has always recognized the importance of vein minerals and approves about 90 per cent of applications.[262] Fortunately some of the deposits are in areas where the landscape is not the highest quality. The problems which extraction poses fall into two main categories. The approximately 100 small fluorspar workings within the park have a cumulative rather than individual impact on the landscape. Although they unavoidably cause visual disturbance on a small but widespread scale while in operation, in many cases at least partial backfilling is possible. The ratio of waste to commercial product obtained during workings is approximately within the range of $2\frac{1}{2}$–3:1, and often waste resulting from the working of dumps is also available to help fill opencast cuts. Where backfilling is possible, this is stipulated in planning consents, which also require progressive working along the vein with backfilling carried out behind the line of workings. There remains the problem of service traffic generated by these workings, often in narrow, unsuitable lanes, a problem to which there is no easy solution and which is causing the Board increasing concern.

The problems posed by the one large operator within the park, Laporte Industries Ltd., are largely of a different type. Laporte obtain a large proportion of their minerals by underground mining, and expansion can probably be concentrated in this sector. This is clearly preferable within the Park since modern fluorspar mines do not cause subsidence, although older mines may do so. However, Laporte also works the only area of large-scale opencast excavations within the Park, at Longstone Edge and Deep Rake. These workings have resulted in a scar, prominent even in distant views from the south across the Wye valley and in the considerable disruption of local rights of way.[263] The workings have been mainly carried out under permissions granted by the Minister in 1951 and 1952 which, in the Board's view, contained inadequate stipulations about site restoration,[264] and the excavations have so far remained partially unfilled in the absence of suitable filling material in sufficient quantities immediately to hand. During 1969–70, Laporte Industries sought the advice of the Board on the form of site restoration to be carried out there when, in the not too distant future, the excavations are completed. Although a substantial measure of agreement was reached,[265] the Board and the firm have subsequently disagreed about the feasibility of utilizing the waste from Laporte's processing plant at Stoney Middleton, some miles away, to complete the backfilling. Very severe problems of waste disposal are presented by the Stoney Middleton processing plant. A white slurry is produced there which has, to date, been disposed of in waste lagoons. In 1969, when two existing lagoons adjoining the mill were almost full, Laporte applied to the Board for permission to construct a new 29·2 hectare reservoir at Blakedon Hollow at the head of Coombs Dale; this reservoir, some distance from the mill, would provide enough capacity to last for just over a decade.[266] The scheme was rejected by the Board as 'totally unacceptable in a National Park'. At this site, three woodlands, an old highway and an area provisionally registered as commonland would be affected by the proposal and the area to be submerged is popular with walkers. Although once the reservoir were full, the water would be drained off and the area could be grassed when the slurry had settled, the natural contours and character of the landscape would be changed. The long-term nature of the problem has also caused concern: the new reservoir, if permitted, would only provide enough capacity to last 10–13 years, and with the escalating demand for fluorspar, the problem is likely to be met with in a more acute form at the end of that time.

Although the question of a new reservoir at Coombs Dale remains finally unresolved, further negotiations between Laporte Industries Ltd. and the Planning Board provided accommodation for the waste at the existing site for an interim period. Laporte were allowed to raise the walls of their two existing lagoons adjoining the mill and to build a third lagoon on the same site. Permission has subsequently been obtained to increase the capacity of the third lagoon such that it will last until 1977, an operation which the firm claims is a most unattractive proposition commercially.[267] Because of this agreement, the appeal to the Minister in respect of Blakedon Hollow would not need to be pursued until 1975, allowing two years for the construction programme there if the scheme were approved. However, the Board's permission for an increase in capacity at the existing site was made conditional upon Laporte's conducting research into alternative methods of disposal.

The Planning Board would approve any one of three alternative methods of waste disposal: pumping the waste by pipeline to tailings dams or old quarries outside the National Park; commercial utilization of the waste, e.g. by concrete manufactures; or total filtration and stabilization by chemical additives to enable the waste to be safely dumped into old excavations.[268] The finding of commercial outlets involves difficulties since the waste varies in composition and is not easily fitted to British Standard specifications for aggregates and the quantity is also likely to be much in excess of local market demand. The creation of tailings dams outside the park, while clearly preferable to those inside it, is an unsatisfactory and expensive alternative. The Board believe that stabilization is the best solution and their consultants have devoted much time to analysing and costing this method. The Board claim that it would be technically possible to treat the waste from the Cavendish mill and transport it to fill local excavations, notably those on Longstone Edge. They concede, however, that the cost of this method of disposal is four times as high per tonne of waste as that of dumping in conventional tailings dams.[269] The costs are £1·97 and 49 pence per tonne respectively and these compare with the approximate 1971 price of £19·68–£23·62 per tonne for the finished product (acid grade). Laporte, on the other hand, consider that there are in fact considerable technical difficulties in treating the material for transportation. Their chief objections however appear to be on the grounds of cost. They point out that the volumetric capacity of the local excavations, including Longstone Edge, is considerably less than has been suggested, and that within four or five years haulage distance of 16–19 kilometres would be involved (39 kilometre round trip).[270] John Bramley, Laporte's works manager, was quoted[271] in 1971 as saying of this scheme that it 'would add about 20 per cent to our production costs and raise serious doubts about our competitiveness'. Laporte themselves have tested a cheaper method of filtering the waste so that it solidified sufficiently to be tipped into old quarries, but the process reportedly failed to produce a material which would remain stable when it rained.[272] Meanwhile, with the question of a fourth conventional tailings lagoon postponed until 1975, the research continued. Since no alternative solution mutually acceptable to the Planning Board and the firm has emerged during that time, the question will undoubtedly come before a public inquiry.

However, the disputed question of the technical possibilities of stabilizing and transporting the waste slurry could only be pronounced upon a third, independent, technical expert in the field. The question of the cost of the scheme is of a more general interest. It is clear that

1A Gravel extraction in progress at Thorpe, near Chertsey, Surrey.

1B Worked out areas at Thorpe reinstated to leisure use as a water park.

2A Merehead, the largest limestone quarry in the Mendip Hills, Somerset, producing four million tonnes a year. The rail link is used to supply most of the output of clean stone to a distribution depot at Botley in Hampshire.

2B The cement works at Hope in the Peak District National Park. Sited because of the favourable proximity of raw materials, the scale of the plant makes it an obtrusive element in the Hope valley.

3A The largest chalk quarry in Britain at Swanscombe in Kent, producing 8·5 million tonnes a year. The working is bounded in the north by the Thames estuary and the urban areas of Swanscombe and Northfleet and in the south by the A2 and the M2 serving London and the Channel ports.

3B An industrial estate at Coulsden, Surrey, developed inside a disused chalk quarry by the former extractive company and the local authority.

4A *Above left:* A Bedfordshire brick clay pit after the usable material has been won leaving conical heaps of clay rejects. The saplings in the foreground are an attempt at screening the excavation.

4B *Below left:* Broughton Moor slate quarry in the Lake District National Park, specializing in the production of decorative cladding materials.

5A *Right:* Slate waste at the disused Dorothea Quarry, Llyffni Valley, Snowdonia National Park. Although its boundaries were drawn to avoid the worst areas, such tips represent a major dereliction problem within the park. Dorothea is being developed for recreational purposes.

5B *Below:* A typical open pit china clay operation at Great Carclaze, St Austell, Cornwall. The working tips of quartz waste can be seen in the centre background; other disused tips in the area have become vegetated.

6A *Left:* Crushed gypsum being carried by aerial ropeway from the underground working at Mountfield, Sussex, to the processing plant over three miles away.

6B *Below:* Opencast fluorspar working on Longstone Edge in the Peak District National Park Some worked-out sections are now being filled, contoured and revegetated by Laporte Industries.

7A *Above right:* Ridges of overburden produced by the opencast working of iron ore at Cranford St John, Northamptonshire.

7B *Below right:* The same area as above restored by the local authority to agricultural use from finance provided by the Ironstone Restoration Fund.

8A Shaft head gear at the new Wheal Jane tin mine near Truro, Cornwall.

8B An opencast coal working at Tinings, County Durham. Rock overburden and soil are tipped separately adjacent to the site for subsequent reinstatement of the landscape which is achieved with the level of success of that following ironstone extraction.

fluorspar profits are not quite as high as the very strong upward demand of recent years would suggest. B. L. Hodge, former chief geologist of Laporte Industries Ltd., has stated that fluorspar production does not yield a particularly high return, the profitability depending to an extent on by-product revenue.[273] Thus although the prices for marginal business, i.e. limited sales which take place outside long-term contracts, almost trebled in value over the period 1969–71 and the demand for the product will grow at a predicted rate of between 75 and 100 per cent over five years, the bulk of production is sold on long-term contracts where the upward movement of prices is less steep.

However, should a public inquiry find that a fourth conventional tailings dam is not acceptable within the Park, it is distinctly possible that the firm will in fact find a viable substitute, rather than go out of business. Experience elsewhere suggests that, if firm pressure is applied to an operator to find more acceptable waste disposal methods, procedures previously held to be either technically impossible or prohibitively expensive may in fact be adapted to a practicable form. English China Clays' solution of their micaceous residue disposal problems on-site is a case in point, and illustrates that when the full technical resources of a large firm are applied with real determination to problems of waste disposal, great advances can be made.

Outside the boundary of the park, the Derbyshire workings do not present problems of waste disposal. The only large beneficiation plant, that of the Guilini Group just outside the southern boundary of the Park, is to dump its waste, which will amount to about 60–75 per cent of tributers' material, into some old silica sandpits close to the plant. The chief problem within the Derbyshire County Planning area is the enforcement of planning conditions upon the large number of small operators.[274] Information from many planning offices relating to different kinds of extractive industry suggests that planning authorities find it easier to deal with a few large companies than a host of small operators, and planning procedures are probably one factor in the trend towards the creation of larger extractive units. The problems of dealing with large numbers of very small operators are exemplified in the case of Derbyshire. The position is complicated by the exemption of some small operators from planning control: where an old tip retains its original appearance of a heap of waste material deposited on the ground, it is considered for planning purposes as a movable possession and permission to work it is not required. However, some irresponsible and highly mobile small operators have been known to work dumps not in this category, using almost fly-by-night techniques and leaving behind numerous small holes in the ground. The administrative effort involved in ensuring that small workings subject to planning control obtain consent and comply with the terms is very considerable. This appears to be more of a problem within the administrative planning area of Derbyshire than within the Peak Park, possibly because avoidance of planning controls, where these apply, would be more difficult within the Park, which is patrolled by wardens and where, it is said, the occupants of the new commuting executive housing estates act as effective vigilantes. One method which would secure compliance with planning conditions in cases of this kind is the implementation of a system of bonds or deposits, sufficient to cover costs of restoration, to be lodged with the local authority before permission is granted and reclaimed when operations are completed and conditions fulfilled. This scheme would also have advantage of providing funds for restoration when a firm goes bankrupt in the course of operations. However, it would clearly do nothing to prevent the illegal avoidance of planning controls altogether. Furthermore, the bond system, like some other planning procedures, bears relatively heavily on the small, responsible, low capital operator. This system, although it has been advocated from time to time,[275] and has indeed found favour at provincial level in Canada, is at the present time outside the power of the British planning authorities.

The Northern Pennine orefield presents considerably smaller planning problems than those in Derbyshire. Although the Grassington Moor workings in the West Riding fall within the Yorkshire Dales National Park, and most of the other workings in the northern field are in 'Areas of Great Landscape Value', the population densities, amenity value and pressures from other users are generally lower than in Derbyshire. The agricultural value of the land is usually lower whereas in Derbyshire some areas of reasonable quality pastureland are involved.[276] The poor employment situation in many parts of the Northern orefield gives fluorspar extraction an especially high social value there. The greater proportion of underground workings and absence of very large beneficiation plants reduce both surface impact and waste disposal problems, and the substantial expansion schemes of the BSC in this field involve underground extraction. In spite of the very considerable areas of land in the Northern field covered by current permission for fluorspar working—26 300 hectares in Durham and Cumberland of which over 21 900 hectares is the Stanhope Common permission of Weardale Lead Company[277]—the planning and amenity problems here are unlikely to be anything like as serious as the very difficult problems encountered in Derbyshire.

BARIUM MINERALS

The barium minerals barytes (barium sulphate) and witherite (barium carbonate) are generally found in Britain as vein minerals and are, like fluorspar, often associated with metal-bearing lodes, especially those of lead and zinc. These non-metallics, which had almost until this century very little commercial value, were known as gangue minerals, that is minerals forming part of the gangue or waste rock. Barytes is not a rare mineral by world standards, and substantial deposits occur in both the United States and West Germany.[278] In Britain, it is found in the Southern Pennines orefield (associated with fluorspar and lead), on the outer fringes of the Northern Pennine orefield (where fluorspar is not present), and in comparatively small deposits in the South-West of England, the Welsh border and parts of Wales and Scotland. Witherite is by world standards extremely rare, but it occurs as a common mineral in the Northern Pennines, and in this respect the field is unique in the world.[279] The vein worked at Settlingstones mine in Northumberland was remarkable in that it contained pure witherite almost exclusively, with only very minor quantities of barytes, lead and calcite. Barytes, which has, in addition to its more widespread occurrence in Britain, much wider commercial application, was in 1916 worked in Durham, Westmorland, Shropshire and the Welsh border, Cumberland, Yorkshire, Derbyshire, Flintshire, Montgomery-shire, Carmarthen and Devon, with one mine only in Scotland.[280] Barytes made up substantially the greater part of the 25 064 tonnes of barium minerals produced in Britain in 1921.[281] Production of barytes was expanded considerably during the 1940s to meet wartime and post-war demand, and expansion occurred particularly in the Northern Pennines where a number of new mines were opened.[282] Witherite production was probably at its greatest from 1932 to 1958 when, in addition to Settlingstones, extraction was carried out at the Holmside and North Moor mines south of Gateshead, and maximum output during those years is estimated to have been 17 300 to 25 400 tonnes per annum.[283] However, extraction of barium minerals in Britain has contracted sharply during the past fifteen years. That of witherite ended entirely with the closing of the Settlingstones mine in 1969; output of barytes fell from 61 000 tonnes in 1960 to 17 300 tonnes in 1969[284] and extraction is now confined to one mine in the North Riding of Yorkshire.

Settlingstones, the most famous witherite mine in the world, ceased operations entirely as a result of the exhaustion of reserves. The mine, a former lead working, had been exploited for witherite since 1873.

Exploration work carried out by the Settlingstones Company from 1957 onwards at various sites in the locality proved abortive,[285] however, and production was run down from 1965 onwards as reserves became depleted at a depth of 268 metres.[286] The site has been bull-dozed to conform to natural contours and natural vegetation is now established. Although virtually the entire output of witherite came from Settlingstones in the period 1958–69, there was only a small demand. The main uses in latter years were in connection with the purification of crude brine, the manufacture of barium nitrate and chloride, and blanc fixe[287] (a precipitated barytes used for instance in the prepar-ation of polished white cards and papers). Consequently, it has not been difficult to replace the mineral for these few applications. There have been reports of the possible beginning of witherite production elsewhere, notably in association with exploitation of barytes at the old Longcleuth lead mine near Ninebanks in West Allendale,[288] but the economic incentives are clearly nothing like the order of those for many other types of mineral extraction, especially of metals.

The reasons for the contraction of British barytes output are consider-ably more complex. The chief factors involved are the exhaustion of some of the more easily accessible known reserves, the doubtful quality of some of the known remaining deposits, the contraction of one particular market, and the competition of comparatively cheap foreign imports. During the 1960s barytes workings ended at the Silverband mine, near Appleby in Cumberland, formerly operated by Laporte Industries Ltd. (closed 1963); at the Gasswater mine near Muirkirk in Ayrshire, formerly owned by Anglo-Austral Mines Ltd., an RTZ subsidiary (closed 1963), and at the Force Crag mine at the head of Coledale in the Lake District, formerly owned by McKechnie Chem-icals Ltd. The most recent closure, in 1969, was that of the Muirshiel mines near Lochwinnoch, Renfrewshire, formerly owned by RTZ and a mine which had been producing about 15 200 tonnes a year.[289] Muirshiel closed primarily because of the approaching exhaustion of its reserves, but the increasing costs of mining and of transporting the mineral overland to the chief market, the Orrs Zinc White Ltd. lithopone plant at Widnes in Lancashire, were also factors in the closure. Lithopone, a paint composed of various zinc compounds and barytes, was in fact a sharply declining market in the late 1960s, when both the Orrs Zinc White plant and another lithopone plant in Widnes, owned by McKechnie Brothers, closed as a result of competition from titanium dioxide. However, the Orrs Zinc White Ltd. plant was taken over and a new company, Barium Chemicals Ltd., formed; the plant was extensively modernized for the production of barium chemicals and Muirshiel continued to supply raw material to the company until the closure of the mine. Nevertheless, barium chemical manufacturers as a whole were in the 1960s coming to rely increasingly on foreign imports of barytes. Barytes is mined world-wide and on a large-scale, with a total output in 1970 estimated at 3·6 million to 4·1 million tonnes per year.[290] Unground barytes could, in that year, be bought almost anywhere for $10.83–$12.80 per tonne f.o.b.; thus at a coastal or near-coastal chemical works imported material was likely to undercut the domestic product brought considerable distances overland, for instance from Scotland to Lancashire. Imports into Britain increased by 66 per cent from 1968–9, from 34 340 to 57 300 tonnes, an exceptionally large increase probably affected by the closure of Muirshiel, and the Board of Trade decided, after representations from the barium chemicals manufacturers, to suspend the import duty of 7 per cent on crude (unground) barytes from 2 April 1970 (see Table 4.4). Apart from the

Table 4.4. *UK production and imports of barium minerals, 1964–9 (tonnes)*

| | Production | | Imports | |
	Barytes	Witherite	Barytes unground	Barytes ground
1964	35 560	7 110	38 392	8 958
1965	30 480	7 110	55 353	12 800
1966	32 510	5 080	47 854	9 947
1967	30 480	6 100	31 137	20 531
1968	26 420	5 080	18 160	15 149
1969	17 270	2 030	31 254	25 236

barium chemical manufacturers, who consume an estimated 15 200–20 300 tonnes per year of lump barytes,[291] this suspension also benefited the paint, rubber and allied industries using ground barytes as an extender, since most of the estimated 30 500–35 600 tonnes per year consumed in these industries[292] is imported in lump form and ground in Britain. The forces at work in this situation are clearly of a circular nature: as a result of the exhaustion of some British deposits, the consuming industries have come to rely more heavily on foreign imports. This reliance has in turn created pressure for suspension of import tariffs, which discourage exploration of new domestic deposits and the development of new mining projects.

The unusual marketing pattern of the British barytes-producing industry has been a further factor influencing its decline. On a world scale, the barytes industry is largely dependent on a single market, that of the oil- and gas-well drilling industry, which consumes some 75 per cent of total world production for use as a weighting agent in drilling muds to control abnormal fluid pressures and prevent blowouts. The muds are poured into oil-wells to hold back gas during boring operations until the casings are inserted. The muds, weighted by the heavy barytes, are pumped down the hollow drill stem, pass through holes in the openings in the drill bit, and rise to the surface between the wall of the hole and the drill stem. Barytes for drilling muds have to be fine-ground, chemically inert, and have a minimum specific gravity of at least 4·2, although the colour is not important and barytes stained red or yellow by iron impurities may be used if other requirements are met. In most areas of the world, barytes sales tend to fluctuate in line with increases or decreases in oil-well drilling activity. Intensive drilling in the North Sea in the 1960s did not, however, bring that expansion to the UK market which might have been expected. Although Closehouse mine, the one remaining working solely for barytes, does supply this market, the industry in Britain, as in the other European producing countries, was developed historically to meet the requirements of the chemical, paint, rubber and allied industries, partly indeed by the chemical companies themselves. Consequently, the barytes mines of Britain, as of Germany, were not geared to produce the large quantities of cheap barytes for drilling muds, and the bulk of the tonnage used by the petroleum industry in Britain or British waters is imported ready ground from regular suppliers to this type of market. Thus this complex of factors has combined to eliminate all but one of the British barytes mines, although the mineral is produced as a fluorspar by-product in Derbyshire.

The Closehouse mine stands on the north side of the Lune valley in the North Riding of Yorkshire, and is located on the outer fringe of the Northern Pennines orefield. The barytes deposits here, of an unusual geological type, are associated with a major fault-zone where the Carboniferous strata have been faulted, folded and intruded by quartz dolerite prior to mineralization. The width of the fault-block is some 92 metres and recent exploration has indicated that mineralization extends for a considerable distance both to the east and west.[293] Early mining for lead in this district began at least as early as the thirteenth century, and continued on a small scale until the London Lead Company acquired the lease of the Lunedale district in 1771. During the period of their control, which lasted until the base metal slump in 1880, there were many indications of the presence of barytes, although production was not at that time a commercial proposition. The first recorded barytes sales from this district occurred in 1886–91 when 2720 tonnes were produced.[294] In 1937, however, a report on the barytes, fluorspar and lead resources of Upper Teesdale and Weardale was produced for the North Eastern Development Board by Granville Poole. As a result a local company, Athole G. Allen (Stockton) Ltd., anticipating a shortage of supplies for its barytes grinding operations and manufacture of barium chemicals, obtained the lease to the Closehouse district.

Production began in 1945, after extensive exploratory trenching and the building of a gravity concentration plant. By 1970 a total of 152 400 tonnes of barytes had been extracted from this site.[295] Extraction is confined to the west side of the Arngill valley, where the mineral has been worked over a length of 549 metres and a vertical depth limited to 37 metres. Five different types of mineral deposit are found here. The most important occurs in the quartz dolerite 'Northern Dyke' which outcrops along the valley and has been worked by both underground and opencast methods. The dyke is in some places more than 50 per cent barytes, partly introduced by dilation along fracture and partly by replacement. A faulted zone to the south of the 'Northern Dyke', known locally as the shale deposits, has also been worked over a length of 153 metres at widths of 10–12 metres, but here the barytes is contaminated by other materials. Mining operations have continued and have touched on promising areas still awaiting full westwards development.[296] Opencast working has been extended and was in 1971 expected to yield more than earlier anticipated; in that year approximately half the output was from opencast and half from underground workings.[297] About 50 per cent of the output was fine-ground for consumption as a constituent in drilling muds, in the rubber/asbestos and allied trades, the paint trade, for coal-wash preparation plants and for other filler purposes. The other 50 per cent was either despatched in lump form for the manufacture of barium chemicals, sold as aggregates for high density concrete (used among other purposes as a shield against X-ray and gamma radiation) or used in the company's on-site brick/blockmaking plant,[298] which supplies similar markets to those of the high density concrete.

Future reserves of barytes at Closehouse appear to be good. These cannot be stated precisely, but they appear to be more than 152 000 tonnes[299]—how much of these will be economically workable is not at present known. Deposits are, for instance, known to exist in depth below the Arngill valley bottom, but no way has yet been found to exploit them, since the quantity of water, flowing through the limestone beds to the north of the vein, is too great for existing equipment to handle. Output during the 1970s is expected to be between 10 000 and 15 000 tonnes per year approximately, and a new milling plant, beneficiating the material to a 96 per cent barium sulphate content, has been commissioned and will be capable of producing up to 305 tonnes per week.[301] The conclusion must be drawn that the prime factor influencing the survival of Closehouse when other barytes workings have closed is the existence of working reserves in quantity at this unusual geological deposit.

At the adjoining Lunehead mine, also held by Athole G. Allen but worked only on a limited scale since 1937, further barytes deposits are known to exist and, after encouraging exploratory work carried out some time ago, plans for development are, in 1974, still under consideration.[301] An exploration licence has been negotiated for the vein extension running south-west into the adjoining property in Westmorland. The Lunehead mine, like Closehouse a former lead working, has in fact a longer history of barytes production, which began here in 1884 and produced an estimated total yield of 71 100 tonnes by 1937.[302] Full-scale operations did not cease as the result of exhaustion, and this site seems the most likely possibility for a new operation dealing mainly in barytes. Recent interest has, however, been reported in the lead/zinc/barytes potential of parts of the Lake District and Argyllshire,[303] at deposits where these minerals could be worked together.

Barytes is already produced in substantial quantities as a by-product of fluorspar production in Derbyshire. Derbyshire barytes is generally of a lower grade than that of the Northern Pennine orefield. The veins occur in Carboniferous limestone, and often an amorphous earthy-looking type known as 'caulk' or 'cawk' occurs interbanded with the normal crystalline type. Much of the material is a granular aggregate of fluorspar and barytes particles.[304] The output of barytes of Laporte Industries' Cavendish mill, which totalled 18 300 tonnes of by-product barytes in 1965, was only approximately 8600 tonnes in 1969,[305] although this decline is the result of special circumstances and is likely to be temporary. In 1969 the company undertook major plant modifications in which the barytes circuit, which suffered most disturbance, was the last to be completed. The engineering was finished by the end of 1970 and the company expect barytes production at least to regain, and possibly to exceed, its 1965 level during the 1970s.[306] This output is now primarily sold as filter-cake. Additional supplies of barytes are expected from the new Guilini Group mill which began commissioning in 1971. Consequently, the percentage of British output produced as by-product in Derbyshire may be expected to increase.

Barytes working in Derbyshire is inseparable from that of fluorspar and consequently its impact on the landscape is simply a contributory factor towards the problems discussed in that connection, although necessarily a minor contributory factor. At Closehouse, the impact of workings is partly modified by the extent of underground extraction. There are some 1·2–1·6 hectares of buildings, plant and shunting yards at the site,[307] and some waste from the gravity concentration plant, part of which they have managed to use in site road construction, is left as waste tips. However, the comparatively small scale of workings means that no prominent scars or serious waste disposal problems are created.

REFRACTORY MATERIALS*

Refractory materials, i.e. those able to withstand and contain heat, are essential requirements of the metallurgical, chemical and brick-making industries, as well as having other miscellaneous uses.[308] They are used to provide a hot enclosure in which certain industrial processes, such as metal smelting, steelmaking, etc., may be carried on.[309] The properties required of refractory materials fall into three categories: chemical, where their compatibility with the process concerned is desired; physical, where their thermal properties and texture are necessary; and mechanical, where strength and ability to withstand stress at the required temperatures are essential. Refractory materials, which are normally processed by mineral dressing or heat treatment, come within three main types: acid, alumina silicate and basic refractories.

Acid refractories, i.e. those with a high silica content, comprise the various types of silica rock, a term which, at its broadest, includes ganister and silica sand. These refractories are essential requirements for coke ovens and may be used in the open-hearth steelmaking process although they have a lower melting point than basic open-hearth refractories.[310] Deposits of acid refractory materials do occur in Britain, although those of the purity required for the processes just mentioned are not common; furthermore, the more easily worked ganisters of Yorkshire and Durham are now nearing exhaustion. Alumina silicate refractories vary widely in alumina content and hence in heat tolerance. The main alumina silicate refractories, in ascending order of alumina content, are: china and ball clays, fireclay and bauxitic clay; andalusite; kyanite and natural sillimanites; bauxite; and the synthetic refractories mullite and tabular alumina. Of the alumina silicate refractories, only the comparatively low alumina

* In this section, the non-refractory uses of minerals used primarily for refractories are also considered. Refractory products are also discussed in the sections on china clay and silica and moulding sands.

materials, china and ball clays, fireclay and bauxitic clay (30–50 per cent alumina) occur in Britain. Most fireclays only withstand temperatures of up to about 900°C, but the Scottish fireclays, averaging 43 per cent alumina, may tolerate temperatures up to about 1100°C.[311] The higher alumina content refractories, such as bauxite, with an alumina content of about 80 per cent, have to be imported. The synthetic alumina refractories, which may have an alumina content of as much as 99·9 per cent and withstand heat of 2000°C,[312] clearly come at the expensive end of the refractory market.

Basic refractories are those chemically resistant to ferruginous slags formed in the course of iron and steel manufacture. Magnesia, contained in large quantities in the mineral magnesite, is the most effective oxide in chemically resisting these slags. Dolomite, a double carbonate of magnesium and calcium and containing smaller proportions of magnesia than magnesite, is very resistant in its dead-burned form* to iron and iron oxide though not as resistant as magnesite to ferric oxide. Dolomite deposits occur in Britain in the Permian magnesian limestone and parts of the Carboniferous limestone series. Dolomite of the purity required for modern steelmaking is however comparatively rare, and that of the necessary specifications for certain other applications such as glassmaking has increasingly to be imported. Natural deposits of magnesite are far less widespread than dolomite on a world scale and do not occur in Britain. However, high quality magnesite is obtained at Hartlepool by a process involving the interaction of dolomite and sea water. Chrome, an imported basic refractory material, may be used on its own for open-hearth furnace linings or steelworks' ancillary plant where prolonged high temperatures are not involved. The use of chrome and chrome/magnesite bricks (used for open-hearth furnace roofs since the 1930s) is however diminishing in favour of magnesite/chrome bricks (70 per cent magnesia), a trend which represents both an increase in cost and an upgrading in refractory quality (see Table 4.5).

The iron and steel industry represented in 1972 about 70 per cent of the total UK refractories market[313] and consequently the levels of demand for the various types of refractory materials are highly susceptible to changes in steelmaking technology. The open-hearth

* Dead-burned dolomite is produced by the firing of the mineral in a shaft or rotary kiln up to 1700–1800°C; during this process, large quantities of carbon dioxide are evolved and the stone is reduced to half its original weight, becoming a fully shrunk, dense and highly refractory material with a melting point which may be as high as 2300°C. The achievement of the maximum melting point depends on a low impurity or flux content.

process of steelmaking may utilize either acid or basic refractories, but since the 1930s basic refractories have been gaining ground in this market as a result of their substantially higher melting point. The newer basic oxygen and electric arc steelmaking processes, which have effected substantial economies of fuel consumption and accounted for 51 per cent of UK steel production in 1970,[314] demand refractories

Table 4.5. Sales of products of the refractory industry (by establishments employing 25 or more persons), 1963 and 1968

	1963		1968	
	Quantity thousand tonnes	Value £000	Quantity thousand tonnes	Value £000
Firebricks	737	9 673	743	10 975
High alumina bricks (44–60 per cent alumina)	16·2	919	25·9	1 422
High alumina bricks (60 per cent alumina +)	38·3	1 841	87·8	4 811
Silica bricks	98·3	2 033	51·6	1 235
Siliceous bricks (75–92 per cent silica)	18·1	186	—	227
Insulating bricks	27·6	1 288	29·5	1 743
Magnesite bricks	42·5	2 117	76·8	4 479
Magnesite/chrome bricks	32·6	1 564	58·6	3 275
Chrome/magnesite bricks	95·4	3 786	89·4	4 074
Other refractory bricks (including chrome bricks and dolomite bricks)	31·6	1 019	62·3	2 499

Source: Department of Trade and Industry, Business Statistics Office, Report of the Census of Production, 1968, no. 125, *Bricks, Fireclay and Refractory Goods*, HMSO 1971, table 5.

capable of withstanding far more difficult operating conditions both of temperature and of chemical and physical attack than the open-hearth process. Consequently, the British refractories market during the 1960s reflected the relative decline of the acid and low alumina products, and the increasing relative importance of dead-burned, high quality dolomite, magnesite, calcined bauxite and tabular alumina (see Table 4.5). In fact, the best European and British dolomites, containing upwards of 2 per cent fluxes, would be considered only marginally acceptable in the United States and Japan, where improved technical performance in the Linz Donawitz (LD) basic oxygen steelmaking process has been achieved by using the higher cost, low flux dolomites, generally containing less than 1·5 to 2 per cent fluxes.[315] The basic oxygen and electric arc steelmaking furnaces have profoundly affected not only the quality and type of refractories in greatest demand, but also the overall quantities of refractories required. The newer steelmaking processes utilize smaller quantities of higher grade, more expensive refractory materials than the open-hearth method. This was the major factor in the sharp fall in refractories consumption per ingot tonne of steel produced, from more than 22 kg in 1945 to approximately 9 kg in 1971.[316] In spite of the costlier refractories involved, the lining for an LD steelmaking vessel in 1971 cost approximately £20 000 and took five to eight days to install, whereas a large open-hearth furnace cost approximately £50 000 and took up to two to three weeks to install.[317] The small quantities of refractories required and the increasing relative importance of the high grade imported materials had a big impact on domestic refractories production during the 1960s. Although British steel production rose by 35 per cent from 1960–70, the total production of refractories fell by 17 per cent.[318]

The trend towards proportionately greater use of the more expensive high quality refractories, very marked in the steel industry, was paralleled elsewhere in the refractories market. Non-ferrous metal industries, for example, were making increasing use of basic and high alumina refractories; the cement industry has tended towards the use of kilns with a much greater capacity than hitherto, a development which favours the use of basic refractories such as magnesite/chrome and dolomite bricks. During the 1960s there was in general an increasing development and use of high alumina refractories, which are dense materials and have longer lives, require less maintenance and have better dimensional tolerances to justify their higher prices. There is a growing tendency to abandon the much-used criterion of refractory cost per tonne of product towards total cost evaluation, i.e. it is increasingly appreciated that in some processes total operating costs may be reduced by increasing the refractory cost per tonne of product.[319] This trend is likely to grow with the use of larger and more expensive equipment, with correspondingly higher costs involved in premature shutdown from refractory failure.

The extraction of British deposits of refractory materials is intimately affected by developments such as these. Most of these deposits provide materials of relatively low heat tolerance for the less expensive end of the market which is contracting. The output of silica bricks, for instance, fell by nearly 50 per cent between 1963 and 1968 (see Table 4.5), representing a very substantial curtailment of silica rock quarrying. Output of fireclay was also falling during the 1960s: extraction is likely to be increasingly concentrated on the higher quality fireclays (those with higher alumina content) and on those which can be most cheaply worked (thick shallow seams, or deposits which can be jointly worked opencast with coal). The shift in emphasis in the refractories market from low to high quality materials necessarily involves an increasing dependence on imported refractory materials, and the relatively greater importance of domestic sources of high quality refractory materials. High purity dolomite, used in its dead-burned form or in the manufacture of magnesite, must be considered of prime importance here.

Dolomite

Dolomite occurs in Britain in the Permian Magnesian limestone and parts of the Carboniferous limestone formations, where it was formed either by direct deposition from sea water or, more often, by the action of magnesian salts contained in sea water which converted calcium carbonate (limestone) to calcium magnesian carbonate (dolomite). The Permian Magnesian limestone, the main British source of dolomite, outcrops from South Shields on the Durham coast to Nottingham, in a continuous belt with an average width of 8 kilometres. The Carboniferous limestone series contains high quality dolomite in Derbyshire—notably the extreme east of the county—Gloucestershire and the Forest of Dean, parts of Shropshire, and the rim of the South Wales coalfield.

Although the overall reserves of dolomite are very large, reserves of chemical and refractory dolomite of the necessary quality for modern markets are comparatively rare. As specifications of material suitable for refractory purposes have become more rigorous, the number of quarries working dolomite for this purpose has decreased. The quarry of Steetley Ltd., at Llynclys near Oswestry, provides a material no longer suitable for refractory usage, and now serves only the roadstone and concrete aggregates markets.[320] Two parts of the dolomite outcrop, on the other hand, contain sufficiently large reserves of high quality dolomite to have given rise to complexes of quarries working refractory or chemical grade dolomite. One of these is the high quality deposit near Worksop on the Nottinghamshire/Derbyshire border. Quarries in this area, notably at Whitwell, Bolsover and Steetley, have traditionally supplied refractory materials to the Sheffield steel industry, and provide the basis for a substantial refractory industry in the area. Apart from the use of locally-worked dolomite for refractory brickmaking, other types of basic refractories, using imported chrome and magnesite from the sea water extraction plant at Hartlepool, are manufactured in this area.[321] A second important complex of refractory grade dolomite quarries occurs in the high quality deposits of

County Durham, north-east of Bishop Auckland, notably at Coxhoe, Cornforth and Chilton, with a less important centre to the south of the county near Darlington. There are also a number of quarries working high quality reserves in Gloucestershire, and the Forest of Dean. The rim of the South Wales coalfield is an area which has traditionally supplied the South Wales steel industry with refractory dolomite products. Isolated quarries working refractory grade material also occur in parts of Yorkshire and Derbyshire.

The location of dolomite quarries and their on-site plant has of course been determined by the rare occurrence of the mineral with the required chemical purity. Fortunately, several of the major deposits occurred in reasonably close proximity to iron and steel centres, notably those of Whitwell, Bolsover and Steetley to Sheffield, of the Taffs Well quarries to the South Wales steelmaking area, and the Durham deposits in the North-East. The first refractory plants were usually sited close to deposits since the product range was fairly narrow and the manufacture of the refractory was an essential part of raw material treatment. Processing plants designed to produce purely dolomite refractories and dolomite for non-refractory use are still located in most cases at the quarry. However, the major refractory plants, utilizing not only dolomite but a range of other materials such as magnesia and chrome, are now concentrated on those areas particularly close to major markets. The Steetley Group's largest refractory plant for the manufacture of bricks, blocks, cements and monoliths,* for instance, is at Steetley village. This is indeed close to local dolomite deposits but the prime locating factor is proximity to Sheffield. Two of the company's four other refractory plants of similar type are also in the Sheffield area. Consequently, it is not now as easy as it once was to identify particular steel complexes supplied from particular quarries as the supply lines, for the more sophisticated refractory products at least, are no longer clear cut.[322]

The increasingly technical processing now involved in the production of refractory and chemical dolomite has affected not only marketing patterns but the structure of the industry since it has undoubtedly contributed to the dominance of large producers with extensive capital for research and development. The largest dolomite extractor in Britain is the Steetley Group, which in 1970 produced about 75 per cent of total British production,[323] from five dolomite quarries (four producing refractory grade material). The Steetley Group, which has played a major part in the development of new applications for dolo-

---

* Complete linings or specialized refractory shapes, constructed at the consumer's site.

mite, is now an international company, the largest manufacturer of refractory materials in Western Europe and operator of dolomite quarries in Spain and Canada and a sea water magnesia plant in Sardinia.

The overall British output of crude dolomite grew by 54 per cent between 1964 and 1969 (see Table 4.6). During that same period, how-

Table 4.6. UK production and imports of dolomite, 1964–9 (tonnes)

	1964	1965	1966	1967	1968	1969
Production of crude dolomite	3 759 200	3 860 800	4 267 200	4 775 200	4 978 400	5 791 200
Imports	12 254	13 988	19 631	22 111	22 998	27 049

Source: Institute of Geological Sciences, Mineral Resources Division, *Statistical Survey of the Mineral Industry,* 1964–9, pp. 190 and 195.

ever, imports of the mineral grew by 120 per cent. The growth in home output reflects increased demand from non-specialized, and hence less valuable, markets. Home output has been particularly affected by the increasing demand for aggregates.* The growth in imports, on the other hand, reflects the growing demand for certain tightly specified products such as dolomite raw material for glass manufacture, of which adequate supplies cannot be obtained from British deposits.

In spite of rising home output and rising imports, the total tonnage of dolomite consumed by the iron and steel industry actually decreased during this period, falling from 816 200 tonnes in 1964 to 774 200 tonnes in 1969.[324] A slightly larger proportion of this tonnage consisted of dolomite used, not for refractory purposes, but for fluxing in blast furnace and sinter plants. The fall in consumption by the iron and steel industry during this period is, of course, related primarily to the decrease in dolomite refractory consumption, in turn resulting from a range of factors, not least a reduction in consumption per tonne of steel produced.

The value of the iron and steel market during this period is however likely to have substantially increased as a result of a shift in demand towards the higher purity, more expensive grades for refrac-

* It should be noted that the dolomite output figures must be regarded as approximate, since some dolomite for aggregates is worked at quarries which also supply limestone. Operators of such quarries may not distinguish between the two minerals in their returns, since in this instance there is little significance in the chemical differences between the minerals.

tory purposes. In view of the heavy demand from the iron and steel industry for these grades, it may in a sense still be legitimate to call this the dominant market,[325] although the industry consumed directly only some 13 per cent of total British dolomite output in 1969 (apart from that used indirectly via the sea water magnesia plant).

The use of dolomite for refractory purposes in steelmaking dates from the late nineteenth century. The Gilchrist–Thomas process, perfected in 1878–9, employed dolomite refractory linings to make possible for the first time the use of phosphoric ores in the Bessemer converter and open-hearth furnace. By introducing limestone into the charge, the slag was turned alkaline and the phosphorus oxidized and passed into the slag. The Gilchrist–Thomas process involved the development of an alkaline refractory brick, consisting of dolomite, and unaffected by this 'basic slag' which at high temperature destroyed the acid silica linings used hitherto. The Gilchrist–Thomas process was of great significance in the British steel industry since it made possible the use of the abundant phosphoric ores of the Jurassic strata in the Bessemer and open-hearth processes, where very substantial cost reductions were possible. The extraction of dolomite for steelmaking refractories developed rapidly as a result, notably in the Worksop area, where the mineral had previously been worked for lime. Dolomite refractories did, however, until the more recent advent of the tar-bonded block, have the drawback that the material hydrates rapidly when exposed to any sort of humidity because of the free lime content. Acid linings continued to be used for steelmaking based on the less abundant British haematites, and on imported non-phosphoric ores. At Middlesbrough, for instance, it was cheaper to manufacture steel by the acid process using ores imported from Spain than by the basic process using ores from the nearby Cleveland Hills.[326]

Dolomite refractory linings continue to be used as an alternative to the more expensive magnesite for the working hearths of open-hearth furnaces. Much of its current importance, however, relates to its use, generally in tar-bonded blocks, a good, economical refractory, as a lining in the basic oxygen furnace. For the Kaldo basic oxygen process, the severity of operating conditions is such that the more chemically resistant magnesite linings are necessary, but for the LD process dead-burned dolomite refractory linings are a cheaper alternative to magnesite. However, dolomite/magnesite blocks, which incorporate different proportions of dolomite and magnesite according to the severity of furnace conditions involved, achieve lining lives well in excess of those achieved with dead-burned dolomite alone, and will probably be of increasing importance. Large quantities of processed dolomite (not necessarily of the highest chemical quality) are being supplied for the working repair of both open-hearth and electric arc furnaces. The annual tonnages for this purpose over approximately the next ten years are expected to be at least as great as those supplied for block-making.[327] Dolomite also makes an important contribution to the iron and steel refractory market indirectly through its use as a raw material in the manufacture of magnesite. Initial experiments to produce magnesia from sea water and dolomite began in 1936, stimulated in the first instance by the absence of domestic sources of natural magnesite and then by the interruption to supplies of imported dolomite during the Second World War.

The sea water magnesia plant of Steetley Ltd. at Hartlepool is now the largest of its kind in the world with an annual capacity of a quarter of a million tonnes.[328] The location of the plant was necessarily confined to the Durham coast, the only area where the Permian Magnesian limestone abuts the sea. Within that area, the specific site at Hartlepool was dictated by the presence there of sea water free from dilution from rivers. Dolomite for this process is quarried from the high quality deposit some 22–24 kilometres inland from Hartlepool at Thrislington, near Coxhoe, where in 1969 approximately two thirds of the quarry's production of 1 million tonnes per year was supplied to the sea water plant.[329] The dolomite is crushed, washed, graded and calcined in rotary kilns on-site, processes which involve weight losses and consequently effect some transport economies. The material is transported to Hartlepool by rail and is slaked before being reacted with sea water in large 97·6 metre diameter settling tanks to precipitate magnesium hydroxide. Since sea water contains about 1 part of magnesium to 800 parts of water,[330] complex chemical engineering processes are involved, but the magnesium obtained is of better quality than that obtained from natural magnesite or magnesium salts. The sea water process is very versatile in that a number of different grades of sea water magnesias may be produced by the use of suitable additives.[331] The Hartlepool plant is clearly of great importance in view of the scarcity in Britain of deposits of refractory materials which are effective at high temperatures, and is likely to become more important as demand for higher grade refractories grows. In 1969 British magnesia was exported to 12 countries and sales in the UK represented an estimated saving of more than £6 million on the balance of payments.[332]

It is convenient at this point to refer briefly to the non-refractory outlets for the mineral dolomite. The specialized market for dolomite of importance second only to that of the iron and steel industry is that of glass manufacture. In 1970 the annual consumption of British dolomite by this industry exceeded 274 000 tonnes,[333] or just over one-third of the total iron and steel direct consumption. For both glass manufacture and steel refractories very tightly specified materials are required. For glass manufacture, dolomite of small particle size is required, and the level of impurities such as iron, manganese, vanadium, chrome and lead must be very low since these may discolour or cause physical defects in the glass. The tolerance on calcium oxide (CaO) and magnesium oxide (MgO) may be as narrow as ±0·5 per cent.[334] Although the total reserves of dolomite in Britain are large, there is difficulty in obtaining sufficient domestic supplies of raw materials with low enough iron levels and this has led to increasing dolomite imports from Norway and Mediterranean countries.[335]

The comparatively non-specialized dolomite outlets, which will be briefly noted, are of comparatively high tonnage and low value. Chief amongst these is the rapidly expanding aggregates market, in which dolomite is suitable for ready mixed concrete manufacture, for asphalt road surfacing and coated macadams, for bulk fill and for railway ballast. In some instances dolomite aggregate is supplied by quarries serving mainly specialized markets and is in a sense a by-product consisting of materials not meeting the specifications for other purposes. The Thrislington quarry at Coxhoe of Steetley Ltd., supplying mainly the sea water magnesia plant, produced 3050 tonnes a week of dolomite aggregate in 1970, much of it used as a bulk fill for factory sites.[336] Elsewhere quarries working grades unsuitable for specialized purposes may concentrate almost exclusively on aggregate production. The output of the Whitecliff quarry in Gloucestershire of Man–Abel Holdings Ltd., for instance, consisted in 1972 of 67 per cent for coated macadams and 27 per cent for railway ballast.[337] In the agricultural market, where substantial tonnages of dolomite are also involved, dolomite usage largely overlaps with limestone, as it does in the aggregates market. Ground dolomite may be used as a conditioner to counteract excessive acidity and is particularly applicable where the soil has a magnesium deficiency. Specifications for this purpose are nothing like as tight as those for refractory purposes, or glass manufacture, but the neutralizing value and fineness must reach certain levels before the product can qualify for a Ministry of Agriculture lime subsidy. Ground dolomite is also used as a raw material in fertilizer manufacture and in the late 1960s significant amounts of this purpose were exported to the Continent.

Small quantities of dolomite are used in a variety of very minor markets. Ground dolomite is used as a cheap filler in markets such as the rubber industry. Dolomite dust, i.e. dolomite pulverized to a standard particle size, is used to neutralize the combustible matter in coal dust and so minimize the effect of explosions in coal mines. Small amounts are used for water purification; dolomite, calcined at a low temperature, acts as a porous filter which reduces any corrosive effects which water may have. Dolomite powders are used as elements in animal feed. The mineral is also used in the manufacture of magnesium carbonate, known also as 'technical carbonate' and 'magnesia alba', for use, mixed with asbestos, for buffing metals to produce for instance the deep blue tone of highly polished nickel.[338]

The extractive processes involved in dolomite winning, whatever its ultimate purpose, are essentially similar to those of limestone. A similar tonnage per hectare is normally obtained and, from a planning viewpoint, similar problems of noise, dust vibration and visual impact are involved. Whatever the markets served, dolomite quarries normally have a substantial on-site processing plant, including rotary or shaft kilns for dead-burning, refractory brick or cement manufacturing plant, and crushing, screening and coating plant. However, dolomite extraction is clearly on a much more restricted scale than that of limestone—representing only 6·8 per cent of combined tonnage in 1969[339]—and dolomite deposits do not on the whole occur in the finest areas of limestone scenery. The Peak District, for instance, which is under the heaviest pressure for expansion of limestone workings, is scarcely worked for dolomite. Furthermore, natural mellowing of the rock face occurs more quickly in Magnesian limestone, the most important formation for dolomite, than in Carboniferous limestone.

The particular industrial importance of dolomite has, since the earliest period of post-war planning, been recognized and steps taken to protect high quality reserves. In view of the comparatively rare occurrence of refractory and chemical dolomite, the Ministry of Housing and Local Government convened regional conferences in the early 1950s, at which representatives of the dolomite industry, local planning authorities and certain government departments were present. The aims and action of the conferences were to allocate sufficient land within Development Plans for the areas concerned to safeguard reserves from sterilization from surface developments. The Durham Development Plan, for instance, contained areas approved for the working of dolomite, in view of the special value of the mineral for use in the metallurgical and chemical industries. It is interesting to note that in 1971 the planning authority refused an application for dolomite working in one such area—near Hetton in north-east Durham, an area of pleasant, comparatively unspoilt rural landscape—since the application was, not for metallurgical or chemical grade dolomite, but for an aggregates working.[340] More conflicts of this type between the industry and local authorities may reasonably be expected since the demand for dolomite aggregate is growing rapidly, while the market for refractory and glass manufacturing dolomite is becoming more selective.

Silica rock and ganister

The term 'silica rock' at its broadest includes those rocks with a high silica content, such as quartzites, ganisters, quartzitic and quartzose sandstone, and silica sand. The narrower definition, adopted by the Geological Survey[341] and followed here, denotes those sandstones and quartzites able to be used for silica brickmaking and excludes ganisters, which are distinct in their process of formation and characteristics. Silica rock and ganister used for the manufacture of silica bricks contain at least 97 per cent silica, less than 1 per cent alumina, less than 0·3 per cent alkalis and very little lime.[342] Alkali-bearing silicates such as felspar, muscovite and sericite are particularly undesirable constituents. Particle size as well as chemical composition is tightly specified for refractory usage; the ideal grading of the rock after crushing and milling should be made up of equal proportions of fine and coarse particles, with very few of intermediate size.[343]

The quartz grains in silica rock are usually derived from sand debris transported by rivers. The sandy particles have been largely separated from the other, finer grained, components during transportation, and most of the remaining silicates decomposed either by the humic acids emitted by decaying vegetation on the rock surface (also transported rather than growing on the sand) or by mineralizing solutions seeping up through them. In the latter case, only those rocks in which the silicates have been decomposed without the introduction of undesirable minerals such as galena, lead, fluorspar or barytes are suitable for silica brick manufacture. The texture of silica rocks may be broadly classified into three types, determined by their degree of compaction and the pressure to which they have been subjected: very compact silica rock of quartzite, which is tough, glassy and homogeneous and produced by severe earth stresses; very loosely consolidated material or quartzose standstones, which crumble easily; and material of intermediate compaction, i.e. quartzitic sandstones. Of these types, the compact quartzites, with very low porosity, are most likely to contain suitable particle size gradings for silica brick manufacture. The porosity of the rock after firing should be as low as possible and even the toughest particles derived from the softer quartzose sandstones tend to have higher porosity after firing than those of the harder rock. Consequently, silica bricks made from quartzose or even quartzitic sandstones have shorter lives than those made from quartzite.

Ganister, which differs both in process of formation and characteristics from silica rock, consists of the sandy seat earth of coal seams. The quartz sand, transported by rivers, once contained silicate minerals, which have been decomposed by the weak organic acids given off by the decaying vegetation which gave rise to coal. The formation of ganister was normally associated with large amounts of vegetation, whereas that of silica rock was associated with small amounts of vegetation, or none at all. Ganister beds usually vary in composition from top to bottom. The bottom, relatively unaffected by vegetation decay, may contain a large proportion of silicates and thus be unsuitable for silica brick manufacture. The best quality ganisters usually underlie thin coal seams[344] since a thick vegetation growth draws its mineral salts from underlying levels of decayed vegetation rather than from the sandy seat earth. The same conditions which favour decomposition of the silicate minerals also corrode the quartz grains so that they interlock, giving a compact texture. In its typical form, ganister may be distinguished from all other quartz rocks used for refractories, by the fineness, angularity and even grade of the quartz particles and by its splintery fractures.[345] In quality ganister resembles the higher grade silica rocks such as quartzite: the silica content is higher than that of some grades of silica rock and may be as high as 98–99 per cent with less than 0.3 per cent alumina.

Vitrified silica has a very low coefficient of expansion, which enables it to withstand sudden changes of temperature: it can be heated to redness and then plunged into cold water without cracking. The properties of silica were first exploited for silica brick manufacture in the early nineteenth century in South Wales, where the Dinas firebrick, based on the quartzite of the Vale of Neath, was put into production for refractory use. In the 1860s the pioneer of the Dinas firebrick began manufacture in the Sheffield district, utilizing local ganisters, which bear a strong resemblance to Dinas quartzite. As demand for silica bricks increased, plants were built in other parts of Britain. For a time flints from the Thames valley and chert* from Denbighshire were utilized for silica brick manufacture, although these raw materials were later rejected as being of insufficiently pure silica. Silica brick demand grew in the late nineteenth and early twentieth century in response to the need for open-hearth linings, and after the First World

* Flint and chert are essentially nodules of silica contained in chalk and limestone respectively.

War a further impetus was given as silica bricks became, as they still remain, the standard refractory for coke-ovens. Silica stone consumption (including ganister) more than doubled between 1918 and 1937.[346] There was a marked trend away from ganisters during this period, as the reserves of easily accessible ganister are much smaller than those of silica rock, and the costs of working are correspondingly greater.

During the past thirty years there has been a trend towards replacement of silica by either basic or high alumina products: furthermore, outlets have diminished in other ways. The phasing out of gas manufacture, for instance, is eliminating an outlet for those types of silica rock, such as the pocket silica deposit at Friden in Derbyshire, with up to 10 per cent alumina content which are suitable for refractory use in gas retorts. Demand from the glass industry has also been decreasing. The chief impact on reduced consumption, however, has been made by the iron and steel industry, the chief consumer of silica rock in most areas. In 1959 about 98 per cent of South Wales, output of silica bricks was sold to steelworks[347] (although this included consumption in steelworks' coke-ovens, a continuing market). As noted earlier, silica rock and ganister usage in this market has contracted as changing steel technologies have led to increased demand for higher performance and basic refractories. Silica bricks are still used as an alternative to magnesite/chrome or chrome/magnesite bricks for open-hearth furnace roofs but this is bound to continue to be a contracting demand as an increasing percentage of steel output is derived from basic oxygen furnaces. Silica brick consumption in this market has also been affected by more economical usage. Thus diminishing demand from the iron and steel industry was the chief factor in the sharply declining output of silica bricks during the period 1955 to 1969 with total UK production falling from 293 003 tonnes to 69 810 tonnes during the period. Output of siliceous bricks (75 to 92 per cent silica and made predominantly from imported diatomite and perlite) also fell from 24 955 tonnes to 10 268 tonnes.[348] While output will almost certainly diminish further as demand from steelworks continues to contract, there is bound to be a limit to this contraction, in view of continuing demand from coke-ovens. No major silica rock producing area has been entirely eliminated by contracting markets, but quarrying in all areas is now more limited than formerly.

Ganister production has been necessarily affected by the general trends in silica refractory consumption outlined above, but certain special factors do apply in this case. Good quality ganister is one of the best silica refractories and in some areas, notably the Pennines, demand has increased relatively to that for the lower grade silica rock of the area, in spite of the greater expense and difficulty of ganister extraction.

Even at the height of demand, quarrying of silica rock and ganister was necessarily localized. Since the chemical and physical characteristics of silica rock and ganister suitable for silica brickmaking are very specific, these raw materials have a highly restricted distribution. Very few Pre-Carboniferous quartitzes (i.e. where no vegetation was present during formation) contain sufficiently pure silica to be suitable for silica brickmaking. The Ordovician quartzites (Stiperstones) of Shropshire, for instance, contain too high an alkali content for this purpose.[349] Similarly, the Cambrian quartzite of the Wrekin and Nuneaton, important for aggregate production, contains too much clay mineral for silica brick manufacture. The Cambrian quartzite, which outcrops in a narrow band from Cape Wrath on the north coast of Scotland in a south-westerly direction to Skye, contains too much felspar, and is, in addition, inaccessibly located. Distance from markets is a material factor in the exploitation of silica raw materials which, in common with most indigenous British refractory materials, come at the cheaper end of the refractory market. One deposit relatively distant from markets is however still exploited; the Pre-Cambrian quartzite of Anglesey was in 1969 worked for silica rock by three quarries in the neighbourhood of Holyhead.[350] The Holyhead quartzite contains immense reserves of silica rock, but scale of working has been affected by the physical nature of the deposit, where good stone is irregularly distributed amongst low grade materials of much greater bulk. The isolation of the deposits has however been partially offset by the availability of cheap transport by sea from Holyhead. The majority of silica rock quarries active in 1969 worked material of Carboniferous age, mainly in North and South Wales. In North Wales, the Cefn-y-Fedw sandstone, which outcrops in a long strip from Oswestry northwards to Halkyn mountain, was in that year worked by seven silica rock quarries in Flintshire and Denbighshire. High quality quartzite suitable for silica brick manufacture is found only in very restricted parts of this outcrop, that is parallel to the Bala and Minera faults, where mineralized solutions have leached out the silicates.[351] Softer silica rock, of similar chemical purity, is abundant, but is used mainly for silica flour for scouring soaps, abrasives, ceramics and cheap fillers. The best quartzite occurs where mineralization and earth stresses have been sufficient to weld the quartz grains together, without introducing deleterious minerals, such as metal ores. The mode of occurrence of high grade silica in this area presents difficulties of working; the lithology of each lenticular bed may change rapidly both laterally and vertically. Consequently, a certain amount of hand selection is necessary and the scope for mechanized extraction and grading is limited. In the past, a larger number of small silica rock quarries operated here, working without the aid of detailed sampling and borehole analyses, and with only low investment, and with changing points of extraction as the quality of the mineral altered. Many of these have now closed down.

Silica rock of varying types occurs extensively throughout the Millstone Grit series of South Wales, which outcrops in a long narrow band from Abergavenny to Kidwelly in Carmarthenshire. The Basal Grit of this formation has been the most important source of silica rock here. The texture of the silica rock varies from section to section of the outcrop. In the east, from Aberdare to Abergavenny (i.e. from south Breconshire to north Monmouthshire) the Basal Grit contains quartzitic sandstone and coarse quartz conglomerates. Local faulting has, on a limited scale, produced quartzite of economic importance here. Further west, the major Vale of Neath fault in Glamorgan has produced tough quartzites, much worked in the past, and including that of Craig Dinas, the earliest location of silica rock working. In the Black Mountain to the west, most of the Millstone Grit consists of quartzose and quartzitic sandstones, the numerous cross faults not having been severe enough to produce quartzite. From the Black Mountain to Kidwelly, localized thrust-faulting has altered parts of the outcrop to quartzite, of current economic importance. Anlaysis of the properties of various deposits since 1945 favoured the development of south-east Carmarthenshire and south Breconshire deposits, rather than the earlier Vale of Neath area, and by 1959 these two areas were considered to 'contain the greatest known resources of high grade silica rock in the British Isles'.[352]

Since that time, however, quarrying for silica rock in South Wales has fallen sharply, particularly in view of the very great dependence on the steel market in this area. By 1969 only six silica rock quarries remained active in South Wales: three in Carmarthenshire, one in Glamorgan, one in Monmouthshire and one in Breconshire.[353]

Silica rock is worked only on a very limited scale in England. It was in 1969 worked only by some four quarries in England, two in Derbyshire, one in Durham and one in Staffordshire.[354] In west Derbyshire and east Staffordshire, small 'pocket' deposits of silica rock ('crowstones') occur in the Carboniferous limestone, in some instances more than 30 metres deep. The pocket silica consists of quartzitic sandstones not of the highest purity nor of the highest compaction. Although large tonnages are available, their constitution is not acceptable to most manufacturers. Notable among the crowstones are those at Friden and Parsley Hay near Hartington and at Harborough, west of Wirksworth. In the North Pennines quartzitic sandstone, of similar composition to the crowstones, occurs in groups of sandstone beds contained in the Millstone Grit. Although easier to work than the ganister of the area, since they form prominent hillside terraces, the silica rock deposits of this area are almost entirely unworked now since the material is not of the highest quality. The material is not so pure and compact as the ganister, and careful selection was always needed in this area to avoid sections of the beds containing too much clay. Furthermore, great care needed to be taken with the crushing and grinding.

Although neither silica rock nor ganister are now worked extensively in England, ganister is currently the more important of the two in the North Pennines, the reverse of the position in 1947.[355] In that year the less expensive but lower quality silica rock was in greater demand; now the market demand which remains is primarily for the higher quality material, i.e. ganister, in spite of its relatively higher cost. In 1969 ganister was exploited at 11 quarries in Durham and Yorkshire.[356]

The mode of occurrence of deposits in these two areas is somewhat dissimilar; in the Northern Pennines, between Teesdale and South Tyne, where sandstones occur in both the Millstone Grit and the Lower Coal Measures, ganister and quartzitic sandstones are found at some 15 different levels in the sequence. The South Tyne, Wear and Tees and their tributaries have cut valleys into this sequence, and terraces of varying width have been developed on the valley sides. Working is normally on the sides of valleys above 300 metres, since below this height deposits are covered with boulder clay which it would be prohibitively costly to remove. The silica rock beds of this area can be relatively easily worked since they form prominent terraces covered by overburden whose thickness increases only gradually. The ganister beds of this area, on the other hand, although hard, tend to be thinner, not forming prominent terraces like the silica rock, and hence the depth of overburden increases more sharply in relation to the workable mineral (unless the ganister beds happen to occur immediately above a thick, hard bed). The amount of overburden which can economically be moved is consequently less than that of silica rock, since it relates to the thickness of the deposit. Although a few ganister mines have been operated in this area in the past, the bulk of working has always been by opencast methods, the normal procedure being to work a terrace outcrop until increasing depth of overburden makes operations uneconomic. There are consequently a very large number of abandoned ganister quarries in County Durham. Half of the quarries still active in 1969 worked ganister in association with other products, namely fireclay or sandstone.[357]

In the Sheffield district of Yorkshire, where ganister occurs in the Lower Coal Measures, the mineral attains its most perfect development. (Ganister also prevails over a fairly wide area of south Yorkshire and in the Moor Grit of the North York Moors, not now of economic importance.) The chief ganister horizon forms the floor of the coal seam known as the Ganister or Alton Coal. These ganisters, formerly worked at accessible points by opencast methods, were by 1917 exploited largely by mining under shallow cover, mostly by clayholes. The need for mining in this area between the wars, given the techniques of opencasting then available, meant that the winning of ganister here became progressively less economic as the use of more easily won quartzite developed, and by 1947 there were only six mines in the Sheffield district compared with 40–50 thirty years earlier. Currently very limited amounts of this ganister are worked by opencast methods—which can now of course economically move a higher ratio of overburden to ganister than hitherto—and the remaining economically workable deposits are small. For many refractory purposes, locally-won dolomite has taken over the markets once held by ganister, and where it is still positively required, e.g. for coke-oven lining bricks, some of the demand has to be met by ganister brought from Durham or silica stone from South Wales.[358]

The opencast winning of silica stone and ganister involves similar extractive techniques to hard rock quarrying for aggregates, i.e. blasting, crushing and screening. The silica brick (or, on a small scale, silica cement) making plant is likely to be on-site. The scale of silica and ganister working is, of course, very small indeed by aggregates standards and becoming steadily smaller. In most areas—such as the Durham and Yorkshire ganister regions—worked-out sites far outnumber those still active. The small scale of present working is unlikely to pose environmental difficulties even when it occurs in high amenity areas. The few small workings in the silica deposits of the southern Peak Park, as a case in point, have, in the words of its planning chief, given rise to no particular problems, although several of the excavations have not been backfilled to ground level.[359]

Fireclay and bauxitic clay

Fireclays consist principally of the clay mineral kaolinite, with variable amounts of quartz, mica, anatose and the iron minerals such as siderite, pyrite and haematite.[360] Fireclays usually form the floor or seat earth of coal seams, and are believed to represent the muddy ooze in which the swamp forests grew. The geological association of fireclays with the coal measures has in the past enabled the iron and steel industry to line its furnaces from local sources. The steel market is now of only very minor importance, although fireclay is still used extensively for blast furnace linings. Fireclays are very variable in thickness, in a manner unrelated to the depth of the overlying coal seam, and often have marked vertical or lateral variations in their chemical and physical properties. Although their refractory performance is affected by physical properties such as the capacity to withstand pressure, generally speaking a high alumina content indicates high quality material. Alumina contents vary from 30–32 per cent of the fireclays of the Monmouthshire section of the South Wales coalfield to an average 43 per cent of first-class Scottish fireclays.[361] The different types of fireclay tend to have differing outlets, not all within the refractories market. Refractory outlets include firebricks used for blast furnaces and to a small extent steel furnaces (for high alumina grades only), retorts, crucibles, nozzles and tuyeres,* i.e. where temperatures are low or where exposure to high temperatures is short and the temperature gradient steep. Fireclays with high flux and low alumina contents are used for vitrified ware, notably sanitary products, acid-proof ware, and salt-glazed pipes and tiles. The durable glaze on the products is obtained by firing at high temperatures and consequently they require refractory rather than non-refractory clays. In some instances, fireclays are also used for high grade building bricks. Total UK output declined from 2 194 000 tonnes in 1960 to 1 731 000 tonnes in 1970.[362] The most important factor in diminishing demand was the trend towards greater consumption of high performance refractories for use at high temperatures, within an overall contracting refractories market (by tonnage). Not only was more economical refractory usage being obtained by use of high grade materials, but the growing practice of 'gunning' was replacing the lining of cupolas† and furnaces with firebricks. By this process the refractory material is sprayed on to the furnace walls, a method which is cheaper, just as effective, and involves a smaller volume of refractory materials.[363] Some sections of the refractory market, such as that of gas retorts, were, as indicated earlier, contracting sharply in the 1960s as natural gas gained ground at the expense of manufactured gas. An exception to the general trend, however, was the rising consumption of casting-pit hollow ware, based on fireclay. Such hollow ware is only used once and overall consump-

* Pipe through which air is forced into the furnace.
† Furnace for melting metals.

tion is consequently directly proportionate to the tonnage of ingot steel produced.

The difficulties of obtaining a consistent fireclay product have also played their part in declining demand; since seams vary extensively in character, it is not possible to produce a totally consistent product over a long period without recourse to complex blending,[364] which can price fireclays out of the cheaper end of the refractories market. Since continuing sales in this market rely heavily on their comparative cheapness, difficulties of extraction which raise operating costs have also assumed some significance. In 1960 a large proportion of output was derived from mines, some of them licensed coalmines, or those working other minerals such as ganister. Fireclay mines tended throughout the 1960s to be small operations, and neither economies of scale nor a high degree of mechanization were usual.[365] In any event, fireclay mining must be a labour-intensive process, and output per manshift in 1972 was estimated to average only 2 tonnes by this extractive method.[366] The growing costs of deep-mining, particularly in terms of labour, helped to produce a pronounced trend towards opencast extraction during the 1960s. From 1967 to 1968 alone, ten fireclay mines in Britain went out of production,[367] and by 1970 deep-mining was largely confined to Scotland.[368]

Opencast winning of fireclay dates back in the case of the Swadlincote Clays of Derbyshire as far as the 1840s, but it has assumed an increasing importance as improvements in earth-moving machinery have tipped the economic advantages further in favour of this extractive method. In 1972 it was estimated that the cost of deep-mined fireclay in the west Midlands might average £7·38 per tonne whereas fireclays from opencast sites might average about £1·97 per tonne.[369] However, the heavy capital investment involved in opencast working equipment has effected a change in the structure of the fireclay extractive industry. Whereas refractory manufacturers at one time played a considerable part in extracting their own raw materials, much more extraction is now undertaken by independent producers who supply the material to refractory goods manufacturers and do not process it themselves.[370] Since high cost earth-moving machinery must not be allowed to stand idle, the average refractory goods manufacturer can buy fireclay more cheaply than he can opencast it. Very substantial reserves of fireclays are accessible to opencast winning; opencast operations for coal have reached depths of 150–180 metres. Where the operation is confined to fireclay, a maximum ratio of clay to overburden of 1:7 would probably be economic.[371]

Clearly, the cost advantages of working fireclay in association with opencast coal at those sites where both occur in commercial quantities are considerable. Joint fireclay/opencast coal workings fall broadly into three categories. First there are sites where clay and coal are worked and the coal is not owned by the National Coal Board because it was sold by the Coal Commission under the terms of the Coal Act 1938 prior to the nationalization of the coal industry in 1947. Second, there are sites worked for both clay and coal by companies acting under licence from the NCB and where either a royalty per tonne of coal is paid or the coal is handed over to the NCB on payment by the NCB of the additional costs incurred by the operator in winning the coal and delivering it to the NCB. Third, there are sites authorized for working under the Opencast Coal Act of 1958 where contractors work the site on behalf of the NCB. In such cases the contractor would be one experienced in clay operations and the cost of working the site is shared between the NCB and the mineral owner according to the relative values of the respective minerals. However, coal is the more valuable product per tonne and in most cases it is the presence of the coal which determines the working of the site rather than that of the fireclay. The NCB's Opencast Executive claim that in the past companies have sought licences to work coal in order to permit clay working, when their real interest has been in the more profitable exploitation of the coal.[372] This can have very real disadvantages for the NCB since the coal produced in association with clay is rarely of good quality and its production at times of coal surplus could be detrimental to the NCB's own disposals and cause additional stocking costs. Such companies tend to strip away rapidly all the on-site coal, often on the grounds that, in the event, the clay has proved unsaleable. In order to prevent this practice, the Opencast Executive have sought to ensure that a market for the clay is established, that only coal necessarily removed to win the clay is taken, and that the rate of coal production is geared to clay requirements.[373] Although, as a general rule, costs of working and restoration of the coal/clay sites are shared by both mineral owners on the basis of the relative values of the respective minerals, the Opencast Executive maintain that, through their willingness to enter into joint schemes, sites have been worked which would be totally uneconomic to work for clay alone.[374] In view of the Opencast Executive, fireclay has tended to be an underpriced product, since its extraction has in many cases been subsidized to a greater or lesser extent by the more profitable extraction of coal. Had this not been the case, it is fair to assume that, during the 1960s at least, the decrease in fireclay output would have been even more pronounced.

The relationship between the Opencast Executive and fireclay operators involves complex legal, administrative and technical issues. The complaint is frequently voiced by fireclay interests that in the past coalmining damaged millions of tonnes of fireclay as a result of the crude methods of extraction and a poor appreciation of the various grades of fireclay.[375] The Opencast Executive point out that opencast mining for coal only began during the Second World War and it was operated by the Government until the NCB took over in 1952. In the early days, it was essential in the national interest to extract the maximum amount of coal as quickly as possible and it was during this period that fireclays may well have been damaged. The Executive have no reason to disbelieve the allegation that millions of tonnes of fireclay may have been lost. They point out, however, that it is impossible to place any estimate on the actual loss of fireclay. It is still in the ground and it is arguable that it is the fact that the coal has gone that makes at least a proportion of the clay 'lost'.[376] In recent years, the Executive claim that their operations have always been planned to ensure the exploitation of any commercially viable minerals other than coal in opencast sites. Nevertheless, the critical view taken by many fireclay operators of the past record of opencast coalmining in this respect has been in at least one instance a delaying factor in the attainment of a joint working agreement.

From the general survey of trends in fireclay extraction made at the beginning of this section, it emerges that certain underlying criteria may be used to explain the distribution of fireclay workings. Fireclay is only likely to be mined in those areas, such as parts of Scotland, where the mineral has an exceptionally high alumina content to justify the comparatively high costs involved in this method of extraction. Fireclays are only likely to be worked opencast on their own either where thick seams occur at comparatively shallow depths (with a maximum ratio of overburden to clay of 7:1) or where the clay is of exceptionally high quality. In the case of other deposits which come outside these categories, the distribution of clay winning is likely to be heavily affected by the existence of interstratified coal suitable for winning by opencast methods. There can be occasional exceptions to this, such as the Streets Lane site near Cannock in Staffordshire, where clay deposits of unusual and special quality occur. Only very rarely will the need for coal production be the determining factor in the choice of joint sites since the presence of clay can slow down the rate of working and the NCB would normally look to coal-only sites for their main source of opencast coal production.

In England, which in 1969 produced 923 000 tonnes or more than half the British total,[377] fireclay deposits are widespread, more so, in fact, than any other refractory raw material. Fireclays underlie the Upper Coal Measures of Lancashire, Warwickshire and north Staffordshire, the Middle Coal Measures of Lancashire, Cumberland, Cheshire, Northumberland, Durham, Derbyshire, Leicestershire, north and south Staffordshire, Shropshire and Warwickshire, and the Lower Coal Measures of Lancashire, Durham, Northumberland, Yorkshire and north Staffordshire.[378] There are in addition some fireclay deposits in the Millstone Grit of Lancashire, Cheshire and the Forest of Dean, and some fireclays resulting from decomposed granite in Devon and Cornwall. The balance of importance has shifted markedly within this wide range of deposits, as opencast operations have assumed increasing importance. In 1969 substantially the largest English producing area, contributing 30 per cent of the English total (see Table 4.7), was Shrop-

Table 4.7. Fireclay production in Britain by area, 1969 (in thousand tonnes)

Northumberland and Durham	167
Cumberland and Yorkshire	163
Lancashire, Derbyshire and Lincolnshire	144
Shropshire	285
Staffordshire, Leicestershire, Northamptonshire, Worcestershire and Cornwall	164
Flintshire, Carmarthenshire, Denbighshire and Monmouth	132
Stirling, Fife, Dunbartonshire and Lanarkshire	275
Midlothian, West Lothian and Ayrshire	334

Source: Department of the Environment.

shire. In 1961, when the Geological Survey was preparing its special report on fireclays in Britain, Shropshire was only of very minor significance, with a few workings at Coalbrookdale.[379] The recent importance of the Shropshire fireclays relate particularly to the existence of thick fireclay seams near the surface. The chief fireclay deposits, now worked exclusively by opencast methods, occur in an area 9·7 kilometres by 11·3 kilometres extending from Wellington nearly to Much Wenlock, in the vicinity of Telford New Town. The greater proportion of workings in this area are joint coal/clay workings; extensive mining has taken place in the past and deposits can economically be worked for their coal remnants by opencast methods with simultaneous recovery of fireclays. However, this is one of the few areas where it is economic to work opencast for fireclays alone, and some workings in this area are solely for fireclay. Although the other English county figures are so grouped together by the Ministry for reasons of confidentiality as to make analysis difficult, it is clear that a pronounced shift of emphasis has occurred. Yorkshire, formerly a producing area of high importance and one where fireclay deposits occur over a wide area, is substantially less important than hitherto. This relates partly to the exhaustion of some of the more easily worked fireclays and associated ganisters and partly to the low level of opencast coal getting in this area throughout the 1960s (see Table 6.5). Fireclay output from Northumberland and Durham, on the other hand, is relatively more important than formerly; this reflects primarily the high level of opencast coal winning in this area during the late 1960s, second amongst opencast coal regions only to that of the South-West region (including South Wales). In 1970 three licensed mines working fireclay and associated coal were also in operation in Durham.[380] Fireclay output from Derbyshire, the most substantial contributor to the Ministry's Lancashire/Derbyshire/Leicestershire grouping, derives from two main areas, in both of which fireclay extraction is associated with opencast coal getting. One is the north-east of the county from the locality of Sheffield southwards to Ilkeston, and the other a small area in the neighbourhood of Swadlincote. The Bottle Clay of the Swadlincote area, long worked by opencast methods, serves primarily the important local industry of sanitary ware and salt-glazed pipes, rather than the refractory market. (A similar local industry is based on the fireclay deposit of the Stourbridge, Worcestershire region.) Of greater importance in the Swadlincote neighbourhood are the truly refractory Derby and Deep fireclay beds. Lancashire fireclay output is of declining importance; only one (at Billinge) of the nine fireclay mines active in the county in 1960 was still in operation in 1970, and the fall in mining activity was not balanced by a corresponding increase in opencast working. Opencast coal getting in this area remained at a very low level throughout the 1960s (see Table 6.5) and joint clay/coal workings were in 1972 confined to a small area between St Helens and Widnes.[381] Fireclay output from Wales (including Monmouthshire) represents only a small percentage of British output but did in fact slightly increase during 1960–70 from 6·1 to 7·6 per cent,[382] in spite of the low average alumina content of most Welsh fireclays. This development is related primarily to the very high degree of opencast coal getting in South Wales and Monmouthshire during the period; from 1963 onwards, except for 1967–8, opencast coal output was higher from the South-West opencast coal region than from any other. In Monmouthshire, a part of this region, four clay levels in the Lower Coal Measures produce fireclays with the low average alumina content of 30–32 per cent; these clays, which are not economic to work opencast on their own, are extracted on a scale larger than their quality alone would justify, in view of the widespread opencast coal-getting in this area, where schemes involving the clearance of dereliction are of importance. The

Buckley Fireclay group in Flintshire, North Wales, in 1958 the main Welsh fireclay producing area,[383] contains beds that are very variable in character, with the result that in some places as many as thirty different kinds of material have to be handled. The alumina content is not sufficiently high for many refractory purposes, but the material remains of importance for a variety of applications, of which the chief are acid and fireproof goods, paving and ridge tiles, and common bricks. The extraction of the Buckley fireclays does, however, involve considerable difficulties. In many parts of the field economically valuable deposits were sterilized by brickworks, built before the geological structure of the clays was appreciated.[384] Extraction of the clays, long worked by quarries or large open pits, now involves operating to increasing depths with attendant problems of increasing overburden removal and drainage.[385]

Scotland contributed 36·5 per cent of British fireclay output in 1969. Here, as elsewhere, opencast extraction increased strikingly during the 1960s,[386] as a result of the production economies involved. However, Scotland remains the one area of Britain where fireclay mining still exists on any scale. In 1960 there were a total of approximately 37 fireclay mines, 22 producing only fireclay and the balance producing fireclay in association with coal, ganister, blaes* or, very rarely, ball clay.[387] By 1970 the approximate total number of active fireclay mines in Scotland remained a substantial 26, of which 19 worked fireclay only.[388] The main complexes of active mines in that year were at Bonnybridge, Stirlingshire, Bathgate, West Lothian and Kilwinning, Ayrshire. The survival of fireclay mining in Scotland, in contrast with other parts of Britain, reflects essentially the higher average alumina content of Scottish fireclays. As can be seen from Table 4.5, consumption of refractory bricks containing more than 40 per cent alumina was increasing during the period 1963–8 and this category includes the higher quality Scottish products. These high alumina clays are also in demand for export. Their enhanced value, relative to most fireclays elsewhere, renders mining economic in this area where it would not be elsewhere.

The Scottish fireclay reserves, contained mainly within the Central Valley, occur primarily in the Millstone Grit. The Lower Fireclays at the base of this series are of prime importance in a belt running from Plean in east Stirlingshire southwards to Coatbridge in Lanarkshire. The Lower Fireclay is also worked at Linlithgow, West Lothian. The Upper Fireclay of the Millstone Grit is of particular importance in the area of Bonnybridge. In some cases there are two or three seams, both

* A type of shale.

of fireclay and ganister, and in others ganister lies between two thick clays, while an impure coal is generally associated with the deposits.[389] Bonnybridge has for long been the centre of a refractory goods manufacturing industry. Millstone Grit fireclays are also worked in north Ayrshire while Coal Measures fireclays are worked to a small extent in the Central Valley, notably at Roughcastle near Falkirk.

The Ayrshire bauxite clay, which extends over a wide area and probably underlies the whole of the Ayrshire coalfield,[390] is of a different chemical composition and geological origin from fireclay. It is probably always present where contemporaneous igneous rocks are associated with the Millstone Grit series. The association of the bauxite clay with decomposing igneous rocks suggests that its origin was similar to that of bauxite, i.e. as a direct product of the decomposition of igneous rocks. The alumina content varies considerably from area to area but is on average unusually high by fireclay standards. In the Saltcoats area, average alumina content is as high as 45–50 per cent, while at Sanquhar, in West Dumfries, it falls as low as 26–34 per cent.[391] Consequently, modern operations are concentrated in the Saltcoats and neighbouring Kilwinning and Galston areas. In 1971, ten sites in this part of Ayrshire were allocated for the winning and working of bauxitic clay; four by opencast methods, five by deep-mining and one by both underground and opencast methods.[392]

The trend away from deep-mining to opencast winning, apparent in Scotland although less marked there than elsewhere, has naturally altered the impact of extraction on land use and amenity. Some fireclay mines have in the past given rise to subsidence; those to the east of Kilsyth in Stirlingshire, where instability resulting from workings has made the land unsuitable for building, are a case in point. However, many fireclay mines, such as those elsewhere in Stirlingshire, do not give rise to subsidence and their visual impact on the landscape is clearly smaller than that of active opencast operations. The impact of combined coal and fireclay workings is necessarily very great during their active phase—there is, for instance, said to be considerable visual damage in the Avonbridge area of Stirlingshire.[393] There is an initial disruption caused by opencast working, which may go as deep as 183 metres. In such instances, the amount of overburden to be stored for eventual replacement is very great. The storage of graded stockpiles of fireclays over considerable periods of time has been an important factor in visual disturbance, especially as the falling demand for certain types of fireclay has tended to increase stockpiling.[394] However, the restoration of combined opencast coal/fireclay sites is of a comparable standard to that generally high one achieved elsewhere on opencast coal sites.[395] In Shropshire, the main producing county, all vacated fireclay sites (including those worked for fireclay alone) have been either fully restored or graded prior to final restoration.

The inescapable disruption caused during opencast workings has led to resistance to such operations in areas where fireclay deposits underlie high quality landscape. Since these areas are comparatively few in number, the mineral is not of rare occurrence and overall output is declining, such objections have carried some weight. One such instance concerned the deposits on the Sheffield fringe of the Peak District, where a small number of opencast workings are active. Although the standard of restoration of these workings is said by the Planning Board to be generally good,[396] the Board rejected an application for twenty acres of new workings at a particularly prominent site at Bradfield near Sheffield. The Minister upheld the Board's decision, since he was not satisfied of the need to work this mineral, not of rare occurrence, in the National Park in the face of a strong landscape objection.[397]

In Shropshire, too, the planning authority has attempted with some success to resist the expansion of workings in high amenity areas of the county and hopes to concentrate workings in the area of Telford New Town,[398] where extensive deposits occur. As part of the Telford New Town reclamation programme, a plan of phased opencast extraction of coal and clay prior to restoration for the town's development had in 1972 been agreed with the NCB.[399] The necessary cooperation between the parties concerned was, however, at times still being hampered by difficulties in obtaining a working agreement between the Opencast Executive and the fireclay operators. Since the successful resistance to extended workings elsewhere in high amenity areas of the county depends on successful resolution of this problem and since phased working of minerals prior to restoration for surface development represents one kind of optimum solution to land use planning of this type, the successful formulation and implementation of such a plan is highly desirable.

SILICA AND MOULDING SAND

Sands containing the special properties required for glassmaking or metal castings are of much rarer occurrence in Britain than sand for aggregates. The bulk of demand from these industries is met by silica sand, used as a raw material in all types of glass and crystal manufacture and for foundry moulds and cores. Glass sands must be composed of 98–99 per cent silica and be virtually free from iron (less than

0·015 per cent for optical glass, 0·025–0·030 per cent for colourless glass containers and about 0·05 per cent for coloured glass containers).[400] Silica sands for use as a refractory material in the manufacture of foundry moulds in which iron and non-ferrous metals are cast contain a wider variation of silica content than those produced for glass manufacture, with silica contents ranging from 87–99 per cent.[401] Silica sands for foundry use require the addition of a bonding agent, i.e. they are essentially the major raw material in the manufacture of synthetic mouldings sands. Naturally bonded moulding sands, which are of limited occurrence in Britain, contain sufficient quantities of clay, and in some cases iron oxide, to give moulds made from them the necessary strength to retain their shape when receiving molten metal, except in the case of the more advanced foundry techniques.

Although glass sands are a highly specialized commodity, their costs are low in comparison with other materials used in glass manufacture, notably the chemical elements and the oxides of metals magnesium, aluminium or lead, and constitute a small proportion of total manufacturing costs. In 1971 prices ranged from 74 pence per tonne for a sand suitable for coloured glass containers to approximately £4·92 per tonne for the highest quality glass sand suitable for optical and crystal glass.[402] The price of sands for the major market of colourless glass containers is intermediate between the two, but closer to that for coloured containerware. Consequently, even at their most expensive, glass sands are a comparatively high bulk/low value mineral and transport costs make up a substantial element of their delivered price.

It is only possible to produce the highest quality sand for optical glass and crystal from the main British deposits such as the Cretaceous Lower Greensand by using expensive and sophisticated beneficiation techniques. Since this is a small market, it would not be possible to spread the processing costs involved over a large tonnage: consequently, the resultant prices would be uncompetitive with high grade sand from deposits where beneficiation techniques are not required. Only one British deposit produces untreated glass sand of such quality, a small isolated outcrop of Cretaceous sandstone at Loch Aline in Argyllshire, on the northern coast of the Sound of Mull. This mine, worked by Tennant Loch Aline Ltd., part of the Consolidated Goldfields group, had by 1970 produced a total of some 2 million tonnes[403] of high quality material from workings which extend for more than 32 kilometres. In spite of its quality, however, the deposit suffers from two disadvantages: the occurrence of the mineral, overlaid by Tertiary basalt, necessitates mining by the comparatively wasteful room-and-pillar method which involves leaving about 40 per cent of the mineral as pillars for support. A more serious disadvantage is the location of the deposit, remote from the main glass manufacturing centres. Although sand is shipped from the port of Loch Aline for markets as distant as St Helens, Stoke-on-Trent, Stourbridge and Waterford,[404] its freight charges to most British factories are comparable with those of high quality glass sand imports. The main source of such imports is Belgium and Holland, where extensive deposits of sand, suitable for optical and crystal glass manufacture without any beneficiation, occur adjacent to the extensive canal system connected to the Rhine. (High grade sand from a deposit at Fontainebleau in France is not generally marketed in Britain since this involves the high costs of overland transport to Rouen before shipment.)

The market for coloured and colourless containers makes up the bulk of the glass sand market; the production of containers, whose total value was £86·6 million in 1970,[405] had been growing over the previous two decades but in the late 1960s was given added impetus by the increasing use of non-returnable bottles for food and drink. British deposits such as the Cretaceous Lower Greensand can compete very successfully in this market, since the cost of beneficiation can be spread over the large tonnages required. Until the 1940s, however, sand for the container market, as well as those for optical and crystal glass, was imported. Belgian and Dutch sands, requiring no beneficiation, benefited from the low freight rates then operative from the Continent. It is believed that in the mid-1930s Lancashire glass manufacturers were buying Belgian glass sand for less than £1 per tonne, delivered into their works.[406] In such circumstances, there was little incentive to develop the processing techniques necessary for the exploitation of British deposits, and the first plant for anything more complicated than simple washing started only in 1938, with the opening of a plant for the chemical purification of sand for glass manufacture at King's Lynn.[407] The Second World War provided the first real stimulus to domestic glass sand extraction; supplies of continental sands were cut off and of necessity new domestic sources were exploited and the beneficiation techniques necessary to purify them developed. (It was only during the war that the high grade Loch Aline deposit was first exploited.) Although imports of continental sands were resumed after 1945, they never recovered their dominant position, and an import duty and the steadily rising freight charges stimulated the expansion of British operations. In 1969–70 freight charges for imported Belgian sand carried by a 1000 tonne vessel chartered for 2 voyages per month for 12 months might average £1·97 per tonne.[408] Large bulk carriers, which can contain rising freight costs by their economies of scale, cannot be used in this instance because of the limitations of the canal system. Consequently, output of British sands for glass manufacture more than doubled between 1950 and 1969 (see Table 4.8) and in 1970 constituted about 85 per cent of annual consumption.[409] Foreign imports at that time were largely restricted to high quality glass sands for optical and crystal glass, except for lower grades imported to serve certain Scottish factories. In the absence of sufficiently large Scottish supplies, foreign imports to Scotland were competitive with supplies brought from the English Midlands. These remaining lower grade imports were, however, likely to be further reduced and could be eliminated as a result of the development of a deposit at Devilla Forest, Clackmannanshire, which began deliveries in 1970.

The Cretaceous Lower Greensand outcrops in one arc formation in Kent, Surrey, Hampshire and Sussex and in another running from Lincolnshire through Norfolk and Suffolk (see Fig. 4.8). The main workings in the former occur in Surrey at Redhill, Godstone and Reigate. Here the best seams are equivalent in colour and quality to Belgian and Dutch sands, but they represent only a small proportion of the total tonnage quarried, and it is necessary to combine the different grades of sand extracted, for processing purposes. In 1970 the two Surrey quarries of British Industrial Sand Ltd., the largest silica sand producer contributing an estimated 80–85 per cent of British glass sands,[410] had a total output of 508 000 tonnes of silica sand, of which some 406 000 tonnes were marketed for glass manufacture.[411] Smaller quantities from this deposit serve the important foundry markets of London and South Wales. Another centre of extractive operations in the Cretaceous Lower Greensand occurs in the northern outcrop near King's Lynn, an area where workings for glass sands, foundry sands and building sand has taken place over a long period. The complex of quarries worked by British Industrial Sand Ltd. in this area produced a total of approximately 528 000 tonnes of glass sand in 1970,[412] mainly for Yorkshire and north Midlands markets. The small quantity of best sand here, as in Surrey, is equivalent to that of Belgium, although rather darker in colour. The Greensand deposits are unconsolidated or loosely consolidated, requiring little crushing, but for colourless containerware the material may require acid leaching, i.e. the removal of the surface coating of each grain by an acid wash to remove surface contamination.

A number of isolated deposits in the Millstone Grit contain a higher percentage of clay than those in the Lower Greensand, as much as 20 per cent compared with 1 to 2 per cent, and are consolidated; the extra loss of material during washing and the additional crushing and screen-

Table 4.8. Production of silica and moulding sands, 1950–69

	SILICA SANDS				MOULDING SANDS		Total production all classes
Year	For making synthetic moulding sands (including core sands)	For acid open-hearth furnaces	For glass manufacture	For other purposes	Naturally bonded for iron, steel or non-ferrous foundries	For other purposes	
	tonnes	tonnes	tonnes	tonnes	tonnes	tonnes	tonnes
1950	480 743	94 899	739 245	480 262	766 091	31 540	2 592 780
1951	742 833	99 763	850 504	493 365	825 271	92 349	2 104 085
1952	757 896	61 382	762 466	466 071	894 613	86 470	3 028 898
1953	715 587	62 661	739 877	469 180	819 030	75 531	2 881 866
1954	831 786	94 839	829 187	448 279	638 691	135 110	2 977 891
1955	973 068	120 567	1 105 956	431 701	760 109	82 869	3 474 270
1956	931 219	99 253	1 103 678	464 208	855 969	60 701	3 515 028
1957	1 043 367	142 268	1 058 992	519 425	713 648	175 968	3 653 668
1958	941 353	53 332	1 043 425	512 444	593 161	104 802	3 248 518
1959	1 070 176	—	1 000 042	789 064*	592 046	208 484	3 659 812
1960	1 253 028	—	1 170 992	730 519*	770 029	110 531	4 035 099
1961	1 418 811	—	1 152 946	702 865*	631 084	132 718	4 038 424
1962	1 319 739	—	1 161 122	572 260*	670 495	138 741	3 862 358
1963	1 395 033	—	1 244 554	505 998*	833 434	91 309	4 070 329
1964	1 781 452	—	1 417 912	735 767*	742 499	139 817	4 817 447
1965	1 596 389	—	1 390 221	1 078 264*	735 845	135 590	4 936 309
1966	1 558 505	—	1 461 540	967 928*	724 827	90 190	4 802 991
1967	1 414 749	—	1 445 628	1 137 367*	557 870	123 506	4 679 120
1968	<2 008 643	—	>1 528 770	<1 382 574	....	....	>4 919 987
1969	<2 351 976	—	>1 589 101	947 638	621 922	39 095	5 549 732

* These figures also include silica sand for acid open-hearth furnaces.

Fig. 4.8 *Silica and moulding sand extraction*

ing required add significantly to production costs. Deposits of silica sand occur in this formation in the south-west and north-east of Staffordshire, but only one location is worked primarily for glass sands, that of Oakamoor 19 kilometres from Stoke-on-Trent. In 1970, 152 000 of the 356 000 tonnes extracted here by British Industrial Sand Ltd. was for the manufacture of colourless glass containers, and a similar quantity for the production of silicates such as sodium silicate, a process closely allied to glass manufacture.[413] A new purifying plant for glass sand which was brought into production in 1972 at Oakamoor reflects the growing shortage of good quality glass sand in Britain and the trend towards more intensive upgrading of lower quality sand which can still undercut foreign imports. This plant is designed for an advanced type of process using hydrochloric acid during leaching, and makes possible the processing of some of the more heavily iron-contaminated rocks found in the lower beds of the quarry, hitherto uneconomic to process. The main markets served from this deposit are those of the Lancashire glass industry, although lesser quantities are sold to the ceramics industry in the Potteries.

The Lower Greensand of Surrey and Norfolk, and the Millstone Grit of Staffordshire, provide most of the British glass sand suitable, with beneficiation, for the manufacture of colourless glass. Sands of lesser quality, suitable for coloured containerware, are also worked at Chelford and Congleton in Cheshire, Messingham in Lincolnshire and West Lothian in Scotland, all deposits which yield primarily foundry sands. Glass sand for coloured containers is also extracted from the glacial deposits known as the Shirdley Hill Sands of south-west Lancashire. For many years Pilkington Brothers Ltd., the largest British glass manufacturers, have extracted part of their requirements for coloured glass, approximately 396 000 tonnes in 1970,[414] from these deposits which lie north-west of the company's main St Helens factories. Direct control of extraction by the consumer, prompted in this case mainly by the fortuitous proximity of deposit to factories, is still an unusual feature of the glass sand industry, which has been until recently a buyer's market. However, there was, significantly, in the late 1960s another instance of backwards integration to secure supplies. The quarrying operation at Devilla Forest in Clackmannanshire, which began deliveries of sand for coloured and colourless glass manufacture in 1970, is controlled by a consortium which includes Pilkington Brothers Ltd., United Glass and Sir Alfred McAlpine and Sons Ltd. The factors which prompted such a move are clear. The price of domestic supplies had been rising steadily, as a result of the gradual exhaustion of much of the higher grades over the previous 20 years, and the additional cost of the more complex processing techniques required for purifying lower grade materials. Even the increasingly costly domestic material was undercutting that of foreign imports, affected by rising freight charges. In view of glass manufacturers' dependence on only a few British suppliers, there may be further moves by manufacturers into glass sand extraction, but the sophisticated beneficiation techniques now involved could deter all but companies with very large capital resources, or consortia.

In view of the small element of total manufacturing costs made up by silica sand, and the relatively recent exploitation of domestic deposits, it is clearly unlikely that glass sand deposits have been the chief locating factor for glass manufacturing centres. An analysis of the 78 factories operated in 1971 by members of the Glass Manufacturers' Federation[415] indicates extensive dispersal throughout Britain. Only three sites were situated in close proximity to deposits: that of the Wedgwood Glass factory at King's Lynn, of the United Glass factory at Alloa, Clackmannanshire, and the St Helens complex, dominated by Pilkingtons and United Glass. In fact, at all three sites the proximity of factory to local deposits is fortuitous: the King's Lynn factory, using mainly imported Belgian sands, was primarily attracted to the area by facilities provided by King's Lynn Corporation, while both the Alloa factory and the St Helens complex pre-dated the exploitation of local reserves of glass sands. At St Helens other factors, such as proximity to the chemical industry of south Lancashire and Cheshire, to coal and water transport, have been of much more significance. As far as supplies of glass sands are concerned, the St Helens glass factories now draw on a variety of sources. The Peasley factory of United Glass obtains supplies from Redhill and from Staffordshire for colourless containers as well as from the local deposits of Lancashire and Cheshire for coloured containerware. The nearby Ravenhead factory obtains the highest quality sands for tableware from Loch Aline and Belgium.[416] Of the other glass manufacturing complexes, that at Stourbridge in Worcestershire was based on a fireclay deposit from which the crucibles used in the manufacturing process were made,[417] and the concentration in and near London owes its importance more to the large metropolitan container market than to proximity to the Surrey glass sand deposits.

Silica sand for the making of synthetic foundry moulds and cores made up a larger proportion of total silica sand output than that of glass sands in 1969 and output had grown more rapidly, having more than quadrupled since 1950 (see Table 4.8). Changes in steelmaking technology had however slightly reduced the very small consumption for refractory linings of acid open-hearth furnaces. Silica sand for foundry use has traditionally been a cheap commodity supplied from domestic sources. In 1971 the great majority of foundries used a low cost, washed, graded silica sand with a delivered price of approximately £2·46 per tonne.[418] However, specialized sands with a phenolic resin coating, a complex artificial bonding agent necessary for certain types of moulds and cores, varied in price from about £11·81 per tonne to as much as £24·61 per tonne.[419]

The chief source of silica sand for foundry use is Cheshire, where deposits in the Chelford/Congleton/Allostock area provide one of the world's largest reserves of general purpose foundry sand. The largest quarry here, located at Chelford and worked by British Industrial Sand Ltd., is a composite quarry extending over several square miles. Since the deposit lies beneath the water-table, the main workings are in the form of a lagoon, from which the raw sand is pumped, and washed simultaneously with extraction. It is probable that some 1 270 000 tonnes of foundry sands were extracted from the Cheshire area in 1970 (of which British Industrial Sand Ltd. contributed 914 400 tonnes);[420] i.e. approximately half of the total silica sand for foundry use extracted in Britain in that year came from Cheshire. The bulk of this output is general purpose foundry sand and the main market is the industrial Midlands, the centre of the British foundry industry. It is estimated that about 60 per cent of Cheshire foundry sand goes to the Birmingham/Wolverhampton area, about 30 per cent to Lancashire, Cheshire and the North-West and the remainder to foundries on the North-East coast.[421]

A smaller deposit of silica sand, worked primarily for general purpose mould and core-making sand, occurs at Messingham, south of Lincolnshire, and consists of blown sands of recent geological origin. At West Lothian in Scotland, an isolated silica deposit in the Millstone Grit provides mainly foundry sand, with smaller quantities for coloured glass manufacture and concrete aggregates. The 'estuarine sands' of the Lower Jurassic yield foundry sand in Northamptonshire, especially near Wittering, and in east and north-east Yorkshire. Although the economies of scale of the large Cheshire workings are not possible at these other deposits, the higher unit costs of production are offset by their location, permitting lower transport costs to markets in North-East England, the East Midlands and Central Scotland. Foundry sands are also extracted from deposits providing mainly glass sand, namely that in Surrey, serving mainly the London and South Wales markets, Staffordshire and Norfolk. British Industrial Sand Ltd.'s King's Lynn works is the site of the company's resin coating plant for foundry sands, the largest such coating plant in Europe or the United

States. The comparative remoteness of this location from most major markets is offset by the very much higher value of resin coated sands than normal foundry grades (selling at from £11·81 to £24·61 per tonne compared with £2·46 per tonne for normal foundry sand). This greatly reduces the significance of transport charges as a percentage of delivered costs.

Naturally bonded moulding sands for use in iron, steel or non-ferrous foundries is a small and slightly diminishing sector of foundry sand in Britain. Such sands, which are relatively cheap to produce since very little processing is required, are of comparatively rare occurrence. The main factor behind the slightly falling output figures during the period 1950–69 (see Table 4.8) is that this is not a suitable material for some modern foundry processes, depending as they do largely on organic binders. The high percentage of fluxing agents such as iron oxide present in naturally bonded sand also makes it insufficiently effective as a refractory for steel casting and for the more sophisticated types of iron casting now being carried on. The chief deposits occur in the East and West Midlands. In the Nottingham and Mansfield area, naturally bonded moulding sand occurs in the Bunter Pebble beds of the Lower Mottled Sandstone, frequently overlaid by glacial sands.[422] The main working is near Mansfield, but a small deposit of lesser quality is worked in the Bramcote Hills, west of Nottingham and near Blidworth. The main markets served are at Sheffield and Chesterfield, although smaller quantities are marketed in Glasgow. In the Trias of the West Midlands, a complex of workings occurs, notably at Wombourn and Swynnerton in Staffordshire and in the Bromsgrove area of north Worcestershire. Smaller deposits were in 1969 worked elsewhere, notably at Castleton and North Cave in Yorkshire, in the West Malling/Rochester area of Kent, the Westbury/Devizes area of Wiltshire and the Gartcosh/Ferniegair area of Lanarkshire.

While output of naturally bonded moulding sand has been declining slowly, demand for silica sand was in the 1960s growing at the rate of about 6 per cent per year. Although estimates submitted by Cheshire County Council's economic geology consultants in 1970 postulated a continuing growth factor of 6 per cent,[423] there is in fact evidence to suggest that the rate of growth will fall during the period 1972–82 as more foundries, which constitute the major silica sand market, reclaim sand for re-use. Indeed, British Industrial Sand Ltd., the major silica sand extractor, believes it would not be unrealistic to predict a decline in the quarrying of new foundry sand deposits in the 1970s and early 1980s, a decline which could result in output falling to as low as 50 per cent of the present level by the end of the century.[424] Demand for glass sands, on the other hand, could well continue to grow at its present rate. If these estimates prove correct, then clearly the planning problems associated with deposits worked primarily for glass sand are likely to be accentuated as pressure for expansion increases, while those associated primarily with workings for foundry purposes are likely to diminish in time.

The chief planning problems associated with silica sand working, like those posed by most non-ubiquitous minerals, are primarily connected with the inflexibility imposed by limited deposits. The planning problems of silica sand extraction contrast strongly with the more serious ones imposed by sand and gravel workings for aggregates, since they are intensive where those of aggregates material are extensive, and are more often of a long-term nature. The sand and gravel industry frequently work a deposit over a short period of time: not uncommonly a greenfield site may be worked-out and restored within five years, whereas silica sand deposits tend to be exploited over much longer periods. Twenty or thirty years is a common length of time for silica sand deposits to be worked because, with the very much more sophisticated methods of treatment, longer periods are needed to amortize capital investment.[425] Two silica sand deposits may be said to present planning difficulties of some seriousness. The Surrey deposits near Redhill and Reigate are within the Metropolitan Green Belt and close to an area designated as being of Outstanding Natural Beauty. These deposits, which are principally exploited for glass manufacture, contain substantial reserves and are likely to be the subject of considerable pressure for expansion. The extraction of these deposits forms one of the two Surrey districts defined by the County Planning Officer[426] as presenting 'a particularly sharp area of [land use] conflict'. The workings have created water-filled pits in an area where demand for land is great, although some, such as the disused Holmethorpe quarry near Redhill, are now used as a source of water for the Redhill washing plant. The amount of traffic generated by the transport of sand by lorry from Godstone to the processing plant at Redhill causes some added congestion to this heavily populated area, although the amount is declining as this quarry nears exhaustion.

The planning problems of the Cheshire deposits are also largely those of land use competition. In 1968, the date of the last full county survey, 10 sites covering 223 hectares had permission for the working of silica sand and in 1971, with small variations, the scale of working remained the same.[427] Land use competition is particularly acute around the town of Congleton, where the deposit extends up to the town and the workings are far closer to a large built-up area than would normally be permitted. This harms the environment of some parts of the town and is a limiting factor on its development.[428] However, the pressure for expansion in this area, worked principally for foundry sand, could diminish in the long-term if forecasts of a reduction in foundry sand output prove correct. Only comparatively minor problems arise elsewhere. The Loch Aline deposit, remote from large centres of population, is located on the Sound of Mull, an area of importance to coastal and scenic preservation, but since the deposit is worked underground there is little in the way of visual disfigurement, although there is a subsidence problem. The working of the Shirdley Hill sands near St Helens does not seriously conflict with the main competing land use, that of agriculture. The sands of this shallow deposit are worked to a depth of only about 1·2 metres, after which the drainage is replaced and the land restored to agriculture.

The planning authorities in the main producing areas claim to appreciate the national importance of silica sand deposits and the special circumstances of their operators compared with those of sand gravel extractors. The Surrey Development Plan recognized that certain types of sand deposits were limited and that the local planning authority should protect them from sterilization from other development.[429] Cheshire County Planning Department have given close consideration to the problems likely to be caused by increasing sand extraction in the county and commissioned a report on the question by Mackay and Schellmann, the county's economic geology and mining consultants, presented in April 1970.[430] The planning authority recognizes that 'Cheshire is a major supplier of silica sand for British industry . . . to such an extent that limitation of extraction in the County would be economically harmful to important industries'. To ensure that adequate supplies are safeguarded, a 'County Reserve' of land with planning permission for extraction is maintained, which is large enough to guarantee ten to fifteen years' supply of each type of sand at estimated production rates. Although new workings at Congleton are not permitted until existing excavations have been completely worked out, the normal criteria applied to permitted mineral extraction are modified there in view of the 'exceptional national importance' of the deposits.[431] Silica sand operators in the county may also apply for relaxation of the week-day limitation on hours of loading, unloading and movement of vehicles which is otherwise made on sand working operations 'to permit more continuous use of the substantial capital investment involved'.[432]

In spite of this, the largest silica sand operator feels that the importance of working these deposits is only fully appreciated at national level and that too many applications are rejected at local level, with the decisions only reversed after a public inquiry and long-delayed ministerial approval.[433]

DIATOMITE

Diatomite or diatomaceous earth consists of the fossil remains of minute organisms known as Diatomaceae or diatoms, primitive plant forms which live in fresh or salt water.[434] One cubic inch (about 16 cubic centimetres) of diatomite contains the silica shells of from 40 to 70 diatoms, whose organic parts have decomposed.[435] Most of the world's economically workable deposits were laid down during the Tertiary period in freshwater lakes or swamps, usually in districts made up of resistant rocks. However, diatomite is still accumulating, where suitable conditions exist, especially in the Arctic and Antarctic regions. The substance formed is fine-grained, similar in appearance to chalk or white clay and is easily reduced to powder when dry. The purest deposits are white, but the presence of impurities, notably clay, peat or iron oxide, causes discoloration to grey, yellow or brown tones.

Diatomite has a unique combination of physical and chemical properties which include non-conduction of heat and sound, chemical inertness, and high absorbency—good quality diatomite will absorb four times its weight of water.[436] Consequently, it is widely used in insulation against heat, cold and sound, either in the form of powder or of bricks; in filtration, especially in water purification plants and in sugar refining. The cheaper grades are used as a lightweight filler for such products as paints and rubber, and some of the low grade diatomite and diatomaceous shales are made into lightweight aggregates for concrete by burning out the organic matter which they contain. The combination of low density and insulating properties is useful for this purpose. Diatomite is no longer used in the manufacture of dynamite, formerly its principal use, but does form a convenient carrier of nitroglycerine explosives. The production, consumption and import figures are somewhat contradictory; *Industrial Minerals* suggests that consumption has been increasing by about 5 per cent per year[437] but the domestic production figures fell slightly between 1964 and 1969 and imports fell sharply (see Table 4.9). Of the estimated total world production of 17·8 million tonnes,[438] Britain produced only 12 982 tonnes in 1969, and that in an impure form unsuitable for filter-aid manufacture. Most of the rest was extracted in the United States. Consequently, substantial quantities of most types of diatomite are imported, especially the type known as Danish 'moler' used in water purification. The one British deposit now worked commercially is near Kendal in Westmorland. The deposit, about 820 metres long by 270 metres wide, was once no more than a marsh, but has become a lake as a result of excavation.[439] It is worked by Cape Insulation Ltd., a member of the Cape Asbestos Group, which acquired the working from Kencert Products Ltd. in 1943. The deposit, dark-coloured and impure, is used almost entirely for insulation purposes, and is worked by dredging. In 1961 the dragline then operating was replaced by a pontoon equipped with 0·48 cubic metre mud grab to improve selec-

Table 4.9. UK production and imports of diatomaceous earth, 1964–9 (tonnes)

	Production	Imports (Chiefly 'moler' from Denmark)
1964	13 936	57 138
1965	15 320	46 582
1966	14 932	43 041
1967	12 684	47 210
1968	14 936	43 322
1969	12 982	39 848

Source: Institute of Geological Sciences, Mineral Resources Division, *Statistical Summary of the Mineral Industry, 1964–9*, HMSO 1970, pp. 121 and 123.

tivity at the excavator stage. The earth is conveyed by barge to the jetty, and then transported by aerial conveyor to 'weathering dumps' where as much of the moisture as possible is dried out. The material is then taken to the factory for calcining. Although these operations take place within the Lake District National Park, they are on a comparatively small scale and do not, in the eyes of either Westmorland County Planning Department or the Lake District Planning Board, appear to cause very serious amenity problems.[440] Although the planning consents stipulate that, should activities cease, the area must be restored, it could well be argued that the creation of the lake has actually improved amenities, and it would probably be left as such should working cease.[441] The factory buildings are largely screened by trees.

Although there were, in 1972, no other active diatomite workings elsewhere in Britain, several Scottish and Welsh deposits are known to exist. The Institute of Geological Sciences published in 1972 a report on diatomaceous deposits in Snowdonia[447] where many mountain lakes may contain the mineral. Unestimated but small reserves were found in Llyn Geirconydd, Llyn Crafnant and Llyn Elsi. However, it was believed that Llynau Mymbyr, a pair of lakes connected with Llyn Dyffryn Mymbyr, may have a volume of 1 000 000 cubic metres of diatomite. All these are deposits similar in origin to that at Kentmere, but small by international standards. Nevertheless the Institute of Geological Sciences report concluded that total economic appraisal of all deposits in Snowdonia would require better sampling techniques.

The Scottish deposits, unlike the Welsh, have been exploited commercially in the past. Chief amongst these is the deposit at Loch Cuithir in the north of Skye, made up of pure material believed to be about 12 metres thick.[443] This was formerly worked by the British Diatomite Company and the Skye Mineral Syndicate Company. Diatomite is said to occur in small quantities elsewhere on Skye, namely in Loch Mealt, Sartil, Loch Cleat, Loch Smisdale and Glen Uig, and some of these have been worked in the past on a small scale. It is possible that the diatomite working on Skye could be resumed in the 1970s, since the high price of the pure mineral, in 1972 in excess of £19·70 per tonne, could outweigh the long distances to market involved in extraction in this remote location. Diatomite working on Skye was recently the subject of a special feasibility study by the firm of mineral consultants retained by the Highlands and Islands Development Board. The board's policy is to act as a trigger mechanism by uncovering mineral prospects; their mineral consultants carry out both regional mineral assessments, and specific studies of selected minerals, such as the Skye diatomite deposits. Although no definite application for working has yet been made, the board maintain that there is some scope for a small extractive operation, employing less than 40 men.[444]

A second, once-important deposit in Scotland, is near Ballater in Aberdeenshire. This was discovered under a layer of peat near Loch Kinord in 1880.[445] However, it was of poorer quality than that from the major Skye working and was only intermittently extracted as the workings were liable to flood. Almost the whole output served the explosive works at Ardeer, Ayrshire. Other, smaller, diatomite deposits occur at Kirkibost and North Tolsta on the Isle of Lewis and Loch Ba on the Island of Mull and Loch Leven in Fifeshire. These last two are of inferior quality. However, as far as Lewis is concerned, Ross and Cromarty County Planning Authority, in consultation with the Scottish Council for Development and Industry, pursue an active policy of seeking fuller investigation into the mineral resources of the island, including the diatomite deposits.[446] Inasmuch as it is appropriate here to point out that some of the local authorities for the remote areas of Scotland, supported by such official bodies as the Highlands and Islands Development Board and the Scottish Council, take a much more active role in encouraging mineral extraction in their areas, which contrasts strongly with that of many English planning authorities, who tend to regard mineral extraction in the light of competing demands for land use. The official encouragement of mineral exploitation in the north of Scotland is entirely understandable, bearing in mind the problems of unemployment and population imbalance in such areas. The Highlands and Islands Development Board point out that even a small-scale extractive operation—all that was envisaged for any mineral in any part of their area in 1971, employing perhaps 12 to 40 men—would provide a very significant amount of employment in terms of the size of the local population.[447] However, any deposit within the area covered by the Highlands and Islands Board, such as the Skye diatomite deposit, must inevitably make some impact on a landscape of which the chief value at the present time lies in the tourism it attracts. However, although there is a possibility that Scotland may see in the 1970s the beginning of new operations resulting from the prospecting referred to in Chapter 1, the Highlands and Islands Development Board considers that none of the prospects yet uncovered would result in serious conflict with Areas of Outstanding Scenic Value, and that they can rely on the local planning authorities to frame the conditions necessary to prevent damage to amenity. At the same time, it is most important that the desire for the local employment which mining might bring should not prevent the framing of stringent safeguards to protect the interests both of amenity and of the tourist industry, which contributed more than £100 million to the Scottish economy in 1970.

This dictum must apply with much more force to a matter hardly considered in the early 1970s—the need for construction sites for North Sea oil platforms. The problems raised by this issue art dealt with in Chapter 6.

5

METALLIFEROUS MINERALS

BRITAIN is a metalliferous province with a long and extensive history of extraction of ferrous and non-ferrous ores. The non-ferrous ores are found in three main types of geological environment; the granite masses of Devon and Cornwall; the Lower Palaeozoic rocks of the Highland zones such as Central and North Wales, the Welsh border, the Lake District and the Southern Uplands of Scotland; and parts of the Carboniferous limestone outcrop of Derbyshire and the Northern Pennines, the Mendips and Flintshire. Ferrous ores occur in much larger quantities and are substantially more widespread. Haematite, the richest of the British ores, occurs in Cumberland and north-west Lancashire in irregular deposits in the Carboniferous limestone[1] and in the Forest of Dean and South Wales.[2] Bedded iron ores occur extensively throughout the Coal Measures; clayband ironstone, essentially iron carbonate, occurs most importantly in south Staffordshire, Shropshire, South Wales, Derbyshire, the West Riding, and Southern Lowlands of Scotland and blackband ores, carbonaceous ironstones, in north Staffordshire and Scotland. (The Coal Measures ores are now costly and difficult to work but a huge reserve remains.) The bedded ores of the Jurassic series occur from Yorkshire to Oxfordshire. Minor occurrences include the ironstone of the Wealden rocks of Sussex and Kent. Both ferrous and non-ferrous ores have been worked extensively in Britain since the pre-Roman period but their history, current extractive position and attributes are sharply distinctive. Ferrous ores, which are on a world scale of much wider occurrence and much lower value than non-ferrous ores, approximate more closely to the category of commoner minerals (the second group of non-metalliferous minerals as given in Chapter 1). Britain has very substantial deposits; the total UK resources have been calculated at approximately 5500 million tonnes including about 3150 million tonnes classified as

309

reserves.[3] Thus supplies of ferrous ores have never been depleted to anything like the same extent as the rarer and more valuable non-ferrous ores. Nevertheless the lower value ferrous ores are being worked increasingly in the context of world markets; their higher metallic content than the non-ferrous ores makes viable their transport in substantially untreated form over large distances and modern transport improvements by sea have intensified the international movement of ferrous ores. The world market conditions prevailing for ferrous and non-ferrous ores have differed sharply in the past century; iron ore production has been much less volatile than that of the non-ferrous ores and British output has not been subjected to the precipitate slumps as witnessed, for instance, in base metals in the late nineteenth century. On the other hand, very large discoveries of iron ore deposits overseas in the 1950s and 1960s has made the market an increasingly competitive one for iron ore suppliers. The reverse is true for suppliers of non-ferrous metals.

The non-ferrous metals may be divided primarily on the basis of value into the precious metals (gold and silver) and the base metals, of which tin (cassiterite, tin oxide), lead (chiefly galena, sulphide of lead), zinc (calamine, zinc carbonate or blende, zinc sulphide), copper (chiefly chalcopyrite, copper pyrites, or cuprite, copper oxide), tungsten ore (wolfram), arsenic and nickel have at various times been extracted in Britain.[4] The precious metals have never been located in any great quantity in Britain. Silver, usually found in association with lead, has been obtained from argentiferous ores of lead in Derbyshire, the Mendips and the Isle of Man. A little gold has been obtained, notably from the Dolgellau area of North Wales; at least 13 gold mines have been operative here and recorded production from 1844 to 1938 was 3633·364 grammes of gold.[5] A well-known working, the Ogofau gold mine, was also in production near Pumpsaint in Carmarthenshire. Alluvial deposits of gold have been worked in streams in Selkirkshire and Sutherland. The base metals, lead, copper, zinc and tin have, on the other hand, been located and worked in very substantial quantities in Britain, notably lead from the Pennines, Mendips, Flintshire, Shropshire and the Scottish borders, copper from Anglesey, Shropshire and Cornwall, tin from Devon and Cornwall and zinc from the Mendips and Pennines. Although lead, copper and tin were worked substantially in Roman times (zinc was of little commercial value until the end of the eighteenth century), the height of extractive output occurred in the nineteenth century, interacting with the rapid industrial expansion of the period. During that century a greater British tonnage of copper, lead and zinc was produced than in the whole of previous historical times.[6] In the early nineteenth century Devon and Cornwall alone were producing about half the world's copper ore, and a whole hill of copper ore discovered in Anglesey in 1768 was gradually being worked-out. In 1800 approximately 100 zinc mines were operative in the Mendips alone. Lead mining was approaching its most active phase; there are now some 4000 disused lead mines in Derbyshire alone. The peak period for lead mining was 1850–70 when an average of more than 91 000 tonnes of ore were produced annually[7] (chiefly from Derbyshire, the North Pennines and North Wales). Cornish tin mines achieved a maximum output a little later, in 1871, and production continued to be high until the 1890s.[8] However, all these base metals were severely affected by a recession in demand and sharply falling prices during the late nineteenth century, affecting different metals at slightly different times. The sharp decline in British base metal mining resulted from the discovery of new large deposits overseas, notably copper from the United States and Chile, lead from Spain and tin from Malaya and Bolivia. In important instances, the deposits occurred in countries over which Britain then enjoyed economic or political influence. The rapid growth of steam shipping facilitated imports at prices which greatly undercut home supplies, obtained in many cases from areas where mining conditions were becoming more difficult as the best and/or most accessible ores were being worked-out. From 1872 to 1881, for instance, imports of lead rose from 70 958 tonnes to 94 894 tonnes, and the price of its ore fell from £13·43 to £12·94. Total British lead production dropped from 74 595 tonnes in 1870 to 60 277 tonnes in 1882.[9] By 1913 lead ore output had fallen further to 24 671 tonnes, zinc ore to 17 571 tonnes, tin ore to 8489 tonnes and copper ore, most affected of all, to 2 610 tonnes.[10]

Output of all these base metals has remained at a continuously low level this century and that of copper has virtually died out. In 1970 the domestic mining of metallic ores provided less than 2 per cent by value of metals consumed.[11] That necessary prerequisite of continued mining activity, an active search for new ore bodies to replace those that had become exhausted, was, until recently, hardly undertaken. In only two instances was there a partial revival, in the period 1950 and 1970. The output of lead and zinc ores (principally lead) increased by 39·7 per cent (from 4332 tonnes to 6055 tonnes). However, the most striking revival occurred in the case of tin with the output of these ores (including a small quantity of tungsten) rising by 121 per cent (from 1474 to 3767 tonnes).[12] The reasons for this are explored in detail in the next section. A few major points only need be noted here. Tin is, on a world scale, one of the rarest of the base metals; tin deposits, unlike those of lead and zinc, occur in only a few parts of the earth's crust. By far the greatest percentage of current world output is obtained from alluvial and eluvial deposits which have a limited life, and it is believed that the future supply of tin will have to be obtained from known tin fields.[13] Special circumstances in Cornwall favoured the likelihood of substantial reserves of tin remaining, a point to be taken up later, while the major deposits of lead and copper are likely to be exhausted. At the present time, however, tin is the most valuable of the base metals of known existence in Britain; its January 1973 price of over £1600 per tonne may be compared with £450 per tonne for copper and £130 per tonne for lead.[14] Tin is even more valuable than nickel, a metal produced in only a few areas of the world; this metal, of which recent exploration has found some favourable indications in Aberdeenshire, had an average price in 1973 of £1300 per tonne.[15] The comparatively high value of tin, and the existence of regional investment grants for much of Cornwall, made economic both the expansion of investment in the two mines with a continuous history of operation in Cornwall, which had managed to survive harsh overseas competition, and the opening up of new mining operations.

The smaller-scale revival of lead output during the 1950s and 1960s was brought about under very different circumstances. In many areas the opportunities for a revival of lead mining as a self-sufficient economic enterprise were much more limited than those for Cornish tin. In Derbyshire, for instance, centuries of active prospecting by thousands of miners on the exposed limestone areas, where anyone was legally able to register a claim provided he worked his discovery, left little chance of any new discoveries being made near the surface, and in 1959 it was postulated that if anything remained undiscovered it was unlikely to be large enough to attract modern enterprise.[16] In 1970 more lead was produced in Britain than any other base metal, including tin, due almost entirely to its coincidence in the Pennines with fluorspar, in earlier centuries considered a waste mineral, but for which demand in the 1950s and 1960s was accelerating rapidly. Of the total British output of lead in 1970, most of it, approximately 4600–5100 tonnes, was produced in Derbyshire by Laporte Industries Ltd. as a by-product of the company's fluorspar operations.[17] This lead output, obtained through flotation treatment of ores worked by deep-mining and open-casting by the company itself, as well as from material worked by tributers over a wide area of the country (see Chapter 4), had almost quadrupled since 1960. Lead concentrate is also obtained in small quantities as a by-product of fluorspar working elsewhere in Derbyshire; for example, at the Guilini (Derbyshire) Ltd. plant, south-west of

Matlock, which also produced some zinc, and in the Northern Pennines at the BSC Blanchland plant and the Weardale Lead Company plant at Rookhope. In North Wales at the Olwyn Goch mine in Flintshire, lead is worked in association with another commercially valuable product, the almost pure calcium carbonate (limestone) used for glass manufacture or agricultural purposes. The owners of the mine, the Hollywell and Halkyn Mining Tunnel Co. Ltd., hold a lease covering the larger part of the lead bearing area of central Flintshire and in 1971 produced about 1000 tonnes of about 63 per cent lead and 10 per cent zinc concentrates.[18] However, the operators are working on the fringes of ore left from previous operations and now have no calculated reserves. Thus, the factors influencing the increase of lead output in the 1950s and 1960s were not related essentially to the economics of lead mining itself, and for that reason the increase in output is not strictly comparable to that of tin. Therefore lead is not considered separately in the section which follows. Zinc is not listed separately in the official mineral output figures; production only amounted to 372 tonnes of dressed ore in 1968,[19] the last year for which independent figures were given, and was derived essentially as a by-product of other operations, since it is usually found in association with lead. However, output levels are lower than those of lead as the lead–zinc deposits in Britain consist for the most part primarily of lead. Galena (lead sulphide) has a lead content of 86·6 per cent and sphalerite (zinc sulphide) a zinc content of only 67 per cent. No copper output was recorded in the official British mineral statistics during the 1960s although copper was obtained in small quantities as a by-product of tin mining in Cornwall. Cornish tin mines have recently also been producing small quantities of by-product tungsten and arsenic. In the case of tungsten, an important steel alloying metal, only 11 tonnes were produced in 1970.[20]

Non-ferrous metal mining has for the most part remained at a very low ebb in Britain this century principally because the economic stimulus to exploration and development of what are not easily accessible deposits was lacking. The limited amount of mineral exploration that was carried out consisted of the re-opening of old mines to see whether substantial quantities were left in the ground, an approach unlikely to be profitable since earlier miners knew their business.[21] However, by the late 1960s, the increasing world demand for non-ferrous metal products, the availability of new techniques in locating and exploiting deposits, a change in government policy towards actively encouraging such activity, and, to a lesser extent the discovery of commercially workable lead–zinc deposits in Eire (some of them such as

313

the new Tara mine at Navan, large by international standards), were factors which encouraged prospecting in the UK.

Of these, certainly the prime factor, must be considered the rapidly expanding world demand for metals, in itself a product of both demographic and economic expansion. A few examples of the anticipated range of future demand, based on calculations of the US Bureau of Mines, may appropriately be cited here, although such long-term predictions may easily be invalidated, by product substitution or technological change. In 1970 world production of copper (excluding the 18 per cent produced in Communist countries) was 5·1 million tonnes.[22] The average annual increase in world consumption of all types of copper is likely to be about 4·5 per cent (the rate prevalent in the 1960s), and estimated world demand for primary copper in the year 2000 between 19·7 and 38·8 million tonnes.[23] Even the current rate of depletion necessitates the annual discovery of about 1000 million tonnes of ores, to hold reserves constant; as consumption rises and ore grades fall, it is believed that this annual discovery rate may need to be doubled in ten years.[24] The world production of refined lead in 1970 was 4 million tonnes; world demand for lead in 2000 has been estimated at between 6·67 and 9·63 million tonnes.[25] World production of zinc in 1970 was 5 million tonnes; world demand for zinc metal in the year 2000 has been estimated at between 8·2 and 14 million tonnes.[26] Demand of the scale anticipated can only be sustained if more inaccessible or more disseminated deposits of lower grade ores are worked. This will be a continuation of a trend already apparent in this century. Whereas in 1910 copper ores of 5 per cent or more metal content were predominantly worked, the average in 1959 was well under 2 per cent and large tonnages were being mined from ores with about 1 per cent metal content.[27] Such ore bodies may well exist in Britain, despite its long and intensive mining history, since these were types of ore body which earlier miners could not easily identify or handle. Their unsophisticated methods were unable to deal with either complex or finely disseminated ore. Such ore may now, if found in sufficient quantities, be worked economically with modern, capital-intensive mining equipment. There is the further possibility of locating by modern methods substantial ore bodies undetectable by earlier methods. These bodies are unlikely to be near the surface since the general practice was to put down trial bores where there were any mineral indications at the surface. Modern exploration techniques however include airborne photography (coloured, infra-red and X-ray), airborne geophysical surveys, ground geophysics and the geochemical study of trace elements in plants and soil.[28] Such methods can be used over large areas to help identify the most promising locations to be tested by diamond drilling, though they are both lengthy and expensive and non-ferrous metal mining remains the most speculative of all branches of mineral exploration. The science of geology has so far not provided such reliable guides for non-ferrous metal exploration as for hydrocarbon exploration,[29] which may partially be related to the fact that non-ferrous metal operators have not devoted as large a part of their exploration budgets to geologists as have oil companies.[30] Furthermore, as implied in Chapter 1, the non-ferrous metal industry in Britain suffers a further onerous disadvantage compared with oil prospectors since they* have to deal with a multiplicity of mineral rights holders, whose claims are nowhere officially registered. On the other hand, oil companies are dealing in a commodity whose mineral rights are nationalized. The disadvantages of the non-ferrous metal operatives are considerable now that exploration techniques and development may well involve large areas of land. It is for these reasons that most non-ferrous metal interests consider that the attitude of the Government is of particularly crucial importance in the extraction of this type of mineral.

At the opening of the symposium of the Institution of Mining and Metallurgy on the Future of Non-Ferrous Metal Mining in Britain, R. M. Preston commented that it was hardly possible to envisage a successful revival of mining in Britain without the support of the Government.[31] This view was spelt out later in more detail by J. F. McDivitt, in a report on the status of mineral exploration in Europe, prepared for the Organization for European Economic Cooperation. He argued that

Government plays a very important part in determining the level of exploration activity in a country. The direction of this interest may be indicated by the extent of a Government's sponsored prospecting, or by the way in which it handles control of the tax structure and of the system of allocating mineral lands. Thus the level of mining activity may not be directly related to the mineral potential of a country, but rather to the Government attitude towards mineral development.[32]

During the 1960s strong Government interest in mineral development, although by no means new, was increasing in many European countries; France, Greece, Norway, Portugal, Spain, Sweden and Turkey all had Government agencies directly concerned with search for minerals; Eire pursued a policy of stimulating mineral exploration through indirect subsidies and tax concessions. In Britain, however, although

---

* Somewhat different criteria apply in the case of gold and silver, to which the Crown has a pre-emptive right.

individual prominent politicians expressed interest or concern, little in the way of very positive Government action was taken during the 1960s to encourage or promote specifically non-ferrous metal or other mineral extraction. Although a number of mining enterprises such as the Cornish tin mines benefited substantially from regional investment grants in the 1960s, these were not specifically designed for high risk metal operators. Such inactivity was not exceptional in the context of British history; three times this century Government committees had been appointed to look into the state of metal mining in the UK[33] and in every case no action had been taken on the ensuing recommendations. Non-ferrous metal operatives were, however, more critical of such inactivity at a time when many other European governments were adopting more positive roles, nor were they unduly impressed, as Chapter 1 makes clear, when in 1971 the Government announced the Minerals Exploration Bill. This, so the Government claimed, was a specific measure to encourage exploration for non-ferrous metal ores, barium minerals, fluorspar and potash. However, the exclusion of the ferrous ores from the provisions of this Act is a reflection of the entirely different considerations applicable in this case. The most salient distinctions are that the extraction of ferrous ores in Britain has never yet been run down to the same extent as that of non-ferrous ores, that very large reserves of such ores are known to exist, and that the current world market is a buyer's rather than a seller's one. During the 1960s the delivered price of imported ore was becoming relatively cheaper than the delivered price of home ores, which are of relatively low average iron content. The period saw the development of very large new overseas ore bodies (in some respects comparable to the large overseas discoveries of base metals in the late nineteenth century), helping to make competition in world iron ore markets, among new and old producing districts, very keen. At the same time, delivered costs were being held down by a steady reduction in per unit transport costs by sea, achieved by larger ore carriers and handling terminals, and to some extent by the expansion of the practice of upgrading metal content or ores at source to reduce bulk for transport. In spite of the additional cost of higher imports to the balance of payments, it is to the advantage of BSC, and ultimately to the economy as a whole, that British steel, itself marketed in competitive world markets, should utilize the cheapest available raw material. Consequently, while an expansion of British non-ferrous base metal output may confidently be expected during the 1970s, output of ferrous ores is likely to contract by one third, from 12 million tonnes per year to 8 million tonnes per year, in 1970–5.[34]

The decline of extraction of ferrous ores should provide little consolation to conservationists and planners since most current extraction is covered by the unique terms of the Ironstone Restoration Fund by which past and present excavations are restored to a high standard. The potential revival of non-ferrous ores, on the other hand, has caused considerable disquiet. This is certainly not justified in every case. The underground mining of tin in Cornwall, for instance, can, under modern conditions, cause little surface disturbance. Generally speaking, the ore bodies of Devon and Cornwall do not fall into the category of those suitable for exploitation on a large scale, because of their mode of occurrence and comparatively small size. However, the opencast working of non-ferrous metal ores, which does not exist in Britain at the present time, undoubtedly poses environmental problems of a high order, problems which may well seem particularly alarming since there is no tradition of such operations in this country.

Any generalizations about the nature of probable opencast workings for non-ferrous ores in Britain need to be treated with caution, since every ore body and hence every site will be unique. Ore bodies may be either flat horizontal deposits which may be worked by a stripping process and accompanied by progressive restoration, or vertical or steeply inclined ore bodies or disseminated zones which may have to be kept unfilled for the duration of the active working. A wide range of possibilities exist between these two extremes. Nevertheless, certain common difficulties are likely to arise. First, such operations are likely to take place in areas of high quality landscape, since the mineralized zones of Britain coincide with such areas of Upland Britain. It is unlikely that shallow deposits still remain unexploited, and deeper deposits are unlikely to lend themselves to full restoration. The workings are likely to have a very high ratio of waste to produce; over 90 per cent and sometimes up to 99 per cent of the rock removed from the working face remains, either as solid waste which would probably be deposited on waste rock tips or as slurry from the treatment plant deposited in the tailings lagoon (which might be sited anywhere within a radius of 16 kilometres of the working). While rehabilitation of the site to create acceptable new land forms could be carried out after the closure of the working through contouring and vegetation of the waste tips and the vegetation of the tailings areas, disturbance, both visual and audial, would inevitably occur during its active life, which might well be of the order of 20 to 30 years. In all these respects, the potential opencast operations for non-ferrous minerals may be contrasted with opencast excavations for ironstone, and with opencast coal working, the most successful surface mineral operations from an environmental point of view. Such workings are, in contrast, predominantly in low-land areas, susceptible of full and on-going restoration, have a low ratio of waste and a shorter duration of working.

The scale of possible opencast non-ferrous workings has been illustrated by two hypothetical cases which were postulated by the Zuckerman Commission. One was an openpit copper mine with total reserves of 60 million tonnes, grading 0·7 per cent metal and worked at the rate of 4 million tonnes of ore per year, and the other a lead–zinc opencast working with reserves of 10 million tonnes, worked at a rate of 666 000 tonnes per year, a size comparable to that of mines now operative in Eire. The hypothetical copper working might occupy a surface area of 300–600 hectares with an additional surrounding area bringing total land requirements to between 600 and 1200 hectares. Of this total, rock dumps might occupy between 100 hectares and 200 hectares, and the tailings reservoir between 100 hectares and 220 hectares.[35] In the case of the smaller lead–zinc working, a surface area of 90 to 180 hectares might be involved, including an openpit of 20–40 hectares, a tailings disposal and water reservoir area of 35–50 hectares and a waste rock dump of 4 to 8 hectares.[36] No opencast workings of this scale have yet, as far as the Zuckerman Commission are aware, been backfilled and fully restored anywhere in the world. Apart from the massive amount of rock removal which such restoration would involve, there is the additional difficulty of keeping stored top-soil in good condition for up to twenty years.

The comparatively extensive scale of surface disturbance involved in these hypothetical workings may be compared with that posed by the new Wheal Jane tin mine in Cornwall, an underground working with an initial capacity of 150 000 tonnes per year, and occupying not more than 70 hectares (175 acres) at the surface. To find excavations of comparable size to a small to medium opencast excavation in high quality British upland scenery, one has to look outside the field of non-ferrous metal extraction altogether, e.g. the Penrhyn slate quarry, where the excavation itself covers 41 hectares and penetrates to 366 metres, or the even larger 284 hectare Dinorwic slate quarry nearby, not now actively worked. However, it is apparent that different attitudes now prevail towards the establishment of new enterprises on this scale or larger, at a time when pressures on space and the value attached to high quality landscape are growing rapidly. Consequently, the issue of opencast working of non-ferrous ores is likely to be one of the most controversial in the field of mineral exploitation in the 1970s.

NON-FERROUS METALS: TIN

The Cornish tin mining industry produced 3573 tonnes of tin in 1973.[37] This may seem a rather small amount, particularly in comparison with the annual consumption of tin in Britain of 17 to 18 000 tonnes a year,[38] but it saved the country over £5 700 000 in foreign exchange. Since it was recently suggested that Cornwall stands at the beginning of a 'considerable renaissance'[39] in this once important industry, the prospects for the national economy and that of South-West England could be exciting indeed. Yet any visitor to the Duchy cannot but be impressed by the large number of derelict engine houses scattered across its cliffs and moors instead of the surface accoutrements of a present-day dynamic extractive industry. In fact, out of the 250 active tin mines in 1840,[40] the only producers of tin ore until very recently were the mines of South Crofty, between Camborne and Redruth, and Geevor, near Pendeen on the Penwith peninsula, though tin from mine effluent has been recovered in the Red River and Carnon River valleys for some time.

From a peak figure of 11 100 tonnes of tin metal produced in 1871,[41] the industry declined through a combination of technological, economic and managerial factors and found itself unable to compete with the alluvial ore fields of Malaya, Indonesia and Bolivia after their discovery in the late nineteenth century. Most Cornish mines were worked on a 'cost-book' system, or as unlimited liability companies often reaping from a trifling outlay enormous dividends which were shared out at once, leaving little capital in reserve to survive a recession or to carry out improvements. In many cases, the narrow and steeply inclined shafts and working tunnels prevented improved haulage techniques or mechanized working.[42] Further, the significant fact that tin can exist in quantity below copper ores, but separated from them by a barren zone,[43] only became generally known in the second half of the nineteenth century; consequently many companies merely exploited the copper, failing to appreciate that tin might exist in the veins at greater depths.[44]

Thus the knowledge that there may still be large reserves of tin ore left in Cornwall, as well as the stimulus of the current excess of demand for tin over supply, have led to renewed interest in the possibility of expansion and redevelopment. Also, the ore fields of Malaya, Bolivia and Indonesia, now accounting for 76 per cent of the world output, are gradually being worked out.[45] Labour and freight costs have also been rising. Additional reserves must become increasingly difficult to find. Indeed, it was calculated in 1961 that, at the then current rate of consumption, the known reserves of tin could only last another 30 years.[46] All these factors have been reflected in world markets where the price of tin has soared from below £886 per tonne in 1961 to over £1600 per tonne in January 1973 and £3000 a year later.[47] Meantime the short fall in production has been met from the fast-diminishing United States' strategic stockpile.[48] The impetus so given to Cornwall has been reflected in the share prices of one of the major current producers, Geevor Tin Mines Ltd. In January 1954 the 25p ordinary shares stood at 49p.[49] A quotation made in 1972 from the London Stock Exchange has put them as high as £3·43.[48] The impetus has also made itself apparent in the impressive number of British, Canadian and American companies that have been considering the possibilities of the old mines of Cornwall, concentrating their efforts in districts which the Cornish Mining Development Association recommended as worthy of closer investigations in a series of reports entitled *Mineral Areas in Cornwall Worthy of Investigation*, the first of which was published soon after the Second World War. Fig. 5.1 is a map of the recent developments in tin mining in Cornwall.

Immediately to the south of Camborne in the area of Troon are the old Grenville mines, situated in a valley which separates the granite masses of Carn Brea and Carn Menellis. The Grenville United mines, which closed in 1920, in their time had produced 32 000 tonnes of black tin*[50] mostly from the rich Great Flat Lode.[51] Promising parallel lodes are now thought to exist and planning permission was given at the end of 1961 to Camborne Tin Ltd., a company formed to prospect and work these by the Siamese Tin Syndicate.[52] Siamese Tin were later joined in the project by the Union Corporation (UK) Ltd., who have since taken over control of the company. Camborne Tin Ltd. have also been prospecting and drilling in the Godolphin area about 11·3 kilometres south-west of Camborne,[53] where the West Godolphin and Godolphin mines were in production in the nineteenth century. Camborne Tin have since withdrawn from both sites.

Between Redruth and Scorrier lies the Great North Downs mine and, separated from it by a major fault, Wheal Peevor. Great North Downs, an early copper working, was exploited for tin between 1861 and 1870, and between 1871 and 1873, but was abandoned because of a major slump in the metal market. Wheal Peevor, on the other hand, to the west and on a different lode, had enjoyed a period of high production from 1872 to 1885. Together with West Wheal Peevor it was re-opened in 1911 and worked until 1915 when wartime difficulties

* Black tin is the concentrate which is sold to smelters and usually contains about 70 per cent tin metal.

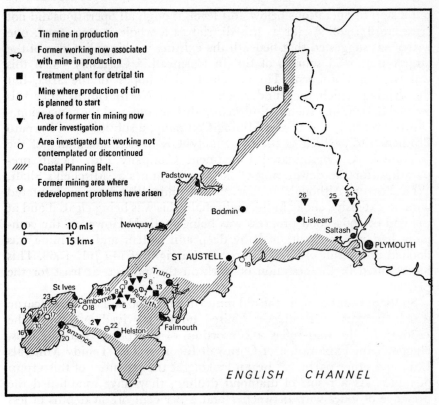

Fig. 5.1 *Recent developments in Cornish tin mining*

Key to locations shown by numbers on the map:

1 Grenville mines
2 Godolphin mines
3 Great North Downs mine
4 Wheal Peevor mine
5 Pendarves United mines
6 Falmouth Consolidated mines (Janes)
7 Mount Wellington
8 South Crofty mine
9 East Pool and Agar mines
10 Geevor mine
11 Boscaswell Downs mine
12 Levant mine
13 Carnon Valley (effluent deposits)
14 Red River (effluent deposits)
15 Basset and Frances mines
16 St Just Airport area
17 Ding Dong mine
18 Lelant
19 Par Beach (alluvial deposits)
20 Newlyn
21 Giew mine
22 Wheal Vor mine
23 Carnelloe mine
24 Gunnislake area
25 Hingston Down area
26 Caradon Hill (Upton Cross) area

put a stop to operations below adit level, though all operations did not cease until 1920. As far as this district as a whole is concerned, one writer has suggested that beneath the existing workings lies 'one of the largest untapped sources of tin' in Cornwall.[54] Certainly when this was written Camborne Tin also had 'high hopes' of the area, but the drilling which they undertook at Great North Downs after this seemed to belie any such optimism and they abandoned the concession.

More recently the Barcas Mining Company, a subsidiary of Barnato Brothers Ltd., which is itself a wholly UK-owned subsidiary of the Johannesburg Consolidated Investment Company Ltd., began preparations for the dewatering of the Peevor mines at Mitchell's Shaft, West Peevor. Although at first serious difficulties were encountered with an extensive choke in the main shaft, this was being cleared and at the end of 1967 good progress was being made.[55] However, the company had not reconditioned the deep adit system and the mine was flooded as a result of a cloudburst on the night of 1–2 July 1968. This has resulted in the cessation of work on this project, at least for the present.[56]

South of Camborne lie the old mines of Tolcarne and South Tolcarne which, as part of Pendarves United mines, survived only until the 1880s.[57] In the mid-1960s a consortium of Camborne Tin Ltd. plus, Guggenheim Exploration of Cornwall Incorporated, Tehidy Minerals Ltd., and other partners[58] began looking at the potential of this group of mines. As a result of diamond drilling, they have established the presence of lodes with between 1 and 2 per cent ore at depths of less than 91·4 metres, and in May 1965 planning permission was given for a trial shaft. By January 1969 this had reached 259 metres and tunnelling had begun from it at two horizons.[59] In the same year work began on dewatering the nearby old Tryphena mine, not only to prevent flooding, but also to provide a second access to the new working.[60] Although the consortium eventually began operations shortly after, in early 1973, financial difficulties arose and working ceased. The mine has how been bought by South Crofty Ltd. with whom its operation, now restarted, will be integrated.[61]

One of the most interesting of the proposals to rework old tin mining areas is that in the Gwennap/Baldhu area. This district, formerly important for copper mining, consists of the tributary valleys that converge to form the valley of the River Carnon. Near Baldhu, Wheal Jane and West Wheal Jane, which amalgamated with a number of other mines in 1905 to form Falmouth Consolidated Mines,[62] were once important. Beyond these mines, and westwards acrosss the Carnon valley, is the old Mount Wellington mine and a very large group of abandoned copper and tin mines extending over a large part of the parish of Gwennap and St Day. International Mine Services Ltd., a Canadian company, have shown interest in this area. On their behalf Cornwall Tin and Mining Corporation of New York (one of the Hirshorn group of companies) announced in 1969 that they would sink a new 4·5 metre (15 foot) diameter circular shaft, following successful diamond drilling which began in 1968[63] on the Mount Wellington lode. Provided that the developments were satisfactory, it was thought that the mining operation will eventually yield 500 to 1000 tonnes a day.[64] It is interesting to note that attempts to investigate the potential of the Mount Wellington lode were made close to the village of Twelve Heads even before the last war and exploration and development were in progress from 1935 to 1941.[65]

More recently the shaft put down by Cornwall Tin and Mining Corporation had reached 198 metres with five levels established, at 49 metres and then at intervals of 33 metres. Developments in the exploration of the lode have now confirmed the tonnage and grade of ore indicated by the surface drilling. The only hindrance to further progress has been the large amount of water that has had to be handled, at times nearly 23 million litres a day, but this is now being overcome.

The Cornwall Tin and Mining Corporation have also acquired prospecting leases on ten square kilometres of land between Perranporth and St Agnes and a drilling and sampling programme of the old Cligga workings, formerly mined from Wheal Prudence, is planned for the immediate future.

Meanwhile in east Cornwall the predecessors of Cornwall Tin and Mining, International Mine Services, had, in 1968, begun a drilling programme on Hingston Down and Caradon Hill. This was continued by the new company who were then granted planning permission to investigate the old Phoenix United mine which closed in 1914.[66] This project has subsequently been abandoned and Cligga shelved in order to devote company resources to the development of Mount Wellington.[67]

It is in the neighbouring area of the old Janes mines, however, that the major developments are at present taking place. Here, now that planning permission has been granted, Consolidated Goldfields are spending £6 million[68] on a new mine which J. H. Trounson, chairman of the Cornish Mining Development Association, recently described as a 'really major mine—the biggest thing Cornwall has seen'.[69] The first encouraging results from geochemical investigations and diamond drilling were reported early in 1967[70] but it was not until 1969 that, with laboratory and pilot scale tests carried out on the ores obtained and with the detailed engineering studies completed,[71] it was decided to go ahead and bring the mine into production under the company title, Wheal Jane Limited. This new mine, which opened at the beginning of October 1971, now ranks as a producer second only to one of the two extant mines, South Crofty, at a capacity of 152 400 tonnes of ore per year.[72] Reserves of ore are thought by Consolidated Goldfields to be, at a conservative estimate, about 5·1 million tonnes. With a percentage of tin of about 1·25, the mine is providing between 1500 and 1600 tonnes of tin in concentrate a year. Against the total investment of £6 million, future profits now look very promising. Because of its location in a Development Area, it was originally estimated by the company that the Government would contribute up to £2 400 00 in grants. Though this sum was probably not realized because of changes in Government policy towards such areas, undoubtedly cash received from this source will have contributed substantially to the ultimate success of the mine. The mining rate will be built up in the early years and both high and low grade tin concentrates may be produced. The company has leased about 607 hectares (1500 acres) with mineral options purchased for £6000, but royalties will amount to about £60 000 a year. By the end of 1971, not only had the lateral underground development of the mine exceeded 2440 metres and early estimates of the amount and grade of the ore confirmed, but a second shaft had already been completed to aid production.[73] At present the Janes employs over 450 men,[74] expanding eventually to 500,[75] and as a profit-earner the mine has taken first place from South Crofty, a mine with a long and continuous productive history.

South Crofty began operations in 1854 and worked the southern half of the old East Wheal Crofty sett which had been rich in copper in the 1830s. By 1894, with 154 men in its employ, it had sunk to a depth of 314·5 metres. In 1902 the company took over the adjacent but small and abandoned undertaking, New Cook's Kitchen mine, and then in about 1916 it pushed northwards into what had been the sett of North Wheal Crofty. By the outbreak of the First World War, workings had reached a depth of 567 metres with 480 men employed. It is interesting that South Crofty managed to survive the early 1920s, when the price of tin fell to record low levels and when heavy expenditure on drainage was incurred as a result of the closure of the adjacent Tincroft mine and the collapse of the engine shaft at the East Pool mine immediately to the north-east. By 1935 South Crofty had acquired a number of other old setts to the west, and more recently took over the old East Pool and Wheal Agar mines which closed in 1945. After the takeover, the newest section (Taylor's) was dewatered and in

1968 it was entered from South Crofty. The task of pumping out the rest of the East Pool mine was completed in 1971.[76]

Today the whole South Crofty undertaking is a thriving one, exploiting, in all, more than a dozen lodes of tin. It has reached a depth of 689 metres and employs 470 men. In 1964 a modernization scheme, which had taken six years to accomplish, was completed. In that year receipts totalled £828 489, with a working profit of £321 741. The mine had produced in the previous twelve months 1010 tonnes of black tin from 89 825 tonnes of ore, representing a recovery grade of 1125 kilogrammes per tonne of ore milled.[77] Up to the end of the year 1963, it had produced over 38 600 tonnes of black tin since its opening in 1854. In 1968, however, the board of South Crofty decided that the potential of the mines warranted even greater output and a programme of expansion was geared to increasing production of ore from a total of 112 530 tonnes in that year to 203 200 tonnes in 1971,[78] 'doubling its output or thereabouts'.[79] In order to achieve this the company has needed additional hoisting equipment and treatment plant. The rate of underground development has also been increased and one of the main shafts deepened. All this meant an expenditure in the two-and-a-half year period up to 1971 of £650 000, to be met from internal resources;[80] it also meant that South Crofty would keep in front of the forecast production of ore from the Janes by a narrow margin. Latest figures for South Crofty suggest that the target figure for 1971 is likely to take longer to achieve.[81]

The other important tin mine with a long history of production is Geevor, about 9 kilometres north of Land's End, a mine which had made a long-standing contribution to the economy of west Cornwall and is currently a much needed source of employment in the area. The forerunner of this undertaking was the North Levant mine where work really began as early as 1810; its name was not changed to Geevor until 1905. In the twentieth century, in spite of minor recessions brought about by fluctuating tin prices and the trade cycle, output has expanded steadily, with the company acquiring adjacent setts. Two acquisitions have been of particular importance. One of these, the Boscaswell Downs mine, is situated in a half-mile sett running south-east through Pendeen. But it is adjacent to, and to the immediate north-east of, the original Boscaswell lode that the main development work in this part of the Geevor company's holding has taken place. An old shaft (Treweek's) has recently been reconditioned and deepened to enable the further development of the Boscaswell main lode as well as other subsidiary lodes, and a new lode, the Simms, to be worked efficiently. Over 1524 metres of Simms lode has now been developed and it looks very promising for the future, particularly the north-eastern area.[82] The Levant mine, the other notable acquisition, had been one of the major sources of tin and copper in west Cornwall. From 1820 to 1930 30 500 tonnes of black tin were produced,[83] but after the abandonment of the mine in 1930 the sea broke into the workings, a result of their having been unwisely carried up close to the sea bed. Nevertheless, it was the possibility of the seaward extension of Geevor into the lodes that had once been Levant's that suggested the acquisition of the latter and it was proposed that an attempt be made to seal the sea breach and drain the mine.[84] The first attempt to do this in 1961 failed and, after a review of Geevor's prospect, further efforts in this direction were postponed.

It became clear, however, that, if further work was to be done on the extension of the Geevor mine into Levant, additional finance would be needed. This was obtained by an arrangement with Union Corporation by which they share the estimated cost of £250 000.[85] In July 1964 work on the Levant project began again. The breach was subsequently successfully plugged and the area sealed off from the rest of the mine by St Just Mining Services. Since then the process of pumping the water out of the mine has been in progress. A number of deep boreholes were drilled in 1966 in order to test the seaward extension of the known lodes south-west of Cape Cornwall and in 1968 exploratory diamond drilling south of Levant to 2691 metres had been done.[86] These investigations, according to Geevor's managing director, Douglas Batchelor, have given 'some very good results'.[87] Although subsequent development carried out at three levels from the old Levant mine proved less promising, evidence encountered in a seaward drive from Geevor's lowest level along the Coronation Lode, indicates the need for deeper development beneath the sea from Levant for the best results.[88] Apart from the development of some of the potential of the adjacent Boscaswell and Levant mines, Geevor itself has undergone during the last ten years a comprehensive programme of rationalization. In 1968, with a manpower total of 282 workers, the mine produced 759 tonnes of black tin worth £561 343 from 78 589 tonnes of ore,[89] and for 1969 output was up 30 per cent.[90] By 1973 it has reached 111 584 tonnes of ore, proceeds of sales from the mine realizing £961 564.[91]

Two other more modest undertakings have been recovering tin ore by streaming. Effluent deposits have been worked for years in the Carnon River valley at Bissoe, first by Hydraulic Tin Ltd., and—after 1966—by the Continental Ore Company Ltd., who acquired this business and who propose to develop its potential.[92] In 1970-1 about 101 600 tonnes of sand and slimes were treated, yielding 203 tonnes of 45 per cent tin concentrates and 76 tonnes of 10 per cent concentrates.[93] Meanwhile, to the north-west of Camborne tin streamers have for years worked the ore deposited in the Red River from the mines of Camborne and Poole. In 1966 the Cornish Tin Smelting Company Ltd. erected a tin concentration plant capable of dealing with 254 tonnes a day of residual materials from the Red River flats,[94] and elsewhere. Five years later this dealt with 51 114 tonnes of material in a twelve-month period, giving 243 tonnes of concentrates.[95]

The same company was also actively pursuing underground sources of tin and has prospected in the last few years in the Camborne and Redruth district.[96] Twelve shallow diamond drill holes were made in 1966, as well as geochemical sampling, and in 1967 exploratory dewatering operations were carried out at Lyle's shaft of the old North Wheal Basset mine at Carnkie, one of a group of five mines which closed in 1919.[97] In 1970, further rights were obtained for underground prospecting in areas adjacent to this mine.[98]

Across the Penwith peninsula close to St Just Airport, Penwith Mineral Explorations Ltd. have also been drilling and carrying out geochemical surveys. The results achieved by 1968 prompted the company to acquire further leases to the north of the present area, as well as in other parts of the St Just area and the Penwith peninsula, though the company had to raise new capital to the extent of £30 000[99] in order to push ahead with these developments. Since then they have concentrated their activities on exploring known adits. For example, in 1970–1 the workings of the old Wheal Hermon were unwatered in order to inspect and assess the potential of workings running under the sea. Samples taken so far have been encouraging and it seems that the mine is flooded with surface water and not by the sea.[100]

But, in spite of all this activity, the redevelopment of the Cornish tin mining industry has serious problems. First of all there is always the possibility of failure to find sufficient ore to justify commercial exploitation, even after heavy investment in exploration. Four examples of this spring to mind. At the historic Ding Dong mine 4 kilometres west of Penzance, Consolidated Goldfields Ltd. have recently carried out diamond drillings to estimate its future potential,[101] but results have been disappointing and it is unlikely that the mine will be reworked. At St Ives Bay, Coastal Prospecting Ltd., a subsidiary of Union Corporation (UK) Ltd., converted a motor vessel to extract tin from dredged sand and in 1967 completed a processing plant at Lelant.[102] This began to operate and shipments of tin were actually made[103] but for various reasons, including the low tin content of the sand in the bay and the problems of running the ship into the port of Hayle in bad weather, the project has been abandoned. On Par Beach English Clays Lovering Pochin and Company Ltd.[104] began exploratory drilling for alluvial tin in 1968. The work was not expected to be completed until 1970[105] but it was prematurely abandoned in 1969 and it must be presumed that the results obtained were unsatisfactory. Another shore line exploration started in 1967 in Mount's Bay, where Amey Roadstone Corporation Ltd., Newlyn, worked at the end of a 52 metre steel-tube pier jutting out from the foreshore at Penzance. Drilling was carried out to evaluate the tin-bearing elvan dyke which proved so productive in the famous under-sea Wherry mine between 1778 and 1798[106] but the results of the drilling were poor. It is, known, though, that these stanniferous elvan dykes do not necessarily persist over any great length or depth and so the chance of failure in this last case must have always been high.

Another problem is that of identifying the owner of mineral rights and of reaching agreement with him before extraction can be contemplated. For example, Baltrink Tin Ltd. was formed by Rhodesia-Katanga, Kleinwort Benson and the Canadian Westfield Minerals in order to examine the extension of the lodes of the old Giew mine at Trink Hill, south-west of St Ives;[107] the mine had been worked intermittently until 1922 when the low price of tin on world markets finally caused it to close.[108] Baltrink Tin pursued an intensive programme of drilling and geochemical soil testing in order to confirm the nature of the easterly continuation of the old Giew mine's main lode, but found, because of cross faulting, that the prospects for development were not favourable. Perhaps this would not have been so unfortunate if Baltrink had been able to expand the boundary of their concession but the problem of identifying the owners of the mineral rights of the adjacent land was insoluble[109] and Baltrink has withdrawn from the field. A director of the company, E. W. J. Tyler, is reported as saying of this venture, 'It is just too difficult, too impossible. You spend hours and hours just going round in circles. There is the rest of the world where people can go and look for minerals.'[110]

It is clear that Baltrink Tin is not the only company to have been frustrated in its efforts to identify the owners of mineral rights. There are, in addition, other companies who, having eventually discovered the mineral owner after a time-consuming search, find themselves further frustrated in their attempts to obtain a licence to work the minerals on reasonable terms. Certainly mining interests in Cornwall believe that there is a good case for Government legislation to relieve these quite avoidable frustrations. As a writer in the *Financial Times* reported, following a visit with a large party of transatlantic and British mining men, to new mining fields in the Irish Republic, 'the visitors were as enthusiastic about Ireland's . . . far-seeing legislation whereby it is reasonably easy to acquire land necessary for mining developments as they were unenthusiastic about the UK in [this] respect'.[111] The writer added that 'perhaps the Government might at least start taking steps to smooth the path of the miner in his often frustrating search for even who owns the mineral rights, let alone whether they are willing to part with them'.[112]

Other problems have arisen which may best be described as those arising from land use competition. Here two particularly interesting cases spring to mind. The first involved the reworking of the old mine at Wheal Vor near Helston. This is situated close to the granite of Tregonning Hill and was not only a very ancient mine but also a rich one. During its most productive period from 1853 until 1877 the mine produced 9774 tonnes of black tin[113] and profits reached over £99 000.[114] It is now thought, however, that the company which exploited this area failed to locate several ore bodies which may be commercially exploitable. Certainly Camborne Tin Ltd. thought it worth while to carry out a series of preliminary investigations, as a result of which they submitted an application for planning permission to re-open the mine. It seemed likely that this application would receive favourable consideration since the mine was in a Development Area and, if re-started, it might employ about 400 men in a locality where the unemployment rate was 6 per cent. Further, it was situated in a zone scheduled in the Cornwall Development Plan[115] for possible mining activities. A public inquiry into the proposed re-opening of the mine was held but, in spite of the application finding favour with the inspector, the Minister of Housing and Local Government refused to grant planning permission on the ground that the Helston and Porthleven Water Company obtained part of its water supply from the adit stream flowing from Wheal Vor. Permission for the water company to use this water had been given in 1956, and although this was strenuously opposed at the time by the Cornish Mining Development Association, they only succeeded in persuading the Minister to insert a saving clause in the order to the effect that nothing should prejudice the rights of the mine owners to resume operations. At the 1964 inquiry the water company pointed out that they could eventually replace the Wheal Vor source by pumping from the Looe Pool. The Minister did observe, therefore, in giving his ruling that it was without prejudice to a further application being made by the mining company when the alternative water supplies had been finally secured. He also expressed his hope that the water company would press on urgently with its scheme for obtaining alternative supplies and agreed that the re-working of the mine could be beneficial in an area of heavy unemploy-ment.[116] However, when the water company eventually went ahead with their proposal to use Looe Pool as an alternative source, they were opposed by various local authorities on the grounds that the pool was polluted by sewage. This necessitated a further public inquiry which led to a prolonged wrangle over the costs of a scheme to treat the source of pollution. Meanwhile, other difficulties arose at Wheal Vor concerning the already mentioned problem of mineral ownership. The major part of the area to be developed was in the hands of the Treworlis Estate, which was willing to cooperate with Camborne Tin. The Wheal Vor lodes, however, dip north at a fairly flat angle and in the deeper areas pass under the land of the Duke of Leeds. Negotiations started with Leeds Estates were prolonged, mainly because the latter had already begun discussions for the transfer of all mineral rights to another landowner in Cornwall. Just as matters seemed to be settling in favour of Camborne Tin, the Duke died, followed shortly afterwards by his successor to the title, thus leaving probate to be settled in two cases. There were further delays before the estate was finally sold. So it was that, after four and a half years, Camborne Tin were no nearer beginning their work at Wheal Vor. Meanwhile, the water dispute dragged on and the frustrated company applied to go ahead with at least a trial drilling in the area of the mine. Planning permission was given, provided that drilling in no way polluted the water supply. But unfortunately the Treworlis land borings were the only ones available until permission to work in what had been the Leeds land was obtained and it soon became clear that important finds were only likely in this last area. By this time, the delays had been so lengthy that Camborne Tin felt they could tolerate the difficulties of this situation no longer. They decided to concentrate all their efforts on their Pendarves concession, an enterprise which has now come to fruition.[117]

Thus ended a sorry story, the details of which must cause concern to those who are anxious to see mining encouraged in Cornwall. It is ironical to note that Camborne Tin abandoned their schemes at Wheal Vor just before the negotiations for working the ex-Leeds estate could have been completed; more important, the local water company has now become part of the South Cornwall Water Board and the additional supplies to forgo the Wheal Vor source are piped in from another area altogether.

Another illustration of the problems of land use competition concerns attempts that were made, beginning in the spring of 1961, to re-open Carnelloe, one of a series of mines running along the cliff tops west from St Ives as far as Morvah.[118] This mine, situated close to an unscarred stretch of coastline of outstanding natural beauty, was closed nearly 90 years ago and the plan of W. T. Harry to re-open it encountered the resistance not only of a 300-strong pressure group but also of the National Trust and the county Development Plan. Put briefly, the objectors' case was that the mine, if exploration proved successful, would grow until the adjacent village of Zennor developed into a second Pendeen, the sprawling home of the Geevor mine. If it were unsuccessful, the damage to the landscape would be irreparable.[119] Harry, however, forecast that the mine, for which he had already acquired the mineral rights and could raise £200 000 capital, would soon employ 200 to 300 men. He stressed that the mine was in any case well away from the village and that there was no question of spoiling the landscape. At the public inquiry set up on 11 May 1961, he stated that the mine would be developed in three phases. The first would be exploratory, involving little in the way of above-ground structures; the second would involve excavating one or two new shafts; and the final phase, the actual working of the mine, would be carried out under the sea.[120] The inspector agreed that a case for re-opening the mine had been made. The few buildings needed could harmonize with the landscape and the mine would provide local employment and a valuable source of tin for the nation. Nevertheless, the Minister of Housing and Local Government overruled this recommendation on the grounds that the intrusion of this kind of mining development into an area with an unspoiled coastline could only be allowed in quite exceptional circumstances and that in any case the success of the mine was uncertain.[121] In March 1963 a further application by Harry to erect two huts and to begin prospecting work on the mine only was successful but by this time the original backers for his proposal, concerned over what they thought to be unreasonable delays, had withdrawn their financial support and invested elsewhere. Since then the planning permission granted to prospect has expired. However, at least one mining expert believes that in this area of highly altered slates and greenstone resting on granite, rich tin ore is likely to be found, as the output of earlier mines between Pendeen and St Just bears witness.[122] It is known that the company working Carnelloe on a very small scale about a hundred years ago worked a narrow but rich tin lode there which 'came down on the grey elvan' (the greenstone sills) before it quite typically died out. The company were unable to find the money to sink through the elvan,[123] which is a very hard rock.

Indeed, it was only by sinking through the greenstone sills that the Levant mine, situated in a similar geological position, ultimately proved so successful.

From these two case histories, it is clear that tin mining development can conflict in certain instances with other land use interests and that these conflicts may obstruct viable mining projects, in that prospecting companies or financial backers will move their resources elsewhere if difficulties prove formidable. For the future the question of land use competition will most probably arise where mining expansion is attempted in areas which the local planning authority recently designated as part of the 4·8 kilometre deep coastal planning belt. This zone, with some exceptions, extends right round the county,[124] and in it the county council have attempted to interrelate all land use demands, laying particular emphasis on tourism and the preservation of the coast.[125] However, it should be noted that the planning authority has for some time accepted the fact that, in many areas of Cornwall both on and off the coast, it may be necessary to consider planning applications for mining development. Such zones were identified in the county Development Plan and named, as it was pointed out in Chapter 1, consultation areas. This was because it was believed that all interests would best be served if a decision to allow or reject a new mining development in these areas was made the subject of consultation between the Cornish County Council and the Cornish Mining Development Association. These consultation zones, originally defined on the advice of the Cornish Mining Development Association, are at present undergoing considerable revision, in view of the number of new mining developments now under way.[126] This system will be necessary if a properly planned expansion of the mining industry is to be achieved and reconciled with other land use interests. Moreover, the possibilities of conflict may be further lessened when it becomes more generally realized that the relatively few 'above-ground' activities of this industry can be housed in buildings which blend with the landscape. Present-day engineering methods mean that comparatively few shafts are required, a single one perhaps serving an area 3·2 kilometres or more in length underground.[127] In addition, modern technology means that although present-day mines are much larger with the four 1973 producers embracing forty old mines,[128] they are able to function without the environmental pollution characteristic of the nineteenth century.[129] The waste dumps of that period were, in any case, more characteristic of Cornish copper mining. In contrast to this present-day mining and concentration of tin give rise mainly to clean washed sand and gravel which is in demand for building and making concrete or coarse stone which is readily saleable as hardcore. Indeed, problems of an environmental nature are today minimal where tin mining is concerned. In the case of Wheal Jane the method of underground mining causes little surface subsidence; the plant has been constructed so as to be a relatively minor intrusion in the landscape and its high value/low bulk output in the form of concentrate generates no more traffic than about two lorries a day.[130] The greatest problem is caused by the disposal of fine-ground waste material from the plant (tailings), at present amounting to 147 300 tonnes a year.[131] This is impounded by a dam in a valley below the mine, and, apart from highly acid water caused by the processing of the tin that runs from these residues, their collection will eventually cover a site extending over 24·3 hectares.[132] However, the environmental effects of the dam will be ameliorated by screening. Furthermore, the damage done to the landscape through the extraction of tin, when compared with a large opencast copper mine which would utilize many of the same raw material processes, is modest in the extreme. Even though it has been estimated that the total extent of underground tin workings could rise to 104 square kilometres, this would only represent 3 per cent of the land area of Cornwall and since in the case of the currently working mines the land they occupy on the surface averages 3·2 per cent of their underground area, it is possible to infer that the fully developed tin mining potential of the county would only result in a mere 0·096 per cent of the surface of Cornwall being occupied by this land use.[132] This is, of course not to say that the visual impact would not be more widely apparent. None the less, given all the circumstances of modern tin mining it is increasingly likely that, in the future, planning permission for new developments will not be withheld. Thus the contrast between the planning prospects for tin and those for the possible exploitation of low grade copper ores etc., by opencast methods at present envisaged as a possibility elsewhere, is a strong one.

The problems that have arisen over mineral rights as far as tin is concerned, however, have no immediate prospect of being eased, as Chapter 1 made clear. All the same, tin interests in Cornwall consider that the key to the ultimate prosperity of the industry must lie in a revision of the taxation system which will give concessions to prospecting and mining by means of some kind of 'tax holiday'. In this respect the UK strongly contrasts with Ireland. Until a few years ago, mining in Eire was moribund, but as a direct consequence of the adoption of a new tax code, culminating in 1966, when total tax relief for twenty years was granted, the industry was reborn and is expanding rapidly. Recent figures show that prospecting licences have been granted for about a third of the Republic's total area. Substantial discoveries have already been made and new mines are coming into production, whilst the output of lead and zinc from the Tynagh mine in County Galway is now the largest in Europe.[134] Indeed, in 1971 the output of Irish non-ferrous metal ores was worth well over £15 million.[135] It is interesting to note therefore that in 1961 Harold Wilson advocated tax concessions in England similar to those available in Eire. In a debate in the House of Commons on the taxation of non-ferrous mines, he pointed out that a world shortage of tin—together with the problem of UK balance of payments—made it imperative for the nation to develop its own supplies. For this reason and 'because of the difficulties and risks of tin mining due to the disposition of the metal by nature, special tax concessions are required'.[136] He might also have mentioned the advantages to regional employment that might accrue from such tax concessions in an area of high unemployment and the fact that the savings in the outflow of currency would have amounted, even at that time, to £1181 for every tonne of tin produced at home.

Nothing was done to grant tax concession up to 1964, and if anything the situation deteriorated between then and 1970. Admittedly, a moderate concession was made by the Government to the mining industry in Cornwall when it was announced that the rates payable by them would be reduced by half with a 25 per cent cut in April 1971 and a further 25 per cent reduction a year later.[137] On 15 May 1970, however, the details of tax concessions for owners of mineral rights were published in a new clause to the Finance Bill. This welcome change should have some beneficial effect on Cornish tin mining, although it does not go nearly as far as mining interests feel is necessary.

The excuse for making such a small tax concession—and that only to owners of mineral rights—seemed at the time to be that the scheme of investment grants given under Part 1 of the Industrial Development Act 1966 provided reasonable assistance to the mining industry itself. However, the announcement of October 1970, heralding the discontinuance of investment grants, has worsened the situation, since, as discussed in Chapter 1, the new legislation no longer distinguishes the key difference in the capital investment structure of the mining industry as against other industrial activities. The Mineral Exploration Act 1972 can only be but a small palliative and only to those companies still in the exploration stage. The fact remains that this Act with its emphasis on repaying loans and the new system of depreciation rates does not go far enough for a high risk industry like non-ferrous metal mining in which investment in prospecting is no guarantee of commercial success. Moreover, the 1972 budget legislation giving a regional development grant of 20 per cent for plant, machinery and mining works, only to some extent restores the position enjoyed before investment grants were terminated.

Given the need to maintain a healthy balance of payments situation in Britain, the increasing long-term world shortage of tin and the tax concessions offered to mining in Eire, as well as in Canada, Australia, the United States and elsewhere, it is surprising, so Cornish tin interests argue, that the present Government has been so negative in its attitude towards offering the tax incentives really needed. At a more local level, they have also emphasized the importance of tin mining in terms of regional development, not only as a direct provider of much needed employment, but as a generator of other wealth through the multiplier effect; indeed they have recently stated that the two longest established mines, South Crofty and Geevor, between them disbursed in 1972 about £1·5 million of real new wealth through the county in the form of wages, salaries, dues, rates, stores and services.[138] But in spite of the strictures of those who feel the Government is niggardly in its attitude towards mining, the industry is making progress with a 10 per cent increase in output from 1967–8, a more than 10 per cent increase in 1969. Now that Wheal Jane has begun production, the new plant at South Crofty has come into use, and Pendarves is operational, a doubling of the 1970 production figure was achieved by the end of 1973.

FERROUS METALS: IRON ORES

In contrast to the recent expansion in British tin mining, and the extensive search for commercially workable deposits of other metals, the extraction of iron ore in Britain is now rapidly contracting. This contraction is a recent phenomenon and involves a major change of policy. The Iron and Steel Board, in a special report in 1957,[139] advocated the maximum economic use of home ore and forecast large increases in home ore production by 1965. In the early 1960s, when the European Coal and Steel Community (ECSC) ore industry was shrinking rapidly, the British output level was almost constant, falling only slightly from 17 360 800 tonnes in 1960 to 16 586 900 tonnes in 1964.[140] Within the ECSC, on the other hand, output dropped from 97 743 400 tonnes in 1961 to 81 483 200 in 1964, 42 mines were closed (24 in Germany) and 18 mines significantly restricted output (10 in Germany).[141] Since 1964, however, British ore production in its turn has taken a sharp down-turn, falling to 12 297 200 tonnes in 1969, a drop of 25·8 per cent from 1964. The Development Coordinating

Committee of the British Iron and Steel Federation envisaged in 1966 'a progressive withdrawal from the use of home ore resources'.[142] This decision is particularly far-reaching in view of the concurrent expansion of the British iron and steel industry, and the large-scale growth planned for the future, to take BSC capacity from 24 million tonnes in 1968 to 33–35 million tonnes a year by the late 1970s and 36–38 million tonnes a year in the first half of the 1980s.[143]

While a sharp decline in home output is a comparatively recent phenomenon, the growth of imports relative to home production is of long standing; virtually all the growth in total ore requirements between 1954 and 1964 was provided from imports, which increased by 48 per cent. In fact, home ore had taken second place to imported ore since 1946 in terms of pig potential[144] and since 1964 in terms of weight (see Table 5.1). The tonnage of imported ore more than

Table 5.1. UK ore consumption 1950–69 (thousand tonnes)

Year	Home iron ore (in terms of raw ore)	Imported iron ore and manganese ore
1950	12 980	9 184
1951	14 231	8 993
1952	16 402	10 230
1953	16 839	10 941
1954	16 141	12 340
1955	16 622	12 870
1956	16 665	14 365
1957	17 253	15 998
1958	15 093	14 118
1959	15 055	12 880
1960	17 347	16 877
1961	16 753	15 292
1962	15 558	13 640
1963	15 237	14 816
1964	16 523	18 231
1965	15 744	18 687
1966	13 790	16 730
1967	12 852	15 790
1968	13 824	17 615
1969	12 311	18 565

Source: Iron and Steel Industry Annual Statistics, 1969.

doubled between 1950 and 1969. The factors affecting the home ore/imported ore balance are clearly long standing, but have intensified the impact on home production since 1964.

The delivered cost of raw home ore is still less than the delivered cost of raw imported ore, but the cost advantage has been steadily narrowed since the 1950s (see Table 5.2). Home ore costs have risen partly as a result of the need to work ore at greater depths, a rising cost only partly offset by increasing efficiency in ore extraction. Imported ore prices, f.o.b. loading ports, had, until 1969 when the trend began to be reversed, decreased largely as a result of substantial expansion of world ore-mining capacity. From 1966 to 1969 it is estimated that the world production of lump iron ore, pellets and fines suitable for sintering increased by about 71 million tonnes to reach a record level of just over 710 million tonnes in 1969.[145] In the period 1950–65 major new mines within the widespread UK catchment area were opened

Table 5.2. Movement of delivered cost of ore, 1957–64

	1957	1958	1959	1960	1961	1962	1963	1964
Home ore index	100	111	112	124	129	131	127	123
Imported ore index	100	91	85	79	79	78	74	72

Source: Stage 1 Report of the Development Coordinating Committee of the British Iron and Steel Federation, July 1966, appendix 11. Later figures are not available.

in Venezuela, Canada, Liberia and Mauretania, as well as big expansion of older capacity in Sweden and Brazil. Since then Australian output has grown spectacularly, increasing from 6·8 million tonnes in 1965 to 39·1 million tonnes in 1969.[146] Parallel with this increased output have gone changes in freight rates, a factor of great importance. Since the value of iron ore is low in relation to its bulk, transport costs constitute an important part of the total delivered cost of the ore, as much as two-thirds in extreme cases. There have been striking improvements in the transportation of imported ores since 1950, notably the employment of large specialized ore carriers, usually on long charters, as opposed to earlier dependence on tramp shipping. There has also been a partial advance in British docking facilities, making possible the accommodation of bigger carriers and their faster turn-around. The greatest impact of improved docking facilities is likely to be felt in the 1970s, however, with two new terminals, designed to secure the economies of scale which stem from giant carriers, coming into full operation at Immingham and Redcar, in addition to that already operating at Port Talbot. These new developments enable vessels of 100 000 tonnes to be docked at all three ports, and approval was given in 1973 for a fourth major terminal in Scotland, near Hunterston. Improvements in the UK ore carrier fleet are likely further to reinforce this impact.

Progress has also been made in the transportation of home ores, with

337

the use of specialized rail and discharging facilities. Northampton-shire ores are despatched in diesel-hauled block trains, each carrying 100 tonnes of ore in 27 tonne tippler wagons, making the journey from Wellingborough to Middlesbrough, for instance, in fourteen hours.[147] But the technical advances in home transportation have been less significant than those in shipping, and have been largely negatived by the general rise in the UK freight rates. From 1954 to 1965 the standard tonne/kilometre freight rate from home ore movements rose by 61 per cent,[148] and between 1965 and 1971 by just over 20 per cent. It is difficult to be optimistic about a reversal of this trend in the 1970s.

But probably the most crucial factor affecting the home/imported ore balance is the low iron content of home ore. The great bulk of home ore is derived from the low grade Jurassic ironstones of the Humber–Severn belt (see Fig. 5.2). The average iron content of these ores as used has fallen from 30 per cent in 1948 to 28 per cent in 1969. In the future, the iron content of home ores is likely to remain static or diminish further. Imported iron ores, about twice as rich, have a rising average iron content, which grew from 55 per cent in 1948 to 61 per cent in 1969 (weighted by arrivals).[149] The average iron content of imported ores is likely to increase to about 64 per cent by 1975,[150] and there may be a shift to still richer iron-bearing materials such as pre-reduced pellets, 75–85 per cent iron content. There is the further point that considerable quantities of home ore, notably from the North-ampton Sand orefield, have a high phosphoric content which makes them unsuitable for the LD (Linz Donawitz) steelmaking process. These ores can however be used for steelmaking by an adaptation of the LD process, called the LD/AC process, which costs a little more but is used very successfully at Corby.

As a result of the difference in iron content, the use of home ore involves more coke for smelting and more capital equipment. In 1971 home ore furnaces used about 200 kg more coke per tonne of iron than imported ore furnaces,[151] 700 kg for home ore as against 500 kg for imported ore. This, together with the progressive rises in coking coal prices, has aggravated the relative disadvantage of home ore users. In 1970 a world shortage of coking coal became apparent. British coking coal rose in price by 16 per cent and the gradual decline of suitable qualities of this commodity in some areas was necessitating transfer from other areas for blending, which increased transport costs. The shortage of home coke is bound to continue and currently the steel industry is importing the material. These developments make the higher coke consumption associated with the processing of home ores a grave handicap. Moreover, increased expenditure on blast furnace

338

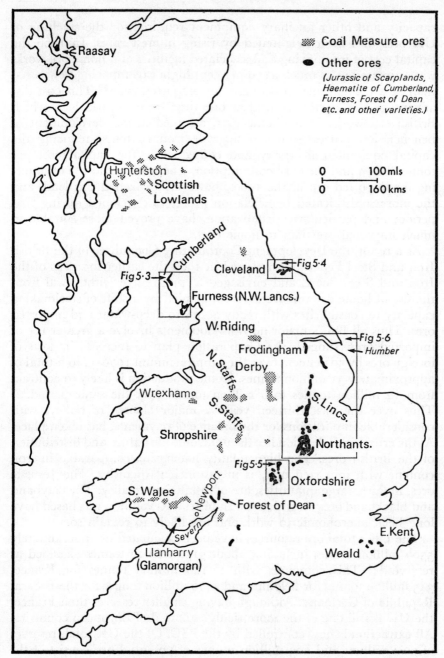

Fig. 5.2 *Iron ores of Britain*

Coal Measure ores

Other ores
(Jurassic of Scarplands, Haematite of Cumberland, Furness, Forest of Dean etc. and other varieties.)

0 — 100 mls
0 — 160 kms

Raasay

Hunterston

Scottish Lowlands

Cumberland

Cleveland — Fig 5·4

Fig 5·3

Furness (N.W. Lancs.)

W. Riding

Fig 5·6
Humber

Frodingham

Derby

Wrexham

N. Staffs.

S. Staffs.

S. Lincs.

Shropshire

Northants.

Fig 5·5

Oxfordshire

S. Wales

Newport

Forest of Dean

Severn

E. Kent

Llanharry (Glamorgan)

Weald

capacity and other ancillary equipment required for the smelting of UK ores, has been heightened by rising interest rates. In 1966 the capital cost of ironmaking and associated facilities at a home ore works was estimated at as much as 70 per cent higher (comparing new costs) than at a comparable works based on imported ore.[152] This cost disadvantage was partly reduced at one time by the world lead which British steelworks, using home ores, assumed in the development of beneficiation processes, which upgrade iron contents, reducing the capital equipment necessary and consequently the capital cost per tonne of iron and the coke consumption. The widespread use of sintering for imported ore in the 1960s, however, weakened this lead, and the more sophisticated beneficiation processes developed during that period, and particularly pelletization, have proved more suitable to much imported ore than to home ores.

As a result, the Development Coordinating Committee of the British Iron and Steel Federation reversed in 1966 the earlier forecasts of the Iron and Steel Board and envisaged a 'progressive withdrawal from the use of home ore resources', accompanied by a shift of steelmaking capacity to coastal sites with ready access to deep-water and imported ores. Thus all BSC's major new developments involve a greater use of imported ores. Indeed, the Corporation plan to increase imports of foreign ores by 50 per cent over the quinquennium 1970–5, to a total of approximately 31 million tonnes. Home production is likely to contract from 12 million tonnes to 8 million tonnes over the same period.[153] Thus over the past thirteen years a major change of policy, with considerable implications for the balance of payments, has taken place. At the crux of this decision lies the unfavourable nature and distribution of the British ores. The high quality haematite, comparable in iron content with imported ores, is in insufficient quantity. The Jurassic ores, in fairly large quantities, are of insufficient quality. The clayband and blackband ores on which the Industrial Revolution was based have long been uneconomic to work and are likely to remain so.

The UK's total ore resources have been calculated at approximately 5500 million tonnes including about 3150 million tonnes classified as reserves.[154] This compares with 11 180 million tonnes for France, 345 million tonnes for Belgium and 4470 million tonnes for the Federal Republic of Germany. Although having smaller reserves than France, the UK is still one of the more richly endowed of European countries. All extraction is now controlled by the BSC. Of the UK total, reserves of 90·4 million and 203 million tonnes of potential ore consist of the haematite deposits near the western coasts. Haematite (an iron oxide ore) occurs in Cumberland and north-west Lancashire[155] in irregular deposits in the Carboniferous limestone and two separate areas have, historically, been important for production (see Fig. 5.3). In the Furness district a number of dish-like deposits occupied great hollows in the limestone and the largest of these, the Hodbarrow deposit near Millom, contained originally more than 6·1 million cubic metres of almost solid ore.[156] Production in this district ended in 1968 with the bankruptcy of the Millom Haematite Ore and Iron Company, although there is a possibility of reworking the slagheaps which total 7·1 million tonnes.[157] The iron content of the 4 million tonne number one slag bank in particular looks promising, since it dates back fifty years, when techniques of extraction were comparatively inefficient.

Further north, just south of Egremont, two mines, Beckermet, opened in 1906, and Haile Moor, which started production in 1941, are currently producing high quality haematite which is non-phosphoric. The high iron content makes possible its use in the furnaces without further treatment. The average per cent of iron from Cumberland haematite, weighted by consumption in 1969, was 48, second only among British ores to Glamorgan haematite, 50 per cent iron, the output of which is currently slightly smaller. Deposits, worked under the control of BSC General Steels Division, lie at depths of 150–610 metres, overlaid by red sandstone and breccia. The deposits are irregular in form and occurrence, posing difficulties in exploration and working, but a high level of mechanization involving considerable investment has been introduced.[158] The BSC annual report, 1968–9, recorded that selective rationalization in this area had produced increased output, improved productivity per manshift and lowered costs.

The slight increase in output in 1967 over the previous year was, however, only a temporary rallying. Production from Cumberland has fallen from 278 700 tonnes in 1964 to 145 300 tonnes in 1969,[159] a drop of 47 per cent compared with the national average drop during that period of 25·8 per cent. The contraction of output from Cumberland has in fact been more pronounced than that from Glamorgan. Locally imported ore is now supplemented by imports from Teesside for the production of foundry iron at Workington, though this plant ceased steelmaking in 1974.

There is only one remaining mine in the Glamorgan haematite at Llanharry, and its output is used by BSC Strip Division. Important ore deposits here are confined to a small area on the south-eastern margin of the coal basin between Taff's Well and Pencoed, with an east–west length of 18 kilometres.[160] Ore has been worked here since 1910, and during the Second World War output reached a peak of over 203 200

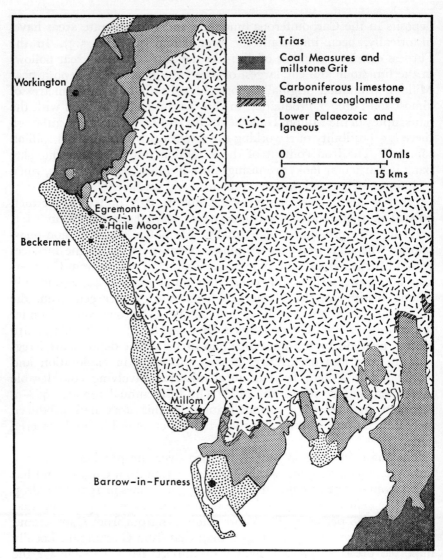

Fig. 5.3 *Haematite ores of the North-West*

tonnes. More recently, production from Glamorgan has held its level comparatively well, falling from 155 250 tonnes in 1964 to 138 200 tonnes in 1969,[161] a 9 per cent drop compared with the national average drop for that period of 25·8 per cent. But these ores, like those of Cumberland, are in the process of exhaustion, which is unfortunate, to say the least, bearing in mind that they are currently the richest worked in Britain and are located less than 32 kilometres from the major steelmaking complex at Port Talbot.

The great preponderance of UK deposits, accounting for 97·6 per cent of output by weight in 1969, occur as bedded, minette (Lorraine) type ores in the Jurassic system and extend intermittently from York-shire to Oxfordshire.[162] The ores occur at several different horizons in the Jurassic sequence: in the Lower Lias formation in north Lincoln-shire; in the marlstone beds of the Middle Lias in the Cleveland Hills and the scarplands from Lincolnshire to Oxfordshire; and in the Inferior Oolite formation in Northamptonshire, Leicestershire, Rut-land and south Lincolnshire (the 'Northampton Sands'). At Claxby in north Lincolnshire there is in addition some ironstone of Cretaceous age which was, until 1969, when extraction ceased, always included with the Inferior Oolite figures for statistical purposes. The Jurassic ores are all lean ores, varying in iron content from 20 to about 35 per cent; they occur in thick beds and are either worked opencast or by shallow mining.

The search for greater efficiency within the home ore industry has led not only to greater concentration on the Jurassic beds, whose share by weight of national output rose from 88·9 per cent in 1948, to 97·4 per cent in 1964[163] and 97·6 per cent in 1969, but to greater concen-tration on the more efficient areas within that system. This has involved the final closing down of production in the Cleveland Hills at the beginning of 1964 and in the Oxfordshire and south-west Northampton-shire areas in 1967. Operations began in the Cleveland Hills in 1846 (see Fig. 5.4), the ore bed being first quarried in the outliers of Eston and Upleatham only a few kilometres from the Tees estuary, where the marlstone outcrops on the hills' northern flanks. The marlstone dips gently south-eastwards and owing to the resistant nature of the overlying beds the ore bed rapidly disappears underground. Almost at once, therefore, adit mining, and subsequently vertical shafts, became necessary. The close proximity of the good coking coals of the Durham coalfield helped, within twenty years, to make this the most important centre of pig-iron production in Britain. In terms of ore extraction too, the Cleveland Hills acquired a dominant position before the First World War, 6 million tonnes being produced from this area in 1913.[164]

The ore was however highly phosphoric and therefore unsuitable for use in the Bessemer converter and ore imports, especially of non-phosphoric Spanish ores, amounted to almost half the ore consumed here in 1900.[165] The growing difficulties and expense of extracting the local ore increased imports between the wars, and by 1945 extraction had been reduced to 8 local mines with an output of 1 218 290 tonnes,[166]

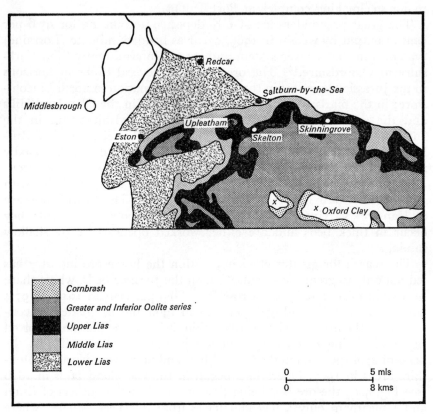

Fig. 5.4 *Cleveland iron ores of the Teesside area.*

about 8 per cent of the national total. Even this much reduced rate of extraction could only have been maintained for less than half a century before the reserves became exhausted. In fact, costs and difficulty of mining increased to such an extent after 1945 that, when the 'ore-based' iron and steel plant of Skinningrove at Saltburn-by-the-Sea closed its Loftus mine in 1958, only 3 remaining mines owned by Dorman Long stayed in operation. The last of these, at North

Skelton, closed in 1964, having been continued for the last few years for social rather than economic reasons.[167]

The Oxfordshire, south-west Northamptonshire and Warwickshire workings in the neighbourhood of Banbury (see Fig. 5.5), which came to an end in September 1967, never had in practice anything approaching the importance of the Cleveland deposits. The workable iron ore of this area, as of Cleveland, belongs to the marlstone rocks of the Middle Lias which is particularly well developed in the area round Banbury, stretching from Fawler in the south to Edge Hill in the west. Iron ore was worked intermittently at Fawler from 1858 and Adderbury from 1859, and regularly at Adderbury and Hook Norton after the opening of the Banbury/Cheltenham railway line in 1887.[168] In the absence of local coal and coal smelting, the ore from this area was always transported elsewhere, the chief destinations being the blast furnaces of south Staffordshire and South Wales. This was always a check on the expansion of the field—the *Victoria County History of Oxfordshire* noted in 1907 that 'the industry is not as fully developed as it might be owing to the heavy railway rates'.[169]

Increased demand during the First World War did however stimulate for the first time the development of the northern part of the iron-stone field on the Edge Hill plateau, north of Banbury. In 1940 the whole field produced 974 650 tonnes, rising to 1 157 120 tonnes in 1945.[170] The most important of the workings in the post-war period was Wroxton in the Edge Hill plateau, worked by the Oxfordshire Ironstone Company: in 1963, as the only remaining working in this area, it employed 135–40 men and produced 917 140 tonnes, which was sent to South Wales and the Brymbo steelworks at Wrexham, Denbighshire.[171]

In the event, output from the Oxfordshire field fell steadily until it closed altogether in 1967, but for a time from 1958–60 a totally different future was envisaged for this area. In November 1958 the Prime Minister announced in the House of Commons that Richard Thomas and Baldwin would construct a large new steelworks at Newport, Monmouthshire, aimed at producing 3 million tonnes of steel by 1964–5, and 6 million tonnes by 1975.[172] The Spencer works was planned with a view to utilizing the maximum economic percentage of home ore, as recommended by the Iron and Steel Board in 1957, and initially 40 per cent (later 30 per cent) of the requirements were intended to be brought from Oxfordshire. The steelmaking process at Richard Thomas and Baldwin's new Spencer works required ore of a low phosphoric content (0·35 per cent), obtainable only in the UK from Oxfordshire, and the silica and lime content of this ore was

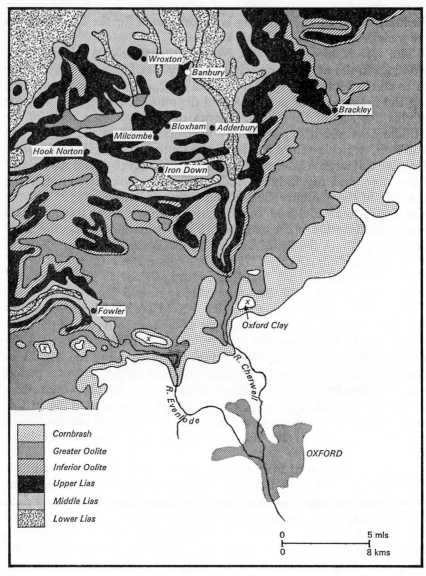

Fig. 5.5 *Jurassic iron ores of north Oxfordshire*

in the correct proportion for the mixture with 60 per cent foreign ore originally intended.[172] Richard Thomas and Baldwin, considering it necessary to obtain ore supplies under their own control as well as purchasing ore from Wroxton, made applications for ironstone workings in four areas: Bloxham Grove, Milcombe, Hook Norton and Iron Down. The applications totalled 1917 hectares which Richard Thomas and Baldwin estimated contained 1163 hectares of recoverable iron ore. If the Spencer works expanded as the company expected, Oxfordshire ore would be required at the rate of 1 million tonnes at the end of 1961, 2 million tonnes in 1964, 3 million tonnes in 1969 and 4 million tonnes in 1975 (including only 1 million tonnes from Wroxton). The ore would eventually be exhausted after 30–35 years.[174] Thus a massive expansion of iron ore production in this area was envisaged, bringing, so the company claimed, a cost advantage of 3 per cent compared with using 100 per cent foreign ore.[175]

The planning application was opposed by Oxfordshire County Council and a host of local objectors whose case rested, not only on the question of local amenity, but that of economic viability: they argued that prices were moving in favour of foreign ores and the workings might well be prematurely abandoned. The objectors were, of course, better informed on this question than the company's experts, and what they envisaged could easily have become a reality, i.e. the devastation of an area, the majority of which was designated as of Great Landscape Value, in the interests of a rapidly vanishing cost advantage.

In what must clearly be one of the most fortunate planning decisions in the field of mineral working in the 1960s—and not least for Richard Thomas and Baldwin—the Inspector, and the Minister of Housing and Local Government, upheld the objectors' case. The Inspector reported that the applicants had not made a case on cost advantage. If this existed it was very small and could easily be reversed by changing economic conditions. Workings could well become unprofitable and be abandoned.[176] Had the verdict gone the other way, it is clear that the changing economic balance of home and imported ores would rapidly have made the new Oxfordshire field, 185 kilometres from Newport, a white elephant. Apart from the grave economic loss which such an error would have involved the damage to the landscape would have been serious. Restoration is, of course, now obligatory on opencast ironstone operators, but the operations themselves involve unavoidable disturbance and restoration does not reproduce the original character of the area.

Fortunately, such a blunder was averted. The fate of the Wroxton field, where planning permission was never in question, clearly reflects the uneconomic nature of ironstone extraction in this area in the 1960s. In 1960 the Oxfordshire Ironstone Company was prepared to deliver 508 000 tonnes a year to the Spencer works and it was stated that in 1963 one million tonnes could be made available.[177] This capacity was never utilized. Output fell steadily from 917 100 tonnes in 1963 to 722 700 tonnes in 1966.[178] The following year this, the last working in the Oxfordshire area, closed down entirely.

The Northampton Sand ironstone, on the other hand, remained in 1969 the biggest producer by area of UK ore. This term comprises the bedded deposits of the Inferior Oolite running southwards from the Grantham area through Kettering and down to Northampton (see Fig. 5.6). This field is the richest and most extensive of the three ore-bearing series of Jurassic age,[179] and its output has, to date, fluctuated only marginally since the end of the Second World War. In 1969 the area (together with the cretaceous bed of north Lincolnshire) produced 7 299 450 tonnes, 59·3 per cent of the national total, compared with 7 899 000 tonnes in 1945.[180]

Extraction of the Northampton Sand ironstone, worked originally in Roman and mediaeval times, was restarted in 1852-3, promoted by the declining availability of clayband and blackband ores, and by rapid railway development, which both stimulated demand for iron and made possible large ore movements. The production of ore here was expanded more slowly than in the Cleveland Hills, largely because of the lack of local fuel, and the bulk of the ore was sent by rail to other areas, notably the West Midlands and Derbyshire. The phosphoric nature of the ore greatly delayed its use for steelmaking: even after the invention of the Gilchrist–Thomas process in 1878 made it possible to make steel from iron smelted from phosphoric ores, doubts about its quality persisted, and not until 1934 was a steelworks, that of Stewarts and Lloyds specializing in the production of tubes, opened at Corby. The steel made here is very suitable for welded steel production because of the fact that the only raw materials used consist of local ore and scrap uprising in the Corby plant, which result in a steel with a very low proportion of impurities. The siting of this works at Corby, approximately the centre of the field, was well chosen. To the south of Corby, the scene of the earliest nineteenth century workings, the bed is fragmented and dissected by streams. To the north of the River Welland, ore could economically be transported to Scunthorpe. The location of the Corby complex, in its turn, has helped to concentrate production on its immediate vicinity in the centre of the field.

In spite of the creation of the Corby works, much of the ore from

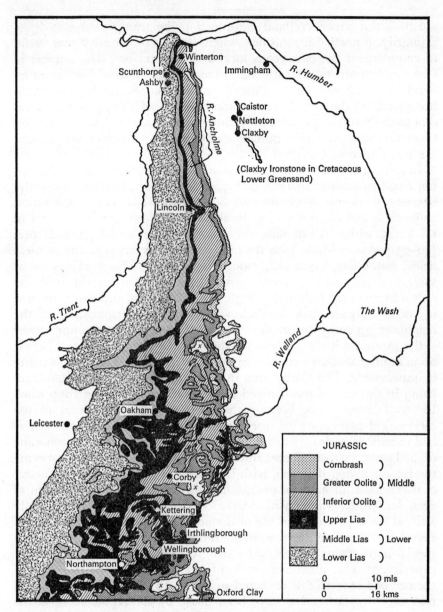

Fig. 5.6 *Jurassic iron ores of Lincolnshire, Leicestershire and Northamptonshire*

Within the map:

Winterton

Scunthorpe
Ashby

Immingham

R. Humber

R. Ancholme

Caistor
Nettleton
Claxby

(Claxby Ironstone in Cretaceous
Lower Greensand)

Lincoln

R. Trent

The Wash

R. Welland

Oakham

Leicester

Corby

Kettering

Irthlingborough
Wellingborough
Northampton

Oxford Clay

JURASSIC

Cornbrash)
Greater Oolite) Middle
Inferior Oolite)
Upper Lias)
Middle Lias) Lower
Lower Lias)

0   10 mls
0   16 kms

north of the River Welland continued to be transported elsewhere, primarily to north Lincolnshire, where its siliceous content was useful to complement the calcareous local Frodingham ore. The decline in Cleveland production meant that increasing amounts of Northampton Sand ironstone were sent to the Teesside furnaces. By 1970 approximately half of the total Northampton Sand ore of 7 229 450 tonnes was sent to the Scunthorpe area, to be sintered in admixture with local ores. Over three quarters of a million tonnes went to the North-East, and the remainder was smelted locally.[181]

In spite of the numerous freight movements involved, the Northampton Sand ironstone has held its high output level, to date, essentially because of its use of Corby and Scunthorpe. The Oolite formation contains a bed of iron ore, generally between 1·8 and 3·7 metres in thickness, which is not only the richest of the British Jurassic ores (30–33 per cent iron), with the most extensive reserves of any of these fields, but offers, above all, ease of extraction. The workings lie at shallow depths and operations are almost all opencast; in 1966 the only mines were at Irthlingborough, opened in 1917, and Eston, opened in 1960.[182] Apart from its shallowness—unlike the marlstone of the neighbouring areas the ore does not deteriorate eastwards under cover —the ironstone is distinctly softer than that of the marlstone. Where it occurs under shallow overburden and is oxidized, preliminary blasting is unnecessary. The Corby area in particular has long benefited from being in the van of mechanized ore quarrying, ever since 1895 when Lloyds Ironstone Co. became the first company in Britain to use mechanical excavators for working ironstone, and in the 1930s Corby had the first electric excavator.[183] The past twenty years have seen some of the largest excavating machines in the world here. In the 1950s came the large walking dragline, with its ability to handle up to 31 metres of overburden at a single operation, and the subsequent evolution of even larger excavators with increased capacity buckets has greatly assisted the economic working of the field. In 1965 excavators, both of shovel and dragline types, were operating with buckets constructed of special high-strength steels and having upwards of 23 cubic metres in capacity.[184] The maximum ratio of overburden to the thickness of the ore bed extracted is expected to rise to 18:1.[185] Where blasting is necessary, improvements have been made by the replacement of the heavy percussive drills with more mobile truck-mounted rotary drills using air and water as a flushing medium. By this means, the speed of blasthole and exploratory drilling has been doubled. The use of ammonium nitrate/fuel oil as a blasting agent instead of the more expensive conventional explosives has also reduced costs.

It is largely technical improvements such as these which have permitted the Northampton Sand ironstone actually to increase its percentage contribution to total output from 1959 to 1969, with only a slight output decline in absolute terms. The future looks very different. This area is likely to feel very strongly the impact of increased foreign imports in the 1970s. With so large a proportion of its ore transported overland, the rising delivered costs of Northamptonshire Sand ore relative to foreign ores have been particularly marked. Even more important is the ore's unsuitability for the LD steelmaking process, the prime reason for the replacement of the Northampton Sand ore sent to Scunthorpe, half the output in 1970, by imported ore. The changeover took place towards the end of 1972. The three quarters of a million tonnes sent to the North-East in 1970 was down to half a million tonnes in the first half of 1971[185] and deliveries ceased altogether in the middle of that year. The future potential of the field is virtually limited to supplying Corby. A new, large iron ore sintering plant has been built, and is fed with a burden of locally mined ores together with other materials.[187] But this expansion will clearly not offset altogether the sharp decline in ores transported elsewhere. Production from deposits north of the Welland was severely cut down in the early 1970s and ceased altogether in 1973. The long-term future of this field, described as recently as 1971 as 'one of the vital factors in the British iron and steel industry', [188] now appears to be one of sharply declining national importance. However, the southern area around Corby is likely to be important locally for some time to come. It is unlikely that it would be practicable to operate the Corby works entirely on foreign ore.

The marlstone beds of the Middle Lias in south Lincolnshire and Leicestershire (see Fig. 5.6), very close to the northern, more difficult areas of Oolitic ironstone, are much smaller in extent and have felt the impact of competition and of exhaustion earlier than the Corby area. The Middle Lias is found in a clear horizon of about 3·7 metres average thickness at the top of the marlstone and is consequently exposed on the dipslope of the escarpment. The gentle angle of dip of the ore beds (2–5 degrees) usually produces broad outcrops,[189] and the ironstone is therefore worked opencast, although there was from 1933 to 1943 underground mining in the Holwell are of north-east Leicestershire.[190] The diminution of output from this area, 66·8 per cent from 1964 to 1969 compared with the national average drop of 25·8 per cent, stems from the closure of several East Midlands pig-iron producing plants in the 1960s, the high rail freight rates and the less extensive nature of the deposits. The large earth-moving and ore-recovery equipment of the

Corby and Scunthorpe area was much less in evidence here. Quarries closed in the north-east Leicestershire area at Eaton in 1965 and Eastwell in 1967. The end of working in this area, forecast in 1971, came about two years later.

Paradoxically, the Jurassic ore bed whose future looks much more assured than any other British field apart from Corby area is the Frodingham deposit around Scunthorpe. The iron content here is only 20–22 per cent, well below any other British field, and probably the leanest ore currently being commercially exploited anywhere. The deposit has been described as 'the worst iron ore field in the world'.[191] It produces more slag per tonne of iron than any other field, and its properties are extremely variable. In a fully developed face of 9·8 metres there may be up to 24 different seams, with wide chemical variations vertically between beds and horizontally within a bed.[192] Furthermore, the deposit has the added disadvantage of a higher percentage of underground mining than the other Jurassic beds. The worked-out areas occur, naturally, towards the outcrop along the southern and western edges of the orefield, and it has been necessary to work eastwards in the direction of the dip to maintain a continued supply of ore. The increased proportion of mined output involves, of course, a higher proportion of skilled men, and does not make possible the total extraction of the ironstone. However, unlike the Northampton Sand ironstone, the ore is not highly phosphoric, and thus is not ruled out for use in the LD steelmaking process. Its high lime content makes it an attractive ore for fluxing and the thickness of the bed—up to 9·2 metres—makes it a more attractive operation than the thinner beds.

The Frodingham Ironstone is located in the Lower Lias between the River Trent in the west and eastwards to the River Ancholme (see Fig. 5.6) extending from the River Humber in the north about 16·5 kilometres south to Ashby Ville. The concealed deposit dips from the west at 1 in 65, changing to 1 in 35 in the most easterly areas currently being worked at the Dragonby mine. It is economic to exploit only the central part of the field between Winterton and Ashby. The reserves of the bed are substantial: the total of proved, probable and possible reserves were estimated at 1449 million tonnes in 1944.[193] The ironstone consists of limonite* oolites in a matrix of chamosite† and siderite‡ mixed with a considerable proportion of shells and shell fragments which partly account for the low iron content but also make the ore self-fluxing.

* Yellowish to brown hydrated oxide of iron.
† Greenish hydrous iron silicate.
‡ Iron carbonate.

Apart from some extraction in the Roman period, the Frodingham ore was first worked in 1859. In the early days of working, only the more completely oxidized parts of the ore bed were extracted, a process which involved selective hand-digging. When it was realized that the Frodingham ironstone could be used as a ferruginous/calcareous flux in the smelting of the siliceous Northampton Sand ore, extraction began to take place over much greater areas of the bed. The first blending of this kind was carried out in late 1870 or 1871, and by 1875 all but one of the works were using such ore from south Lincolnshire, in proportions varying between one eighth and one quarter.[194] In the twentieth century further efforts to improve the performance of the ore have led primarily to crushing, screening and sintering of both local and Northampton Sand ore. This has made possible greatly improved blast furnace performance. Parallel with the improvements in this field have gone expansion of steelmaking capacity, growing slowly from 1890 onwards, and helped by the proximity to coal.

Between the First and Second World Wars the area increased its proportion of the national output of pig-iron from 6 to 14 per cent and of steel from 3 to 10 per cent.[195] In 1969 its three integrated works plus a plan to expand steel capacity seemed to offer a significant furture for Frodingham ore. In fact, an additional steel plant has completed and opened at Scunthorpe in 1974.[196]

Until a slight downturn in the second half of the 1960s, iron ore output had increased steadily from 2 512 100 tonnes in 1934 to 5 636 600 tonnes in 1961. During 1964–9 output fell by 18·9 per cent compared with the national average fall of 25·8 per cent. The opencast section of the field is worked by large-scale mechanization and up to 46 metres of overburden is removed. It is considered that up to 61 metres can be economically removed, although to date this has yet to be proved in practice. In that year approximately 20 per cent of the output was mined and underground methods are more advanced here than anywhere else within British iron ore fields. The two sections currently mined are Winns, opened in 1938, and Dragonby, opened in 1950, combined into one mine, Santon, in 1969. Dragonby, much the larger of the two, had had a substantial investment programme, and considerable increases in productivity had been achieved. In 1957 Dragonby mine employed 171 men to produce 11 180 tonnes per week, with Joy Loaders and shuttle cars for loading and transporting the ore to the conveyor system. In 1971 Santon Mine produced 20 300 tonnes per week, employing 134 men and using diesel loading shovels to load and transport the ore on to the conveyor system.[197] The output of the mine may double between 1971 and 1979.

353

The Frodingham bed remains, apart from Corby, the only British deposit with, as far as can be seen, a major long-term significance. The planned output is 102 000 tonnes a week (5 304 000 tonnes per year), compared with the 4 478 500 tonnes produced in 1969.[198] The decisive factor is proximity to the large Scunthorpe iron and steel complex which is capable of absorbing all the local ore produced. So great have been the changes in the balance of home and imported ore costs, and especially the rises in cost of overland freight, that proximity to a large enough complex now outweighs several natural difficulties.

With the prospect of further closures in almost all the extraction districts, it is indeed fortunate that the industry possesses, in the Ironstone Restoration Fund, a system for restoration unique among extractive industries. In the early 1930s there were still a few quarries in the East Midlands where ore was hand dug, but on the whole the increasing depth of overburden involved complete mechanization of the working face. The largest of these operations caused such widespread devastation, and public concern, that the Kennet Committee was set up in 1938 to consider the question of restoration. Although at the time of the inquiry there were 1200 hectares of derelict ironstone land,[199] techniques of restoration were at an early stage,* and the committee did little beyond recommending afforestation. The great demand for increased output during the Second World War could have created devastation on a vast scale. In fact, the increasingly large-scale earth-shifting machinery made possible the first real breakthrough in restoration techniques, i.e. restoration as an integral part of the extractive process, and the wartime demand for the quickest possible return of land to agriculture provided the impetus.[200] In 1946 another committee, the Waters Committee, was able to consider the restoration question in a much more informed way than its predecessor, and its findings[201] led eventually to the Mineral Workings Act of 1951, which set up the Ironstone Restoration Fund.

The Ironstone Restoration Fund provides money for the restoration of land worked opencast for iron ore within the geographical counties of Leicester, Lincoln (excluding parts of Holland), Northampton, Oxford, Rutland, Warwick and the Soke of Peterborough. For every ton of ironstone worked, the producer contributes to a central fund 3 pence for which he can recoup from the mineral lessor between 1·5 pence and 0·468 pence (dependent on the royalties paid) and a further

---

* Restoration of a primitive kind considerably pre-dates the Reclamation Fund. Samuel Lloyd's first lease in the Corby area, dated 11 August 1881, stipulated that the land surface should be fully restored for agricultural use. Sir Frederick Scopes, *The Development of Corby Works*, Stewarts and Lloyds 1968, p. 8.

0·308 pence is then added by the Exchequer to provide an overall income to the fund of 3·308 pence per ton. (The Ironstone Fund still uses statute tons and acres for calculation purposes.) As the yield is usually between 14 000 and 20 000 tons of ironstone per acre, a sum of between £463 and £661 usually becomes available for restoration. The producers' contribution to the fund, given above, was substantially increased by an Act of Parliament in 1971, which was prompted by the Fund having liabilities of more than £1 million in excess of its assets. The producer also became liable for the first £260 instead of the first £110 per acre of restoration costs imposed by planning consents, and this is likely to rise again shortly to £330.[202] The two main payments out of the fund are to iron ore producers who can claim from the fund the excess where their cost of complying with planning conditions exceeds £272 per hectare, and to landowners and farmers for bringing the land back to agriculture. The payments made to local authorities were fairly substantial in the early years but are now less important. The majority of the older workings have been reclaimed without the use of topsoil, but more recent permissions to operate usually stipulate the replacement of existing topsoil for restoration to agriculture or, more rarely, forestry. All applications to operate are 'called in' by the Minister for the Environment, who draws up conditions in association with the local planning authority. The Ministry of Agriculture is responsible for ensuring that the restored land is returned to agriculture, with adequate fencing, the planting of hedges and the provision of water. All these costs, as well as a grant for afforestation, are met from the fund, although no payment is made for landscaping.

The scheme has in general worked well. A 1952 survey, for instance, revealed 567 derelict hectares from ironstone working in Northamptonshire. Restoration began in 1953 and by 1965 486 hectares had been restored, all except 89 of them by Northamptonshire County Council.[203] No permanent new dereliction is created as the producers are obliged to restore the land at the end of the operations: in 1965 1110 hectares in the county had been restored by the producers, and of these 903 were ready for agriculture. This brought the total of land restored in Northamptonshire to more than 1620 hectares.[204] Little backlog now remains throughout the whole ironstone district.

Techniques of restoration have improved, and some areas were left in the early years in a condition which would not be considered satisfactory today.[205] In any event, even with the most advanced techniques, the character of the landscape may be changed as a result of operations. The level of land in relation to buildings is sometimes altered, as roads may be left on embankments and trees take long to recover their original size. In the worst instances, as the County Planning Adviser for Oxfordshire said of lands restored by the Oxfordshire Ironstone Company, 'the effect was to transform ordinary English countryside into bare, bleak, uninteresting prairie without trees and hedges . . . this utilitarian land was devoid of all beauty'.[206] However, this is not true of most of the restored ironstone land in Oxfordshire. In the better areas, such effects are reduced by contouring, but unfortunately the use of landscape consultants is not always stipulated in planning consents.

During the period of exploitation, of course, large-scale opencast workings as at Corby and Scunthorpe cause great and unavoidable disturbance. The presence of extensive ironstone quarries and associated iron and steel works to the north and east of Scunthorpe acts as an important constraint on the direction of the town's development.[207] However, much of the approximately 1620 hectares of land already worked in the planning area for (Lindsey) opencast ore winning has been restored, with the help of the Ironstone Restoration Fund, and the shift in emphasis from opencast to underground working at Scunthorpe, necessary for technical reasons, will further reduce the impact of workings on amenity. The underground workings have not, in this area, caused any appreciable subsidence.[208] In Northamptonshire, where the area being worked for ironstone in 1971 was 1013 hectares (including buildings and ancillary plant) and the annual take 57 hectares,[209] ironstone was much the largest consumer of land among extractive industries. However, the problems of land use competition or amenity posed were less than those caused by the substantially more restricted sand and gravel and limestone extraction. This is largely due to the role of the Ironstone Restoration Fund and the sophisticated techniques of reinstatement which have been evolved.

The Ironstone Restoration Scheme does not cover the counties where haematite is worked. Consequently, waste dumps associated with disused iron ore workings, a very rare sight in the Midlands, still present problems of unsightliness at Millom and in the Egremont area of west Cumberland. In Glamorgan, however, the main problems arise from subsidence resulting from the Llanharry mine, which restricts residential development in the area,[210] and even an extension of the Restoration Fund could do little to ameliorate this.

The restoration of opencast iron ore workings, like that of opencast coal, is required by law. In both cases, the high standards attained owe much to the comparative ease of the task involved: in many cases a thin seam of mineral underlies a thick overburden, thus eliminating the need for fill obtained from outside. The technical advances in earth-moving equipment and the development of sophisticated techniques of land reclamation have also played a part. The special contribution of the Ironstone Restoration Fund lies in its role in clearing past dereliction: as a result ironstone working, an extractive industry with a long and extensive history far pre-dating planning controls, has left an incomparably small legacy of damage on the landscape. It is largely for this reason that many planners and conservationists argue[211] that the principles of the scheme, originally intended as a pilot experiment, should now be extended to cover other extractive industries.

6

CARBON AND HYDROCARBON FUELS

COAL

AFTER ten years of rapid contraction, the coal industry still remained in 1969 the largest extractive industry in the UK, in terms of tonnage produced. Total coal output from all sources was 155 651 200 tonnes[1] compared with sand and gravel, the second largest extractive industry, with a total output of 105 950 500 tonnes (including silica sand).[2] The primacy of coal may endure throughout the 1970s, although the gap will almost certainly narrow further, in view of the expected annual growth rate of sand and gravel of some 3·5 per cent.[3] However, the NCB, seen as a single organization with a turnover of about £900 million in 1970,[4] will continue to overshadow in size any other extractive enterprise in the country. Indeed, in terms of assets, turnover and manpower, the NCB ranks as one of the largest industrial concerns in the world.

The position of UK deep-mined coal, relative to mining and quarrying as a whole, altered sharply in the years 1960–9. In 1960 the tonnage of NCB deep-mined coal represented 47·1 per cent of total tonnage raised by all mining and quarrying, in addition to 7 721 600 tonnes of opencast coal and 1 117 600 tonnes of other production (licensed private mines). In 1969 the NCB deep-mined total represented 30 per cent of an estimated total of 478 147 100 tonnes produced by UK mining and quarrying as a whole.[5] In terms of numbers employed, the percentage contribution of NCB deep-mines varied by a smaller amount over that same period. In 1960 the average number of wage-earners in NCB mines represented 78·8 per cent of the total average number employed in all mining and quarrying. In 1969 the percentage was 69·2.[6] This comparatively smaller change in the relative position of the deep-mined coal labour market occurred in spite of the sharp overall contraction in the size of that market which fell by nearly one half, from 602 100 wage-earners in 1960 to 305 100 in 1969.[7] The greater fall in percentage of total tonnage than in percentage of total manpower means that the productivity of deep-mined coal relative to mining and quarrying as a whole declined from 1960–9, in spite of the considerable productivity advances made in coalmining (see Table 6.1). This declining relative productivity reflects the greater advances

Table 6.1. The position of deep-mined coal relative to mining and quarrying as a whole, 1960–9

	Tonnage produced		Average no. employed	
	1960	*1969*	*1960*	*1969*
Gross mining and quarrying	396 443 200*	478 147 100†	764 000	442 000
NCB deep coal	186 740 800	146 507 200	602 100	305 100
Coal as per cent of total	47·1	30·0	78·8	69·2

* Excluding lead and zinc.   † Estimated.

possible in modern opencast working techniques, and the impact of diminishing returns on coal as an old extractive industry.

The changing position of coal in relation to extractive industries as a whole in terms of value is more difficult to assess in the absence of reliable statistics for mining and quarrying as a whole for 1960. The gross estimated value of mining and quarrying in the UK (at mine or quarry) in 1970 was £1 024 000 000,[8] of which coal contributed 70·3 per cent. The much higher percentage contribution of coal by value than by tonnage is largely caused by the low value of the other bulk minerals, mainly aggregates. Clearly, however, the fall in the percentage of total value made up by coal during the 1960s must have been considerably larger than the actual fall, which was only a marginal one, from £760 430 000 in 1960 to £715 583 000 in 1969.

One of the most striking changes in the position of the coal industry relates to marketing. The contribution of coal to the UK energy market fell spectacularly from 61 per cent to 47·1 per cent in 1970.[9] The chief challenge to coal during this period came from oil. In the second half of 1970 oil replaced coal for the first time as the chief UK primary energy source. The size of the challenge presented by oil may be indicated by the fact that the average annual value per tonne of crude and processed oil entering the UK between 1965 and 1969 was less than that of ten years earlier (ranging from between £5·88 and £7·43 and from between £7·73 and £9·70 respectively).[10] This reduction reflected not only the diminished price for Persian Gulf crude oil f.o.b. during that period, but also world market surpluses and the economies in oil transport costs brought about by the use of larger tankers and more advantageous charger rates. Coal had maintained its predominance in the energy market longer in the UK than in most other major industrial countries. In the United States oil with natural gas became the leading energy supplier in 1950; oil by itself took the lead in Japan by 1962, and in the EEC by 1964. Oil became the leading energy supplier in the world in 1966. The most striking exception to this general trend is the USSR, the world's largest coal producer, where coal in 1968 still met some 58 per cent of the total energy demand.[11]

The longer predominance of coal in the UK energy market compared with most other industrial nations reflects a variety of factors. The UK economy was geared historically to coal as a major source of energy and the significant percentage of British industry still located on the coalfields, compared for instance with the United States, gave coal a transport cost advantage. Political decisions to protect coal, reflecting strategic and social considerations, operated to reduce the contractions of coal in the 1960s more strongly in the UK than in the EEC. The British Government were also concerned not only to limit the cost of fuel to the balance of payments but the dependence on imported oil whose supply, they believed, could not be guaranteed (a wise assumption in the light of events which followed the 1973 Arab-Israeli war). They also considered the general coincidence of the loss making coalpits with areas of high unemployment to be an important consideration in controlling the rate of decline of the industry. The revenue tax on imported oil, the various measures to protect coal in the increasingly important power station market, consuming 46·8 per cent of total inland consumption and exports in 1969–70,[12] and the writing off of £415 million of unproductive assets in 1965, were the chief manifestations of this policy. The Coal Industry Act 1971, which raised the statutory limit on the NCB's deficit from £50 to £75 million and gave powers for this to be further increased to £100 million, also helped to blunt the impact on coal of competition from other energy sources.

While the coal industry was not exposed to full market competition in a decade which marked the changeover from a two to a four fuel economy (incorporating the primary energy sources natural gas and nuclear energy as well as coal and oil), the distribution of production during the decade underwent a marked locational change under the impact of the NCB's increasing concentration on high reserve, low cost pits. This was a continuation of the trend already showing strongly during the 1950s and which was reflected primarily in the increasing importance of east central England coalfields and the declining importance of Scotland, Wales and Northern England, except Yorkshire. E. S. Simpson, commenting on the area production figures from 1950 to 1962, wrote that,

Coal output is becoming increasingly focused on a belt of country from the Leicestershire coalfield in the south through Nottingham as far as the River Aire in Yorkshire to the north. Almost exactly one-half of British coal now [1966] originates in this area of east central England. The centre of gravity of coal production has moved from Highland Britain to the English Lowland.[13]

During the seven years 1963–4 to 1969–70 this general trend has been reinforced, with the NCB areas (see Fig. 6.1) of North Yorkshire, Doncaster, South Yorkshire, North Nottinghamshire, South Nottinghamshire, South Midlands and Staffordshire increasing their percentage contribution of total deep-mined output, and Scottish North, Scottish South, Northumberland, North Durham, South Durham, Barnsley, Northwestern, North Derbyshire, East Wales, West Wales and Kent contributing reduced percentages (see Table 6.2). The Staffordshire division, which made a declining percentage contribution during 1950–62,* increased it percentage contribution during the period 1963–4 to 1969–70 and had the highest profit per tonne of any area in 1969–70. The Staffordshire area increased productivity by 9 per cent over the previous year compared with the national average of 2·1 per cent. It will be seen from Table 6.2 that all the areas with increased percentage total, 1963–4 and 1969–70 had an overall drop in output levels during that time, with the exception of North Nottinghamshire whose overall output level rose despite the severe contraction in the industry as a whole.

The chief factor influencing expansion of production in one region rather than another is the availability of reserves and access to them. The major Yorkshire/Derbyshire/Nottinghamshire field has the greatest known reserves of any British field.[14] However, other very important factors were productivity and production costs per tonne (see Table 6.4), which in turn were influenced both by geology and the exhaustion of the more accessible reserves in the older fields. The correlation between above average output per manshift in 1969–70, above average output power loaded, overall profit per ton saleable coal and increasing percentage of total production was almost complete.

* The change in NCB area organization means that exactly equivalent figures for the present Staffordshire area are not available for 1950–62. However, the contribution of the North Staffordshire section of the West Midlands area to national output fell from 3·3 to 2·7 per cent during that period (E. S. Simpson, *Coal and the Power Industries in Post-war Britain*, Longmans, 1966, p. 107).

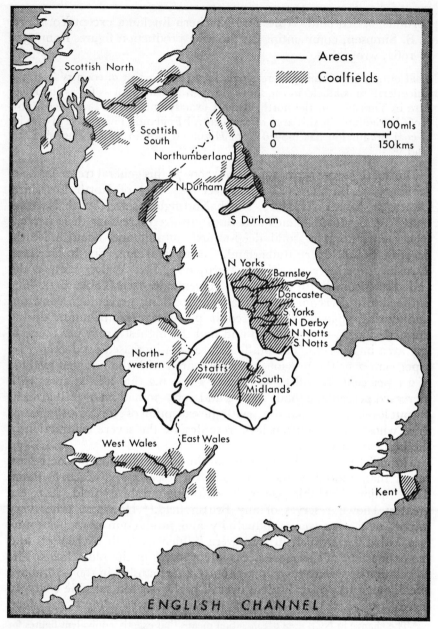

Fig. 6.1 *National Coal Board areas*

Table 6.2. Output, productivity, mechanization and cumulative absence by areas

Area	Percentage of total (deep-mined) 1963–4	Percentage of total (deep-mined) 1969–70	Tonnage change 1969–70 on 1963–4 (thousand tonnes)	Output per manshift 1969–70 (tonnes)	Percentage of output power loaded 1969–70	Cumulative absence percentage 1969–70
Scottish North	4·0	3·6	− 2 565	1·956	93·0	19·08
Scottish South	4·8	4·6	− 2 633	1·809	79·6	17·89
Northumberland	5·9	4·9	− 4 189	2·154	73·5	13·40
North Durham	5·0	3·8	− 4 102	1·697	86·7	14·53
South Durham	6·4	5·9	− 3 837	1·844	91·5	16·10
North Yorkshire	5·5	6·6	− 1 163	2·510	95·2	18·38
Doncaster	5·2	6·1	− 1 339	2·433	97·2	21·97
Barnsley	6·3	5·7	− 3 755	2·134	91·9	21·80
South Yorkshire	6·0	7·2	− 1 080	2·347	96·7	19·14
Northwestern	6·8	5·0	− 5 847	1·829	96·3	17·86
North Derbyshire	7·8	7·6	− 4 045	2·845	98·1	18·00
North Nottinghamshire	5·9	8·4	+ 711	2·982	99·1	17·94
South Nottinghamshire	7·4	8·0	− 2 861	2·977	98·4	16·25
South Midlands	5·9	6·6	− 1 853	3·033	94·6	13·87
Staffordshire	5·8	6·1	− 2 418	2·565	95·3	18·74
East Wales	6·3	5·5	− 4 228	1·382	81·2	21·58
West Wales	4·1	3·6	− 2 686	1·509	77·7	21·57
Kent	·9	·8	− 512	1·351	89·6	18·59
AVERAGE				2·187	92·3	18·32

Source: Figures calculated from NCB Annual Reports; cumulative absence percentage figures supplied by the NCB.

North Derbyshire was the only area with above average output per manshift 1969–70 which had reduced its percentage contribution to total production during the previous seven years. This probably reflects the fact that the North Derbyshire area does not face difficult working conditions but is located on the oldest section of the major Yorkshire/Derbyshire/Nottinghamshire field where reserves have been most depleted. Only the Scottish North and Northwestern areas had above average per cent of output power loaded and below average output per manshift in 1969–70. Northumberland alone of the areas with decreased percentages showed a profit per tonne in 1969–70; and North Yorkshire and Doncaster alone of the areas showing increased percentages made a loss per tonne in 1969–70.

The varying geology of the coalfields, and the exhaustion of reserves in parts of the longer worked fields, affect not only their respective rates of production, but the related question of productivity and production costs per tonne. In the East Midlands and South Yorkshire areas, shallow angles of dip, generally thicker seams and low incidence of faulting make mechanization particularly effective. The Leicestershire/South Derbyshire field, for instance, has a high proportion of production from thick seams[15] and the existence of shallow seams favourable to drift mining has also been an important aid to productivity. On the other hand, in the anthracite producing districts of the South Wales coalfield, the second largest British coalfield, both inaccessible main seams and difficult working conditions at the seams helps to bring about very high production costs. Minor structures disrupt mechanized mining; furthermore, the variance in the quality of the coal from seam to seam, and in the thickness of the seams over short distances, as well as the presence of dirt bands, all reduce output.[16] Because of the special properties of these coals, smokeless fuel of a quality second to none in the world, heavy investment schemes were implemented here after nationalization in 1947, but the problems involved in merchanizing mining in such an area were underestimated.[17] Here, as elsewhere, the NCB's concentration on fewer coalfaces lengthened production delays when adverse geological conditions were encountered. The difficulties attendant on mechanization here were the chief reason why many private mines in the area, employing less than 30 men and chiefly manual methods, enjoyed, in the early 1960s at least, higher productivity and profitability than the large NCB collieries. The average output per manshift in the large collieries in 1961 was 0·884 tonne, while a sample of licensed mines in that year showed the lowest output per manshift to be 1 tonne whilst several averaged more than double this quantity.[18]

Perhaps surprisingly, the area productivity levels bear little relationship to cumulative percentages for absenteeism, although a high level has very disruptive effect on the necessarily coordinated teamwork of a modern mechanized face. The greatest cumulative absence percentages for 1969–70 were from the Doncaster and Barnsley areas, both of above average productivity. However, the area variations in levels of absenteeism are not very large, all areas having what must be considered an unfortunately high level.

The major changes in the pattern of coal utilization in the 1960s, altering the levels of demand for the various types of coal produced, did probably affect the locational change in production. The influence of demand was always subject to availability. There was, for example, an almost steady demand for good quality coking coal, but the Durham areas, producers of very high quality coking coal, contributed declining percentages from 1963–4 to 1969–70 because of the exhaustion of the most accessible reserves. The coke-oven market contracted slightly (see Table 6.3) as a result of the British Steel Corporation's increasing use of higher grade imported ores which require smaller amounts of coke for smelting. The biggest overall contractions during the 1960s, however, occurred in the industrial, railway and gas markets. The steady fall in the gas market from 1963 was caused mainly by the Gas Council's increasing adoption of oil-based gas; the much sharper fall after 1967 coincided with the first deliveries of natural gas from the North Sea.

The largely unforeseen slump in the gas market produced severe problems in some areas, especially in Durham and Yorkshire. During the 1950s a major reconstruction at Westoe colliery, County Durham, costing £6 million, was planned on the basis of supplying more than 75 per cent of its output for the gas industry. By 1966 the percentage of this colliery's output taken by the gas industry, as a result of conversion to oil, was little more than 25 per cent[19] and the discovery of natural gas merely intensified difficulties of this kind. On the other hand, the size and importance of the power station market increased very substantially. The continued emphasis in the 1960s on the siting of power stations in the East Midlands and Yorkshire was both the cause and result of expanded production there. The last coal-based power station, started in 1966, was at Drax in Yorkshire. The trend towards greater conversion of coal to electricity has enhanced the importance of those areas producing suitable low grade coal, and those well placed for delivery to stations serving the major power consuming areas such as South-East England. The East Midlands was of importance on both counts. However, the permission of the 1971–4 Conservative Govern-

Table 6.3. Coal consumption in million tonnes, 1960–1970/71

	1960	1961	1962	1963	1964	1965	1966	1967	1968	1969	1969/70	1970/71
Power stations	52·7	56·3	62·1	68·6	69·1	71·1	69·7	68·3	74·4	77·1	78·1	74·7
Gas works	23·0	22·9	22·8	22·8	20·8	18·5	17·2	14·8	10·9	7·0	6·1	3·5
Coke-ovens	29·3	27·4	24·1	24·1	26·3	26·7	25·2	24·0	25·3	25·7	25·8	25·0
Industry	35·5	33·1	31·3	29·6	28·4	27·7	25·6	23·3	23·0	21·7	21·0	18·7
Domestic	36·1	33·8	34·3	33·6	29·4	28·9	26·9	24·5	23·6	21·3	21·3	18·6
Rail	9·0	7·8	6·3	5·1	3·9	2·8	1·7	0·8	0·2	0·2	0·1	—
Others	14·2	13·6	13·4	13·3	12·3	11·9	11·2	10·7	9·7	10·1	9·0	10·1
Total	199·8	194·9	194·3	197·1	190·2	187·6	177·5	166·4	167·1	163·7	161·4	150·6

Sources: Ministry of Technology, *Digest of Energy Statistics*, 1970 and National Coal Board Report and Accounts, 1970–1.

ment to move towards much greater consumption of oil and to a lesser extent natural gas could well have reversed this trend in the 1970s had it not been for the oil crisis of the winter of 1973–4.

Predictions of the likely market for coal in the 1970s have to be seen not only against the rising cost of oil, but also against a background of repeated failures of forecasting and unexpected changes of demand dating back to the 1950s. Between 1947 and the end of 1956 coal was not so much sold as allocated and emphasis was put on producing the maximum output, with relatively little attention paid to either cost or marketing techniques. Between those dates, the average annual increase in inland demand for coal was 3·25 million tonnes[20] and hundreds of loss-making pits were kept open to help meet demand. Although a heavy investment programme was begun, average productivity rose very slowly from 1·258 tonnes per manshift in 1951 to 1·263 tonnes per manshift in 1957.[21] The 1950 *Plan for Coal* assessed its likely demand as far ahead as 1961–5 at between 234 and 254 million tonnes per year (home and overseas markets) and a long-term increase of 18 per cent in national deep-mined output was planned for 1950–65. In 1965 home consumption reached a peak of more than 218 million tonnes and in May of that year a report by the Organization for European Economic Cooperation forecast that the demand for coal would continue to exceed supply.[22] During 1957, however, a totally unexpected surplus was accumulated; home consumption fell by more than 5 million tonnes and exports by 2 million tonnes. The decline, originally thought to be temporary, was reinforced in 1958 and 1959; during these three years the total market for British coal contracted by some 34 million tonnes, or about 15 per cent, while deliveries of oil in direct competition to coal almost doubled.[23] In fact, the forecasts of energy consumption were not markedly inaccurate; it was the reduction in coal's share of the market in relation to oil which had not been foreseen. The unexpected downturn in the coal market necessitated the *Revised Plan for Coal*, published October 1959, which reassessed home demand in 1965 at 193–208 million tonnes per year and exports at 10 million tonnes. The Revised Plan initiated a period when new priorities emerged in the management of the coal industry, notably improving the competitive position of coal by greatly increased productivity, concentration on the more efficient pits and improved marketing techniques. Although market demand was again reassessed downwards in the course of the 1960s, these remained the priorities during 1960–70 when Lord Robens was chairman of NCB. The number of pits fell from 737 at the beginning of 1960 to 299 in 1970, the average percentage of output power loaded rose from 38·2 in

1960 to 92·2 in 1970 and productivity rose from 1·417 tonnes in 1960 to 2·205 tonnes in 1970.[24] The increasing productivity was due at least in part to the inevitable benefits of the pit closure programme. The last study of the Prices and Incomes Board which investigated the coal industry in the late 1960s[25] attempted to estimate increasing efficiency apart from the automatic benefits of pit closures, through a sample of existing collieries which had not formed part of any extensive re-organization. Here the Prices and Incomes Board found an increase in output per manshift of approximately 25 per cent during 1964–70. However, despite these overall improvements in productivity during a period when the British coal industry became probably the most technically advanced in the world, official forecasts continued to pre-dict declining markets. In 1965 the National Plan estimated a reduced demand of 173–83 million tonnes in 1970. The 1967 White Paper on Fuel Policy, produced largely as a result of the discovery of substantial indigenous gas reserves under the North Sea, estimated a much more drastic curtailment of the inland coal market to some 146 million tonnes in 1970 (to be raised to 156 million tonnes by asking the Central Electricity Board and the Gas Board to burn more coal). Total coal production in 1970 of as much as 157 million tonnes was envisaged, based partly on the NCB's submission that 'it should technically be possible to obtain by 1970–1 an increase in labour productivity of about a third on the 1966–7 level'.[26] Total coal production for the year 1969–70 was 152·5 million tonnes, however, and in 1970–1 the NCB produced only 144 million tonnes. This resulted partly from a failure to reach the expected productivity level—output per man-shift overall for 1970–1 was 2·245 tonnes compared with the 2·479 considered technically possible—and partly from the unofficial strike on several coalfields in November 1970. The result was that even allowing for substantial withdrawals from stocks, the coal industry was unable to take full advantage of the energy shortage, which had come about largely as a result of technical difficulties in the nuclear energy programme and a much greater demand for energy than the White Paper had anticipated.[27] Thus in 1970 an excess of demand over supply led to the importation of coal for the first time since 1958.

Although output was low, the prospects for the coal market during 1970–1 thus seemed brighter than for some time: the NCB produced 144 million tonnes, sold 155 million tonnes and total UK consump-tion was 160 tonnes. The NCB made a profit of £500 000 after paying all interest and other charges. The various national and international coal bodies were optimistic that the buoyant market would continue during the 1970s, particularly after the threat of interruption to oil

supplies by members of the Organization of Petroleum Exporting Countries, which was only averted by a substantial increase in prices. As in late 1973 the threat became a reality and oil prices rose again by a factor of four, the prognostications of the coal interests look like becoming realised. Even in 1971 the Association for Coal in Europe had predicted much greater pressure on oil supplies in the future.

Cumulative requirement over the next 20 years would be about 81 280 million tonnes of oil. Proved reserves amount to 74 170 million tonnes. On a 15 to 1 reserves to production ratio, about 81 280 million tonnes of fresh reserves need to be found by 1990. If the present 30 to 1 ratio of reserves to production is to be maintained, about 182 900 million tonnes would have to be found between now and 1990, equivalent to discovering several 'Alaskas' each year.[28]

The Association predicted that the United States would come to rely increasingly on oil imports from the Middle East and Africa, thus strengthening the competition for supplies which Western European customers might then be facing from Japan, the Soviet Bloc and developing countries. This would inevitably be reflected in price levels.

The NCB believed that the British coal industry, by far the largest in Western Europe, was in a good position for entry into the European Economic Community. In 1971 the EEC imported more than 25 million tonnes of coal, much of it from the United States and some from as far distant as Australia. The German coal industry was facing continuing problems. Ruhrkohlea AG, an amalgamation of almost all the Ruhr mines which in 1971 accounted for more than 80 per cent of Germany's coke and coal output, and half the European Coal and Steel Community output, had lost money since its formation in 1968. Although the contribution of coal to the French energy market was expected to fall from 30 per cent in 1969 to about 8 per cent by 1980,[29] imports were seizing an increasing share of the market, rising from 16·1 million tonnes in 1969 to 17·8 million tonnes in 1970. In the British market, there was likely to be a continuing demand for coking coal, of which there is a world shortage, and the NCB is likely to be able to sell as much as it can produce. Although the best grades of coking coal, especially from Durham, were becoming exhausted and the BSC estimated in 1970 that 20 per cent of its needs might have to be imported by 1980,[30] the NCB claimed to have made a major advance during 1969–70 by demonstrating that blends of lower qualities of coking coal could be combined with certain additives to produce acceptable foundry coal.[31] But the factor most stressed by the protagonists of coal is the seemingly assured growth in world energy demand. The Association for Coal in Europe estimated that world energy consumption, nearly 7100 million tonnes of coal equivalent in 1970, would be between 11 200 million tonnes and 12 200 million tonnes of coal equivalent by 1980.[32] The World Energy Conference meeting in Bucharest in 1971 also emphasized the increase in demand for energy resulting from the industrialization of developing nations,[33] and the possibility of an energy crisis of some size resulting from the future exhaustion of fossil fuel reserves was also raised. Indeed, although the world contribution of coal to total energy consumption fell sharply during 1955–70, the total world coal output rose slightly. Provisional figures suggested that total world production of coal and lignite in 1969 increased by about 1·6 per cent compared with the previous year and reached approximately 2845 million tonnes.[34] Both the USA and USSR were anticipating major increases in coal output. The USSR planned to double coal output during 1965–80.[35] In the USA coal had since 1961 made up much of the ground lost in the 1950s; total sales in 1965 exceeded 508 million tonnes after falling below 406 million tonnes in the 1950s and the United States Bureau of Mines forecast that annual production might need to reach 914 million tonnes in the 1980s.[36] Although coal is obtained in those countries under generally much more favourable geological conditions, the continuing world demand which their production plans anticipate could also provide opportunities for the older, more complex British industry. In terms of reserves at least, the British industry is in a strong position. Workable reserves were in 1971 considered to be sufficient for about 50 years' working, at the then current rate of extraction. Recent investigations have revealed a deep bituminous coal seam in Oxfordshire which raised Britain's total reserves by more than a third. Moreover in July 1973 the richest coal seam ever discovered in Britain was located extending 77 square kilometres north of Selby in Yorkshire. This alone adds a further 508 million tonnes to the reserves but, unlike that of Oxfordshire, the seams, varying between 2·1 and 3·4 metres in thickness, are only 275 metres below the surface and could easily be worked-out for coal-burning power stations in the area.[37] Doubts about the future of the British coal industry centre, not on the existence of future marketing opportunities or on the existence of reserves, but on the NCB's ability to exploit those opportunities by remaining competitive *vis-à-vis* other sources of energy.

The disadvantages of coal in relation to other energy supplies are of a formidable kind. Compared with those of nuclear electricity, gas and petroleum, the coal industry is highly labour-intensive. The pressure of wage inflation in excess of productivity shows no sign of abating. In 1971 a successful strike added about 25% to the NCB wage bill whilst by March 1974 similar action had raised the price of coking and industrial coals from the Midland and Yorkshire pits by 48% and from other areas, 28%. Even though the latter increase must be seen against a four-fold increase in the costs per barrel of oil in the winter of 1973–4, it can be said that these considerable increases in coal costs have not markedly improved its competitive position. The steady raising of productivity, which will be vital in the rest of the 1970s if coal is to maintain any kind of real advantage, is likely to be more difficult than in the 1960s since rapid mechanization and substantial pit closures, with their automatic productivity benefits, are likely to be less widespread. Further improvements in productivity will largely depend on maximizing the use of the capital equipment already installed. In 1970 British coalmining machinery in the USA was yielding four times the tonnage per manshift than in the better British mines.[38] The easier geological conditions in the USA were only one factor in this differential. Great productivity improvements could be made in Britain by securing more continuous working, both more shifts per day and more days per week, and by reducing absenteeism. Absenteeism, both voluntary and involuntary, which averaged 18·32 per cent overall in 1969–70 and reached much higher figures on certain days, e.g. Mondays, becomes more disruptive the more complex the mechanization, and its present level is an obstacle to maximizing the use of capital equipment. The increased profitability which could arise from more shift workings is also substantial: Lord Robens stated in 1966 that a pit which changed from a two- to a three-shift working had in general a tonnage increase of approximately one third while the profit virtually doubled.[39] Similarly, the profitability of seven- as opposed to five-day working is greater than the increased tonnage. However, the experience at Bevercoates colliery, which in 1970 reverted to five-day working after two years of seven-day working as a result of what were alleged to be disruption to miners' lives, was not an encouraging sign.[40] The removal of such obstacles to profitability and the maximizing of the use of capital equipment is likely to be a priority of the management during the 1970s, as are efforts to keep the machines running more minutes out of each hour, within the framework of existing working hours. The solution of this problem depends on better maintenance and detailed improvement in mining techniques. Any estimate of the future markets for coal in the 1970s must depend on the success with which these problems can be solved. It would be difficult to overstate the difficulties involved.

Improvements in the distribution system of coal are also essential to remaining competitive. Coal is a high bulk/low value commodity: the average costs of production per tonne in 1969–70 were £5·43 (see Table 6.4) and consequently the ex-pit prices bring it within the

Table 6.4. NCB areas in 1969–70 showing costs per tonne, output, men employed, overall profit/loss and profit/loss per tonne

Area	Production cost per tonne of saleable coal (£)	Output thousand tonnes	Average no. of wage-earners on colliery books (thousand)	Overall profit/loss before charging interest (£ thousand)	Profit/loss per tonne saleable (pence)
Scottish North	6·10	5 056	13·3	2 527 L	52·1 L
Scottish South	5·93	6 491	17·3	1 142 L	17·6 L
Northumberland	5·04	6 962	14·7	76 P	1·2 P
North Durham	6·32	5 445	14·9	4 011 L	73·8 L
South Durham	5·64	8 422	21·0	822 L	10·7 L
North Yorkshire	4·57	9 365	18·0	2 748 L	29·5 L
Doncaster	4·92	8 666	17·9	2 957 L	34·0 L
Barnsley	5·21	8 194	19·5	4 613 L	56·6 L
South Yorkshire	4·84	10 267	21·8	2 219 P	21·7 P
Northwestern	6·12	7 126	17·8	2 P	0·0
North Derbyshire	4·25	10 761	17·5	62 L	0·4 L
North Notts	4·03	11 973	18·8	4 617 P	38·5 P
South Notts	4·08	11 331	16·9	2 330 P	20·5 P
South Midlands	4·19	9 405	13·5	1 306 P	13·9 P
Staffordshire	4·81	8 697	15·7	4 318 P	49·6 P
East Wales	6·79	7 839	26·1	2 061 L	26·2 L
West Wales	7·39	5 154	16·5	3 260 L	63·2 L
Kent	7·58	1 114	3·9	2 357 L	211·6 L
Total	5·43	142 268	301·1	11 752 L	8·2 L

Sources: Ministry of Technology, *Digest of Energy Statistics*, and National Coal Board Report and Accounts 1970–1, volume II, table 2.

cheaper categories of minerals. In consequence, transport costs make up a high percentage of the delivered price. In 1969 nearly 70 per cent of all coal movements were by rail. Although freight charges between some pits and some power stations were reduced during the 1960s, partly as a result of the introduction of merry-go-round trains, overall freight rates were increased. This badly affected coal's competitive position, especially since the other energy suppliers were able to make substantial improvements to their distribution systems, which lay to a much greater extent within their own control. Gerald Manners has contrasted the highly integrated production–supply systems of the gas, electricity and petroleum industries with the highly fragmented distribution system of the coal industry, involving very large numbers of virtually independent wholesalers and retail coal merchants, who make difficult the rationalization of marketing.[41] There is substantial scope for improvements, however, particularly in transport: the great advances achieved in the transport of aggregates, lower value minerals than coal, is a case in point. During the 1960s, very little was done to exploit possible cheaper means of transporting coal, for instance through application of the experimental technology of slurried transportation through pipelines. During the next decade, very substantial cost reductions will be needed to meet the challenge of such phenomena as the completion of the gas industry's new distribution system, or the construction of further oil pipelines.

The coal industry is at a further disadvantage, particularly in relation to oil, in terms of the extensive variation in its delivered costs throughout Britain. As can be seen from Table 6.4, the NCB's profit-making pits are concentrated in a comparatively small area of the Midlands and Yorkshire. The variations in production costs per tonne between these areas and, for example, Kent, are very substantial, although the resultant variations in delivered costs to customers in some parts of Britain were largely ironed out by cross-subsidization. So great are these variations in costs that, despite the transport costs involved, additional marginal tonnage produced in the East Midlands could undercut local coal marketed only 30 kilometres from the pit in high cost areas such as Wales, Scotland and Kent.[42] The scope for the production of marginal tonnage is clear from Table 6.4. All the profit-making fields with the exception of North Nottinghamshire had reduced overall output during the period 1963–4 to 1969–70. Staffordshire, whose output fell by more than 2 million tonnes during this period, showed the highest profit per tonne of any division in 1969–70 (49·6 pence per tonne). The labour shortage in the East Midlands which limited the opportunity for producing increased marginal tonnage in this region in the 1960s is unlikely to be a problem, at least in the early 1970s. But even if a greater marginal tonnage was produced to undercut the local ordinary bituminous coals* in distant markets, with the undeniable political and social difficulties which that would entail, this marginal tonnage would still be at a disadvantage compared with the petroleum industry, which can market its products throughout Britain with comparatively little variation in delivered costs.[43]

The high cost imposed on coal users in the industrial sphere in terms of anti-pollution equipment is a further disadvantage imposed

* The scope for this type of substitution is of course limited to some extent by the existence of special coals, which tend to come from the high cost areas.

on coal. How far the coal industry will enjoy during the 1970s the degree of protection afforded it during the 1960s is a matter for conjecture. In that decade the position of coal in the important power station market, for instance, was a preferential one. The coal-burn subsidy paid to the Central Electricity Generating Board for using coal rather than a cheaper alternative fuel source was removed in 1971 and already in the previous two years permission had been sought for oil burning at 19 new or converted power stations, in addition to conversions from coal to gas (on an interruptable basis) at Hams Hall C station near Birmingham and West Thurrock in Essex. In 1969–70 the Central Electricity Generating Board and the Scottish Electricity Generating Board increased their oil consumption by the equivalent of just over 4·5 million tonnes of coal equivalent (although some allowance has to be made for abnormally high oil burning resulting from the policy of conserving coal stocks during the shortage).[44] In the long term, nuclear energy, in spite of its early problems and larger than estimated capital costs, is bound to make a major contribution to electricity generation. Having largely lost the former major railways and gas markets, the coal industry would be very badly affected by big oil inroads into the power station market. There is in addition the threat posed to coal by the gas and oilfields in the British sector of the North Sea. There was sufficiently commercially exploitable gas located by October 1970 to sustain production at more than 113 million cubic metres per day envisaged in the 1967 White Paper, while the strikes of oil in the British sector are likely to provide substantially for expected UK oil demands. The discovery of these large indigenous reserves diminishes the force of the NCB claim to special treatment as the only secure source of energy. The Labour Government which came to office in February 1974 has begun talks with the NCB and the NUM and the resultant policy of restoring production to the 1969 figure will at least postpone the problems which a large-scale overall contraction of output would bring. The country has made a massive investment in coal-mining since nationalization. The costs of re-opening mines, once closed, to meet a resurgence of demand, are of an extremely high order. Furthermore, substantial problems would be involved for the coal industry in meeting fixed charges such as interest from a contracting overall tonnage. These problems will probably be averted, but the heavy emphasis on making up production from new schemes at existing collieries and from new collieries themselves (especially Selby, with a projected output of 10 million tonnes[45]) means that continuing contraction in the less economic fields is bound to occur. This need not be regretted. It is at least arguable, in this connection, that the very necessary help required for areas affected by coalmining contraction should not take the form of keeping open loss-making pits, but rather the form of compensation, re-training and removal grants. The impact of coalmining on the landscape of such areas throughout its long history is indeed one factor in their lack of appeal to modern investment. The environmental problems which are still inseparable from deep-mining suggest that their perpetuation in uneconomic circumstances for purely social reasons may be short-sighted.

Lord Robens, Chairman of the NCB from 1960 to 1971, admitted that 'my own industry has, historically, been responsible for more disfigurement of the countryside than any other'.[46] This disfigurement is not just a matter of the remote past. Since nationalization in 1947 the concentration of attention first on maximizing output in the period up to 1957 and subsequently on improving the industry's competitive position has been at the expense of close attention to questions of land use and restoration, although the 1947 act which established the NCB required it to 'further the public interest in all respects'. The run-down state of the industry's assets at the time of nationalization, and its insecure profitability since that time, have also been handicaps. Another factor is even more important: the long history of the coal industry before the existence of planning controls has not only left an immense legacy of dereliction but continues to affect both current working practice and attitudes.

Normal planning controls, although applicable to the deep-mining of coal only in the case of those workings started since the 1947 Town and Country Planning Act, have been modified from time to time. In 1950 the Town and Country Planning General Development Order stated that, where a site had been used for tipping on 1 July 1948, the NCB or its licensees could continue tipping on that site without further permission, including extending the height or area of the tip. There has been some dispute about the meaning of the term 'site' which, according to one interpretation, means land within the promoter's ownership on the appointed day. In any event, the majority of pits being worked in 1971 pre-dated the operation of the development order. Only 35 per cent of waste resulting from deep-mined operations in that year was deposited on to tips subject to planning control, i.e. begun after 1 July 1948.[47] Many of the sites pre-dating 1948 have substantial reserves of tipping land still in hand: e.g. one colliery in pleasant countryside alongside the A1 near Doncaster, pre-dating planning controls, has sufficient waste capacity in hand to last well into the 1980s. The problem facing many planning authorities is clear: within the boundaries of the pre-1948 sites, where 65 per cent of waste

375

was still in 1971 being tipped, the conditions governing height, shape, method of tipping, topsoiling and planting, usually imposed by planning consents on new sites, cannot be exercised. A planning authority might find it possible to apply persuasion about practice at sites outside their jurisdiction when extensions are applied for. Durham Planning Office have, for instance, reached agreement with the NCB that all tipping questions, whether entirely within sites pre-dating 1948 or not, should be the subject of consultations covering the whole technical process.[48] There are, however, clear limits to the extent of such persuasion: the authority has not been able to prevent the disposal of colliery waste on a ten kilometre stretch of the county's beaches.

The widespread existence of collieries pre-dating planning controls, and the special modifications governing their working, had resulted in much ignorance on the part of planning authorities of the extent of deep-mined coal operations in their areas. The survey of county planning authorities revealed that much less information was obtainable there about the land consumption of the deep-mined coal industry than about other extractive industries. Opencast operations, however, which began only in the 1940s, have been carried out largely within the context of planning controls, although specially modified in their case also. Not only are planning authorities better informed about these operations but the operations themselves make a much less damaging long-term impact on the landscape. Indeed in a number of cases they have effected an improvement by making economic the clearance of previously derelict land.

Although the bulk of its operations lie underground and do not compare in horizontal extent with, for instance, the sand and gravel industry, the deep-mined division remains one of the largest holders of land amongst extractive industries. The total area in NCB ownership, excluding that held by the Opencast Executive, in 1971 was 108 614 hectares.[49] Of this, 25 671 hectares were colliery lands. Clearly a large part of the remaining acreage consisted of working and disused tips, for which the NCB do not have figures, and in addition a number of disused tips are in private or other hands. Estimates of total extent of the accumulated waste heaps, and the area they cover, vary widely, in the absence of precise information. In 1961 three geographers[50] reckoned that there were 2000 existing colliery waste heaps, covering about 12 150 hectares in England and Wales. In 1970 the Secretary of the Durham and Northumberland Shale Contractors' Association estimated that there were 1000 million tonnes of shale throughout Britain covering an area larger than the National Parks.[51] Probably about one third of the derelict acres in England and over half those in Wales and Scotland are made up of spoil heaps. Although current deep-mined output is less than that for most of this century, the problem of present waste disposal is not decreasing proportionately since the exhaustion of thicker, higher quality seams and increasing mechanization result in a larger proportion of waste material being brought to the surface. In 1954 it was thought that the extraneous matter removed from the coal raised and weighed was increasing by about 0·5 per cent per year.[52] This percentage increase is now likely to be greater since the proportion of fully mechanized pits more than doubled between 1960 and 1970. The ratio of waste to saleable coal varies from 1:5 to 1:1·25, with the higher ratio of waste generally operating at the larger, more mechanized pits. The average ratio of waste to saleable coal was 1:2 in 1970[53] and a total of 61 million tonnes of waste were then being tipped each year.[54] The largest proportion of this is dumped in surface tips as close as possible to the colliery to minimize transport costs.

The calculation of tonnage tipped per hectare is complex. The height of conical tips covering 0·41 hectare (one acre) is usually about 31 metres at the peak but many old conical tips cover more than 0·41 hectare and are higher than 31 metres. The height of modern contour tips may be affected by planning controls and may vary between 6 metres and 31 metres. Tips on inclined ground—and few sites are exactly level—will vary in shape and thickness according to circumstances and hence their volume per hectare will differ. Finally, the dry density of spoil varies from one coalfield to another and according to the amount of compaction given. The dry density of spoil is generally within the range of 1·21 to 1·59 kg per cubic metre.[55] Hence the following estimates must be very approximate. It is believed that an average of about 250 900 tonnes of waste per hectare can be deposited using conical tips not exceeding 31 metres in height or 100 300 tonnes per hectare using contour tips.[56] The Clean Air Act 1956, which required the NCB to take all practicable measures to prevent spontaneous combustion on the tips, has resulted in the creation of fewer conical tips, which are more likely to combust, and more low extended ones.*

The problem of land consumption by tipping is gravest in the East

* It was tipping by overhead bucket conveyor which created these conical mounds and allowed air to get into them and made them more liable to spontaneous combustion. Thus the recent change to tipping by dumper truck has led not only to the achievement of far better shapes in the landscape but has also meant much greater consolidation, and very much less likelihood of firing of the tips.

377

Midlands and Yorkshire. The two English counties of Nottinghamshire and Yorkshire contributed in 1969–70 42 per cent of total NCB deep-mined output, more than the Scottish, Welsh, Northumberland, Durham and Northwestern areas put together. These latter areas, however, have a greater backlog of dereliction stemming from their long mining history and large share of pits closure. In 1965–6 to 1970–1 71·4 per cent of all colliery closures were located in the Scottish, Welsh, Northumberland, Durham and Northwestern areas. If greater marginal tonnage were to be extracted from the low cost fields, at the expense of loss-making pits elsewhere, the division between those areas facing primarily problems deriving from a backlog of dereliction and those facing present and future tipping problems could become more marked.

It is worth looking at the problems of Nottinghamshire in more detail. In 1969–70 the North and South Nottinghamshire area (see Fig. 6.2) produced between them 16·4 per cent of total NCB deep-mined output, and the North Nottinghamshire area, alone of any, had increased its tonnage output during the previous seven years. The Nottinghamshire section of the major Yorkshire, Derbyshire and Nottinghamshire field, which has the greatest reserves of any British field, falls into two sections, the exposed one to the west, mainly in Derbyshire, in which the Lower and Middle Coal Measures appear at the surface, and a 'concealed' portion to the east, mostly in Nottinghamshire, where the coal measures extend eastwards to an as yet imprecisely determined limit under a Permo-Trias cover. The Nottinghamshire portions of the concealed field were developed late, the first colliery, Shireoaks, being sunk in 1859. In the 1860s others were opened in the concealed coalfield at High Peak, Hucknall (nos. 1 and 2), Cinderhill, Annesley, Bulwell and Silverhill (number 1). In 1870–80 16 new collieries were opened and in 1880–1910 a further 25, mainly between Nottingham and Mansfield, along the western edge of the county. During the twentieth century new collieries were located further east on coal measures which became progressively deeper. In 1902 the first colliery east of Nottingham, at Gedling, was sunk through the Keuper sandstone as well as Bunter and Permian rocks.[57] During and immediately after the First World War, exploitation of the Measures beneath the Sherwood Forest area of mid-Nottinghamshire began. The collieries here, which included Rufford (1915), Clipstone (1922), Ollerton (1925), Blidworth (1926), Bilsthorpe (1926) and Thoresby (1928), as well as Harworth (1924) and Firbeck (1925) in the north of the county, were larger scale and more spatially disparate operations.

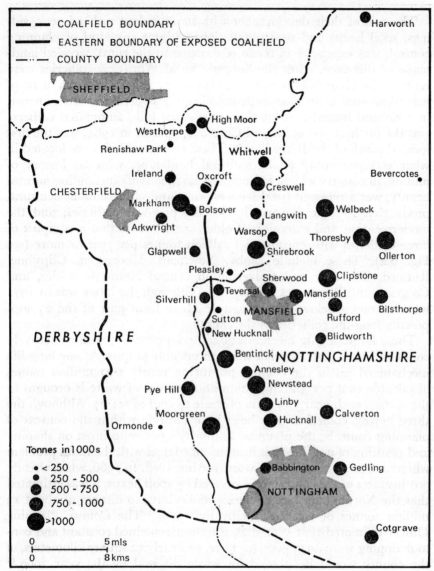

Fig. 6.2 *Collieries in the North and South Nottinghamshire coalfields*
Source: National Coal Board

The cost of their development with its attendant pithead gear, sidings, spoil heaps and new population, without any kind of planning control, was expensive in terms of damage to the rural, wooded landscape of this area. After the Second World War, new collieries were built by the NCB still further east. Calverton, a shaft first sunk in 1939, was completed as an independent colliery in 1952; Bevercotes, opened in 1960 and intended to be the world's first fully automated colliery, was the furthest east of all and Cotgrave, opened in 1964, was the first located south of the River Trent. These recent collieries are located in what was previously an agricultural landscape, with no history of mining, in country which, although by no means of outstanding natural beauty, was a pleasant rural scenery with land of medium agricultural productivity.[58] The construction of the post-war collieries, and the modernization and extension of older ones, has created a complex of large collieries with outputs of 1 million tonnes per year or more (see Fig. 6.2). These include Linby, Newstead, Moorgreen, Clipstone, Rufford, Thoresby and Calverton in central Nottinghamshire, and Cotgrave and Bevercotes further east (although the latter was in 1971 working much below this capacity). These form part of the 27 supposedly long-life collieries in the county.

These large, highly mechanized collieries produce, within relatively confined areas, high ratios of waste to saleable output. At one long-life mechanized pit in the county, producing nearly 1·27 million tonnes of saleable coal per annum, one million tonnes of waste is brought to the surface each year,[59] a ratio of waste to coal of 1:1·27. Although the three newest collieries have been built entirely within the context of planning controls, the planning authority's power to insist on shaping and planting of new heaps is insufficient to deal with the main problem when such large quantities of waste are involved. In 1966, when already 901 hectares of the county were covered by spoil heaps, it was estimated that the Nottinghamshire collieries would have to dispose of about 13 million tonnes of waste annually by 1970.[60] The County Planning Officer estimated that year that, if output remained constant and contour tipping were used, 5000 hectares, or nearly 52 square kilometres, of the county would be needed for waste disposal by the year 2000.[61]

In Yorkshire, the accumulated backlog of spoil heaps is somewhat greater than in Nottinghamshire—an estimated 2005 hectares of dereliction[62] caused by spoil heaps and subsidence compared with 901 hectares of spoil heaps in Nottinghamshire in 1966—but the demand for new land tipping is believed to be somewhat less. The Yorkshire and Humberside Economic Planning Council estimated in 1966 that 81 hectares per year were needed for tipping colliery and other mineral

waste within their area compared with some 360 per year in Nottinghamshire. Although the four Yorkshire areas of the NCB produced
between them 25·6 per cent of total NCB deep-mined output compared
with 16·4 per cent from the two Nottinghamshire areas in 1969–70,
the acreage needed for waste disposal is less because of the smaller
proportion of output from very large collieries with high waste ratios
in Yorkshire. In both counties, as elsewhere, the relatively small area
with which the NCB finds it economic to move the waste produces
inflexibility and resulting land use conflicts. In 1971, for instance, the
NCB applied for permission to extend the spoil tip at Cadeby colliery
by 40 hectares, which would encroach on a nature reserve noted for
its insect life. The heavy land demand for tipping in Yorkshire and
Nottinghamshire may be contrasted with that from the two Welsh
areas which, although having vast accumulations of past spoil heaps,
require only the comparatively small amount of 40 new hectares per
year for colliery waste disposal, according to a recent estimate by the
Council for the Protection of Rural Wales.[63] One other particular
instance of tipping is deserving of notice at this point, although not an
instance of large-scale land consumption. In 1970 approximately 2·79
million tonnes of colliery waste per year from the Durham coalfield
was being deposited on a 10 kilometre stretch of the county's beaches,[64]
to be scattered over much larger distances by the action of the sea.
Tipping on these beaches has been carried out since 1919.

However, by no means all of the shale produced annually from NCB
deep-mines is dumped. Some of the newer collieries, dating from the
era of planning controls and located within what is considered to be
economic distances of sites to be filled, have disposed of their waste as
fill. Planning consents for the large, modern Kellingley colliery in the
West Riding of Yorkshire were able to stipulate that waste should for
a ten-year period be deposited in disused limestone quarries some 2·4
kilometres away at Knottingley. At the end of that time, when the
capacity of the quarries would be exhausted, it was planned that the
waste should be used to reclaim marshland to the south of the colliery.[65]
Waste from the drift mine at Harry Stoke, Filton, in the small Bristol/
Somerset coalfield and dating from the mid-1950s, was initially used
to make playing fields nearby.[66] A pit and some railway cuttings have
been successfully filled with colliery shale at Loughborough in Leicestershire, and there are other examples. However, the power of county
planning offices to make stipulations of this kind is severely circumscribed not only by the absence of suitable sites for filling in many
areas but also by the cost of transportation. In Nottinghamshire, for
example, this latter constraint prevents the moving of vast quantities

of colliery shale in the western half of the county to the sand and gravel excavations either in the far north or along the eastern boundary within the Trent valley.

The total quantity of waste to be tipped is also becoming increasingly reduced by commercial sales. In the year 1971–2 this total rose to more than 7 million tonnes.[67] The main demand has traditionally been for burnt shale, which is utilized for road surfacing, tennis courts and paths, and brickmaking. The Board's brickworks in England sold more than 300 million bricks in 1972–3 although all subsidiary brickworks have since been sold off by Government direction.[68] In 1971 the NCB established the Minestone Executive to increase sales of shale and find new applications. The Executive has concentrated on the possibilities of unburnt shale, hitherto regarded by prospective customers as potentially volatile and liable to spontaneous combustion. Progress has been made in the creation of a non-skid road-surfacing material incorporating unburnt shale and the Minister of Transport has now prepared a specification permitting its use. Progress has also been made in processing the shale into a good quality aggregate, and it may prove possible to make satisfactory building blocks and concrete using burnt spoils.[69] Even more important, the Department of the Environment has introduced a system of dual tendering for the fill material used in motorway contracts. Contractors are now asked to submit tenders with a set of prices based on the use of unburnt shale as fill in addition to pricing their own choice of material. This procedure was first used for a section of the M62 in Yorkshire and as a result unburnt shale was selected as the fill material.

The NCB believes that good propects for substantially increasing sales of colliery shale lie in the export market[70] despite the transport costs involved. There is, they believe, considerable scope for shale usage in reclamation work in Holland. However, the laboratory experiments of D. L. Levi on chemical extraction techniques from colliery shale suggest that aluminium could be removed from colliery shale at about half its present costs, with, in addition, a whole range of valuable by-products including potash.[71] Analysis of colliery shales from the major coal-producing areas revealed between 25 and 30 per cent of aluminium silicates and 10 per cent iron oxide. One major advantage of the method of chemical extraction envisaged would be that a large proportion of the energy required for the process is contained in the spoil—about 20 per cent of modern colliery spoil consists of non-recoverable coal, and older spoils contain a larger percentage. The possibility of utilizing such a process on any scale involves the resolution of many problems and the NCB claim to have examined the possibility of metal extraction

from shale and to have found it uneconomic.[72] There is no firm assurance that laboratory experiments would scale up satisfactorily to commercial production levels, but chemical extraction from shales is a standard practice in Russia. If the process could be employed at commercial levels, several national economic difficulties would arise from the vast amounts of aluminium, much greater than current consumption, which would become available: it is estimated that 41 million tonnes of shale—two thirds of current annual output—contains aluminium which in its refined state and at 1971 world prices was worth well over £1000 million.[73] The problems in terms of the recent large capital investment in traditional aluminium plant would clearly be severe, as would the impact of cheaper aluminium on the consumption of other metals. However, the combination of economic and environmental advantages of chemical extraction from shales is potentially so great that investment in a pilot plant would be desirable.

Unless a big breakthrough is made in any of these possible commercial uses of shale to entirely alter the scale of shale utilization of recent years, very large amounts indeed will inevitably remain. In this event, there may be cases where transportation or backstowage in exhausted underground workings would be justified on environmental grounds. Two instances of the possible non-commercial transport of shale have been investigated. In Durham a coastal survey in 1966 produced two alternatives to the depositing of spoil on the beaches: barging the waste out to sea, or crushing it and depositing it in 31 metres of water. Both the alternatives to tipping were rejected on the grounds of cost by the NCB, who are only likely to adopt such methods when they are satisfied that they can be operated on a permanent basis at a cheaper or equal cost to the present system.[74] It could be that a broader based inquiry, attempting the very difficult costing of damage to amenity, might indicate that a national subsidy to operate such disposal methods might be justified on environmental grounds. This would of course entail a national, political decision outside the present planning framework. There are grounds for believing, discussed in Chapter 7, that the present planning framework is inadequate to deal with the very large national issues which the coal industry, and particularly its waste disposal, pose.

The second investigation of non-commercial transport of shale concerned its disposal from Nottinghamshire. In June 1966 the NCB, having lost an appeal to the Minister to tip spoil on 91 hectares of agricultural land near Kirkby in Ashfield, were asked to study other alternatives to surface tipping, one of these being to deposit the waste in the fletton brick pits of Bedfordshire. The scheme investigated involved transporting the spoil from four collieries, producing a total of about 3·25 million tonnes of waste a year, sufficient to fill Common Farm no. 1 pit in Bedfordshire (7·8 million cubic metres) in four years.[75] The overall distance by rail is about 130 kilometres and the price quoted by British Rail, approximately 74p per tonne, involved a cost per year of £2 400 000, a clearly unacceptable figure. The level of British Rail freight charges, it may be noted, not only hamper the competitiveness of the coal industry's distribution and marketing system, but constrict its possibilities of waste disposal. Since the shelving of the rail scheme, however, there has been some investigation of the possibilities of a pipeline for slurried coal waste, by which the costs could, it is believed, fall to as little as 12·3p per tonne, or £460 000 per year. The possibility has subsequently arisen of obtaining much larger quantities of fill in Bedfordshire from refuse, but, nevertheless, the space available in Bedfordshire is vast, and it is to be hoped that research on the economics and technical problems of slurried coal waste transport will continue, and the costings be made public, so that open and informed discussion may take place.

There remains the possibility of backstowage which is, however, only technically possible at some of the newer pits. In February 1968 *Colliery Engineering* reported a new method of hydraulic stowage, using a chemical reagent mixed with the slurry which, it was claimed, reduced operating costs by 30 per cent. Backstowage has, of course, the special advantage, in addition to waste disposal, of helping to reduce subsidence. Although backstowing is carried out to some extent in Germany, the NCB have always ruled it out on the grounds of cost. The NCB state that 'extensive research has been done in the past into the economics of backfilling but all research has come to the conclusion that it is exorbitantly expensive'.[76] The NCB assert that 'no definite costings are available'. These figures must, however, exist, and it is surely in the national interest that they should be disclosed. Against these costs would have to be set the lack of expenditure to the NCB for land acquisition, fencing, and tip safety, and the bonus to the community in terms of non-sterilization of land and amenity conservation. Although it may be difficult to adequately cost amenity and safety in these calculations, it is important that the evaluation that has been done be made public.

There are grounds for thinking that an Exchequer contribution to colliery waste disposal schemes of the kind indicated above would not be entirely inappropriate. Since 1960 the contribution of the Exchequer to local authority schemes for clearance of dereliction has become widespread and in 1970 stood at a minimum of 85 per cent of

the cost of such schemes, with larger percentages available in most development areas; in that year Durham, for instance, was receiving approximately 91 per cent. No such subsidy is available to prevent additions to the backlog of shale heaps. Although that part of current tipping which is subject to planning and hence stipulations on contouring and planting is unlikely to create dereliction, it is at least consuming land at an alarming rate, especially in the East Midlands. The 65 per cent of tipping which in 1971 was still uncontrolled may well be creating dereliction requiring to be cleared at some future date, largely at public expense. It does appear anomalous that those authorities with clearance schemes for their backlog of tips receive substantial assistance while similar help is not available for the solution of current tipping problems. There is, furthermore, the precedent of the Exchequer contribution to the Ironstone Restoration Fund, which deals with the much smaller problem of restoration in the ironstone fields. If a similar scheme were adopted for coal, the NCB would pay 3p per tonne of deep-mined coal extracted, from which it could recoup 0·468p to 1·5p from the lessor in respect of leased land, and the Exchequer would pay 0·308p per tonne, making a maximum contribution from the NCB of £4 395 216, an Exchequer contribution of £451 242 and a total income to the fund of £4 846 458, at the 1969 rate of deep-mined output. There is, of course, no reason why the proportions should be identical. A national fund on these lines could, as in the case of ironstone, be called upon to pay the difference between total costs of restoration and what the NCB could realistically be expected to pay. Such a scheme might well bring within the bounds of possibility some more preferable waste disposal alternative to tipping, such as backstowage or the transport of waste to available open pit excavations. However although any extra charge to the NCB cannot, of course, be taken lightly, at a time when rising energy costs are of vital importance in the economy, a greater contribution by the NCB to the restoration of surface damage is probably not unreasonable. In 1969–70 the NCB spent a total of £6 281 000 on surface damage, including restoration of opencast sites which is obligatory by law.[77] This compares with £810 508 000 of total expenditure on revenue account, or 0·77 per cent. This must be considered a low percentage compared with the restoration costs which most large-scale extractive industries would expect to pay.

A considerable proportion of the NCB's expenditure on surface damage arises out of its liability to pay compensation for subsidence damage. The extent of land damaged by coalmining subsidence is much more difficult to assess than that consumed for tipping[78] and the problems involved concern mainly damage to buildings and communications, and to agriculture resulting from disruption of drainage causing waterlogged subsidence hollows. The planning problems caused by subsidence are a major limiting factor on development in many parts of the coalfields. The expansion of Coalville and adjoining communities in Leicestershire, for instance, is restricted by subsidence. Problems of subsidence, often from very old workings, have prejudiced development in many areas of Fife. In Nottinghamshire deep-mining causes problems of subsidence over a very wide area of the county and these are likely to loom even larger in the future with growing areas of concentrated development and sophisticated communications. The great advances in the understanding of mining subsidence which have been made in recent years relate not to its prevention, but to predicting the degree of physical damage to the surface so that surface development and coal exploitation may be coordinated. The three most important factors governing the extent of subsidence may be classified[78] as: orthodox ground movements relating to the dimensions of mineral extraction; geotechnical conditions, e.g. site stability prior to subsidence; and the tolerance of surface structures towards the transmission of ground movements. In all the British coalfields, site measurements have been taken to determine the geometry of troughs of subsidence; analysis of the results makes possible the prediction of likely subsidence, based on statistical averages. Reasonable assessment of the probable effect of mining subsidence is now possible in every case, and most authorities follow such policies as insisting on structural precautions in surface development which is at risk, refusing surface development altogether in some instances or, in the case of proposed workings, obtaining the NCB's agreement not to mine in certain areas which could prejudice surface development. Two well-known examples of the phasing of development and coal-mining so that surface buildings are on stable ground are Peterlee and Washington New Towns in County Durham. When plans for Peterlee were first prepared in 1947, about 30 million tonnes of coal remained under its 948 hectares.[79] By the taking of precautions such as aligning the houses broadside to the expected subsidence waves, however, it was found possible to build on land below which as many as three seams of coal remained to be worked. Similar phasing of coal extraction with motorway development took place when that section of the M1 which crosses the Nottinghamshire/Derbyshire coalfield was constructed, and in places the motorway profile was built up to allow for subsidence. However, while the coordination of the NCB, planners and developers has done much to alleviate the worst effects of subsidence on surface development, these are necessarily palliatives, much inferior to the prevention of subsidence at source. Subsidence can be reduced at point of origin if, using the pillar-and-stall method of extraction, substantial amounts of coal are sacrificed or if the worked-out seams are packed with rubble or shale. The first of these methods has been used at particularly vulnerable points at most coal-fields[80] but its widespread use is clearly uneconomic; the potential value of the second cannot be assessed in the absence of detailed costings but is certainly incompatible with modern mechanized longwall face mining as practised by the NCB. This is because this method of extraction allows the roof to collapse after the coal has been removed and the face has moved forward. Thus there is no space to fill. Under present circumstances, subsidence, albeit largely measurable and predictable, is an inescapable feature of deep-mining. The effect on the landscape is usually blighting. However, in one area of the Midlands, at least, natural revival has set in: a chain of pools produced by subsidence became by natural processes a haunt of rare wildlife and now form part of the Alvecote Pools Nature Reserve. Some such resuscitation of flooded subsidence hollows may be possible, by artificial means, elsewhere.

The comparatively small opencast coal operations avoid both the major land use problems of deep-mining, tipping and subsidence, apart from temporary settlement. Opencast operations were introduced in 1941 as a wartime measure and have had a somewhat precarious existence ever since. Although they are of necessity disfiguring during their active phase, the restoration expertise developed by the Opencast Executive and recently the contribution made to clearance of existing dereliction means that their operations could arguably be extended at the expense of the less economic deep mines on the grounds of amenity.

In 1969–70 the total output from opencast operations was 6·7 million tonnes, i.e. 4·2 per cent of the total coal output and equivalent to about $2\frac{1}{2}$ weeks' output from the deep-mines. Opencast operations have for the most part been permitted with some reluctance. They were introduced in 1941 'as a measure necessary in an emergency', under the Directorate of Opencast Production of the Ministry of Power. Hundreds of sites were worked during the war, but at shallow depths only and by comparatively unsophisticated equipment. Operations, originally envisaged as a wartime expendient, were continued afterwards as a result of the continuing coal shortage, and to help NCB output during the early reconstruction phase which followed nationalization. The Attlee Government prolonged workings until

1951, after which they were intended to diminish year by year. Operations were again temporarily continued and responsibility for them transferred from the Ministry of Power to the National Coal Board on 1 April 1952. In the 1950s contractors' operations were concentrated on the Northumberland, Durham, Yorkshire, Derbyshire and Nottinghamshire coalfields, where structural conditions were favourable to opencast working compared with other British fields, though not, of course, compared with many larger and less complex deposits abroad. In 1958, a peak year, 14·5 million tonnes were raised by these methods. Although the average proportion of overburden to coal increased by more than 20 per cent between 1952 and 1958[81] opencast operations during those years made a total profit of £8·21 million.

In spite of its profitability, however, opencast output was cut back under Government directives to 10·8 million tonnes when coal stocks rose to unexpectedly high levels in 1959 and under the *Revised Plan for Coal* issued that year would eventually have been eliminated. During the slump which followed many machines were sold to overseas customers at a substantial loss. During the 1960s output remained stable at about the comparatively low level of 7·1 million tonnes, although the percentage contribution to total coal output was growing as a result of contraction elsewhere. The 1967 White Paper on Fuel Policy stated that the Government had decided not to give further authorizations for opencast production except in special cases where, because of quality or location, the coal to be produced was not in competition with coal from deep-mines. As a result, opencast production of coking coals, anthracite and dry steam coals amounted to 2·5 million tonnes or 40·4 per cent of total opencast output in 1969–70 and this policy, with that of working wherever possible sites with dereliction to be cleared, has produced some change of regional emphasis from that of workings in the 1950s. The three opencast regions with largest output in 1969–70 were, in order of size, Southwestern, Northumberland and Durham, and Scottish (see Table 6.5). Applications for more workings could not be made as long as demand of coal exceeded supply and only the energy problems of the early 1970s promised an expansion of output beyond the 7·1 million tonnes per year level.

The rationale behind the guarded official attitude to opencast operations throughout their history is not difficult to establish. As the NCB point out, opencast operations are more flexible than deep-mined ones—the investment required to re-open a closed colliery is very large indeed—although the flexibility of opencast is of course limited. The NCB complained in 1969[82] that the Government's policy of only allowing new permissions when stocks prevented them from

Table 6.5. Opencast operations by regions in thousand tonnes, 1950–1969/70

	Northumberland and Durham*	Yorkshire	East Midlands	Northwestern†	West Midlands	Southwestern‡	Scottish	Total
1950	3 168	2 248	3 099	885	642	1 739	598	12 380
1951	2 840	1 960	2 473	996	799	1 353	742	11 162
1952	3 485	2 164	3 161	985	755	1 115	640	12 304
1953	3 106	2 159	3 402	944	391	1 260	624	11 885
1954§	2 355	1 590	3 078	874	544	1 338	441	10 220
1955	2 530	1 731	3 052	1 222	590	1 707	715	11 548
1956	2 686	1 757	3 552	1 222	688	1 670	699	12 274
1957	4 133	1 836	3 540	1 448	744	1 409	677	13 786
1958	4 278	1 840	3 407	1 678	912	1 606	854	14 668
1959‖	3 256	1 728	2 297	1 136	419	1 553	617	11 006
1960	2 609	1 028	1 015	700	407	1 599	315	7 674
1961	2 711	976	993	674	577	1 807	927	8 664
1962¶	2 217	1 128	1 399	560	778	1 363	792	8 238
1963	1 427	679	850	382	729	1 427	741	6 236
1964	1 461	655	955	301	905	1 900	742	6 919
1965	1 679	828	850	221	1 062	2 014	795	7 449
1966	1 562	675	647	43	905	2 373	934	7 138
1967	2 203	593	709	0	660	2 239	885	7 198
1967/8	2 282	604	776	1	425	2 184	940	7 212
1968/9	1 874	651	793	0	300	2 258	804	6 679
1969/70	1 997	538	772	3	131	2 076	1 158	6 676

* Including Cumberland.
† Including North Wales.
‡ Made up of South Wales, Monmouthshire, Somerset and the Forest of Dean.
§ The figures for 1954 and subsequent years exclude all screening and washing losses.
‖ The figures of production for 1959 include 39·6 thousand tonnes put to stock prior to that year but not previously included and a reduction of 95·5 thousand tonnes due to screening losses not previously accounted for.
¶ From 1962 the figures include the output of certain licensed sites previously classified with deep-mines.
Source: Ministry of Technology, Digest of Energy Statistics, 1970, table 25, p. 51.

securing continuity of output on the most economical basis, and forward planning was made extremely difficult. Flexibility of output has clearly been necessary in the years since 1956 when supply and demand have been difficult to balance. But a further, less publicized reason for the curtailment of opencast working has undoubtedly been the attitude of the National Union of Mineworkers which, during the 1960s, was hostile to large-scale coal winning by opencast contractors during a decade when deep-mined manpower was nearly halved. However, the policy of subordinating opencast output to that of the deep-mines has involved major disadvantages, not least concerning the profitability of opencast operations. In 1970–1 the opencast operating profit, before charging interest, amounted to £16 385 000, or £2·03 per tonne and the total profits for the years 1960–1 to 1970–1, when opencast operations were persistently restrained, was £74 047 000. If opencast operations had been allowed to maintain output at higher levels the profit margin could of course have been substantially improved and the opencast contribution to the relief of the NCB's deficit during the period, when it was permitted by the Government to write off £415 million of loan capital, correspondingly increased. A further disadvantage to the curtailment of opencast operations is the smaller long-term damage which its operations involve to the environment.

Opencast operations make, of necessity, a devastating impact on the landscape during their active life and applications often face organized and determined opposition, although some schemes, notably recent ones in Derbyshire and Nottinghamshire, have, because of their essential land reclamation value, been steered through with little or no opposition. Although the average size of sites in Britain—of the order of 305 000 tonnes—is insignificant in comparison with the vast openworks abroad, they do represent, in terms of earth moved and traffic generated, major upheavals in a country with the great pressures on space which Britain has. In 1971, the Opencast Executive occupied about 12 150 hectares in Britain, 7695 for workings sites and 4455 under agricultural restoration[83] (i.e. 0·0018 hectare per tonne produced compared with 0·00076 hectare per tonne held by the deep-mined division). Although most sites are worked at a depth of 61–92 metres, much greater depths than this are worked in some places. At Westfield in Fife the Opencast's contractors have penetrated to depths of 215 metres, in a great machine-built canyon which probably represents a record depth for hard coal surface mining and is by any standards a massive earthwork. In Wales opencast operations are approaching depths of 153 metres. But, while certain features of landscape can never be restored—wildlife may be irreparably damaged and wild country is, once excavated, unlikely ever to be wild again—the work of the Opencast Executive in the field of restoration has achieved extremely high standards, comparable with any in the world. The consumption of land for opencast working is, then, an essentially temporary affair* and after working and restoration programmes are complete the land will technically be suited for any purpose. In this respect, opencast coal workings may be contrasted both with deep-mining of coal, which, under most current conditions, is leaving a permanent mark on the landscape, and with wet gravel workings, which, in most cases, are only subsequently suitable for wet recreational or other uses.

Opencast operations, which at one time did not need to meet formal planning consent, are now subject to special provisions under the Opencast Coal Act of 1958 and the Town and Country Planning Act of 1962. Applications are authorized by the Department of the Environment, in other words, planning decisions on opencast coal workings, as on ironstone workings, are automatically, and not only in special circumstances, made at national level. The consent of the local planning authority is not expressly required although they, and all other interested parties, must be notified: if any of these parties object, a public local inquiry must be held. Restoration of workings is required by law. In the late 1960s, when the Opencast Executive's reputation for restoration was established, local authorities in South Wales and North-East England actively supported applications for opencast workings as a contribution to the clearance of dereliction. In 1971, for example, Northumberland County Planning Department were discussing with the Executive plans for an opencast coal operation to be subsequently restored to form a country park. Much greater care is taken with restoration process than with most of the larger workings abroad where pressures on space are not so intense. The topsoil and subsoil are first stripped and stacked separately; the rock and shale overburden is removed by dragline or shovel extractor and the coal seam bared for working. After extraction of the coal, the overburden is then replaced and graded to prearranged contours to conform with the surrounding land; the subsoil is spread and rooted to avoid compaction and assist drainage before the topsoil is replaced. If the land is to be used for agriculture, as is usual, fencing, hedges or walls are

* Most of the NCB's sites have a working life of only 34 months to complete coaling and restoration normally takes place progressively behind the coaling operations (E. Brent Jones, 'Methods and costs of land restoration', reprinted from *Quarry Manager's Journal*, October 1971).

built, ditches dug, before the land is given a five-year course of remedial treatment, directed by the Ministry of Agriculture with participation by the Agricultural Land Service and the Agricultural Development and Advisory Service. Permanent tile drainage is installed after about five years. The restored land may be used for building ten years after restoration or even earlier if special precautions are taken, but since at least half of the land taken is used for ancillary purposes rather than excavation this is available for building immediately. However, use of sites for urban and industrial purposes, which are cheaper to restore as less after-treatment is involved, is only possible on a few suitably located sites.

Whenever possible trees are not destroyed in the preparation for opencast operations. The NCB had, Lord Robens claimed,[84] 'given up a lot of coal to preserve copses and hedgerows'. Where trees have been removed, special machinery for transplanting mature trees has, since 1963, been used. The Council for the Protection of Rural England has criticized the tree-planting programme for lacking sufficient after-care which is necessary following the difficult transplantation of mature trees. Some planning authorities have also criticized poor tree maintenance and, even more so, the replacement of former hedgerows by post and rail fencing.[85] However, most local planning authorities are relatively pleased with the results. According to a Derbyshire County Planning Office spokesman, the Opencast Executive does 'an excellent job'.[86]

The policy of concentrating production wherever practicable on areas where a contribution to the clearance of dereliction could be made is a particularly welcome feature of recent policy. An example of a site combining the two desirable characteristics of special coal to be extracted and derelict land to be restored is Llanilid in South Wales, for which a contract to extract 7·1 million tonnes of coking coal was issued in 1970. The 122 hectare site consisted of rough pasture and dereliction resulting from earlier underground workings. But opencast sites where clearance of dereliction is a by-product are not difficult to find: during 1969–70 permission was given to work such locations in Durham, Yorkshire, Shropshire and Derbyshire.[87] At such sites agricultural land can be obtained from previously unproductive land. At the Westfield site in Fifeshire, for example, approximately 122 hectares of new agricultural land will ultimately be created from what was previously largely peat bog.

Since 1959, when G. P. Wibberley contended that the cost of full agricultural restoration of land to agriculture after opencast coal working was unjustifiable in terms of return on capital invested,[88] the economics of the operation appear to have altered substantially in favour of restoration. Wibberley calculated that the cost of agricultural restoration in the early 1950s ranged from about £987 to over £5432 per hectare, depending on site conditions. Costs for after-treatment averaged approximately £247 per hectare for a five-year treatment. The resultant agricultural productivity, however, was valued at only about 60 per cent of an agricultural site's previous worth, or even less where compaction or liability to further settlement occurred. He stated: 'If we take the lowest figure of the range of costs of restoration, i.e. £400 per acre (£988 per hectare) and add to it a weighted average of the cost of agricultural pre-treatment, there is a minimum capital charge of £500 per acre (£1235 per hectare).' The agricultural productivity of most of the land earmarked for opencast coal being at or below average, he calculated that the agricultural average return of the restored land, at 1955–6 values, would be £62 or below. When fixed costs had been deducted, he estimated that the net return would be unlikely to average more than 57 per cent, or a return of only 1·4 per cent on capital invested. If higher costs of restoration were entailed, the net return on capital would, according to these figures, fall to well under 1 per cent. He also pointed out that, on his figures, the capital costs of replacing the agricultural production of the land used for opencast working were much higher than those involved in schemes of improvement on hill and upland farms or on coastal reclamation for agricultural use.

Since the early 1950s to which these figures apply, the costs of restoration appear to have been substantially reduced, in spite of generally rising prices, largely as a result of the use of larger, more sophisticated earth-moving machinery. Currently the costs of earth-moving, i.e. restoring the land to the required contours and the replacement of subsoil and topsoil, are covered by the coaling contract, so that the Opencast Executive's restoration costs start with cultivation and the replacement of farm fixtures. On a national basis in 1972, these costs averaged some £568 per hectare which covers such things as the restoration of ditches, fences, hedges, roads and tracks, the installation of permanent drainage and the laying on of water to fields.[89] The costs of remedial treatment carried out by the Ministry of Agriculture in the Leeds area at the same time averaged £160 to £173 per hectare over five years.[90] Not only have costs been substantially reduced for land restored after opencast working, but the efficiency of the process has improved so that it would no longer be true to say that the resultant agricultural productivity was valued at only 60 per cent of the site's previous worth. The Ministry of Agriculture expects that following the five-year treatment, productivity will be as high or, in some cases, higher than it was before the land was worked.[91] The Cwmgorse site near Ammanford in Carmarthenshire is an instance of a site where the agricultural value will actually be improved after restoration. The present situation is also altered because of the increasing tendency to work sites where agricultural enterprise was non-existent or very poor, and then to restore them to agriculture. Prices paid per hectare for land restored to agriculture after opencast coal working do not now fall on average below, and may even rise above, those paid for other-wise comparable land in the surrounding area. It is clear that the economics of the restoration operation have greatly improved during 1955–70.

The scale of opencast operations, restrained during most of the 1960s, began to revive in 1968–9. The national coal shortage in 1970, aggravated by two crippling unofficial strikes which lost the NCB about 3 million tonnes' worth of coal, led to the extension of opencast operations in many parts of the country. In 1971, 10 new sites were opened, which in addition to the existing 40 resulted in an increase of more than 2 million tonnes to opencast output in 1973.[92] A further stoppage in the winter of 1973–4 and the reappraisal of Britain's energy needs following the oil crisis has also benefited opencast operations since the Executive have been asked to raise output to 15 million tonnes by 1977–8.

If production of coal must be increased to meet national energy demands, there are strong grounds for welcoming the contribution from opencast workings, both the most profitable and the most environmentally acceptable branch of coal production. Perhaps a connection may be seen between profitability and environmental standards here. The generally poor record of the deep-mined division in terms of land use since nationalization has been connected, not only with its long pre-planning history, but also with is insecure profitability. Only an economically sound coal board is likely to be able to tackle the formidable problems of land use which it faces.

HYDROCARBONS

The development of British hydrocarbon potential has occurred exclusively in the twentieth century. The existence of oil was first realized from accidental discoveries of traces in coal mines and coal borings and this had led to the founding of the British shale oil industry. However, a deliberate attempt to locate reserves, sponsored by the Government, came only as a result of the pressures of the First World

War. Only one find of any size resulted from this search, a well at Hardstoft, Derbyshire, which was put into production and yielded the very small amount of 2640 tonnes of oil by 1938. This was not sufficiently large to encourage widespread exploration programmes once the war was over. All the same, the very low level of production of a mineral for which British demand was large and growing had led in 1934 to the creation of an unusual official incentive: the Petroleum (Production) Act of that year simplified the search for owners of rights by vesting all rights of ownership of petroleum in the Crown. This measure, which would not have been conceivable at that time in relation to a mineral with an established history of production, puts exploration for petroleum on a different, and more favourable, footing than that for most other minerals found in Britain. In 1936 the d'Arcy Exploration Company, a subsidiary of the Anglo-Iranian Oil Co. Ltd. (later British Petroleum), started a systematic search for the mineral. The first discoveries of importance were, however, not of oil but of natural gas, i.e. petroleum in its gaseous form. Natural gas, which may either be gaseous at its point of occurrence or become gaseous when it reaches the surface, consists usually of some 90 per cent methane, with small quantities of ethane, propane and butane. The first located reserves of natural gas in Britain, at Cousland near Edinburgh and Eskdale near Whitby in Yorkshire, were not considered commercially exploitable in the 1930s. Anglo-Iranian's discovery of oil in 1939 at Eakring in the Nottingham area of the East Midlands coalfield, on the other hand, was rapidly exploited as a result of the outbreak of the Second World War, and production rose quickly from 3634 tonnes in 1939 to 114 800 tonnes in 1943.[93] In 1941 a southward extension of the Eakring structure was found at Duke's Wood and a separate oil-bearing structure was discovered at Kelham Hills, 13 kilometres away. Two years later a fourth field was located at Caunton in the same area. The four fields made a valuable contribution to wartime oil supplies and produced a total of 409 799 tonnes by 1945. The high octane values of the oil at Kelham and Caunton were especially useful. A renewed exploration programme for hydrocarbons was initiated in November 1953 with agreement between Anglo-Iranian on the one hand, and the Gas Council on the other. This was brought about by the need to find a substitute for the increasingly expensive use of coal for gas carbonization. The agreement, for five years in the first instance, provided that any oil discovered should be the responsibility of Anglo-Iranian and any gas that of the Gas Council. Anglo-Iranian exploitation was concentrated on the East Midlands where, by 1966, the company, now British Petroleum, had drilled 601 wells.[94] Of the sixteen minor oilfields put into production in Britain by that date, ten, including the most important, were located on the concealed section of the East Midlands coalfield and derive from the Basal Coal Measures. Five of these, Corringham, Gainsborough, South Leverton, Bothamsall and Glentworth, were discovered from 1958–62 at depths of less than 1525 metres in Pre-Permian structures beneath a cover of Permian and Triassic rocks.[95] Gainsborough, the largest of these, was in 1969 the most productive single oilfield in Britain. The East Midlands oils in their crude form are a waxy dark brown to green and the gasoline distillates have predominant naphthenic characteristics with high octane values. They are expensive to work as the oil, contained in sandstone interleaved with the coal measures, has to be pumped to the surface; there is insufficient gas dissolved in the oil to pressure the oil to the surface, as happens in the large Middle East oilfields. Recently, however, greatly improved oil recovery has been achieved by hydraulic fracturing of the oil-bearing rock and the injection of high pressure fluid.[96]

In the south of England, exploration of the petroliferous potential of the Cretaceous and Jurassic systems led eventually in March 1959 to the striking of oil at 546 metres at Kimmeridge on the Dorset coast, the first British oilfield discovered in the Jurassic and with proved dimensions of just under 1·6 kilometres. The extension of the East Midlands oilfields and the discovery of the Kimmeridge field brought the output of home produced oil from 81 300 tonnes in 1958 to 132 100 tonnes in 1964.[97] From the beginning of 1965, however, the preferential rate of excise duty enjoyed by products obtained from indigenous crude oil was removed, in accordance with the regulations of the European Free Trade Association. This measure led to the concentration of production on the larger oilfields and the smaller ones were plugged to be available for production should circumstances make this economic. Anticipation of this measure also dealt the final blow to the Scottish oil shale industry, which had been dwindling for many years. Consequently, production of crude oil fell to 77 236 tonnes in 1969, when the percentage of UK oil consumption met from indigenous production was 0·09 per cent[98] (see Table 6.6).

The discoveries of natural gas in the 1950s were very small. A gas field was located at Calow in Derbyshire, in the Carboniferous rocks of the East Midlands coalfield, which was for a time put into production for local consumption. Natural gas in non-commercial quantities was also found at Trumfleet in Yorkshire and Ironville in Nottinghamshire. The natural gas field at Cousland, discovered in 1937, was put into production for the first time in 1957 and in the years before 1966 yielded 1960 cubic metres a day.[99] In 1956 a reserve of natural gas

Table 6.6. Production of crude oil by fields (tonnes)

Field	1960	1961	1962	1963	1964	1965	1966	1967	1968	1969
Eakring and Duke's Wood	20 234	18 863	17 967	16 916	13 583	4 924	57	—	—	—
Kelham Hill and Caunton	8 652	7 272	5 935	5 208	3 987	214				—
Egmanton	26 996	25 330	23 348	33 765	27 521	28 388	20 637	15 334	16 436	14 570
Bothamsall	18 949	17 058	14 980	14 434	14 342	22 971	25 026	25 895	22 958	18 184
Plungar	3 480	2 869	2 274	2 167	2 009	118	1 235	1 031	856	1 124
South Leverton	558	7 530	7 441	4 906	4 265	55		—	—	—
Corringham	3 552	7 118	7 276	6 186	5 087	27				
Gainsborough	4 021	10 323	19 469	26 855	41 081	15 663	17 191	22 793	19 650	25 608
Glentworth	—	2 173	3 614	1 934	1 802	5				
Kimmeridge	45	8 879	10 343	11 153	13 352	11 145	13 730	16 967	16 943	17 238
Formby	72	19	—		156	124		6 812	4 504	511
Others*	86	31	—	1 132	2 378	105	143			
Total	86 645	107 464	112 647	124 656	129 563	83 739	78 019	88 832	81 347	77 235

* Includes Apleyhead, Wareham, Torksey, Boyncotes, Dalkeith, Beckingham.

Source: Petroleum Information Bureau.

was found in the Lower Permian limestone at Eskdale in Yorkshire, close to the 70 000 cubic metres a day of almost pure methane discovered in the Upper Permian in 1937, and in 1960 both wells were put into production to supply the nearby town of Whitby. The combined output from Cousland and Eskdale was 1·06 million metric therms in the year ending 31 March 1962.* The total gas available from all sources in that year was 3245 million metric therms. Thus in the early 1960s natural gas, like indigenous oil, met only an insignificant percentage of home demand. The British figures compared badly with those of Europe in the pre-North Sea era: in 1964 approximately 10 per cent of Europe's total requirements of oil and natural gas came from indigenous sources. The low level of success resulting from prospecting was undoubtedly one factor in the Government's decision in 1964 to import natural gas from Algeria. In that year a 15-year contract was signed for the annual supply of 711 200 tonnes of liquefied methane, to be landed at a terminal on Canvey Island, and preparations were begun for the construction of a national gas distribution grid. Had domestic supplies of natural gas not subsequently been found in large quantities, further gas imports, probably from the Netherlands and Nigeria, would have been likely.

In 1966, shortly after gas was located in that part of the North Sea, which, for the purposes of mineral exploitation, comes within British jurisdiction, the first substantial onshore gas strike was made at Lockton, a few kilometres west of Eskdale in the North Riding of Yorkshire. The operating company, Home Oil of Canada, began exploration in Yorkshire in 1963, under a 'farmout' arrangement with British Petroleum, by which Home Oil earned a percentage interest of British Petroleum's licences in return for an agreed work programme. The gas, 94 per cent methane, was struck at 1800 metres in the Permian Middle Magnesian limestone, a rock which allows high production per wellhead as it is sufficiently strong not to be broken down by substantial flow rates. The Gas Council signed a 15-year agreement to take about 2·1 million cubic metres per day from Home Oil at an average price of 1·002 pence per metric therm. This compares with the prevailing 1967 prices of gas from coal which cost 4·7 pence to 5·9 pence per metric therm, gas from oil feedstocks which cost 2·37p and Algerian natural gas which cost 2·96p.[100] The price paid for Lockton gas is less than that for North Sea gas, reflecting the lower development costs of an onshore site. Deliveries from two wells began in 1971 when Lockton gas constituted some 4 per cent of British natural gas supplies.

* Metric therm = 100 megajoules.

The producing wells at Lockton are 29 kilometres inland within the boundaries of the North York Moors National Park and special planning considerations were involved in their development. Gas production has, however, the advantage from amenity point of view that on-site facilities may be kept to a minimum. Its treatment involves little waste and small reduction in volume, and consequently a processing site may be selected further along the distribution line if necessary. The well sites at Lockton have, because of their rural location in the National Park, the minimum of equipment on site and are relatively unobtrusive. Gas from wells is fed by pipeline to a field gathering station, and from there by a single Gas Council owned line $14\frac{1}{2}$ kilometres to the processing plant near Pickering, which is screened by a grove of trees. Technical considerations mean that some treatment would have been done, in other environmental circumstances, at the wellhead. The gas contains small quantities of water which, at low temperatures, could combine with the natural gas to form ice-like substances called hydrates which block the pipeline. Hot water has to be circulated in small bore pipes alongside the gas pipe, and the heating and pumping facilities for this operation are situated at the field gathering station. Planning permission for the Pickering plant was subject to landscaping and screening, approved measures to prevent the escape of noxious gases into the atmosphere and restoration of the site after exhaustion of the reserves. The potentially noxious elemental sulphur contained in the gas is removed in solid form and sold as a by-product. Condensate, a liquid hydrocarbon similar to petrol, is also a by-product.

The intrinsic advantages of natural gas, compared with minerals which necessitate on-site processing, and the special stipulations imposed, have done much to limit the impact of its exploitation on the landscape of the National Park. However, Home Oil's subsequent drilling programme did run into planning difficulties. Applications for permission to drill a well at Ralph Cross on Westerdale Moor were refused on two occasions, although permission for a slightly altered location was eventually obtained. Applications for drilling at Stony Ridge on Baysdale Moor, one of the loneliest stretches of the moors, were refused on three occasions, but at the resultant public inquiry which followed Home Oil's appeal against this decision, the inspector returned a favourable recommendation. One of the first decisions of Peter Walker, as Secretary of State for the Environment, was to reject Home Oil's appeal, in spite of his inspector's recommendation. While this decision would, whatever its verdict, have been bound to be controversial one, it does illustrate the lack of a coordinated policy for mineral exploitation in the National Parks. Within the preceding two years, permission had been given by the Labour Government for three large-scale operations to extract the nearby potash, discovered during much earlier oil borings. The potash operations would necessarily constitute a much bigger intrusion into the Park than natural gas wells are likely to do. The need for some agreed framework within which decisions on extractive industries within National Parks should be taken is clear.

Since 1966, when Lockton was discovered, the pace of on-shore hydrocarbon prospecting has quickened. This is partly a response to the rising price of Middle East crude oil, and partly to offshore finds, although there is not necessarily a strong relationship between the geology of the two. The much lower development costs for onshore strikes have also been an incentive. Relatively small finds, which would not be economic to exploit if found offshore, can be commercially workable if found on land. Modest finds, made valuable by their proximity to the sizeable British energy market and by the fact that they represent a stable home source over which there is total control, are all that can be expected. The Department of Trade and Industry (which has now taken over the Ministry of Power) has put on offer, under the Petroleum (Production) Act of 1966, production licences covering almost all of England (except the Lake District and the South-West), South Wales, and the Central Valley of Scotland, thus excluding the predominantly older rocks of the North and West Britain which are not petroliferous. (The promising structures occurring off the coasts of North and West Scotland have no counterpart onshore.) By March 1971 a total of 34 groups had taken up 148 of these licences covering some 63 702 square kilometres.[101]

As can be seen from Fig. 6.3-4, the licences have been taken up for certain highly localized areas. The concentration of licences taken up along the east coast of England is largely a reflection of the finds made in the adjoining North Sea areas, although the interest in the Permian prospects of Yorkshire has clearly been stimulated by the Lockton gas strike. Prospecting on the south coast, in Kent and Sussex, reflects the view that Mesozoic strata of the basin extending from the Weald across the Channel may have good hydrocarbon-bearing potential. Oil sands have, for instance, been recorded at Pevensey in Sussex. Interest in the Hampshire Basin stems from encouraging results of recent seismic surveys made in the English Channel. Attention has been directed to the potential of the Purbeck anticline on the Dorset coast before the discovery of the Kimmeridge field there; oil sands had been discovered in the Wealden formation

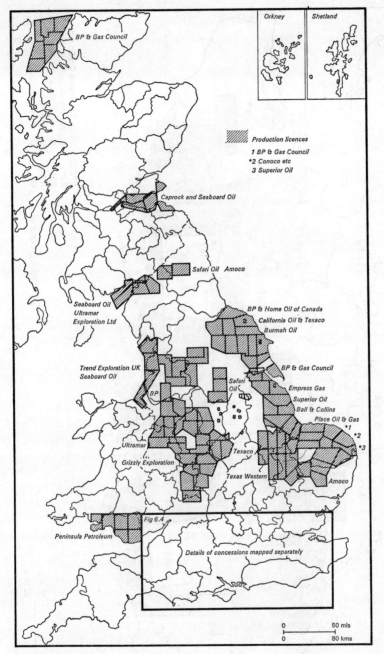

Fig. 6.3 *Hydrocarbon exploration: landward allocation of licences, 1971*

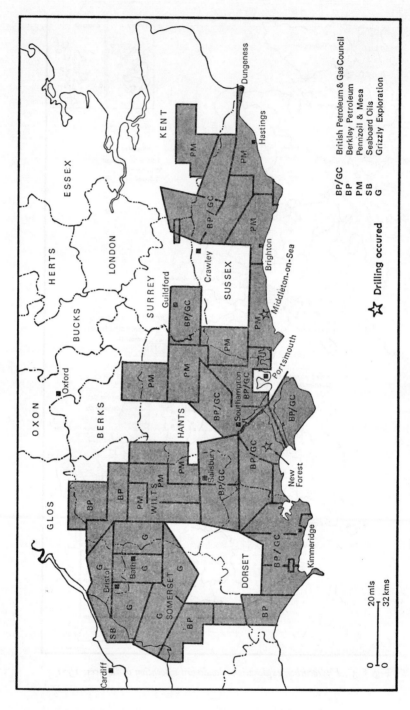

BP/GC	British Petroleum & Gas Council
BP	Berkley Petroleum
PM	Pennzoil & Mesa
SB	Seaboard Oils
G	Grizzly Exploration

☆ **Drilling occured**

Fig. 6.4 *Hydrocarbon exploration: allocation of licences in Southern England, 1972*

near Lulworth and an active seepage of impregnated oil in the Corallian rocks near Weymouth. The recent discovery of a concealed Carboniferous basin below Jurassic rocks north-east of Witney in Oxfordshire has focused attention on this area, particularly around Steeple Aston. Interest in west Lancashire and the Cheshire Basin has been stimulated by extensive seepages of oil at Formby, which has in the past yielded a small commercial output. The Carboniferous strata of the Eastern Central Valley of Scotland, in the region where natural gas was in the past discovered at Cousland, are also being explored.

The policy of the Department of Trade and Industry has been to issue production licences over very extensive tracts of country, irrespective of the quality of the surface or the use to which it is put. The assumption has presumably been that it is in the national interest that hydrocarbon reserves should be located and that any planning difficulties can be dealt with by the normal planning machinery. Although seismic surveys do not require planning permission, the drilling of an exploratory well does. The actual production of oil from any well would require both planning permission from the local authority, or failing that from the Secretary of State for the Environment, and a mining licence from the Department of Trade and Industry. The granting of exploration rights in what is virtually a blanket fashion has led to opposition in some areas, especially in the South of England. At Climping in west Sussex, where seismic surveys had indicated a promising structure, the parish council, among others, opposed in 1970 the plans of Pennzoil United Incorporated to drill holes up to around 3000 metres deep. Fears of despoliation were aroused by British Petroleum's prospecting in the New Forest. Protest meetings were held at Bridport against the exploratory activities of Page Petroleum around Powerstock and West Milton in Dorset, and at Steeple Aston in Oxfordshire against the exploratory drilling plans of the Consolidated Oil and Gas Company. However, planning permission for exploratory drilling has generally been forthcoming,[102] probably because the disturbance caused by the erection of rigs, the noise of drilling and seismic explosions and the generation of a certain amount of traffic, is purely temporary.

But it seems likely that protests have been activated more by a fear of subsequent development than by the immediate effects of exploration. Anxiety has been expressed that these exploration licences are in effect 'a foot in the door' and that once oil companies have spent large sums of money on exploration, subsequent permission for development of any finds would be difficult to refuse.[103] This need not be the case.

The licences are clearly issued subject to the normal planning constraints. The risk of locating a commercial oil or gasfield, and subsequently being refused permission to exploit it, is one which the concession holders knowingly run when they take out a licence. It is arguably in the national interest that hydrocarbon reserves should be pinpointed, even if they are not exploited immediately but left in the ground unless or until changed circumstances dictate their development. This knowledge would not have been forthcoming had the Department of Trade and Industry, as has been suggested,[104] consulted with the Department of the Environment before licences were granted, with a view to excluding certain sensitive areas, such as those of Outstanding Natural Beauty. The allocation of blanket concessions does mean, however, that careful attention must be given to all objections and amenity considerations if new hydrocarbon development is proposed. All the same, it may well be demonstrated that hydrocarbon extraction, which takes a negligible amount of land, can be carried out with minimal damage to amenity. Gas need not and oil certainly will not be processed on-site; oil is of such value and its refining involves so little volume loss or wastage that it can economically be transported long distances in its crude state. Crude oil from the Midlands, for instance, is sent to Ellesmere Port, Cheshire, for refining. It is improbable that an oil strike on land could be made on sufficient scale to alter the established location of British refineries, large units based primarily on imported crude oil. Consequently, the apparatus at an extraction site may be minimized, the wellhead unobtrusive, storage tanks screened and pipes buried. Careful stipulations would need to be made in planning consents but an oil- or a gas-well does not, by general mining or quarrying standards, pose difficult planning problems. Indeed the Kimmeridge wellhead, barely 90 metres from the beach, does little or nothing to impair the scenery of this unspoilt Dorset coast.*

The results of onshore prospecting in Britain by 1964 would never, of themselves, have justified the intensive search for hydrocarbons under the North Sea which began to get under way that year. The cost of developing a submarine oilfield is approximately four times that of one on land. Conditions in the North Sea, with its complex tidal system, fog and surprisingly violent storms, are worse than those found in other parts of the world, such as the Gulf of Mexico or the Niger delta, where offshore drilling had been successful. An expert

---

* This must be in strong contrast to underground coal operations and it is clear that the anxiety being expressed over the certain development of the newly discovered coalfield between Selby and Tadcaster in Yorkshire, very similar in terms of its rural appeal to south Dorset or Oxfordshire, is a very different order of magnitude.

has judged operating conditions there to be 'among the most difficult in the world'.[105] The impetus to tackle this formidable enterprise came almost entirely from the Groningen gas discovery in the Netherlands, with the small Yorkshire gasfields then discovered acting only as minor geological corroboration of the petroliferous potential of the intervening area.

Exploration for hydrocarbons in the Netherlands began in 1933 and in the mid-1940s oil was found at Schoonebeck near the German frontier. The first natural gas deposit was located in 1948 but by and large the success rate of the very intensive post-war drilling programme carried out by Nederlandse Aardole Maatschappe (NAM), a joint Shell/Esso enterprise, was not encouraging. NAM's discovery of the Slochteren gasfield in Groningen province on 14 August 1959 put an entirely new perspective on the search. The Groningen field, extending under the Ems estuary into West Germany, proved to be some 32 kilometres long by 24 kilometres wide, and was situated at about 2898 metres in the Rottliegendes (Permian) sandstone. The estimated reserves are 1·8 million cubic metres,[106] which makes it the world's largest gasfield yet found. It was a field large enough to change the energy balance of North-West Europe, and its discovery multiplied the known hydrocarbon reserves of Europe by four.[107] Its greatest significance, however, lay in its location. Groningen is uniquely situated in the world's most concentrated area of energy use and close to the industrial heart of Western Europe, in contrast to most earlier large gas finds, notably in the United States, Algeria and the Soviet Union, which are remote from large energy consuming areas. This powerful consideration reinforced the impetus which the Groningen discovery gave to hydrocarbon prospecting in Northern Europe.

Groningen gas is probably derived from the action of heat and pressure on the coal measures which lie below the Permian reservoir rock although some petroleum gas from marine sediments may be mixed with it.[108] The geological formation of the big reservoir at Slochteren, however, is much more similar to the large Middle East oil structures than anything hitherto found in Europe, and its discovery, followed by substantial Dutch strikes at Middelie and Schermer in Noordholland province, transformed the view generally held of European hydrocarbon potential. The area of apparently closest geological resemblance to the Northern Netherlands is the North Sea marine sedimentary basin. The North Sea belongs to the same geological province as North Holland, their histories being the same during the Carboniferous and Permian periods, and the broad correlation of the Permian rocks of the Northern Netherlands with those of North-East

England suggested the possibility of a large stratigraphic trap extending north-northwest across the North Sea. The interest thus focused on the North Sea was reinforced by two further considerations: in addition to proximity to the fastest growing energy market in the West, the surrounding area was a politically stable one. By a fortunate coincidence, international action was nearing the point where division of the North Sea continental shelf among its adjacent states according to an agreed formula was possible. Furthermore, a valuable body of experience of submarine drilling techniques had been built up, though not enough, as it transpired, to cope easily with the difficult North Sea conditions. But Groningen indicated the possibility of hydrocarbons under the North Sea just at the time when the legal and technical problems of its investigation had at least been substantially reduced.

Before the twentieth century the claims of individual sovereign states to ownership over the sea bed were theoretical rather than practical since undersea mineral resources could only be extracted by tunnelling out from the coast, an operation of limited scope. In the 1920s technical advances made it possible to work the sea bed by approaching it from above, an undertaking first successfully carried through off the coast of Louisiana.

Although offshore oil prospecting had already led to some national claims of sea bed jurisdiction, it was President Truman who in 1945 specifically linked such claims with the continental shelf. He declared that, in view of the urgency of conserving and developing natural resources, the United States regarded the subsoil and sea bed of its adjoining continental shelf as United States territory.[109] The rapid technical advances in offshore drilling after the Second World War, pioneered by the United States, led to similar declarations being made by more than a dozen other countries within the next four years. These declarations differed widely in the extent of their terms, some claiming not just rights over the sea bed but jurisdiction over the seas above them, thus greatly extending territorial waters. By 1953 it was generally accepted that states could claim sovereignty over the sea bed of their adjoining continental shelves, but there was no agreed formula for defining the extent of the shelf or its division amongst adjoining states. By this time the extent of submarine drilling made such definition imperative. It has been estimated that the continental shelves of the world and their adjacent waters contain 27 500 600 square kilometres (7·6 per cent of the ocean surface) of sea bed underlaid by marine sedimentary formations likely to contain hydrocarbon deposits attractive to oil companies.[110] By 1970 some 17 per cent of the world's oil production came from offshore fields.[111]

In 1953 the International Law Commission, the branch of the United Nations responsible for international law, adopted draft articles on the law of the continental shelf, and in 1958 an international conference agreed a convention which was to come into force after 22 states had ratified it. On 10 June 1964 the convention became binding on its 22 signatories which included the United Kingdom. Article one defined the continental shelf using the criteria of depth and exploitability: it is the sea bed and subsoil of the submarine areas adjacent to the coast but outside the area of territorial waters to a depth of 200 metres or, beyond that limit, to where the depth of the superadjacent waters permits the exploitation of natural resources.[112] By the terms of the convention, the coastal state can claim, not full sovereignty, but sovereign rights over the sea bed for the purpose of exploiting its natural resources. The waters above the continental shelf are not sovereign possessions and consequently there should be no unjustifiable interference with fishing or navigation.

Boundaries where possible were to be fixed by agreement between neighbouring states; in cases of difficulty, they were to be determined by constructing a median line, 'a line equidistant from the nearest points of the base line from which the breadth of the territorial waters is measured'.[113] The UK, surrounded on all sides by areas defined as continental shelf, occupied an extremely favourable position, and the extent of sea bed over which she could claim jurisdiction were correspondingly large, almost half the North Sea area in addition to other surrounding areas. By a strict interpretation of the convention, the UK sector of the North Sea would have been even larger, since Norway's claims were technically negatived by the existence of the deep Norwegian trench, separating her from the continental shelf (see Fig. 6.3). Norway in fact delayed signing the convention for this reason and later obtained her sector by agreement with the other North Sea powers, using the median line formula and ignoring the existence of the trench.

The exercise of British rights under this convention is defined by the British Continental Shelf Act which gave the Ministry of Power authority to lay down regulations and grant licences for exploration and exploitation of the British continental shelf. Although policy has changed in some respects, certain basic provisions have remained constant. The areas offered for allocation are divided on a grid system containing blocks of approximately 250 square kilometres; two types of licence, exploration licence, and exploration and production licences are offered. The latter are valid for six years with options for not more than 50 per cent of the area for a further 40 years. Royalty on producing wells is charged at the rate of $12\frac{1}{2}$ per cent of wellhead value—the same rate as for onshore producing wells and a low rate by world standards—with annual payments deductible from the royalty. The applicant companies must be British registered and thus liable to British taxes. The earliest rounds of licences for blocks in the North Sea in 1964 and in the North and Irish Seas in 1965 were allocated on the basis of small fixed initial charges and annual payments, to companies or consortia chosen primarily in the basis of submitted work programmes and their capacity to carry out extensive drilling schedules. The rationale behind this policy, compared with that, for instance, of selling licences to the highest bidder, was clearly that emphasis was placed on procuring rapid exploratory drilling, at a time when the North Sea was still a 'wildcat' (highly speculative) area and there was a world shortage of drilling rigs. This policy avoided locking up large amounts of capital in a competitive bidding system. In the later rounds of 1970 and 1971, both Labour and Conservative Governments altered the original policy in ways designed to increase state participation or state profits. These changes of policy occurred at a time when the Government's hand had been strengthened by encouraging results—not only was the British sector of the North Sea known to contain large quantities of natural gas, but there were good prospects for oil there. Furthermore, natural gas had been produced from a well off the Irish coast, and encouraging results obtained from seismic surveys in the Channel, the Western Approaches and near Rockall. In the 1970 round of allocations, the Labour Government attempted to increase the role of the Gas Council and the National Coal Board, who had participated from the beginning on a similar basis to any other company. The Government's ruling in that year stipulated that applications for blocks in the Irish Sea then on offer could only be made by consortia which included a British nationalized industry. This ruling probably had a disincentive effect, and only 11 of the 42 Irish Sea blocks were initially taken up. The policy of encouraging state participation in what was predominantly a wildcat area, where success on the North Sea scale could certainly not be guaranteed, also had economic implications.[114] Stipulations of state participation were subsequently abandoned by the incoming Conservative Government, which in 1971 introduced for the first time an element of competitive tendering. In that year 15 premium blocks out of a total of 436 on offer were allocated on the basis of competitive bidding, and a total of £37 300 000 was raised by this method. The overwhelming majority of blocks on offer, including 26 very favoured ones which each elicited from 15 to 26 applications,[115] were still allocated to companies on the basis of work programmes for a very low charge. The licensing policies of both Labour and Conservative Governments were in 1973 heavily criticized in a report of the House of Commons Public Accounts Accounts Committee.[116] The committee asserted that North Sea licensing policies were devised essentially to deal with natural gas, for which there is no free market and the chances of companies making excessive profits are small. Licensing arrangements should, in the committee's view, have been modified after the discovery of oil, for which there is a free market and the possibility of excessive profits being made. The committee contrasted unfavourably the likely British gain from oil revenues with that of Norway. There, 'carried-interest' agreements give the government a heavy percentage share in each company, block by block, without necessitating the Treasury subscribing an equivalent proportion of capital. Statoil, the public holding company, participates in exploration, production and transportation and will take a share in pipelines, processing and marketing of oil. The major criticism of the committee however concerned not licensing policy but the tax system as it affected North Sea oil development. The report pointed out that, because of the particular structure of the international oil industry and the operation of Britain's provision of double taxation relief, many oil companies operating in the North Sea could substantially avoid payment of corporation tax on their North Sea oil profits. Under existing tax rules, nine major international oil companies, with important North Sea interests, could write off North Sea profits against tax losses accumulated elsewhere amounting to £1·5 billion. The committee recommended legislation to correct this and other tax anomalies.

The chief spatial development during the exploration of the British North Sea sector has been the shift of attention from the area off the coast of England to a more northerly one off the coast of Scotland. In 1964 and 1965 blocks throughout almost all of the British sector, stretching from the Straits of Dover to just north of the Shetlands, were put on offer. Applications for these blocks were based mainly on preliminary surveying of the North Sea. Geophysical exploration had begun with an airborne magnetometer survey of the entire area from southern Norway to the Straits of Dover, about 373 000 square kilometres, the £350 000 costs being shared by ten companies. The first seismic survey of the British sector, a joint enterprise of Shell, Esso and British Petroleum, began in 1962 and by mid-1964 there were 46 seismic teams at work in the North Sea as a whole. Seismic surveying was concentrated, as far as the British sector was concerned, on three main areas: the Dogger Bank, an area off Eastern England from Norfolk to Durham and an area 160 to 240

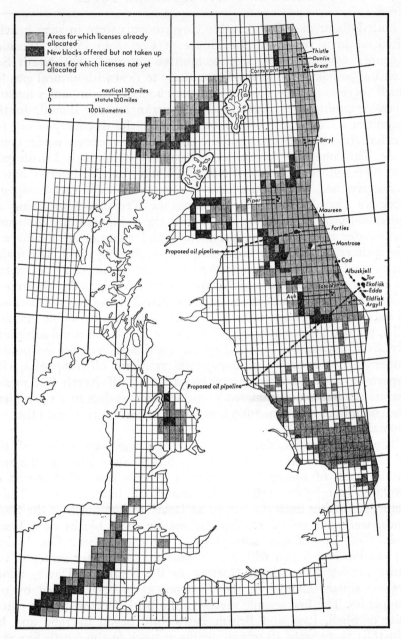

Fig. 6.5 *Hydrocarbon exploration: seaward allocation of licences, 1973* (*Major finds up to March 1974)

kilometres off Aberdeen. The broad correlation between the Permian rocks of the Northern Netherlands and North-East England helped to focus attention on the intervening area, where existing data indicated possible stratigraphic changes; in fact seismic surveys subsequently indicated promising structures off the coast north of Norfolk. Consequently, in the early rounds of licensing in 1964 and 1965, applications were heavily concentrated in the area off the English coast from Norfolk to the Scottish border. Competition was intense here and almost all the blocks on offer were taken up.[117] Applications were also made for a smaller concentration of blocks in the area 160–240 kilometres east of Aberdeen, but none at all in the area north of that, west of the Orkneys and Shetlands. It was off the coast of Eastern England that drilling started, the first three wells, all dry, being 32 kilometres west of the Dogger Bank, and 80 kilometres north-east of Lowestoft. Then came the first strikes of natural gas off Yorkshire and Norfolk and this perpetuated for a time the concentration of attention on this area. Only after the striking of oil further north in the Norwegian sector,

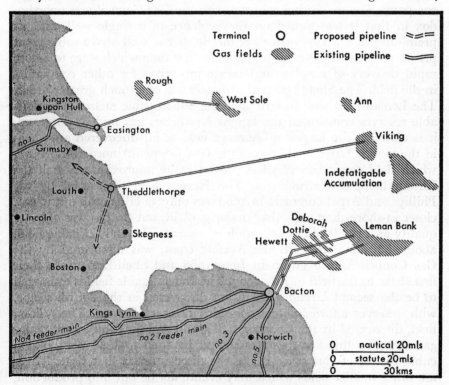

Fig. 6.6 *North Sea gasfields. (Pipelines from Theddlethorpe now completed)*

322 kilometres east of Aberdeen, in 1970, did the centre of attention switch to the more northerly part of the British sector where seismic surveys had, much earlier, shown promising structures. By the 1971 auctions no more than three of the fifteen premium blocks were off the English coast; the majority were east of the Scottish mainland with four in the extreme north, west of the Shetland Islands.

However, during 1964–70, when the focus of activities was the southern part of the British sector, over 200 holes were drilled and something approaching 0·8 billion cubic metres of recoverable gas reserves were proven.[118] During this period five major gasfields were found in the British sector of the North Sea, making it much the most productive sector for this mineral. West Sole, the first field, was struck in 1965 by British Petroleum at a depth of about 3050 metres off the coast of Yorkshire. The gas was of excellent quality, virtually free of sulphur and containing only 1 per cent of unburnable nitrogen, compared, for instance, with 14 per cent at Groningen. This field was to prove unusual in that it lay within the concession area of a single company. The marketing contract with the Gas Council was unorthodox in that it was signed on the evidence of a single well, and its premium price of 1·97 pence per metric therm, well above subsequent prices, reflected the official priorities at that time which were to secure rapid delivery of supplies and create incentives for other companies in the field. The Shell/Esso strike of 1966 was of a much greater order. The Leman field with its estimated 0·4 billion cubic metres of exploitable reserves constituted the largest North Sea gas find to date and, it is claimed, the largest offshore gasfield so far discovered anywhere in the world. Later in that year the Gas Council/Amoco consortium, which held concession of what proved to be approximately half the Leman field, also struck gas. The Hewett field discovered by the Phillips and Arpet consortia in 1968 was only 32 kilometres out to sea, closer in-shore than any other major gasfield, but the gas was of lesser quality as a result of its high sulphur content. The Indefatigable field, about 88 kilometres off the Norfolk coast, was discovered by the Gas Council/Amoco group in June 1966 and Shell/Esso made their first strike in the field in July 1967. The Indefatigable field is estimated to be the second largest gasfield yet discovered in the British sector, with reserves approximately one-third those of Leman. The Viking field, discovered by the Conoco/NCB group and the most recent major gas strike in this area, was estimated in 1969 to hold 0·13 billion cubic metres of gas, one-sixth of the discoveries at that time. There are other smaller fields which may eventually be put into production, although their unit costs would be higher than those of the larger fields.

Gulf Oil's Rough field is such an example and from 1976 it will supply 3 million cubic metres of gas a day. However, subsequent interest in Scottish waters has led to the discovery of the large Frigg field which will supply 30 million cubic metres of gas a day from late 1976.

From 1967, the first year of production, the quantities of North Sea natural gas greatly overshadowed natural gas supplies of British land based origin. In 1967, 3 165 000 metric therms were produced from the North Sea compared with 0·42 million metric therms from onshore production. The North Sea output rose rapidly to 13·8 million metric therms in 1968 and 32·5 million metric therms in 1969.[119] Government royalties from the North Sea concessions rose from £300 000 in 1967–8 to £1 261 605 in 1968–9 and £2 500 000 in 1969–70. The North Sea finds transformed the prospects for the gas industry, which had previously been dependent on high cost coal, imported methane and the gasification of imported oil. After 150 years of producing gas from coal, the industry underwent three technological changes within 15 years, the first the move towards oil-based gas, the second the conversion to natural gas;[120] and finally a rationalization programme which eliminated many small, high cost works was begun. However, by 1970 the enthusiasm for prospecting in the southern area of the North Sea had waned. In 1970 concession holders returned Government drilling licences covering 62 160 square kilometres of this zone, 50 per cent more than they had to surrender under the terms of their original agreement six years earlier. A complex of factors were involved: the ratio of successful to unsuccessful wells in southern waters had declined; the oil strike in the Norwegian sector attracted interest in the potential of adjoining British blocks off the Scottish coast; and there was marked dissatisfaction with the Gas Council's (renamed British Gas Corporation in 1973) pricing policy and its monopoly marketing position.

The 1964 Continental Shelf Act stipulated that the gas extracted from the British sector could only be sold to the Gas Council, provided that body offered a price which was deemed reasonable by the Minister. Although the producing companies could use the gas themselves or sell it directly for non-energy uses such as petrochemicals, the scope for this is limited and it was therefore assumed that most of the gas would be used to meet Britain's own high energy requirements. The monopoly market for gas, compared with the free market for oil, made the latter intrinsically more attractive to producers. The debate over gas pricing was polarized between the advocate of market pricing and those of supply pricing[121] defined by P. R. Odell[122] as 'the minimum price which needs to be paid to the producer to keep him at work both in producing what he has found and in attempting to discover more'. It was clear that if prices were set too high, or sufficiently high to make natural gas uncompetitive with oil and coal, the great economic potential of the North Sea finds would not be fully exploited. If prices were set too low, on the other hand, this would serve to discourage exploration and development, as tended to happen in the United States, where the Federal Power Commission's policy of holding gas prices was, so gas interests claimed in 1970, responsible for the low level of new discoveries.[123] The contract between the Gas Council and the producers were on a take-or-pay basis, i.e. the Gas Council was obliged to pay for the specified daily quantities whether they took it or not. The exceptional first contract with British Petroleum for supplies from the first North Sea discovery, the West Sole field, was concluded in February 1966 and provided for a daily sale of 2·8 million cubic metres a day for three years, half at the premium price of 1·97 pence per metric therm and the remainder at no less than 0·99 pence per metric therm; the purpose of this level of prices was to give impetus to the then nascent North Sea search. This contract, which expired in 1970, was replaced by one more advantageous to the Gas Council, by which 1·15 pence was to be paid for 4·2 million cubic metres a day and 0·81 pence for additional quantities. The average price paid for gas from the Leman, Hewett and Indefatigable fields was 1·13 pence per metric therm, delivered to the Council's transmission system, although the individual agreement took into account a variety of factors including the size of the fields, their distance from the coast and the load factors on producing and pipelining facilities. These prices were only fractionally higher than those paid for gas from Lockton, an average of 1·002 pence per metric therm, although the development costs of an offshore field are considerably higher. North Sea gas substantially undercut all the Gas Council's other sources of gas. Thus the principle of supply pricing prevailed, the emphasis being on keeping the price of supplies as low as was consistent with persuading the producers to contract to make deliveries. This pricing policy was an essential element in the Labour Government's decision[124] to opt for a rapid build-up of supplies. This policy suffered from the disadvantage that it obliged the Gas Council to win markets in the bulk industrial field, where gas commanded only a small premium over other fuels and the savings of real resources were low, compared to the existing market for manufactured gas, where natural gas commanded a very high premium. But the comparatively low resource savings of a rapid build-up, and the shorter life for the gasfields which it entailed, were considered to be outweighed by the benefits to the economy and the balance of payments. The economies of natural gas production favoured a rapid build-up: sales to the industrial market, less subject to seasonal fluctuation than the domestic one, improved the load on pipeline factor. By 1970, however, there were signs that the low cost policy on which this strategy was based had been taken to the point of discouraging exploration and development by the producers. Gulf Oil had suspended operations on its small Rough field rather than accept the Gas Council's price. The contract for the Viking field, signed in 1971, increased the average price payable to 1·42 pence per metric therm, the first increase in prices since deliveries began, and a move which the Gas Council had firmly resisted earlier. This decision probably reflected the Gas Council's recognition that greater incentives for gas exploration were needed now that the main interest focused on the oil prospects further north.

The British discovery of natural gas reinforced in her case what was already an established world-wide trend, the replacement of solid fuels by fluid fuels because of their greater ease of transport, handling, storage, processing and use. The natural gas share of the British energy market would, in any case, have gained ground from its almost unmeasurable position in 1964 because of the contract signed in that year for imported Algerian methane. In Europe, the trend towards natural gas is pronounced. It is estimated that by 1975 natural gas will meet 10–14 per cent of Western Europe's primary energy needs compared with 4 per cent in 1970.[125] This increase comes from indigenous supplies from Groningen, Noordholland and the North Sea fields, as well as from Lacq in South-West France, the Po valley and the Italian Adriatic offshore wells, and from imports from the Soviet Union and North Africa. It seems possible that the Organization of Economic Cooperation and Development prediction quoted above may be an underestimate, and that Western Europe may be moving more quickly than anticipated towards the United States pattern, where 30 per cent of the energy needs are met from natural gas.

The Gas Council's contracts with producers necessitated quadrupling total gas usage within ten years of the first North Sea discovery. By 1975 the Gas Council plans to have a daily flow of 112 million cubic metres of gas from the North Sea, a total daily take from all natural gas sources, including Algerian methane and Lockton, of 114·8 million cubic metres, making a total of 15 825 000 metric therms per year, or 50·8 million tonnes of coal equivalent. The distribution of this amount of natural gas within the British market entails major changes in the pattern of energy consumption. In January 1970 about 7 per cent of the national energy demand was met by gas, with North Sea gas, at 25·2 million cubic metres a day, a small part of that. By 1975 it is estimated that North Sea gas alone will take a 15 per cent share of what will then be a much larger primary energy market, and a 20 per cent share by the 1980s.[126] Meanwhile the manufacture of gas from oil and coal will be abandoned. Until the energy shortage of 1973–4, deliveries of gas to the British market increased still further the competition within the energy market, stimulated in the 1960s by oil, whose price delivered in Britain was falling from the late 1950s to the late 1960s. The marketing of gas has therefore required more energetic and flexible sales techniques than was earlier the case. In the middle and late 1960s the chief expansion in the gas market was the domestic sector, especially gas central heating, which grew more rapidly than the commercial or industrial sector. The industrial market was, however, seen as providing the chief scope for the expanded gas sales necessary in the 1970s, and it is here that the Gas Council has concentrated its efforts. In 1965 gas met only 3 per cent of the fuel needs of industry: the Gas Council's aim was to multiply those sales by six by 1975, which would account for approximately one quarter of the industrial energy market.[127] Anyone using more than 105 000 metric therms is entitled to negotiate his own price with the Gas Council. Contrasts are being offered to bulk users on the basis of interruptible supply, a policy used by many gas companies in the United States, with specially low rates to consumers prepared to switch to an alternative energy supply for defined intervals at an agreed period of notice. The contracts for 'scheduled' gas, supplies of which are guaranteed for 9 months of the year, while the user switches to oil or other power sources during the winter quarter when domestic demand is high, also incorporate reduced prices. Notable among contracts won during the incentive sales drive of the late 1960s were those of Shellstar and ICI to buy gas for chemical feedstock manufacture at a contract price of 1·58–1·78 pence per metric therm. The ICI/Gas Council contract, signed in January 1969, and the Gas Council's biggest ever deal involving 1060 million metric therms per year, doubled the sale of gas to British industry and raised total sales by 20 per cent.[128] Many other new contracts, for smaller quantities at slightly higher prices, were also secured by the Gas Council during the late 1960s in its drive to obtain a larger share of the industrial energy market, mainly at the expense of coal but sometimes displacing oil.

The decision to consume British natural gas entirely within the home energy market was intended to help hold down the fuel costs of British industry, thus making products more competitive for export or for import-substitution. Within the competitive energy market which existed up to 1973, the enhanced competition resulting from this decision was bound to reduce the outlets for coal, particularly if natural gas encroached on coal's vital power station market, and it was for this reason that P. R. Odell advocated in 1970 lifting the Gas Council's monopoly of marketing North Sea gas to allow for exports to Germany, Belgium and France.[129] The position of coal in the power station market was very vulnerable at that time: in the 13 months up to November 1970 the price of coal used for electricity generation rose by 30 per cent, adding an extra £100 million to the Central Electricity Generating Board's costs.[130] The ending of the coal-burn subsidy in 1971 greatly heightened this vulnerability. However, the chief competition for coal in this market was at that time coming more from oil than natural gas. From 1969–71 permission was sought for oil burning at 19 new or converted power stations, mainly at coastal locations in close proximity to oil refineries. Only two power stations, albeit large ones, had in 1971 obtained or were seeking permission to convert to natural gas. In July 1970 the Gas Council and Central Electricity Generating Board announced a five-year agreement for an interruptible gas supply to the five boilers at Hams Hall, Birmingham, power station, where one boiler was already on a dual gas/coal burning basis as a pilot experiment. Hams Hall would burn up to 317 million metric therms per year, making it the second largest gas user in the country after ICI. Application was also made for conversion to natural gas at West Thurrock, Essex, replacing coal brought by sea from the North-East. All the year round burning of natural gas at West Thurrock involved 1060 million metric therms of gas, a load equivalent to ICI consumption, and displaced 4 064 000 tonnes of coal.[131] The marketing of natural gas entirely within the home market has probably intensified the displacement of coal in the power station market, a situation unlikely to be reversed since the most recent increases in coal prices (March 1974) have made natural gas the most competitive of the available indigenous fuels.

The landing of natural gas on the east coast of England has not had, and is unlikely to have, much impact on industrial location, despite the fact that gas costs are lowest at the beach head terminals of Easington, Bacton and Theddlethorpe, and that natural gas transport costs by pipeline are more expensive on a general calculation, per coal equivalent than some other forms of energy transport, notably oil by super-tanker, oil by pipeline[132] and coal by sea. However, other factors have combined to eliminate the price advantages which might have been expected at the beach head. First among these is the national grid. Since the decision to construct a national grid pre-dated the

North Sea discoveries, it was logical to extend and utilize this to the greatest capacity, since the larger the market and the larger the diameter of pipe and its load factor, the lower the therm/kilometre cost of transport. The grid, a 3600 kilometre transmission network of 92 centimetres diameter pipe, was completed in 1974. However, the discovery of the Frigg gasfield bestriding the UK–Norwegian sector off the north-east coast of Scotland has meant extending the grid. A double pipe 885 kilometres long will run from near Peterhead to Bathgate, eventually branching to Partington (Lancashire) and Bishop Auckland. This will bring another 39 million cubic metres per day of gas into the network and because of the energy crisis the lines will be complete by 1976.[133] The use of large diameter high pressure pipelines with high load factors—such as the main transmission lines to the big industrial complexes—means that the cost of gas transport does not rise particularly steeply with increasing distance; Gerald Manners had calculated that between 0·19 and 0·28 pence per metric therm may be added to the beach cost of 0·81–1·04 pence per metric therm by the time gas reaches the more distant markets in the South-West of England and Wales.[134] Much heavier transport costs result from small diameter lower pressure distribution pipes with low load factors, those required for smaller urban or rural markets. Consequently the transport costs of gas vary more within a region than between regions, being higher for the rural areas of the east coast than for the big urban complexes of Western England, Wales and Scotland. What cost differentials are involved interregionally are ironed out by the Gas Council, which sells the gas to the area boards on the basis of a uniform tariff, subject only to variations for the load factor. Prices to consumers reflect differences in the area boards' distribution and other costs, and the size of their own consumption, but not their distance from the beach head terminals. Consequently, there is no cost incentive to high energy using manufacturing industry to move from the established centres of industrial activity to the east coast to take advantages of beach head prices, and the lack of labour and transport facilities would constitute a market disincentive to such a course. The use of gas as a chemical feedstock has not taken place on sufficient scale to justify the very high investment of a new petrochemical complex at one of the beach heads. These complexes continue to be based primarily on products from large petroleum refineries which in turn depend mainly on crude oil imports and consequently require access to deep water. It is clearly more practical to take gas for petrochemical feedstock, or gas condensate for refining, to the existing complexes on the east coast, than to create a new complex at any of the beach heads. Conoco, for instance, obtained authorization in 1971 to construct a 47 kilometre long pipeline to carry gas condensate from the Theddlethorpe terminal to its existing Immingham refinery. There has, of course, been development of service industries for the supply of drilling rigs: several hundred firms have set up operations bases for the supply of such products and services as anti-corrosion marine paints, catering, charter aircraft, general marine contracting, underwater surveying and equipment installation and maintenance.[135] Three terminals, which each include processing plants for the producing companies and a reception station for the Gas Council, have been built at Easington in Yorkshire, Theddlethorpe in Lincolnshire and Bacton in Norfolk. But the prospects are remote for an industrial growth zone along the coast of south Lincolnshire and north Norfolk, such as was predicted in the early years of gas exploitation.[136] Historical changes in industrial location over the past century have mainly reflected a loosening of ties to sources of power and the negative effect of North Sea gas on industrial location appears to be a continuation of this trend. It is interesting that the East Anglia Economic Planning Council welcome the forces which have eliminated the development of a new industrial complex within its region. The council's 1968 report stated that 'we think that the majority of people in the coastal towns of Norfolk and east Suffolk—and many people elsewhere—. . . would be reluctant in any event to allow the considerable loss of amenity to the nation as a whole which such a development would make inevitable'.[137]

The creation of onshore facilities, especially the natural gas terminals, has presented some problems of coastal planning, and mistakes have been made. The first terminal, built at Easington in Yorkshire in 1966–7, was a small one constructed on the cliff edge to deal with 5·6 million cubic metres a day of gas only. The second terminal, at Bacton in Norfolk, was on a much greater scale and may be one of the largest natural gas installations in the world. Its size is in fact to be welcomed, since it embodies the sensible policy of siting a terminal to provide facilities for more than one producer, rather than allowing each producer to build a small individual terminal at his nearest coastal point. The terminal originally proposed was to comprise 16·2 hectares for the Gas Council reception terminal and a 24·3 hectare processing plant for Shell. By December 1966 the proposed site had grown to 48·6 hectares and by February 1967 to 78·9 hectares. The particular site was opposed by Norfolk County Council and the Council for the Protection of Rural England, on the grounds that it would destroy the natural beauty of this unspoilt piece of coastline and take valuable agricultural land. Norfolk County Council pressed for an alternative site at East Ruston, 6·4 kilometres inland and on poorer quality agricultural land, but the inspector at the public inquiry reported in favour of the Bacton site, and in June 1967 the Minister approved the application. Two disturbing features have since emerged. It is now at least tacitly admitted that the claim that natural gas terminals have to be sited right on the coastline where the gas is piped ashore is a spurious one. Furthermore, although assurances were given at the inquiry[138] that only low buildings, less than 9·2 metres high except for the radio mast, would be needed, the situation changed after the discovery of the Hewett field in 1968 by the Phillips and Arpet consortia. The Hewett gas contained sulphur and Phillips made an application and obtained from the county council permission for a 53 metre high chimney at Bacton in connection with burning off this impurity. The Chairman of the Council for the Protection of Rural England was probably correct in asserting in *The Times*[139] that if the chimney had been included in the initial planning application, an inland site would have been insisted upon.

All that can be said about this planning error is that the mistakes appear to have been taken note of in the planning of the third terminal in Lincolnshire, made necessary because no further building is allowed at Bacton and the site at Easington is too limited for expansion. The Gas Council, in cooperation with the Viking field producers, the NCB/Conoco consortium, made an extensive search of the coastline from Easington to Lowestoft for a suitable site, applying what they claimed[140] were rigid specifications on technical and amenity grounds. After consultation with the planning authorities, the ministries concerned, the Nature Conservancy and other interested bodies, the site of Theddlethorpe in Lincolnshire was selected. No amenity objections were lodged, no public inquiry called for and outline planning consent was received in less than four months. This was in spite of the fact that the coastal dunes at Theddlethorpe form an important nature reserve, Saltfleet by Theddlethorpe. The terminal is situated, not on the shoreline, but 0·8 kilometre inland, and the land between the terminal and the reserve has been bought by the Gas Council and is to be retained in agricultural use. The pipelines have a minimum cover of 0·92 metre to a water depth of 4·58 metres below low tide, and the intrusion on the coastline itself is consequently minimized.

The environmental advantages of hydrocarbon extraction are to a large extent enhanced by the advantages they possess in terms of transport. Underground pipelines mean the absence of the road congestion which is manifest in so many other forms of mineral transport, and that no visual disturbance is created compared with the damage done to the landscape by the overhead transmission of electricity. On the debit side, there have been a few reports of gas seepage from pipelines killing trees, but this is a fault which it should be possible to rectify. The capacity to store natural gas underground could be considered as an advantage; as mentioned earlier, the Lockton natural gas structure is to provide an underground storage base and other such structures have been sought. The Gas Council try to use natural underground storage capacity wherever geology allows, although a plan to store gas in geological faults under the city of Winchester had to be abandoned after public protests. However, such storage does involve the above ground building of offtake and compressor stations whilst some liquefied gas storage in future will be situated above the ground. Other surface compressor stations (eventually about 20) are needed to pump gas through the transmissions network.[141] These which may contain up to 15 000 h.p. gas turbine driven compressors, need the most advanced acoustic techniques to ensure that noise is not created outside the site boundaries. Such plant, together with the coastal terminals, reflect the great change which natural gas has brought to the locational pattern of the gas industry itself. Until the building of the national grid for methane in the 1960s, the gas industry was overwhelmingly an urban centred industry, with its production units located close to the major markets. The discovery of North Sea gas has revolutionized the picture: most of the industry's new installations are sited in open country, which makes it essential that high standards of design, screening, and where appropriate soundproofing, are applied. Meanwhile, urban sites such as that on a valuable coastal site separating the beaches of Torquay and Paignton in Devon have become available for redevelopment and amenity improvement as gas manufacturing plants are phased out.

The oilfields in the North Sea are clearly going to have an incomparably greater effect than the gasfields on the British energy market, the British economy, on regional development and on the environment. In 1974 nine fields had target production dates: Forties (1975); Argyll (1974); Auk (1975); Piper (1975); Beryl (1975/6); Brent (1976); Thistle (1977); Ninian (1977/8) and Montrose (1975). However, the limits imposed by the availability of supplies and components, and particularly the world shortage of steel, made it difficult to foresee a substantial flow of oil before 1978. Estimates of future output from the UK sector varied from the Department of Trade estimate of 2 million barrels a day by 1980 (100 million tonnes per year) to 3 million barrels a day (150 million tonnes per year) forecast by Dr J. Birks of British Petroleum.[141]

The first major strike (October 1970) was the Forties field of British Petroleum, located 177 kilometres north-east of Aberdeen. The field is planned to come on stream in late 1975 with production building up to 400 000 barrels a day.[142] The company faced complex technical problems in working in 107 metres of water, compared, for instance, with the 73 metres of the previously discovered Ekofisk field, although subsequently productive fields at even greater depths are to be exploited. The oil from the Forties field will be delivered by submarine pipeline to Cruden Bay on the north coast of Aberdeenshire, and will subsequently travel by underground pipeline to the British Petroleum refinery at Grangemouth near Edinburgh, 225 kilometres from the landing point. A direct submarine pipeline to the refinery had been ruled out on the grounds of the high costs of undersea as opposed to underground pipelines. The underground pipeline from Cruden Bay to Grangemouth was entirely constructed by British contractors, unlike the technically complex subsea pipelines, in the construction of which British firms are not heavily involved. The Grangemouth refinery, previously geared to processing Libyan crude oil, can be expanded to accommodate the refining of North Sea oil which, like the Libyan, has a low sulphur content.

Two smaller fields, Shell/Esso's Auk field, about 257 kilometres east of Aberdeen, and Hamilton Brothers' Argyll field, 290 kilometres east of Aberdeen, are to be put into production although their estimated output of 50 000 barrels a day and 100 000 barrels a day respectively might not justify the construction of a main pipeline for their exclusive use. The fields will be developed by means of floating or fixed production platforms in conjunction with single buoy mooring systems for offshore loading into tankers. These systems are cheaper than pipelines and can be produced more quickly, but they are of course much more vulnerable to weather conditions.

The Brent field of Shell/Esso, discovered in June 1971 (with an extension, owned by Texaco and discovered 1973) was the first major strike in the far northern waters to the east of the Shetlands. Located at a depth of 145 metres (compared with the 122 metres of the Forties field), this was in 1974 believed to be the largest find yet made in the UK sector, with an estimated potential flow of 450 000 barrels per day. Crude oil from this field will be transported by pipeline to Sullum Voe in the Shetlands using a joint line with the Thistle field worked by a consortium headed by Signal Oil. This is located at even greater depths (175 metres) and has an estimated flow of 200 000 barrels a day. Also in these northern waters is the major Ninian field, with an estimated capacity of 400 000 barrels per day. Shell's one million barrels a day,

92 centimetre diameter pipeline to the Shetlands, in water depths of 140–150 metres over much of its 145 kilometres has been described as 'the most audacious submarine pipeline project attempted in the world so far'.[143] The oil from Piper field, developed by a consortium headed by Occidental, with a 250 000 barrels a day capacity, is to be transported by pipeline to Flotta in the Orkneys.

The chief British stake in the oil producing fields, as far as nationalized industries are concerned, is in the 150 000 barrels a day Beryl field, in which the Gas Council has a 10 per cent share, and in the Montrose field, with 60 000 barrels a day capacity, in which they have a 30 per cent share.

The nine commercial oil discoveries outlined above have a total output potential of some 2 000 000 barrels a day (100 million tonnes per year). The oil is of light quality with gravities ranging from 35° to 44° —not suitable for all industrial purposes—and has a low sulphur content. Sulphur is the biggest cause of pollution and is expensive to remove at the refinery stage. The 2 000 000 barrels a day of output would satisfy about 80 per cent of the UK's predicted energy needs in 1980 though there is no legal obligation on the part of the companies to market the oil in Britain and in any event oil of certain kinds would still need to be imported. A recent estimate of gross saving to the balance of payments from UK North Sea oil is £6 980 000 000.[144] It is however likely that by that time further oilfields will have been located in other parts of UK waters. There are a wealth of promising structures west of the Shetlands, towards Rockall, in the Irish/Celtic Sea, the Western Approaches and the English Channel. Mesozoic basins are known or suspected in Cardigan Bay, around the Inner Hebrides, the Moray Firth and on the Hebridean shelf north of the islands of North Rona.[145] There is the possibility of oil-bearing structures west of the Scilly Isles and off the Isle of Wight. The chances of locating such fields are being greatly increased by the development of more sophisticated means of detection, such as electronic sensors attached to computerized systems. The development of fields located in the north west of the UK sector, which present conditions almost as difficult as those of the North Sea, is of course greatly advanced by the experience gained so far in the latter and by technological developments already made as a result. Only in the Channel are special problems presented: negotiations of the median line between Britain and France have been protracted, but the chief problem is the large volume of shipping using this, one of the world's most congested shipping lanes.

It is clear that the increasingly sophisticated techniques of underseas oil detection and development, and the incentives given by the quadrupling in price of Middle East oil in late 1973, make it unwise to extrapolate the importance of North Sea oil on the basis of the present energy shortage. If the value of the North Sea finds was dramatically increased as a result of the 1973–4 energy crisis, there is no guarantee that such price levels will hold. The escalating price of Middle East oil and the threatened interruption of supplies have put a premium value on the location of other reserves of oil, the technological development of other energy sources, the improvement in energy distribution systems, and economics in energy use.[146] The time-span within which these processes could become operative is debatable, and the time-lag could extend beyond the end of the 1970s. It is in this context that the policy of successive British governments to promote rapid development of oil in the North Sea needs to be seen, although all the factors outlined above were not necessarily appreciated at the time. In the light of the probable continuance of high oil prices and heavy dependence on Middle East supplies during the 1970s, the policy of rapid development of the fields seems well conceived. There are clearly now very strong arguments for bringing the British fields into production at the earliest possible time. The Scottish National Party policy[147] of conserving resources by limiting annual output to 70–100 million tonnes seems not only to be based on the ill-founded fears of a rapid exhaustion of supplies but to fail to appreciate the risk of conserving what may be in real terms a diminishing asset.

It is undeniable, nevertheless, that a high price has to be paid for the policy of rapid development. Not only were what now appears excessively generous licensing terms offered, but British firms had little time to adapt themselves to the valuable market of the offshore service industry. British firms have achieved a disappointingly small share of the offshore oil and gas service industry, only 25–30 per cent in 1973,[148] and the bulk of ancillary contracts have been awarded to American firms. The situation may be contrasted with that of Norway, where an oil service and exploration industry has been effectively built up, through joint ventures with American partners, and is now increasingly able to function independently. In Britain the Offshore Supplies Office was set up in 1973 within the Department of Trade and Industry and an official report sponsored that year forecast that British industry could gain a 70 per cent share of the £300–400 million market.[149] In 1974 however American and continental contractors were still dominating the field.[150] It would probably be wrong to see this as an entirely inescapable result of the policy of rapid oil development. Much of the equipment used by offshore contractors and oil companies is of a conventional type produced by British companies, and should be within the scope of British plant and labour resources.[151]

The environmental impact of the North Sea oilfields is of quite a different type from that created by any other kind of mineral extraction in Britain. The problems created at the extraction sites themselves in the northern waters of the North Sea are of course not great: there could indeed by spillages, seepage and even the failure of a mechanism that seals the well in the event of a blowout, in spite of the conditions about pollution contained in the licences. But there is little anxiety about the impact of oil or indeed gas development on the fisheries, the other important economic resource of this area. The Government Fisheries laboratories at Lowestoft and Burnham-on-Crouch have stated that the search for hydrocarbons has so far in no way damaged the North Sea fisheries, nor did such damage seem likely in the foreseeable future.[152] There is potential danger in the event of a large-scale blowout from an oil rig, but in this connection the Burnham-on-Crouch laboratory points out that even the *Torrey Canyon* accident, which discharged 50 800 tonnes of crude oil into the ocean, had no noticeable effect on the catches of fish from the Western Channel in the ensuing three years.[153]

However, the demands made by service and ancillary facilities are most taxing, with the result that the coastal areas of Northern and Eastern Scotland are undergoing rapid change of an unprecedented kind. There were in 1974 about 10 actual or proposed service and supply bases, stretching from Lerwick in the Shetlands down the East coast to Leith. This has brought an important new source of income to many harbours and ports of East Scotland, although some harbour authorities signed leases in the early stages which allotted quayside, transit sheds and berths to developers on excessively advantageous terms. The comprehensive development of the Peterhead harbour by the Scottish Office is an exceptional instance of official planning in the field. In addition to the service and supply bases, there were in 1974 some 21 actual or proposed construction sites, for steel or concrete production platforms, drilling rigs, deck modules and rig components. These construction sites, which can be much more dispersed than the service and supply bases, are making an impact on the west as well as the east coast, and on the established industrial areas of the Central Lowlands of Scotland and North-East England as well as the Highlands. It is important of course, not to lose sight of the stimulus which oil-generated employment of this kind has brought to areas of industrial decline such as the Firth of Forth which have been suffering residual unemployment for decades and which is now, along with Aberdeen and the Cromarty Firth, one of the biggest concentrations of oil-generated activity in Britain. Much needed work has been brought to Clydeside; there were in 1974 actual or proposed concrete production platform sites at Ardyne (with workers to be ferried daily from the South West Clyde) and Toward Point; a jack-up drilling rig site at Clydebank, two deck module sites and a drill ship plant at Glasgow and a concrete production platform site at Hunterston. The offshore business has also brought work to the shipping industry of Tyneside and Teesside. Although the Ekofisk oil terminal at Teesside will provide little employment, important contracts have been won in this area for prebricated parts for oil-production platforms, and the contract for one of the steel production platforms for the Forties field went to Graythorpe. Firms linked in the production of parts for this enterprise include some from Middlesbrough, Hartlepool and Darlington, illustrating the spread effect of oil-generated activity of this type. The provision of employment of this kind in areas of high population and high unemployment and often with traditional shipbuilding or engineering skills and the existing infrastructure to support the workforce, is obviously a most welcome development.

However, it is in the previously non-industrial areas of the Highlands that the potentially damaging effect of oil-generated activity can be seen. Even here, development on a relatively big scale can be sustained with a minimum of disruption if it is not too disproportionate to the existing population and social infrastructure. At Ardersier near Inverness a plant building production platform jackets and employing 600 men has been successfully integrated into the surrounding population of 60 000. Serious problems can arise, both for the workforce and the local community, where a large-scale development is built up rapidly in a sparsely populated rural area. The most publicized instance of this is the Highland Fabricators plant as Nigg on the Cromarty Firth, where one of the steel support structures for the Forties field is being built. The workforce here, built up to 1500 in the space of two years, is housed partly in caravans and partly in two ships moored in the Firth. The firm has faced problems of high rate of absenteeism, labour disputes and a high labour turnover, and the local authority those of pressure on housing and police facilities, as well as other manifestations of stress within the local community. There are signs, however, that some of the features of this development will be specifically avoided in similar but later developments such as those at Arnish Point on Lewis and the construction site as Loch Kishorn.

Nevertheless, the impact of an industrial development of the magnitude required for the building of concrete production platforms on a hitherto rural area cannot be easily modified. The most publicized collision of interest has occurred in the case of the application of Taylor

Woodrow and Mowlem to build these at Drumbuie on Loch Carron. This case has several significant aspects: the rejection of the application by Ross and Cromarty County Council probably partially reflected the disenchantment of the council with earlier developments in the east of the county; the proposed intervention of the Conservative Government to circumvent the lengthy democratic planning procedures illustrates the stresses being imposed on existing planning practice by the emphasis put on the need for speed of development; and the arguments raised about the desirability of this site focus attention upon the overriding question of whether sufficient is being done to encourage oil-based activity in existing industrial areas.

Loch Carron, one of the most beautiful parts of the Western Highlands, offers a particularly advantageous site (Drumbuie) for the construction of concrete based production platforms of the Norwegian Condeep design which, unlike the steel variety which are built on their sides, require water of about 45 metres deep close inshore and access to nearby sheltered water of depths of about 180 metres. It would, of course, be possible to dredge out the Clyde to sufficient depths for such a purpose although this would naturally delay production longer than a ready made site. The creation of a concrete based production platform site at Drumbuie would be an enterprise of sufficient scale to give rise to a town of 10 000 inhabitants, but there would be no guarantee of a lasting demand for the end-product. A Scottish Development Department discussion paper, issued in April 1973, thought demand for such platforms would last only until 1985,[154] although this could be perpetuated if oil-bearing structures were located off the west coast. The Scottish Office has in fact made an attempt in 1973 to produce a planning strategy which broadly divided this coastal area into development and conservation zones. Loch Carron fell into an intermediate category, where conservation might predominate but the importance of the development could justify the resultant environmental consequences.[155] However, the possibility of creating an industrial town which might eventually be abandoned on National Trust Land was an important factor in the rejection of the application by Ross and Cromarty County Council. A public inquiry followed and the Department of Trade and Industry, in evidence to this, urged that the site would afford Britain an unrepeatable opportunity to get in at the beginning of a new era of offshore oil technology. But in January 1974 the Conservative Government proposed to circumvent the normal planning process altogether by introducing a bill allowing compulsory purchase of sites connected with oil development anywhere in the British Isles. Clearly, the Conservatives feared that the delays inherent in the planning process would lead to the loss of valuable contracts to foreign companies. The bill was, however, shelved as a result of the change of government in February 1974. This was a welcome development: not only did the bill pose a most serious threat to the local and democratic element in planning procedures but, as far as the Drumbuie case was concerned, revealed a too great emphasis on the immediate considerations of speed at the expense of serious consideration of the long-term issues involved and alternative options available. Of great significance in this respect is the plan to build two concrete based platforms, of a different design, at Ardyne near the Clyde. There are clearly great merits in encouraging development in this area, where both a large workforce with a high unemployment rate and an adequate social infrastructure exist, rather than to create an industrial town of doubtful duration in the Western Highlands. The subsequent desision of Ross and Cromarty County Council to permit a concrete based production platform site at Loch Kishorn, only a few miles from Loch Carron, may well prove to involve almost all the disadvantages of the Loch Carron site itself.

The question of how far oil-based enterprise should be encouraged in the Highlands is undoubtedly posed in its most extreme form in the case of new oil refineries. In the early stages of North Sea exploration it appeared likely that the refining of oil could be carried out within the existing refinery structure. There are major factors which make economic the overland transport of crude oil considerable distances: these are the high value of the crude oil and its negligible wastage rate and volume loss during refining; the favourable economics of overland oil pipelines (compared for instance with gas pipelines) and the very high capital costs of refinery construction. The overland pipeline transport of oil from the Forties field from Peterhead to Grangemouth reflects these factors, although the suitability of Grangemouth for processing the low sulphur content North Sea oil was quite fortuitous. Subsequently, however, proposals have been made to create three new oil refineries, at Loch Erribol on the north coast, at Nigg on the Cromarty Firth, both in the Highlands, and at Hunterston in Argyllshire. The two Highland refineries would have associated petrochemical works. These proposals reflect the increasing scale of planned oil production, the northern trend of the discoveries and the way in which oil development is shifting the economic balance of Scotland northwards. The development at Hunterston, one of the major growth areas in Scotland and equipped with a suitable infrastructure, appears a sensible choice. The Cromarty Firth, on which the Nigg refinery would stand, is now on the way towards becoming a major industrial area, although formidable social, cultural, economic and environmental problems are involved in the process. The wisdom of creating a major refinery petrochemical complex on the remote north coast, however, rather than in an established industrial area further south, is by no means self-evident.

It is clear that so far the development of oil-generated activity in Scotland has not been coherently planned. The problems involved in oil-based development, which is both to a large degree unpredictable in its incidence and urgent in its pace, must always be formidable. These have been heightened by the emphasis on speed of development, by a lack of initial experience of what such activity entailed, and most seriously, by the lack of any serious overall strategy which attached sufficient importance to the existing industrial areas of Scotland. Many of the expensive mistakes made in Scotland could be avoided should similar developments occur elsewhere off British coasts. A key consideration must be to ensure that such development leaves behind it a lasting communal prosperity, rather than the great enrichment of a few well-placed individuals and multinational companies, and a derelict industrial landscape. The attempts of the Shetlands council to control and participate in oil-generated activity in the Islands, by seeking to obtain through a parliamentary bill powers of compulsory purchase over land needed for oil development, and the formation of a consortium with oil companies to control the development of the Sullum Voe terminal, may indicate one way in which local communities might obtain lasting benefit from controlled, oil-based development.

7

TRENDS IN THE DEVELOPMENT
OF THE EXTRACTIVE INDUSTRIES

The tonnage of minerals extracted in the United Kingdom has shown a very large increase during this century to meet a much higher standard of living and in response to population growth. The rate of increase has been greater in the post-war period than in the inter-war period. Total output of all minerals rose from 287 million tonnes in 1920 to 357 million tonnes in 1938[1] (an average per cent increase of 1·35 per year) and from 353 million tonnes in 1950 to 474 million tonnes in 1970[2] (an average per cent increase of 1·72 per year).

The rate of change of output between different minerals has of course varied greatly. The changes from 1950-70 in the various minerals extracted in Britain are shown in Table 7.1. The minerals with the fastest rate of growth by tonnage are rock salt (4117 per cent increase), sandstone (296·4 per cent increase), china clay and stone (290·1 per cent increase), fluorspar (278·0 per cent increase), limestone (246·1 per cent increase) and igneous rock (223·5 per cent increase). All these minerals more than trebled in output in twenty years. This category is dominated by the high bulk/low value minerals; the increase in rock salt, used almost entirely for winter road clearance, relates to the massive post-war road building programme and the need for higher standards of bad weather maintenance. Apart from rock salt, the other low value, rapidly increasing minerals are all hard rock aggregates. It is highly significant, however, that two high value minerals, fluorspar and china clay, come within the category of rapidly increasing mineral production; unlike the rapidly increasing output of low value minerals, fluorspar and china clay have expanded substantially in export as well as home markets. The increase in tin output (with tungsten amounting to a 121 per cent increase over 1950–70), is a rise of great significance in view of the very high value of this mineral.

Table 7.1. Production of minerals in the UK, 1950, 1960 and 1970

Mineral	Units	1950	1960	1970 (provisional)	Percentage change, 1970 on 1950
Tin ore, dressed	Tonnes	1 412	1 939 ⎫		+121
Tungsten	,,	62	— ⎬	3 259	
Lead ore, dressed	,,	4 260	1 998 ⎫		+39·7
Zinc ore, dressed	,,	72	461 ⎭	6 055	
Ferrous ores	Th. tonnes				
Iron ore and ironstone	,,	13 170	17 360	12 017	−8·7
Other minerals	Th. tonnes				
Chalk	,,	13 137	15 753	16 063	+22·2
Chert and flint	,,	244	160	19	−92·0
China clay	,,	747	1,664 ⎫		+290·1
China stone	,,	69	48 ⎭	3 183	
Potters' clay (plus ball clay)	,,	385	530	837	+117·4
Clay, shale, etc.	,,	23 962	31 307	35 491	+48·1
Fireclay	,,	2 308	2 194	1 742	−24·5
Moulding and pig bed sand	,,	700	838	641	−8·4
Gravel and sand (plus silica)	,,	39 931	74 550	104 931	+162·7
Igneous rocks (plus felspar)	,,	11 423	16 525	36 958	+223·5
Limestone	,,	25 363	40 720	87 808	+246·1
Oil shale	,,	1 475	680	—	−100
Sandstone (plus silica stone, ganister, grit and conglomerate)	,,	4 149	5 038	16 449	+296·4
Slate	,,	150	94	65	−56·7
Barytes					
Not ground	,,	75	42 ⎫ Incl. with		
Ground—unbleached	,,	6	10 ⎭ miscellaneous		
Witherite	,,	17	9	—	−100
Calcspar	,,	18	24	26	+44·4
Fluorspar*	,,	51	86	192	+278·0
Gypsum (plus anhydrite)	,,	2 241	3 653	4 275	+90·7
Salt obtained from brine	,,				
Vacuum	,,	623	1 046	1 686	+170·6
Other	,,	362	206	48	−86·7
Salt contained in brine used for purposes other than salt-making	,,	3 286	4 455	5 698	+73·4
Salt, rock	,,	42	152	1 757	+41·17
Coal					
Deep-mined	,,	207 366	188 976	136 652	−34·1
Opencast	,,	12 090	7 722	7 925	−34·4
Crude petroleum	,,	47	87	83	+78·2
Miscellaneous‡	,,	44	36	50	+13·9

* Fluorspar excludes mineral obtained from some old mine dumps for which returns are not made to the Ministry.

† Coal figures refer to Great Britain.

‡ Miscellaneous consists of: bog ore; celestine (sulphate of strontium); ochre, umber, etc.; diatomite; alum clay; alum shale; block mica; soapstone and talc; arsenic (white) and arsenic soot; iron ore and ironstone used for purposes other than iron-making.

Source: Department of Trade and Industry, *Digest of Energy Statistics*, HMSO 1971, table 125, p. 185 (except for last column, calculated from the same).

There is also a general low level of non-ferrous metal ore production in Britain during this same period.

The main decreases in output during 1950–70 have been in oil shale and witherite (production of which had ended by 1970), chert and flint (92 per cent decrease), slate (56·7 per cent decrease) and coal (34·1 per cent decrease deep-mined and 34·4 per cent decrease opencast). This category may be subdivided into minor minerals, whose decrease has been of relatively small significance in terms of economics and employment, and major minerals whose contraction has been of great economic and social significance. The predominant mineral in the latter category is coal, still in 1970 the country's largest extractive industry, but the less important slate may also be considered in this grouping. No single factor can be discerned affecting all the declining extractive industries but technical changes in manufacturing techniques favouring the use of minerals other than fireclay and moulding sand, the unsuitability of slate for mechanized working, the undercutting by cheaper and/or more easily handled competitors in the case of coal and slate, the exhaustion of known reserves of barytes and witherite, revenue changes making the working of oil shale and to some extent barytes uneconomic and, in the case of iron ores, increasing overseas competition aided by improved shipping have each played a part.

Table 7.2 of mineral output by value is not as illuminating as one would wish, since the broad groupings of minerals at 1970 values conceal many of the more significant differences. The percentage increase by value of, for instance, tin ore, china clay and fluorspar would each be well above that given for their respective groupings with other minerals. As it stands, the increases by value are greatest for the bulk materials, whose increase by tonnage was most marked, although a more detailed breakdown would clearly reduce the significance of their lead. It may be noted that, due to inflation, the value of the total output of a mineral such as coal, which actually decreased by tonnage during 1950–70, grew during this time. The total value of mineral production of £1024 million in 1970 represented 2·3 per cent of the UK Gross National Product of £42 819 million in 1970. However, the contribution of extractive industries to the national economy is in fact multiplied by the indirect contribution to the Gross National Product through the markets they offer to other domestic industries, and their payments for labour and services. A study by the Royal School of Mines[3] of the figures for 1968 found that, for every £1 million which it handled, the mining and quarrying industry bought £356 800 worth of goods and services from domestic suppliers,

Table 7.2. UK production of minerals, by value as at mine or quarry, 1950 and 1970

Mineral	1950 £		1970 £	Percentage increase 1970 on 1950
Non-ferrous ores				
Tin ore, dressed	862 527 ⎫			
Lead ore, dressed	299 291 ⎬ 1 203 642		3 000 000	149·2
Tungsten ore, dressed	41 824 ⎭			
Ferrous ores				
Iron ore and ironstone			11 000 000	
Other minerals				
Moulding and pig bed sand	251 000 ⎫			
Silica stone and ganister	355 000			
Gravel and sand	10 960 000 ⎬ 13 856 000		74 000 000	434·0
(plus silica sand)				
Sandstone	2 290 000 ⎭			
Chalk	1 649 000 ⎱ 12 746 000		61 000 000*	378·5
Limestone	11 097 000 ⎰			
China clay	2 399 000 ⎫			
China stone	181 000			
Potters' clay	769 000			
(plus ball clay)	⎬ 10 768 000		39 000 000	262·1
Clay, shale, etc.	3 297 000			
Fireclay	1 985 000			
Slate	2 137 000 ⎭			
Igneous rocks	6 679 000		30 000 000	349·1
Salt obtained from brine	2 988 000 ⎫			
Salt contained in brine used for purposes other than salt-making	143 000 ⎬ 3 213 000		15 000 000	366·8
Salt, rock	82 000 ⎭			
Gypsum, anhydrite	2 132 000		5 000 000	134·5
Fluorspar	255 000 ⎫			
Chert and flint	162 000			
Barytes and witherite	481 000 ⎬ 1 369 000		4 000 000	194·3
Calcspar	45 000			
Miscellaneous	416 000 ⎭			
Fuel minerals				
Coal, deep-mined	457 789 000 ⎱		720 000 000	
Coal, opencast	⎰			
Natural gas			61 000 000	
Natural gas liquids	⎱		1 000 000	
Petroleum	⎰			
Total			1 024 000 000	

* Includes dolomite.

N.B. The figures for 1950, relating to the total net selling value of the minerals concerned, derive from the Ministry of Fuel and Power, *Statistical Digest*, HMSO 1952, table 50, p. 71. Except for coal, the official statistics of value has been discontinued since 1958. The 1970 figures, therefore, as estimated by the Institute of Geological Sciences and supplied by the Mineral Resources Division of same, are intended to be an approximate guide only.

paid out £633 200 in wages, taxes, salaries and dividends, and imported from abroad only £10 000 worth of materials and services. This means that British extractive industries imported on average less than 1 per cent of their needs in that year, while their contribution to the economy, allowing for the multiplier effect, probably accounted in all for some 4 to 5 per cent.

Whereas the fastest growing minerals by tonnage of the 1950s and 1960s were, for the most part, low value ones, the fastest growing mineral in the next decade in Britain is likely to be the very high value oil from the North Sea, whilst there could, more speculatively, be large increases in the output of certain very high value non-ferrous metallics. The development of the offshore oil industry in the 1970s will inevitably, however, rely much more heavily than British extractive industries as a whole, on foreign goods and services. A report commissioned by the Department of Trade and Industry from the International Management and Engineering Group and published in 1973[4] estimated that the then share of the British offshore oil and gas service industry (worth an estimated £300 million per year) was only 25 to 30 per cent, and that British industry unaided would not be able to increase this share above 35–40 per cent by the end of the decade. This position represents of course a dramatic contrast to the normal very high dependence of British extractive industry on domestic goods and services, as illustrated by the Royal School of Mines study. In 1973 the Government accepted in principle the chief recommendations of the International Management and Engineering Group report for Government intervention and aid to the petroleum service industries, with the intention of raising the British share of the market to 70 per cent (as well as providing opportunities for British firms in the estimated £1300 million per year *world* drilling market). Even if this objective were achieved, the reliance of the offshore drilling industry in British waters on foreign goods and services would remain very high by the normal standards of British extractive industries. While oil drilling, in which the Americans have achieved an outstanding expertise, may be to some extent a special case, it is clear that, where new extractive operations involving techniques not at present practised in Britain are concerned, one cannot assume, as the Zuckerman Commission appears to do, an automatic continuance of the traditional heavy reliance on domestic suppliers. This could well have a bearing on such new developments as the opencast mining of non-ferrous metals.

With the exception of petroleum and tin, all the minerals whose increase by tonnage and/or value may reasonably be expected to be above average during the 1970s and 1980s are surface worked minerals. In the course of this century there has been in Britain, as elsewhere in the world but notably in the United States, a swing away from deep-mining towards opencast working. In Britain this may be discerned in the case of coal (although a much less pronounced swing than would be expected under free market conditions); iron ore and ironstone; slate; fireclay (very pronounced in the 1960s); and ganister. The world trend towards opencast extraction has resulted from a widening gap in their respective productivity brought about by modern, mechanized opencast equipment. In the late 1960s it was estimated that surface extraction of minerals could achieve a productivity rate of 500 tonnes per manshift while, in contrast, a productivity rate from underground mining of 50 tonnes per manshift was common.[5] Aggregates minerals, which have the highest production figures as well as the greatest growth rate for the most part, have always been predominantly surface worked. Whilst such trends continue, the take of land for quarrying, which in 1966 was estimated at 2430 hectares for England and Wales (excluding opencast coal), is bound to grow at a high rate. This will only be partially offset as the balance of aggregate production moves in favour of production from hard rocks since these are relatively economic in land consumption compared with sand and gravel. However, the inevitable large increase in the annual take of land for quarrying would be intensified further if large-scale opencast working of non-ferrous metals, hitherto worked underground in Britain, were introduced in the 1970s or 1980s, as is a distinct possibility. With the notable exception of tin, many prospective non-ferrous metal develop-ments are likely to be opencast operations working disseminated low grade ore, the low grade being offset by the massive scale of opencast operations. This is because the balance of advantage has swung so markedly in the direction of scale economies, most particularly where low grade ores are concerned.

The trend towards opencast working is intimately related to the progress of mechanization in the extractive industries and the asso-ciated phenomenon of increasing capital-intensiveness. These two factors have been equally of vital importance in the change of emphasis in the structure of mining and quarrying away from predominantly small family businesses towards one of dominance (in output if not in numbers) by large national, or even international, companies. The trend in Britain this century towards the creation of very large extrac-tive operators has been considerably more marked than the trend towards opencast working. The main factor has been the need to substitute the intensive use of capital investment in mechanized and

P

larger operations for labour inputs, but clearly official decision-making, at both national and local level, has also had an influence. At national level, the creation of the nationalized industries connected with mineral extraction is the main manifestation of this; less obviously, it is likely that the operation of planning controls, initially at local level, has tended to favour large rather than small mineral operators. To take but two examples of this latter process in practice, some county councils, such as Norfolk, pursue a policy of relating the size of the area given planning permission for mineral working to the capital resources of the applicant firm. Where unfavourable decisions on applications are given at local level, it is the large firms, with the financial resources to employ legal counsel and specialized staff to brief them, that are likely to do best in the time-consuming and costly process of appeal to the relevant Secretary of State.

Unquestionably, the most striking instance of unit concentration at national level was the creation of the NCB in 1947, then as now the largest extractive operator in the world. By a more gradual process, another nationalized industry, the BSC, has come to control all iron ore extraction in Britain. The dominance of these two nationalized industries in their respective fields is approached by that of certain large private firms in other sectors, principally English China Clays with 90 per cent of total output of china clay by tonnage and more by value; and ICI with 90 per cent of total brine output and 100 per cent of total output of rock salt at 1970 levels. Ranking next in terms of dominance come the London Brick Company who produce 95 per cent of national fletton brick output; British Industrial Sand Ltd. with 80–85 per cent of glass sands; Steetley Ltd. with about 75 per cent of total dolomite output; British Gypsum Ltd. who control some 67 per cent of total gypsum output; and Laporte Industries Ltd. with more than 60 per cent of the total output of fluorspar at 1970 levels. The most striking instances of company amalgamation during the 1960s, however, occurred within the aggregates sector, traditionally a field of operations dominated by a multiplicity of small producers and, in view of the bulk product involved, dependent on principally local markets within a 72–80 kilometre radius. The structure of the aggregates industry during the 1960s was remarkable not only for the pace of company amalgamation, but for the degree of integration between extraction of the different types of aggregates, and processing, manufacturing, transport and even civil engineering. The largest combines in 1970 were believed to be Tarmac Ltd. producing about 20·3 million tonnes of aggregates annually from some 80 quarries; Ready Mixed Concrete Ltd. producing about 18·3–19·3 million tonnes of aggregates annually from some 150 pits and quarries; and Amey Roadstone Corporation Ltd. producing about 18·3 million tonnes of aggregates from some 73 pits and quarries.[6] In 1970 the largest aggregates firms had still a multiplicity of extraction points, although the overall number of these is declining and will undoubtedly decline further. The prime reason for company rationalization both within and without the aggregates industry is undoubtedly the need to bring together financial resources for investment in capital equipment so as to achieve economies of scale and reduce output costs, thus ensuring the long-term competitive position of the group. An important result of this has been not only company amalgamation but also rationalization and concentration of extractive operations. This trend has been marked in the case of surface worked minerals, and in those deep-mined operations dominated by large organizations. The number of NCB producing collieries, for instance, fell from 901 at the end of 1950 to 299 at March 1970, a drop quite disproportionate to the fall in total coal output.[7] There has similarly been a very marked concentration in the extraction of brine pumping by borehole, a field of operations dominated by ICI. While economies of scale in production have been the prime motive force in underground deep-mined or borehole operations, the concentration process has only been made possible, in the case of the high bulk/low value minerals, by containing increases in the per unit costs of transport. These transport improvements have made economic the supply of more distant markets from fewer, larger extraction points. In the case of road transport, economies have been achieved by the development of larger capacity vehicles, such as the 10-wheeled articulated tipper lorry of 32 tonnes, and the building of motorways; in the case of rail transport, by the development of larger wagons such as the 101 tonnes gross loading wagons designed to permit speeds of up to 120 kilometres per hour. While the need to reduce production costs has been the main motive force, and transport economies a necessary pre-condition, of pit and quarry concentration, it is likely that here too in at least some instances the implementation of planning controls has helped further the creation of larger units. In the case of sand and gravel, for instance, the officially sponsored Advisory Committee[8] recommended that planning authorities should allow extensions to existing workings wherever possible to economize on existing capital investment and reduce the spread of dereliction. The inevitable result of such a policy has been to encourage fewer, larger pits.

The overall trend in concentration of surface minerals workings can be seen in Fig. 7.1; in 1922 there were 6000 quarries which between

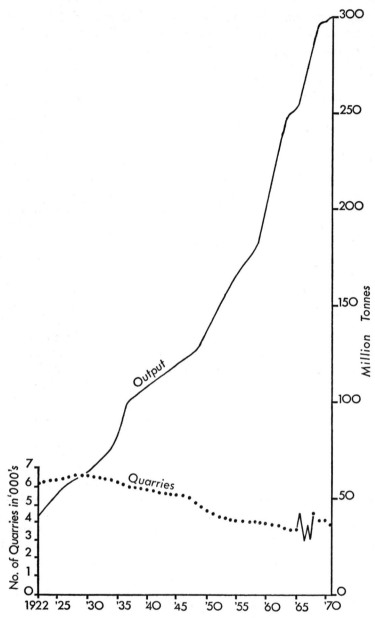

Fig. 7.1 *Changing quarry numbers and output of quarried materials, 1922–72*
Sources: *Annual Abstract of Statistics*, Reports of Inspectorate of Mines and Quarries.

them produced about 40·6 million tonnes of minerals while at the end of 1971 the total number of active quarries was 3975 and the total output of quarried minerals that year was more than 304·8 million tonnes.[9] It is almost certain that the continuing search for further economies of scale will ensure the continuance of the trend towards quarry concentration in the 1970s and 1980s, at least this is the way the director of the Institute of Quarrying sees it. He has further pointed out in respect of crushed stone for aggregates that the case for units up to the size of one million tonnes of annual output is a good one involving as it will a substantial investment of something over £1 million for the plant and basic mobile equipment in every instance.[10] The postulated size of 1 million tonnes output per year for new quarries may be contrasted with the estimated average size of limestone, sandstone and igneous rock quarries in 1969 of some 97 540 tonnes annual output.[11] Clearly, the pattern of the future is likely to be towards fewer, much larger surface excavations.

The concentration of extraction which had been accomplished by 1970 had already made possible, with the help of mechanization, very substantial economies of scale and productivity increases in the field of mining and quarrying. This had been achieved at a time of rapidly increasing labour costs, principally by means of reductions in the size of the labourforce. It can be seen from Table 7.3 that the total number of wage-earners employed in mining and quarrying as a whole (excluding coal) fell by 40 per cent in 1950–70. Average manpower at NCB mines fell from 690 800 in 1950 to 305 100 in the year ending March 1970.[12] Substantial manpower reductions were made, not only in declining industries (in terms of output) like coal and slate, but in dynamic industries such as the hard rock aggregates (limestone, sandstone, igneous rocks) which were expanding rapidly. The only exceptions to this almost universal manpower reduction were the sand and gravel and tin extraction industries.

Every quarrying industry listed improved its productivity during this period; that of the iron ore industry less than doubled; chalk, fireclay, sand and gravel and slate more than doubled; china clay and shale more than trebled; limestone more than quadrupled; igneous rocks more than quintupled; and the sandstone extraction industry increased its productivity more than seven times. It is clear that the biggest productivity advances occurred in the field of hard rock aggregates, a very competitive field which was during the period facing a rapid expansion of demand. The minerals concerned lend themselves to mechanized extraction and processing methods and the buoyant market of the period encouraged a rapid acceleration of company

439

Table 7.3. Employment at mines and quarries and productivity at quarries (excluding coal), 1950–70

	1950		1960		1970	
	Wage-earners	Output per wage-earner at quarries (tonnes)	Wage-earners	Output per wage-earner at quarries (tonnes)	Wage-earners	Output per wage-earner in quarries (tonnes)
Tin ore and arsenic compounds	759		640		1 056	
Lead and zinc ore	271		55		76	
Total non-ferrous metalliferous minerals (including others)	1 087		698		1 136	
Iron ore and ironstone	6 059	4 376	5 742	4 999	2 140	8 587
Chalk, chert and flint	2 280	6 069	1 829	8 709	1 079	14 904
China clay, china stone, mica clay and potters' clay (including ball clay)	3 712	325	3 102	761	3707	1 098
Clay, shale, etc.	6 928	4 424	5 553	8 644	2 777	17 232
Fireclay, moulding and pigs bed sand and silica stone (including ganister)	4 729	1 256	3 527	2 405	1 400	3 627
Gravel and sand (including silica sand)	8 228	4 881	10 057	7 413	9 152	11 505
Igneous rocks	9 444	1 210	6 916	2 392	6 014	6 146
Limestone	13 450	1 921	11 080	3 766	9 414	9 351
Sandstone (including grit and conglomerate)	3 962	914	2 468	1 914	2 331	7 006
Slate	4 656	36	2 401	44	875	84
Total all minerals except non-ferrous metalliferous	64 717		51 910		39 509	
Miscellaneous	5 325		4 031		2 760	
TOTALS	71 863		58 350		42 785	

Source: Department of Trade and Industry, *Digest of Energy Statistics*, HMSO 1971, table 126, pp. 186–7.

amalgamation which in turn provided capital resources for mechanization and concentration of production to produce economies of scale.

It is, once again, highly likely that the trend outlined above towards increasing productivity achieved by the substitution of machinery for manpower will continue in the 1970s and 1980s. It is worth noting that the major new mineral prospects now under consideration are likely to be capital- rather than labour-intensive. The developments in the extraction of oil, most notably, will be accomplished by means of a small, specialized labourforce. Most of the non-ferrous metalliferous prospects now under consideration in many parts of Britain, particularly the upland areas of the west and north (see Chapter 1), too, will in all probability contrast strongly in this respect with the revival of tin mining in Cornwall in the 1960s. Cornish tin extraction, for the most part an underground operation, does not lend itself to large-scale manpower economies, as is borne out by the increasing number of wage-earners employed by this industry during 1950–70 (see Table 7.3). On the other hand, the many other non-ferrous metal projects (including Coed-y-Brenin had it proceeded), would be opencast workings on a large scale of low grade ores, made economic by employing the most advanced techniques of mechanized opencast mining and the maximum of labour economies. It is significant that the chief geologist of RTZ, a company currently evaluating many British metal mining sites, has written that 'any prospective new mines [in Britain] must be large enough so that the maximum use of modern labour-saving machinery can be made. Any new mines brought into production nowadays that are labour-intensive will inevitably struggle to keep going even in countries that have so-called cheap labour.'[13]

Planning considerations: the areas of choice

The planning of mineral extraction for the future will in all probability operate in a context of increasing annual tonnages of minerals extracted and annual take of land for this purpose, more emphasis on opencast or surface working and a pattern of extraction in which fewer larger pits, quarries and mines, and fewer but larger operators, will have increasing predominance. The areas of choice about the amount of minerals extracted in Britain are severely circumscribed. Most prominent in the table of fastest growing minerals are the aggregates, bulk minerals which are still of relatively low value and hence expensive to transport. It is estimated in Chapter 2 that the annual tonnage of aggregates extracted in the UK may rise from 243 million tonnes in 1970 to 762 million tonnes by the year 2010, although there is a very high margin of error involved in this complex calculation. Britain has very little option about whether to extract these materials at home; although they are being moved increasing distances as demand escalates and are even now moved internationally (as witness the growing shipborne trade of igneous rock from Cornwall and North Wales to Northern Europe) there is virtually no chance of any significant amount of British demand being imported. Britain has exceptionally large and varied resources of these materials, which are in short supply along the north coast of the continental mainland. The area of choice that exists is essentially concerned with which of the various aggregate minerals should bear the brunt of expansion (although all will require substantial expansion, especially the hard rocks) and where amongst the outcrops the greatest increases should be concentrated. This choice is of course circumscribed by the quality of the various minerals and their proximity to markets, although the area of choice has widened as transport improvements have helped contain increases in long distance cartage costs. There is also a degree of choice about the desirability or otherwise of expanding the still very small export of aggregate material, notably igneous rock from Cornwall and North Wales and sea-dredged sand and gravel from shallow coastal waters to the continent. In 1969 the Crown Estate Mineral Agent was instructed at the highest level to encourage exports of sea-dredged aggregate to the continent to improve the balance of payments.[14] The present position is that no attempt is being made to influence market destinations of such material. This is clearly an area, albeit very small in relation to total aggregate supply and demand, where choice exists; to encourage expansion of exports in the interests of the balance of payments; to allow free play to market forces; or to discourage export of material for which home demand is growing rapidly, and whose extraction involves substantial environmental cost. Such choice would, hopefully, be exercised in the light of a long-term appraisal of such factors as aggregate supply and demand, rather than on an *ad hoc* basis.

In addition to the aggregate minerals, there are a substantial number of other, low value minerals, which are almost inevitably home produced. In this category are the raw materials of cement and brick manufacture, rock salt for winter road clearance, and speciality, but still cheap, building materials such as gypsum. It is only in the higher value categories (third, fourth and fifth groups of Chapter 1) that any degree of real choice exists about the rate, or even the desirability on any level, of extraction at home. Much less freedom of choice may well be felt to exist about permitting the continued working of those high value minerals such as china clay and fluorspar, whose extraction is already well established in Britain, than in deciding whether to permit the introduction of new operations such as opencast copper mining. Existing operations represent of course an investment of capital and an established source of employment. Even the question of permitting expansion of output of such minerals, about which more choice might be thought to exist, may in fact be intimately linked with the basic question of their continued existence. Such expansion may for instance be necessary to maximize use of existing investment, sustain productivity advances and thus retain a competitive stance to permit continuance of existing employment.

In certain circumstances, the decision to permit exploitation of a hitherto unworked mineral is clear-cut. There has, for instance, been little opposition to the decision to develop an offshore field of oil, a high value commodity for which demand in Britain is accelerating rapidly, for which the foreign supply lines are not entirely secure and which involves, in its extraction, the very minimum of environmental costs. Rather different circumstances apply in the case of the non-ferrous metals such as copper, lead, silver and gold and the rarer non-metalliferous minerals such as potash, which were virtually unworked in Britain in 1970. Very complicated evaluation is needed before decisions can properly be made about the desirability of beginning their large-scale exploitation in Britain. In the first place, such decisions must take account of the likely future pattern of world supply and demand, since these high value commodities operate within the context of world market prices, and in each case the market is subject to fluctuation and may be highly volatile. The metal market most subject to rapid change is undoubtedly that of copper. In January 1971, for instance, when the forecast price of copper had been £787–£984, the price of copper wirebars on the London Metal Exchange fell to only £408·69 per tonne.[15] In purely economic terms, it is only in the national interest to exploit indigenous mineral resources if it is cheaper to do so than to import the same raw material. It does, for instance, make sound economic sense for the BSC to import iron ore from suppliers as distant as Australia if this can undercut delivered prices of comparable Northampton Sands ore. But, bearing in mind that the lapse of time between the beginning of exploration and finally bringing a new project into production may be as much as seven to eight years, the evaluation of the future state of the world market is very difficult in these cases. Such evaluation is carried out in the first instance by the potential developer. However, experience in this field in the 1950s and 1960s shows that it is not enough for the relevant Government department, as final arbiter on planning questions, to

443

take an applicant company's assessment of the future world market on trust, since such companies may not in fact be the best judge of their own interests. Two recent instances of inaccurate forecasting by applicant companies have been dealt with on pp. 345–47 and 23–27, that of ironstone working in Oxfordshire and potash working in Yorkshire. In the latter, insufficient account was taken of market analysis and predictions in the course of the planning appeal procedure. If future mistakes of this kind are to be minimized, much more careful assessment will have to be made, in the national interest, of the complex business of market and resource considerations at local, regional, national and international levels. National and world demand forecasts and the related question of price forecasts could be based on alternative assumptions, as is done by the United States Bureau of Mines. In major new mineral proposals, a national cost benefit analysis would be desirable to enable an informed judgement to be made of the net effect of the proposed working on the national revenue and the balance of payments. Such an analysis would incorporate such considerations as the tax savings of the company concerned, the foreign exchange gains from export sales and import substitution of the mineral to be worked, and the foreign exchange losses to overseas shareholders and equipment suppliers.[16] This task could possibly be undertaken by the Planning Inquiry Commission, first enacted in the Town and Country Planning Act of 1968. Such a commission would consist of from three to five people, and have much wider powers of investigation and research than has an inspector at a normal public inquiry, and could be similar in scope to the Roskill Commission, set up under different powers. The Planning Inquiry Commission has not yet been used, despite requests for it, but one can readily envisage its usefulness.

Even if the strong balance of probabilities is in favour of cheaper production of a hitherto little worked mineral at home, further complex evaluations are required before a balanced decision can be made. The putative saving on costs of the raw material, the security of supply, the contribution of the development to local employment and local rates have to be balanced against the need to maintain strategic reserves of vital minerals against national emergencies and any amenity considerations. It has been argued that, at this point in British history, the country is particularly susceptible to mineral starvation.[17] Whereas the British Empire was short of only two out of more than thirty important minerals, the UK has no appreciable domestic supply at present of copper, bauxite, chromium, nickel, platinum, tantalum, sulphur, asbestos, graphite, mica, diamonds or quartz, and deficiencies

444

of iron, lead, zinc, tin, cobalt and antimony. While it is clearly not feasible that producing countries pursuing deliberately nationalistic policies would interrupt supplies indefinitely, there is a possibility that essential mineral supplies could be withheld for shorter periods, in the interests of obtaining higher prices or of exerting some form of political pressure. The Zuckerman Commission has pointed out that Britain depends on a single source for 75 per cent of her nickel and lead, and that two suppliers account for more than 75 per cent of her total imports of aluminium, bauxite, zinc and tin.[18] If this overdependence on individual suppliers were felt to threaten either the security or the price of metals, however, it could as well argue a case for diversifying the sources of supply where possible as for developing home resources. It is however hard to refute the case for maximum knowledge of the extent and quality of indigenous mineral resources.

Although Britain has a long history of geological investigation, with the work of the Institute of Geological Sciences (now part of the Natural Environment Research Council) and its predecessor the Geological Survey, dating back to 1845, much remains unknown about the location and extent of commercially workable minerals. Although some of the projects of the Institute of Geological Sciences are specially directed towards areas of practical national concern,[19] particularly since 1965 when the Labour Government announced a national economic survey of minerals, most of its work is oriented towards pure geology and the scientific analysis of rock formation rather than to economic geology, and establishing the quantity or quality of workable reserves, which are essentially commercial considerations. The Institute of Geological Sciences' Mineral Assessment Unit does not, under present arrangements, have the resources to undertake more than a few selected projects, and most of the necessary work of establishing the extent of workable reserves has to be done by commercial operators. It has, however, been suggested that the Institute of Geological Sciences is the proper agency for determining the extent of domestic mineral resources and that the Government money at present offered in the form of grants to private companies towards exploration costs of certain minerals (see Chapter 1) should more properly be devoted to them,[20] thus producing a shift from commercial to academic exploration.

The attitude of recent Governments towards mineral exploration has not been entirely coherent. Although the system of grants referred to above gives official encouragement to certain categories of mineral exploration, plans formulated by the Labour Government of 1966–70 for legislation on mineral rights have been shelved, legislation which the industry almost unanimously regard as essential for the efficient

445

exploration of the extensive areas which modern techniques dictate. The problems of exploration for mineral resources, as indicated earlier, apply largely in areas where there is a multiplicity of owners of the land surface and of mineral rights. In some cases it may be difficult to trace or establish the ownership of mineral rights; sometimes operators may be unable to reach a reasonable agreement with the mineral rights owners and the arrangements for overriding this contingency in the case of certain 'preferred' minerals are slow, expensive and little used. Under the proposed, now lapsed, mineral rights legislation, the relevant Government department would have licensed operators to explore for minerals (as it now does for petroleum, of which the mineral rights are nationalized). This would ensure operators prompt access for exploration purposes. No change at all was proposed in the necessity to secure planning permission for operations. A milder alternative to the above scheme would be to require the compulsory registration of mineral rights and the lapsing of rights not registered within a stipulated period of time. The lack of such legislation has seriously hampered the work of potential developers of, for instance, tin in Cornwall.

The Zuckerman Commission has, moreover, recommended that, in the interests of maximizing knowledge of indigenous resources, scout drilling, the preliminary stage of exploration involving the drilling of trial boreholes, should be exempt from planning permission. Whether planning permission is at present required for this activity, which lasts only a few weeks, involves a total area of about 84 square metres and leaves no visible trace after, at most, eighteen months, is at present in some doubt. The Zuckerman Commission recommended that permission for this activity should be granted automatically by deemed planning consent under Development Order,* subject to a detailed code of practices to be officially approved by Ministers, including notification of the local planning authority.[21] Whatever view may be taken of this proposal in detail, it might well seem evident that, as a general principle, it is desirable to encourage the acquisition of full knowledge about commercially workable mineral resources. Those who approve the present system of, for instance, mineral rights, on the grounds that it makes the prospective mineral extractor's task more difficult, may well be short-sighted. The easier it is for the extractor to acquire what he thinks is the best site for exploration, the simpler and more rational it is likely to be for the planning authority to arrive at the right economic and environmental decision, given that that authority has at its disposal a whole range of nationally derived infor-

* A statutory order giving automatic permission, subject to conditions, to various categories of development.

mation. The lack of full knowledge of commercially workable resources acts as a constraint on forward planning by local authorities and their capacity to determine the most environmentally suitable site for extraction available. Those who see many of the present legislative and fiscal enactments as unnecessarily permissive take the view that encouraging prospecting inevitably means that the potential extractor has a foot in the door if he locates workable reserves. This need not be so unless in the last analysis the court of final appeal in any planning decision, the Department of the Environment, the Welsh or Scottish Office, wills it that way. If it did so, against the rationale of all the evidence, including likely future world markets, the decision would probably involve the sacrifice of long-term national interest to short-term political expediency. No aspect of decision-making in Britain is immune from this phenomenon and it can never be entirely safeguarded against. In this connection the Friends of the Earth have suggested a single new ground for appeal from mineral planning decisions to the High Court—i.e. that the grant of planning consent for a particular working has not been proved to be in the national interest.[22]

The very difficult question of weighing present against future needs has been complicated by the argument that reserves of commercially useful mineral substances are in any case likely to be exhausted on a world scale within the foreseeable future. There is however little support for this view from economists in the minerals industry and it has been persuasively argued that ore deposits are immense if one considers the possibility of working deposits less favourable than those currently exploited[23] (i.e. either lower grade or more disseminated deposits, deposits at greater depths or more remote from markets). There would probably be an attendant price rise resulting from this development, likely to be partially offset by substitution if particular minerals became in especially short supply, for instance, by devoting a greater proportion of hydrocarbon resources to the manufacture of plastics to replace metals for some purposes. An historical view would indicate that one should not underestimate the capacity of technology to devise substitutes when these become essential, and the dynamic nature of this technology makes predictions of future need very uncertain. The only other way in which national decision-making can affect the scale of domestic exploitation, apart from exercising choice of home exploitation versus imports or by promoting the technology of product substitution, is by a conscious attempt to limit demand. This involves either more economical usage, or the currently fashionable concept of re-cycling of minerals for re-use (unless a deliberate choice of retarding the growth rate in the standard of living is considered). The scope for the re-use of bulk mineral is at present limited. Some aggregate is reclaimed from abandoned roads, airfields, buildings, etc., and some use has been made of spent railway ballast in road sub-bases. The amount available for re-use is of course small in relation to the needs of similar new constructions. Stone kerbs and setts, a very small fraction of the current market, are often re-used. There is, however, as indicated on pp. 59–60, considerable scope for the conservation of high quality aggregate material, which has hitherto been used for bulk fill purposes if it happens to be the nearest source of such material. Re-cycling of the higher value scrap metals is, on the other hand, already a major industry in Britain—it is estimated that copper re-cycling amounts to 40 per cent of consumption[24]—and it is likely that, if the scarcity value of these metals increases in the future, such re-cycling will become even more important. It might be possible, however, for the government to accelerate this process, in the interest of conservation of metal resources for the future and the minimization of extraction, by giving positive tax incentives for the use of re-cycled metallic material.[25]

Whatever options may be adopted in these respects, the annual take of land for mining and quarrying will probably continue to rise, at a time when other demands on space, for urban development, roads and airports, leisure, etc., will also be growing. Given that there seems little possibility of preventing an increasing annual take of land for mining and quarrying, the only options open appear to be to minimize or ameliorate the impact of this increasing land consumption. This could be done by maximizing restoration of worked-out land, by maximizing the utilization of waste material and thus minimizing the take of land for waste dumping, by encouraging more underground working, or by promoting the development of fewer, larger units. The ideal solution to the problem of mineral land consumption— phased excavation of minerals prior to development for other purposes —is only possible in a small proportion of cases; for instance, sand and gravel extraction in West London prior to filling and urban development or phased opencast extraction of coal and fireclay in Shropshire prior to urban development for Telford New Town. The growing number of sub-water-table workings of sand and gravel designed to be replaced by facilities for water sports and nature reserves, such as the Cotswold Water Park, might also be considered to belong to this category. In other cases, notably where thin strata of minerals are worked at shallow depths, as in the case of much of the Northampton Sands ironstone, full restoration to agriculture or other use is possible; with modern earth-moving equipment it is also possible to achieve a high standard or restoration where a stratum, or indeed several strata, is worked at much greater depths, as in the case of much coal worked opencast. However, there is a very large section of quarrying activity, either involving substantial modification of the topography, such as in bluff working or the creation of very large excavations in areas remote from sources of fill, where total restoration will not be possible in the foreseeable future and where a planned after-use is more limited. Quarries in the older rocks, such as limestone, sandstone and igneous rocks, will not weather and take vegetation as easily as those in softer rock such as sand, clay and chalk, and are more likely to be remote from sources of fill, and to occur in fine upland scenery. The quarrying of the hard rock aggregates from these older rocks has of course been expanding at an exceptionally fast rate (see Table 7.1) and is likely to continue to do so. In every case, however, a substantial amount can be done to ameliorate the visual impact of abandoned sites. Waste dumps can be levelled or contoured and rubbish removed. The natural regeneration which would take place eventually (except on waste dumps of high toxicity), can be accelerated by such devices as layering of working faces to aid tree growth. Scars can be hidden by tree screens or by artificial banks which can also be vegetated. Moreover the expertise developed during the 1960s in establishing vegetation upon inhospitable surfaces, whether they contain high levels of toxic materials or are extremely acid or merely lack an adequately developed soil covering, can be utilized to the full.

Mining and quarrying which operates under the most modern planning consents is unlikely to give rise to dereliction, since the overwhelming majority of modern consents specify that every technique now available should be used to mitigate the impact of working once the site is abandoned, as well as stipulating the least practical disturbance during the active life of the mine. There are, however, three chief problems. The first is the difficulty involved in ensuring that all mineral operators obtain planning consent for working and subsequently comply with the terms imposed. The illicit extraction of minerals without the necessary planning consent is now very rare, being confined to very small transient operations with the minimum of installations or heavy equipment; some of the working of fluorspar dumps in Derbyshire is considered to come into this category,[26] and the administrative resources necessary to eliminate it are very large. The enforcement of every detail of planning conditions imposed is a more serious problem; it is said that planning authorities have often insufficient staff to check on compliance with conditions imposed and that the lengthy procedures for dealing with breaches of planning conditions and the low fines imposed on proven defaulters hinder firm enforcement measures being taken.[27] Secondly, an operating company may go out of business during the active life of the working, leaving no funds available for the restoration or rehabilitation imposed by planning consents. Various suggestions have been made about safeguards against this situation arising, namely the introduction of performance bonds, raised by individual firms from insurance companies (or trusts backed by such bonds) to be lodged with the local authority and forfeited if restoration is not carried out to the required standard as is the case in Canada; the compulsory insurance of mineral extractors against bankruptcy; or the establishment of Renewal Trusts, to take responsibility for holding, spending and accounting for funds paid in annually during the life of a working.[28] The last option differs from the first two in certain significant respects; the special charitable status of a trust would involve some indirect contribution by taxpayers to the costs of restoration through the tax concessions available to such institutions, and the composition of the trust, representative of both mining concerns and landowners, would necessarily be somewhat broader than that of the individual firm. The formation of such trusts for every type of extractive enterprise would be likely to lead to a great multiplicity of such institutions. A further option, to extend to all extractive industries a national restoration scheme similar to that operative since 1951 for ironstone extraction in certain areas, is much broader in scope than a safeguard against the insolvency of individual operators. By this scheme, the producer pays to a central fund a small levy per tonne of mineral extracted, part of which he can recoup from the lessor of mineral rights, and a further, smaller, contribution per tonne is made by the Exchequer. The two main payments from the fund are to operators who can claim the excess from the fund when the cost of complying with planning consents exceeds a given sum, and to local authorities for restoration of long-standing derelict mineral workings. Extensions of the ironstone scheme have long been recommended, notably by the Advisory Committee on sand and gravel for this mineral, and by conservation groups such as the Council for the Protection of Rural England for all extractive industries.[29] The universal application of such a scheme would have certain clear advantages; it would, unlike the bond, compulsory insurance, or trust schemes, provide for the restoration of land made derelict through the laxity of early planning consents, or indeed for land made derelict by mineral extraction before the advent of planning control at all. If the Ironstone Restoration Fund is a valid precedent, it is likely that the backlog of dereliction from mineral workings would be cleared much more rapidly than under the present system of Exchequer grants to local authorities for derelict land clearance of all types, grants which are weighted according to certain regional economic criteria. It shares the advantage of the other schemes that rehabilitation of land under modern consents would not be dependent on the solvency of individual firms. The main difficulties attached to making such a scheme universally applicable to mineral operations are believed to be the heavy administrative costs involved, although it is thought that neither the Department of the Environment, nor its predecessors, have actually costed out the scheme.[30] It certainly involves some complexity; the scheme would partially, but not entirely, supersede the present system of Exchequer grants for derelict land clearance, in that not all land has been made derelict by mineral extraction. Furthermore, there are of course great variations in the difficulty and cost of site rehabilitation, both from industry to industry and within an industry, great variations in the durations of individual workings, and in the degree of rehabilitation which is possible. In opencast coal working, restoration is already provided for under other legislation. Unless a high degree of cross-subsidization is envisaged, very substantial variations in contributions and provision would be required, which would add both to the administration and cost involved. Such a scheme, like the other safeguards against insolvency mentioned earlier, would inevitably bear hardest on the smaller operators and on operators in declining extractive industries. However, in view of some of the intrinsic advantages of the scheme, some more detailed costing of its operation at national level would be welcome.

Apart from the difficulties involved in ensuring that the planning conditions imposed are actually complied with, there remains the problem of ensuring that these conditions are adequately worded to take account of changed conditions which may pertain in the future. Planning requirements may only specify restoration, mitigation of impact or indeed methods of working, which are at present known to be practicable. Yet some modern consents provide permission for working whose life extends into the next century.[31] During the working life of these operations, very substantial technological change is likely which could revolutionize the opportunities for new, less damaging extraction techniques or better land rehabilitation. There are many examples of this phenomenon in the quarter of a century since post-war planning was introduced. To take but one example, in 1950 the Ministry of Town and Country Planning produced a paper on the extraction of rock salt and brine, to guide local authorities, which concluded that it would be difficult to justify a refusal of planning permission for an existing natural brine pumping undertaking, as long as that remained the normal method of extraction. At that time, the advantages of the controlled method of brine pumping, which very substantially reduce the likelihood of subsidence, were not as clear as they now appear. Largely as a result of this advice, a considerable number of permissions to continue natural brine pumping were given in 1951-3 in Cheshire, and elsewhere, without limitations on the amount of brine to be pumped from an approved site; some of these operations are still active at a time when the very onerous disadvantages of this method of extraction are apparent. It is clear that modern planning consents, acting in the best public interest as it now appears and enforcing the most advanced and acceptable techniques now known, may appear equally inadequate in the future. However, as the law stands at present, planning authorities cannot alter, revoke or restrict permissions granted without the payment of compensation, even when such alternations are manifestly necessary to cater for changed circumstances. (Mineral operators, on the other hand, can apply to the local authority for alterations of planning conditions, when improvements in technology have made the conditions imposed unsuitable.) In practice, the legal obligation to pay compensation has acted as a very widespread deterrent to local planning authorities from altering conditions previously imposed. Various suggestions have been made for a more flexible system. The Zuckerman Commission has recommended that the plan for site rehabilitation should be constantly updated in consultation with the local planning authority.[32] The Urban District Councils Association goes further and recommends that when circumstances have changed local planning authorities should be given direct power to impose new conditions or vary existing ones without compensation, which should however be paid if there was a 'wholesale reconstitution of planning permission'.[33] Any kind of review procedure would probably need to guarantee that, except in very exceptional circumstances, the operator would be able to continue to work the mineral for the period of permission (which may need to be a long one to allow for write off of capital invested) at a cost which would not put him out of business in spite of more stringent environmental standards. At the same time such a scheme would probably have to have a built-in arbitration and appeal procedure, and some provision for compensation to be paid if working were brought to an enforced, premature close.

A strong case could be made for making such a review procedure retrospective in application. In many branches of extractive industry, the proportion of workings currently operating under modern planning consents is small. Limestone extraction is a case in point; in the Peak

452

Park a number of limestone quarries still operate under permissions granted by the Minister during the 1950s which in the main only contained conditions about waste disposal, ignoring the possibility of mitigating the impact of extractive operations during their active life, and site rehabilitation afterwards. Many limestone extractors in Somerset are operating on land for which planning consent was obtained during 1946–8 from district councils exercising powers under the Town and Country Planning Act of 1932. These approvals were easily obtained for wide areas with no impositions made about conditions of working or site rehabilitation. By 1 July 1948, when the planning act of 1947 came into force, permission had been given for 70 quarries, nearly all of them limestone, covering an area of more than 1215 hectares.[34] Those operators working under early, permissive consents who have a social conscience, or those who appreciate the relevance of their record when future applications for planning permission are made, voluntarily bring their working methods and site after-care up to current standards, a course which the trade organizations repeatedly urge on their members. However, while there is no legal obligation, there will always be operators who are unwilling to do more than the law requires of them. Unless some action is taken to make modern standards of working and site rehabilitation binding on all operators, dereliction will undoubtedly ultimately be created at some worked-out sites, which can only be cleared, if at all, at the expense of the taxpayer, through Exchequer grants to local authorities for derelict land clearance.

Apart from securing the maximum rehabilitation of worked-out mineral land, a second possibility in reducing land consumption for mineral extraction is to curtail the take of land for dumping of waste material. The three chief solid waste producers amongst extractive industries are slate, china clay and deep-mined coal. Slate extraction, cutting and splitting involves a ratio of waste to saleable product of at least 20:1, making a total at 1970 production levels of about 1 300 500 tonnes of which perhaps 1 244 600 tonnes would be surface tipped. China clay extraction involves a ratio of waste sand to saleable product (apart from other waste such as mica) of from 10·5:1 to 9:1, depending on the pit; this made a total production of waste sand of about 26·4 million tonnes at 1969 production levels, of which at least 24·4 million tonnes were surface tipped. The average ratio of waste to saleable product for NCB deep-mined coal in 1970 was 1:2, and a total of 61–71 million tonnes of waste was tipped in that year.[35] It is apparent that, although deep-mined coal has the lowest ratio of waste to saleable product of the three, the size of its problem is substantially the greatest, because of the much higher tonnage of output produced and the potentially more volatile nature of some of the waste material.

In each of these cases, greater effort was made during the late 1950s and 1960s to devise new outlets for the waste products and to expand markets. Commercial utilization of slate was investigated by the Department of Scientific and Industrial Research and the Rural Industries Bureau, in addition to the research of the larger commercial operators. A certain amount of research into commerical utilization of china clay sand has been carried out by the major producer, although more is required into the manufacture of a synthetic coarse aggregate to market with the sand. In the late 1960s the NCB established a division charged with increasing sales of shale and finding new applications for the material, concentrating particularly on the hitherto more intractable problem of unburnt shale. In each case, total sales of waste products were increasing in the 1960s but these still represent only a fraction of total output. It is questionable whether the operators concerned are being given sufficient incentives to maximize sales of waste products, or consumers sufficient incentives to buy them. In each case, rates are payable on sales of these otherwise waste products. The actual scale of the levy may vary from area to area and, although the element is usually small, it is believed, at least in the case of china clay sand and colliery shale, to have inhibited the removal of the maximum amount of material for commercial usage.[36] D. C. Corner and D. C. Stafford, in their study of china clay production at Lee Moor in Devon, have recommended that the rate at present payable on sales of sand from china clay workings should be abolished and replaced by a low 'amenity tax' payable on sand dumped on the tips.[37] The proceeds of the tax should, they suggested, be used in the first instance for research into the production of a synthetic coarse aggregate to market with china clay sand. The imposition of a mineral rate levy on colliery shale sold for commercial purposes has been widely condemned and it appears that, although almost all parties concerned would welcome the removal of this levy, the necessary legislation to accomplish this has never been forthcoming. The removal of rating levies on sales of what would otherwise be waste china clay sand, colliery shale or slate waste would, in spite of any difficulties of definition involved, appear to constitute a relatively straightforward and uncontroversial method of reducing the land take for waste dumping.

A reduction in the consumption of land for disposal of waste products created by on-site mineral treatment plant is not easy to envisage. The waste created is usually in the form of fine particles carried in suspension in the form of slurries or slimes, and many, in addition to land consumption, pose problems of possible pollution of water supplies. The most notable instances at present are the mica slurry produced by treatment of china clay, the whitish slurry produced by fluorspar processing, and the tailings from tin concentration plants. The mica slurry at present being produced at the major Hensbarrow china clay area of Cornwall is, it is intended, to be disposed of into worked-out pits, deep and hence of large capacity, and consequently a land take of only just over one hectare per year is envisaged between 1969 and 2029.[38] The fluorspar slurry from the major processing mill in the Pennines has no such suitable large capacity excavations immediately at hand; the material is at present disposed of into artificial tailings lagoons which could, at current output levels, require a land take of some 2·4 hectares per year.[39] One way of mitigating the impact of tailings lagoons in the area of the mine appears to lie in a reduction in the unit costs of pipeline transport which would enable tailings to be carried to more environmentally acceptable disposal areas. These might be normal tailings ponds or old quarry workings. In the case of the latter it might be necessary to introduce a solidifying agent to the waste material. Tailings from the new Wheal Jane tin concentration plant, the most recent of the four tin extractive operations in Cornwall, require a 34 hectare disposal reservoir. The creation of artificial tailings dams for waste slurry disposal, involving as they do a higher take per volume disposed of than deep excavations, and the supersession of existing land uses, is an imperfect solution. Over the next 50 years it is estimated that tailings from the South Crofty tin mine will need a 24·3 hectare site filled to a depth of 15–18 metres. Cornwall County Planning Authority have said that this tailings site should not be filled to more than 7·6 metres, in which case 48·6 metres would be required, which is unlikely to be obtainable.[40] It is not possible in the case of slurry, as it is with much solid waste, to reduce the volume to be dumped by promoting its commercial utilization, since the material often varies greatly in chemical composition.

There remains the possibility of curtailing land consumption by the extractive industries by attempting to promote more underground working rather than surface working, i.e. reversing the current trend. This question is a complicated one. It is arguable, for instance, that those minerals whose opencast extraction lends itself to full restoration, with the aid of modern earth-moving equipment, are more advantageously worked this way, from an environmental point of view, than by deep-mining. Opencast coal winning, as a case in point, is on amenity grounds wholly preferable to deep-mining. Deep-mining may cause subsidence and although this possibility is progressively reduced as mines deepen or as the percentage of mineral extracted falls, both of these courses add substantially to operative costs and productivity. There are further general disadvantages applicable in deep-mining; it is, by and large, not possible to extract as high a percentage of a given mineral by underground methods as by surface ones and the utilization of the mineral resource is, in consequence, likely to be poorer if the deposit is mined. Deep-mining is, furthermore, almost always more dangerous than opencast working. In the case, however, of those minerals which can be mined without causing subsidence, and whose opencast workings cannot be restored, deep-mining would probably be preferable on amenity grounds. Moreover in certain instances the backfilling of the underground operation with waste, either rock or tailings mixed with cement, may be economically viable particularly as it is possible using such techniques to mine out the supporting pillars which will, of course, be ore bearing. The additional environmental advantage is a diminution in the surface disposal of waste. Such practices are frequently employed in the winnings of metalliferous ores in Canada and the USA. As far as aggregates are concerned, the Peak Park Planning Board, in its annual report published in July 1972, urged the necessity for a full investigation into the feasibility of extracting limestone by underground mining to prevent further encroachment into the landscape by quarrying. A similar case might be made out for sandstone and igneous rock working; although these two minerals have nothing like the present output level of limestone, all three hard rock aggregates are likely to be under very great pressure of expanded demand during the next thirty years. At present deep-mining of such minerals is largely confined to small speciality mines working block stone (as at Monks Park Bath stone mine in Wiltshire) or the working of stone for particular industrial purposes (as at Middleton by Wirksworth in the Peak District). In the United States, however, impetus has been given to consideration of the deep-mining of bulk minerals, followed by commercial utilization of the resultant hole. This has come about as a result of pressures to conserve surface amenity, especially in urban or near-urban areas. In Chicago a scheme of deep-mining of limestone for aggregate, followed by use of the excavation for water catchment, is under active consideration. Other suggested after-uses for such schemes include underground transport systems, oil or gas storage, waste disposal, chemical processing or other manufacturing plant, floodwater surge systems and pumped storage hydroelectric stations.[41] Clearly such projects would necessitate devising techniques of underground working to improve greatly their rate of productivity, at present very low indeed in comparison with surface working; to produce some kind of advances in underground extractive machinery to parallel the recent dramatic improvements in earth-moving equipment for surface working. In the United States the National Academy of Sciences and the United Bureau of Mines have set up a national committee to study methods of rapid underground excavation. The committee recommended a ten-year research programme into ways of reducing the cost and sustaining the rate of advance of underground mining.[42] There have subsequently been a number of technical conferences on the subject.

As far as Britain is concerned, D. I. Roberts, E. Hoek and B. G. Fish have argued that the likelihood of such an approach being followed depends on the rate of exhaustion of easily accessible reserves and the rate of growth of conservation pressure. They write:

It can be said with some justification that sufficient extraction sites are currently being granted reasonable planning permission to ensure meeting the demand for industrial and construction minerals.

One may, therefore, conclude from these considerations that, although in the very long-term underground extraction of common minerals can become both feasible and desirable, the period up to the year 2000 is not likely to see circumstances forcing such development to any great extent. And without such stimulus there is little prospect of diverting either capital investment or research and development effort on a large enough scale to alter the situation.[43]

If one accepts this view (including the point that sufficient sites are now being made available with planning permission to ensure meeting demand—a questionable point in view of a possible more than three-fold increase in aggregate demand by 2010) then an unfortunate impasse would appear to have been reached. Planning permission is being given for surface working because there appears to be no alternative; no other alternatives are being investigated because planning permission is being given. It is to be hoped in fact that research effort and funds will be allocated to the question of sub-surface excavation of bulk minerals before an exhaustion of accessible surface reserves, or the pressure of public opinion, makes this course a last-ditch expedient.

Finally one must consider the possibility of promoting still further the already well-established trend towards concentration of extraction points in the interests of reducing land consumption. The take of land for ancillary purposes such as the treatment plant and the construction of boundary fencing is clearly likely to be less per tonne of mineral extracted at a large than a small site. Concentration of operations tends to

457

be favoured by planners. As indicated earlier, planning policies have helped, not entirely consciously, to contribute to this trend and some planning authorities openly admit to deliberate furtherance of this tendency. The policy of Westmorland County Council in the National Park area of the county, for instance, 'is to encourage excavation at one large site where reserves are known and expensive equipment is a worthwhile investment, rather than on scattered small sites'.[44] Such a policy, as well as probably minimizing land take, produces a concentration of landscape or environmental disturbance.

In 1970 hard rock quarries had an average annual output of less than 100 000 tonnes per year. It has been suggested that a new quarry, to make maximum use of modern equipment, should approach one million tonnes per year output. Roberts, Hoek and Fish have gone so far as to suggest a consideration of quarries of 10 million tonnes per year annual output on the grounds that 'one ten million tonnes/year quarry is likely to cause very much less disturbance than 10 one million tonnes/year units'. Moreover, the investment in a single large unit is much more able to carry the maximum expenditure on protection of amenities during extraction and on rehabilitation of the site when it is worked out.[45] The authors point out that quarries of this size would require considerable readjustment from all parties concerned. The industry would need to develop relatively new expertise in such matters as geotechnic study and control of operations, and improved distribution systems. Planners would also need to adopt a change of attitude; quarries which at their most favourable geometric shape would cover about 4·4 square kilometres would require very long advance planning permission, abandonment of the concept of automatic or rigid preservation of the skyline and of the sanctity of rights of way or even public highways. Minerals rights legislation would probably be necessary to ensure access to a sufficiently large, compact area.

The parts of the country suitable for such mammoth workings, which would not only cover larger areas but work greater face heights than hitherto, include the present prime producing areas such as the Derbyshire Peak District, and all would be in areas of high scenic value. The concentration of production into fewer, larger units in such areas appears to be inevitable; whether this process should be allowed or indeed encouraged to extend to mammoth quarries of the 10 million tonnes per year type is, however, a matter of choice. The merits and demerits of such a policy need to be considered now.

It also appears inevitable that mineral extraction will in the future be dominated by a diminishing number of larger companies. This trend, too, has advantages from the planner's point of view. Fewer, larger firms are administratively easier to deal with than a plethora of small ones. They are more likely to employ specialist personnel such as landscape architects and to have resources to devote to the amelioration of drainage to their local environment during the active life of their excavations and site rehabilitation afterwards. The large private firms, with widespread and long-term interests, may often, though not invariably, be more concerned than small private operators with the importance of preserving a good public image at a time when conservation of the environment is a matter of great public concern.

However, the growing predominance of the large operator does undoubtedly pose some problems for local planning authorities. While the large national operators may have interests extending to many different parts of Britain, the jurisdiction of the local planning authority, and often its sources of information, are strictly limited. The planning proposals of large companies are likely to be the fruit of a complex decision-making process, quite probably based on computer calculations of least-cost production points and of regional, national or international demand. The policy of Associated Portland Cement Manufacturers, for instance, who control approximately 60 per cent of UK cement output, underwent a marked change in the 1960s away from concentrating expansion on limestone-based works in the Midlands and North, and towards a massive expansion of chalk based production on Thamesside. This was the result of the introduction of linear programming in 1965. Similarly, the proposals of the large aggregate firms are based on expensive research projects and studies to assess demand in various parts of the country. The principal author of the Somerset survey of quarrying in the Mendips has noted that 'research and marketing facts based on a company's own survey, cannot easily be faulted'.[46] Prior to the Somerset survey, such information was undoubtedly superior to the state of knowledge of local authorities on this subject, or indeed to that of the relevant national ministries.

The Ministry's memorandum *The Control of Mineral Working* makes it plain that an assessment of the total amount of land to be allocated for each mineral 'will depend primarily on an appreciation of the future demand likely to be made on the production of the area, whatever the source of the demand'. As market radii of the lower value minerals have widened and the decision-making machinery of large national operators has become more sophisticated, the task of local planning authorities in this respect has become infinitely more difficult. Even if an authority follows largely ad *ad hoc* policy in practice (in spite of nominal land allocations for mineral working on the development plan), pronouncing on each application 'on its merits', it will be difficult to challenge the information which it can require from the applicant on the need for the working in question or to suggest alternative sites. The difficulties are compounded many times over if the local planning authority attempts the more ambitious and more positive policy of clear advance allocation of areas for mineral working, based on the quality and quantity of reserves, scale of future demand and rationalization of the competing land use interests, an approach which has been encouraged by the advent since 1968 of structure plans. The difficulties encountered by Northumberland County Planning Authority in attempting a large-scale transference of sand and gravel extraction from the less environmentally acceptable coastal and river-bed extraction to the working of high level, glacial spreads is a case in point. Somerset, one of the few authorities that have indeed attempted a detailed plan of research, prior to the advance allocation of land for stone quarrying in the Mendips, and has involved itself in the collection of complex data from regions far outside its jurisdiction, has been almost universally praised for its action. It is clear that such projects would involve a massive duplication of effort if adopted by every authority, even if every one had the manpower, resources and initiative to attempt it unaided. However, it would appear desirable that all local authorities should have sufficient access to data on future demand, and the extent and disposition of commercially workable reserves etc., to be able to make such forward allocations based on a framework of national mineral, resource and land use policy, which represent the optimum use of land in every case, rather than to wait upon events. One would, nevertheless, have to recognize an unavoidable element of uncertainty in certain cases, such as the unpredictable incidence of non-ferrous metalliferous ores.

One should not underestimate the immense advances which were made in planning practice as it affected mineral working in the 1960s. In many instances, planning practitioners have developed more professional expertise in this field. The practice of appointing mineral officers, with special responsibility for mineral workings within the authority's jurisdiction, meant a much more specialized treatment of this complex field, which by its nature creates particular problems for planning control. Increasingly more enterprising authorities were calling on independent expertise; for instance, Cheshire County Council's retention of economic geology and mining consultants or the study of china clay waste sand commissioned by Devon County Council from two economists at the University of Exeter. There is, however, a very uneven standard. In some counties, the more pressing problems of urban development lead to a relatively greater concentration of effort and resources here rather than on mineral extraction; some counties have been much quicker than others to appreciate the significance of changing trends in mineral extraction for planning practice; some are unable to afford consultants of the requisite quality for evaluating complex mineral projects. Some local authorities indeed still give the impression of acceding to the strongest pressure brought to bear, whether from mineral operators or some other pressure group. In this connection it may be noted that whereas mineral operators have the chance of getting unfavourable local authority decisions reversed on appeal, no such course is open to opponents of a permitted mineral working. In general, there was during the 1960s a welcome move towards decision-making informed by consultation at a higher or wider level. There is now much more control of mineral extraction at county rather than purely local council level. There is now much more cooperation of planners on a supra-county scale—the work of the regional economic planning councils has obviously been helpful here. Coordination between local planning authorities, manifested in groups such as the inter-county working parties on sand and gravel extraction, or the formation of the Chilterns Standing Committee (including the county planners of Oxfordshire, Hertfordshire, Buckinghamshire and Bedfordshire) are examples. There has always been a certain amount of guidance from the Department of the Environment and its predecessors, and from Government ministries with associated interests. In the late 1960s, however, an awareness of the increasing complexity of mineral extraction from a planning point of view led to greater activity at national level. The Department of Trade and Industry initiated the publication of a series of dossiers on minerals of particular interest in Britain, of which the first, on fluorspar, was published in 1972. The Transport and Road Research Laboratory of the Department of the Environment, continued its assessment of demand for road aggregates (though not of other aggregates.) However, the announcement in 1972 of three major projects in the field of minerals and planning, at national level, was a tacit recognition that not nearly enough was done during the 1960s to provide guidance at that level, especially in the rapidly expanding and complex field of aggregates production. The Department of the Environment and the Department of Trade and Industry announced the setting up of a joint inquiry, under the chairmanship of Sir Roger Stevens, into planning control over mineral working, to examine the operation of statutory provisions under which planning control is exercisable over mineral exploration. The need for such a review of the statutory machinery of planning

461

control over surface mineral working had been urged by both local authority associations, arguing that the present provisions do not always give adequate powers to ensure that environmental damage is minimized, and by the mineral industry, arguing that such current provisions inhibit efficiency and forward planning.[47] The Department of the Environment also announced the formulation of an Advisory Committee on Aggregates, to be chaired by Ralph Verney, to advise the Secretary of State for the Environment, and the Secretaries of State for Scotland and for Wales upon subjects related to the supply of aggregates for the construction industry. The Committee will help in the production of estimates of demand, the appraisal of possible sources of supply, and the investigation of the use of lower grade materials and an examination of the environmental problems arising from the extraction of natural aggregates. The third development was the setting up of a research unit attached to the Department of Mining and Mineral Technology of the Royal School of Mines, Imperial College, London, to investigate the environmental implications of large-scale stone quarrying and opencast mining, research made necessary, in the view of the Department, by the probability of the quarrying of hard rock aggregates on a larger scale than in the past and the possible appearance in Britain of open-pit non-ferrous metal mining.[48]

These developments represent a substantial, though by no means unprecedented, assumption of initiative at national level. If one may isolate one recurrent theme of discontent with modern planning practice from the industry's point of view, it is the operations of controls at local level. R. F. Silverlock, of English China Clays Ltd., has contrasted the concern at national level with the fundamental issue of ensuring a free flow of minerals at economic cost, with the local level of planning 'where parochial views are too often allowed to prevail'.[49] Certainly the present process of appeal against a local decision to the Secretary of State is both time consuming and costly; nearly half (225 out of a total of 471) the appeals against local refusals to give planning permission for mineral working were upheld in 1960–70,[50] amongst the highest success rate by category of planning appeal. This system undoubtedly represents a very large expenditure of time and effort, by operators themselves, and by conservation and environmental pressure groups, particularly in the case of sand and gravel where 332 appeals were heard in the decade. As a result, some spokesmen within the industry, dissatisfied with planning control at the local level, have gone so far as to recommend the assumption of direct national control for mineral extraction in its planning context. John Taylor, formerly of Associated Portland Cement Manufacturers, has argued in favour of a Minister for Minerals. The Committee for Environmental Conservation,* however, while conceding that individual councils do not and cannot have the specialized knowledge needed to examine the complicated technical and economic issues of large-scale mineral working, would oppose the displacement of responsibility to even a regional authority, as this would remove planning 'an unacceptable step away from local public participation'.[51] The Committee would favour rather the availability of expert advice to local authorities from regional planning teams made up of experts on minerals. It would certainly appear that if the present structure of planning control over mineral working is to be made relevant to developments within the extractive industries, more expert guidance will have to be made available to local authorities. It is also likely that some revision of the present planning appeal procedure, which is unsatisfactory to many interested parties, will be necessary. The Zuckerman Commission would like to see more collaboration between opposing parties before the holding of an appeal so that an agreed body of facts not in dispute could be presented to the inspector, to reduce the duration and expense of planning inquiries.[52] The Committee for Environmental Conservation would like to see much more information statutorily made public before an inquiry so that data might be verified and assimilated in advance. In this connection, one should perhaps draw attention to the use of environmental impact statements in the USA by which means a high degree of information about proposed workings has statutorily to be made public at an early stage.[53] These statements, which have to be filed with the Environmental Protection Agency before any federal executive decision regarding allowing an operation can be taken, must specify the environmental impact in question, and in practice usually incorporate a complete cost–benefit analysis of the proposed working.

In Britain the most difficult decisions will undoubtedly involve questions of mineral extraction in National Parks and Areas of Outstanding Natural Beauty, areas which together (allowing for those still in process of designation) make up some 20 per cent of the surface area of England and Wales (apart from the National Park Direction Areas in Scotland) and which contain a disproportionately high percentage of the resources of hard rocks for aggregates, of non-ferrous metals and of some of the non-metalliferous minerals such as fluorspar. At present, as indicated in Chapter 1, no very clear policy towards mineral extraction in such areas, as opposed to elsewhere, exists. During Mr Walker's period as Secretary of State for the Environment,

* Representing the main amenity and conservation interests.

policy in National Parks was defined as a presupposition against development: 'One has to balance the arguments. In the National Parks there is very heavy protection and the balance is strongly against development. An almost incredible case has to be made to go ahead.'[54] The dilemma is clear: to refuse permission altogether for new or expanded mineral extraction in National Parks in the future would, in the case of the widespread bulk minerals, place a very heavy burden on producing areas elsewhere. To take the example of limestone, a mineral for which rapid increase in demand is likely, the Peak Park boundary includes most of the limestone outcrop of Derbyshire, the chief limestone producing area of Britain. In 1970 about 25 per cent of the area's limestone production came from within the Park. An absolute bar on expansion of limestone quarrying inside the Peak Park would necessitate very rapid expansion of quarries elsewhere, probably in other areas of high scenic quality, particularly if the same restrictive policy were applied to limestone expansion in the Yorkshire Dales National Park, the Lake District National Park and the Brecon Beacons National Park. The point is that the limestone outcrop is almost synonymous with highly valued scenery, of which the National Parks represent only a part. In the case of rarer minerals, such as fluorspar, it is likely that a curtailment of expansion in the Peak Park could not in fact be made good elsewhere. On the other hand, to abandon the concept of National Parks as denoting any special protection for landscape would cut right across the growing value being placed on country of this type, measured by the number of visitors annually and the undoubtedly greater mass appeal of the Parks now than when they were designated in 1949. One possible option which has been suggested in various forms would be to recognize that the National Parks themselves contain a wide variety of land and landscape of varying quality each enjoying a different status; National Trust land, sites of special scientific value, nature reserves are examples. Base line maps could be compiled which would help, if constantly updated, in the selection of a smaller proportion of the National Park areas, meriting through their particular character absolute inviolability from mineral (or other) development. In the rest of the Park the existing criteria of presumption against working unless overriding national need were established could prevail.

Mineral exploitation in Britain is clearly taking place against a background of much greater complexity than hitherto, a background composed of increasing concern for the balance of payments, increasing anxiety about the exhaustion of commercially valuable mineral resources, both domestic and world wide, and increasing concern about amenity preservation. One should not underestimate the delays and expense caused by the present climate of environmental opinion, in which virtually every application for mineral working is likely to encounter hostile and probably organized resistance and, as argued earlier, there is a strong case for a more advanced planning strategy, where disputes are settled at one early stage rather than by a series of repeated tactical battles. However, it is indisputable that the increasing environmental concern manifested in recent years has led to greatly improved standards of day-to-day extractive practice, waste disposal and rehabilitation. The opportunities for further improving standards presented by technological change are immense; only *informed* public pressure will ensure that these are invariably used to the full.

REFERENCES

1. THE EXPLOITATION ENVIRONMENT

1. Prices for commodities often vary widely according to type, source, quality, quantity purchased and application but the assignment of specific minerals to value groups has been done in consultation with the relevant extractive organizations and with reference to the journal *Industrial Minerals*.

2. Cornish Mining Development Association, 21st Annual Report, 1968–9.

3. ibid., 25th Annual Report 1972–3.

4. Letter to author from Laporte Industries Ltd. (General Chemicals Division), 2 July 1971.

5. Letter to author from Holywell–Halkyn Mining Tunnel Co. Ltd., 14 June 1971.

6. *Iron and Steel Industry Annual Statistics*, 1969, British Steel Corporation, Table 5.

7. Berry Ritchie, *The Times*, 3 April 1971.

8. Calculated from the *Annual Abstract of Statistics*, 1951 and 1971.

9. Gerald Manners, 'Some economic and spatial characteristics of the British energy market' in *Spatial Policy Problems of the British Economy*, Ed. M. Chisholm and G. Manners, Cambridge University Press 1971, p. 141.

10. ibid., p. 149.

11. ibid., p. 151.

12. P. R. O'Dell, 'The British gas industry; a review', *Geographical Journal* **134** (1), March 1968, pp. 81–6.

13. Victor Keegan, 'Big new North Sea oil flow for BP', *Guardian*, 9 October 1971.

14. Manners, op. cit., p. 147.

15. *The Economist*, 15 January 1974.

16. *Petroleum Economist*, January 1974.

17. T. M. Thomas, 'The North Sea gas bonanza', *Tijdschrift voor Economische en Sociale Geografie*, 59, 1968, p. 57.

18. For a breakdown of minerals and mineral products imported into the UK in 1969 see *Minerals and the Environment*, submitted by the Royal School of Mines.

19. See F. Callot, *Structure, Development and Future of the World Mining Production*, address to the VIIth International Mining Congress, Bucharest, September 1972.

20. Richard Thomas and Jeremy Bugler, 'Quiet minerals rush covering Britain', *Observer*, 3 October 1971.

21. James Lewis, 'Copper mining scheme [in Anglesey]', *Guardian*, 23 October 1971.
22. 'Mining in Snowdonia', *The Ecologist* **1** (12), June 1971, pp. 4–9.
23. Laurence Marks and Jeremy Bugler, 'Copper rush threatens Snowdonia', *Observer*, 7 February 1971.
24. Thomas and Bugler, op. cit.
25. 'Prospecting activities in Wales', *Mining Magazine* **123** (4), October 1970, p. 291.
26. *Sunday Times*, 11 July 1971.
27. *Mining Magazine* **122** (1), January 1970, p. 61.
28. Thomas and Bugler, op. cit.
29. *Mining Journal* **275** (7047), 11 September 1970, p. 226.
30. 'Exploration in Scotland', *Mining Journal* **275** (7040), 24 July 1970, p. 63.
31. Thomas and Bugler, op. cit.
32. 'UK uranium prospects', *Mining Journal* **275** (7045), 28 August 1970, p. 179.
33. Peter Rogers, 'Uranium drilling in Scotland', *Guardian*, 29 September 1971.
34. 'Uranium shortage coming', *Mining Journal*, **275** (7054), 30 October 1970, p. 381.
35. Edwin Arnold, 'Aladdin's caves lying under Britain's National Parks', *Daily Telegraph*, 12 February 1971.
36. R. F. Silverlock, 'Planning and the law', *Quarry Manager's Journal*, Institute of Quarrying Transactions, March 1970, p. 99.
37. *The Economist*, 9 May 1970, p. 70.
38. 2nd Reading, Finance Bill, *Hansard*, **801**, 5 May 1970, p. 279.
39. 2nd Reading, Land Commission (Dissolution) Bill, *Hansard*, **808**, 16 December 1970, pp. 1383–486.
40. Silverlock, op. cit., p. 99.
41. *The Control of Mineral Working*, HMSO 1960, paras. 28–35, pp. 11–12.
42. John Taylor, 'The economic planning of mineral resources', *Cement, Lime and Gravel* **47** (7), 1970.
43. Questionnaire Survey, Gloucestershire County Council, 20 April 1971.
44. 2nd Reading, Mineral Exploration Bill, *Hansard*, **825**, 10 November 1971, pp. 1022–87.
45. *Mining Journal* **275** (7054), 30 October 1970, p. 396.
46. *Mining Journal* **275** (7058), 27 November 1970, p. 478.
47. 2nd Reading, Mineral Exploration Bill, op. cit., Alan Williams, p. 1034.
48. *Mining Journal* **275** (7054), 30 October 1970, p. 396.
49. *Mining Journal* **275** (7058), 27 November 1970, p. 478.
50. Silverlock, op. cit., p. 95.
51. Town and Country Planning Act 1968, section 65.
52. Silverlock, op. cit., p. 96.
53. Verbal comment from Council for the Protection of Rural England, 3 January 1972.
54. *Control of Mineral Working*, HMSO 1960, para. 74, p. 23.
55. J. B. Cullingford, *Town and Country Planning in England and Wales*, London 1970, pp. 198–9.
56. *Control of Mineral Working*, HMSO 1960, para. 71, p. 22.
57. Taylor, op. cit.
58. ibid.; Silverlock, op. cit., p. 96.

59. Council for Protection of Rural England, Report of Working Party on Mineral Extraction, September 1970.

60. Cullingford, op. cit., p. 201.

61. J. C. Wyke, 'Progress in refuse disposal', Council for the Protection of Rural England, Sheffield and Peak District Branch, 1962.

62. E. G. Barber, *Win Back the Acres*, CEGB 1963, p. 8.

63. Cullingford, op. cit., p. 202.

64. Interview, Derbyshire County Planning Office, July 1971.

65. ibid., p. 200.

66. ibid., p. 201.

67. 2nd Reading, Cheshire Brine Pumping (Compensation for Subsidence) Bill, *Hansard*, **502**, 1952, p. 1813. Brine Compensation Board, 2 September 1974.

68. Cullingford, op. cit., p. 201.

69. *Mineral Extraction*, Council for the Protection of Rural England, August 1970.

70. Silverlock, op. cit., p. 97.

71. *Control of Mineral Working*, HMSO 1960, para. 72, p. 22.

72. Silverlock, op. cit., pp. 97–8.

73. ibid., p. 101; Taylor, op. cit.

74. *Industrial Minerals* **2**, 1967, p. 21.

75. *Industrial Minerals*, **8**, 1968, p. 15.

76. Berry Ritchie, *The Times*, 28 September 1967.

77. *The Times*, 19 August 1967.

78. Berry Ritchie, *The Times*, 3 April 1968.

79. *Industrial Minerals*, **24**, 1969, p. 60.

80. Berry Ritchie, *The Times*, 3 April 1968.

81. *Industrial Minerals* **13**, 1968, p. 26.

82. *Industrial Minerals* **11**, 1968, p. 21.

83. *19th Report of the National Parks Commission and 1st Report of the Countryside Commission*, 30 September 1968, HMSO, pp. 39–40.

84. Ronald Raux, *The Times*, 13 April 1970.

85. *2nd Report of the Countryside Commission*, 30 September 1969, HMSO, p. 31.

86. Berry Ritchie, *The Times*, 28 September 1967.

87. 'Pressure on the Parks', *Official Architecture and Planning*, March 1971, p. 207.

88. *2nd Report of the Countryside Commission*, 30 September 1969, HMSO, Appendix D, p. 50.

89. Ronald Faux, *The Times*, 13 April 1970.

90. *The Times*, 11 August 1969.

91. *3rd Report of the Countryside Commission*, 30 September 1970, HMSO, p. 44.

92. *Industrial Minerals* **24**, 1969, p. 59.

93. 'The development of the potash industry in Yorkshire—its economic implications', *Economist Intelligence Unit*, 1969.

94. *2nd Report of the Countryside Commission*, 30 September 1969, HMSO, p. 33.

95. *3rd Report of the Countryside Commission*, 30 September 1970, HMSO, p. 44.

96. Ministry of Housing and Local Government, *Handbook of Statistics*, HMSO 1969, p. 22.

97. J. T. Coppock, 'The recreational use of land and water in rural Britain', *Tijdschrift voor Economische en Sociale Geografie*, May–June 1966, p. 82.

98. Quoted in the *Report of the Commission on Mining and the Environment* (the Zuckerman Commission), September 1972, p. 5.

99. Coppock, op. cit., p. 82.

100. Official Report, Parliamentary Debate, *Hansard* **463**, 31 March 1949, c. 1484.

101. Coppock, op. cit., p. 83.

102. See *Commission on Mining and the Environment*, op. cit., looseleaf map entitled 'Some other types of designated areas within the Snowdonia National Park'.

103. *Commission on Mining and the Environment*, op. cit., p. 24.

104. *The Times*, 17 December 1970.

105. Robert Rice, 'Problems of reviving non-ferrous metal mining in Britain', *Chartered Surveyor*, January 1970, p. 329.

106. *This Island Now*, BBC Radio Four, November 1971.

107. *Commission on Mining and the Environment*, op. cit., foreword.

108. e.g. as in the case of the oil refinery at Milford Haven, see *Commission on Mining and the Environment*, op. cit., p. 32.

109. D. C Corner and D. C. Stafford, *China Clay Sand, Liability or Asset?* Devon County Council, 1972, p. 13.

110. *Commission on Mining and the Environment*, appendix 10, 'Report on the economic effect of a large-scale mining operation on a rural economy', p. 82.

111. ibid., pp. 86 and 87.

112. Bugler, op. cit.

113. 72 per cent of those spending their main summer holiday in Wales in 1961 said they had visited local beauty spots (the highest proportion recorded for any single activity) and 45 per cent of those visiting Scotland in 1956 were particularly interested in the scenery and the countryside. Coppock, op. cit., p. 87.

114. *Commission on Mining and the Environment*, op. cit., p. 88.

115. ibid., p. 33.

116. ibid., p. 31.

2. UBIQUITOUS NON-METALLIFEROUS MINERALS (I): THE AGGREGATES MARKET

1. 'An introduction to aggregates', *Industrial Minerals* **62**, 1971.

2. 66 per cent of sandstone and quartzite and 73·8 per cent of limestone. Department of Trade and Industry, Business Statistics Office, *Census of Production, 1968*, 3, 'Stone and slate mining and quarrying', HMSO 1971, Table 5 (ii), 3/9. This was based only on the returns of larger operators, i.e. those employing more than 25 people.

3. Calculated from the total output figures for these minerals in Britain in 1969, as supplied by the Department of the Environment, and the total number of quarries working these minerals in that year, as listed by the Directory of Pits and Quarries, *Quarry Managers' Journal*, 20th ed., 1969.

4. Average prices in the roadstone market in 1968 were 74 pence per tonne for limestone, 95 pence per tonne for sandstone and £1·20 per tonne for igneous rocks. *Census of Production, 1968*, op. cit., Table 5 (ii). Sand and gravel (including moulding and pig bed sand) averages 63 pence per tonne, *Report of Census of Production, 1968*, 4, 'Chalk, clay, sand and gravel extraction', Table 5 (ii). These figures are based on the returns of larger operators only.

5. Based on data supplied by Mr M. W. Mason Smith of Amalgamated Roadstone Corporation Ltd., South Western Division, 7 July 1972.

6. 'Aggregates in the United Kingdom', *Industrial Minerals*, **64**, October 1971, pp. 13–14.

7. Road Research Laboratory, Road Note no. 24, Roadstone Test Data presented in Tabular Form, HMSO 1959.

8. The estimated total market for aggregates in this category in 1970 was about 254 000 tonnes per year. J. R. Hosking, 'Synthetic aggregates of high resistance to polishing', part I, Road Research Laboratory Report LR 350, 1970, p. 1.

9. 'An introduction to aggregates', *Industrial Minerals* **62**, August 1971, p. 11.

10. The arrangement by which pulverized fuel ash from East Midlands power stations is transported to excavations in the Peterborough brickfield involved £3·5 million for the facilities, annual rental for the terminal buildings, a small charge per tonne tipped and some 39–49 pence per tonne rail charges.

11. e.g. in June 1966 the National Coal Board lost an appeal to the Minister to tip spoil on a 91 hectare site near Kirkby in Nottinghamshire and was asked to study other alternatives to surface tipping.

12. Hosking, op. cit., p. 19.

13. ibid.

14. For an analysis, see Somerset County Council, *Quarrying in the Mendips*, 1971, p. 148.

15. 'Aggregates in the United Kingdom', *Industrial Minerals*, **64**, October 1971 p. 13.

16. *Annual Bulletin of Construction Statistics*, Department of the Environment, no. 12, 1970, table 44.

17. Somerset County Council, op. cit., p. 148.

18. ibid. p. 150.

19. G. J. Mortimer, 'The aggregates industry in the 1970s', *Cement Lime and Gravel* **45** (71), July 1970, p. 173.

20. C. L. Keeler, 'Planning and the quarrying industry in Somerset', *Quarry Managers' Journal*, December 1970.

Sand and gravel

21. *Report of the Advisory Committee on Sand and Gravel*, part I, General Survey, HMSO 1948, p. 17.

22. Ministry of Public Building and Works, *Sand and Gravel Production 1968/9*, HMSO 1970.

23. Henry H. Kirwin, 'After-uses of gravel workings in the US', *Cement Lime and Gravel* **45** (8), August 1970, p. 205.

24. *Sand and Gravel Production, 1963–4*, HMSO 1965.

25. *Sand and Gravel Production, 1968–9*, HMSO 1970.

26. Calculated from Department of Trade and Industry, *Digest of Energy Statistics*, HMSO 1971, Table 125, p. 185.

27. L. M. Dunstan, 'Some aspects of planning in relation to mineral resources', *Cement Lime and Gravel*, **41** (9), September 1966, p. 287.

28. Number of pits as listed in Quarry Managers' Journal, *Directory of Pits and Quarries*, 20th ed., 1969; average output per pit calculated from above and total British sand and gravel output as per *Annual Abstract of Statistics*, HMSO 1971, minus 2 783 042 tonnes from Northern Ireland and 4 888 714 tonnes of silica sand.

29. Calculated from Department of Trade and Industry, Business Statistics Office,

Report on the Census of Production, 1968, 4, 'Chalk, clay, sand and gravel extraction', HMSO 1971, Table 5 (ii); and 3, 'Stone and slate quarrying and mining', HMSO 1971, Table 5 (ii).

30. 'Aggregates in the United Kingdom', *Industrial Minerals* **49**, October 1971, p. 16.

31. Data supplied by the Sand and Gravel Association, 11 January 1971.

32. *Industrial Minerals*, op. cit., p. 18.

33. Calculated from Department of Trade and Industry, *Digest of Energy Statistics*, op. cit., Table 126, pp. 186–7.

34. ibid.

35. S. H. Beaver, *The Geology of Sand and Gravel*, Sand and Gravel Association 1968, p. 44.

36. Dunstan, op. cit., p. 289.

37. ibid., p. 289.

38. A. G. McLellan, *The Distribution of Sand and Gravel Deposits in West Central Scotland and Some Problems Concerning their Utilization*, University of Glasgow 1967.

39. ibid., p. 18.

40. Dunstan, op. cit., p. 289.

41. ibid.

42. *Sand and Gravel Production, 1968–9*, HMSO 1970.

43. *Sand and Gravel Production, 1956–7*, HMSO 1958; and *Sand and Gravel Production, 1968–9*, HMSO 1970.

44. *Industrial Minerals*, op. cit., p. 11.

45. *Sand and Gravel Production, 1968–9*, HMSO 1970.

46. *Cement Lime and Gravel* **45** (9), September 1970.

47. *Sand and Gravel Production, 1968–9*, HMSO 1970.

48. Dunstan, op. cit., p. 289.

49. M. S. Barratt, D. B. Courtier, D. O. Hughes and J. M. Robertson, 'Land use planning and mineral resources with special reference to aggregates for the construction industry', *Geological Aspects of Development and Planning in Northern England*, Yorkshire Geological Society 1970, p. 54. Northern England in this context means Northumberland, Cumberland, Westmorland, Durham, Yorkshire, Lancashire, Derbyshire and Cheshire.

50. Beaver, op. cit., p. 47.

51. From *Sand and Gravel Production, 1968–9*, HMSO 1970; and *Report of the Advisory Committee on Sand and Gravel*, part I, 1948.

52. Dunstan, op. cit., p. 200.

53. Standing Conference on London and South-East Regional Planning, *Sand and Gravel Extraction*, LRP 1640, February 1971, p. 8.

54. In L. G. Robinson, *A Policy for Sand and Gravel Working in the County of Huntingdon and Peterborough*, October 1970, p. 2.

55. ibid.

56. Dunstan, op. cit., p. 21.

57. ibid.

58. Standing Conference on London and South-East Regional Planning, op. cit. (report of the working parties for the Western and Maidenhead Service area, the Middle and Upper Thames Gravel Region and the Wessex Gravel Region).

59. Data supplied by the Sand and Gravel Association, 15 June 1971.

60. John Taylor, 'Economic planning of mineral resources', *Cement Lime and Gravel* **45** (7), July 1970, p. 170.

61. Quoted in *Cement Lime and Gravel* **45** (4), April 1970, p. 83.
62. Standing Conference on London and South-East Regional Planning, op. cit., p. 9.
63. Letter from Joint Director of Planning and Transportation, Greater London Council, 7 June 1971.
64. For an example of the type of stringent planning conditions recently being imposed on workings in such areas see an outline of those imposed in 1968 on Henry Streeter (Sand and Ballast) Ltd. for the works close to Harlington village near the M4, *Cement Lime and Gravel* **45** (4), April 1970, p. 89.
65. Dunstan, op. cit., p. 290.
66. *Sand and Gravel*, Report of Survey, Staffordshire County Council, 1966, p. 9.
67. A. G. McLellan, *Cement Lime and Gravel* **45** (6), June 1970, p. 156.
68. McLellan, op. cit., pp. 24–5.
69. ibid., p. 32.
70. *Report on the Supply of Sand and Gravel in Scotland*, HMSO 1956.
71. *Report of the Advisory Committee on Sand and Gravel*, op. cit., p. 29.
72. Dunstan, op. cit., p. 291.
73. 1948 figure calculated from *Ministry of Power Statistical Digest, 1956*, HMSO 1957; 1966 figure obtained from taking the mean between 1964 and 1968 figures (larger establishments only) calculated from *Census of Production, 1968*, op. cit., Table 5 (ii).
74. Dunstan, op. cit., p. 291.
75. Interview, Derbyshire County Planning Office, 28 July 1971.
76. Standing Conference on London and South-East Regional Planning, op. cit., p. 38.
77. Data supplied by the Sand and Gravel Association, 31 December 1971.
78. *Humberside, a Feasibility Study*, Report by the Central Unit for Environmental Planning, HMSO 1969, p. 9.
79. Standing Conference on London and South-East Regional Planning, op. cit., p. 38.
80. ibid., p. 5.
81. D. C. Corner and D. C. Stafford, *China Clay Sand, Liability or Asset?* Devon County Council, 1971.
82. Standing Conference on London and South-East Regional Planning, op. cit., p. 38.
83. G. J. Mortimer, 'The aggregates industry in the 1970s', *Cement Lime and Gravel* **45** (7), July 1970, p. 174.
84. Dunstan, op. cit., p. 288.
85. ibid., p. 289.
86. ibid.
87. Data supplied by the Sand and Gravel Association, 15 June 1971.
88. Dunstan, op. cit., p. 289.
89. ibid., p. 290.
90. Standing Conference on London and South-East Regional Planning, op. cit., p. 28.
91. *Report of the Advisory Committee on Sand and Gravel*, part II, Greater London, Map B.
92. Dunstan, op. cit., p. 290.
93. Letter from Surrey County Planning Officer, 2 December 1971.
94. John Barr, *Derelict Britain*, Harmondsworth 1969, p. 169.

95. J. G. Orr, 'Mineral extraction and the countryside with particular reference to the sand and gravel industry', *Cement Lime and Gravel* **45** (4), April 1970, p. 87.

96. Lee Valley Regional Park Authority, *Report on the Development of the Regional Park with Plan of Proposals*, London 1969.

97. Nottinghamshire County Council, Holme Pierrepoint, 1969.

98. Gloucestershire County Council, The Cotswold Water Park, undated.

99. Orr., op. cit., p. 88.

100. ibid., p. 86.

101. Taylor, op. cit., p. 170.

102. Christopher T. Paris, 'Gravel pits and planning policies', unpublished dissertation, Glasgow University 1971.

103. Orr, op. cit., p. 83.

104. L. G. Robinson, *A Policy for Sand and Gravel Working in the County of Huntingdon and Peterborough*, Huntingdonshire County Council, 1964.

105. L. G. Robinson, *A Policy for Sand and Gravel Working in the County of Huntingdon and Peterborough*, Huntingdonshire County Council, 1966.

106. J. H. Barratt, *Sand and Gravel*, Report of Survey, Staffordshire County Council, 1966.

107. ibid., p. 9.

108. ibid., p. 41.

109. ibid., p. 2.

110. Taylor, op. cit., p. 170.

111. J. B. Ross, *A Policy for Sand and Gravel Workings*, Northumberland County Development Plan, March 1966.

112. ibid., p. 7.

113. ibid., p. 18.

114. ibid., p. 22.

115. See *A Policy for Sand and Gravel Working in Huntingdonshire*, 1964, p. 15.

116. Interview, Leicestershire County Planning Office, July 1971.

Limestone

117. Data supplied by the Department of the Environment, 29 November 1971, total figure for limestone minus 5 790 000 tonnes of dolomite, Institute of Geological Sciences, Mineral Resources Division, *Statistical Survey of the Mineral Industry 1964–9* HMSO 1971, p. 190.

118. Calculated from the *Annual Abstract of Statistics*, no. 108, 1971, Table 200, p. 184.

119. Defined as Cheshire, Cumberland, Durham, Lancashire, Northumberland, Westmorland, Yorkshire and part of Lincolnshire.

120. A. Please and D. C. Pike, *The Demand for Road Aggregates*, Road Research Laboratory report LR 185, 1968, Table II, p. 26. This table applies specifically to 1966–7, but the relative regional positions are likely to have remained constant for a longer period.

121. Calculated from the *Annual Abstract of Statistics*, no. 108, 1971, Table 200, p. 184.

122. J. R. Hosking, *Synthetic Aggregates of High Resistance to Polishing*, part I, Road Research Laboratory report LR 350, 1930, p. 2.

123. Verbal information, Mr Leslie, British Quarrying and Slag Federation, 3 November 1971.

124. Department of Trade and Industry, Business Statistics Office, *Report of the Census of Production, 1968*, 3, 'Stone and slate quarrying and mining', HMSO 1971, Table 5 (ii); and 4, 'Chalk, clay, sand and Gravel extraction', HMSO 1971, Table 5 (ii). These figures are based on the returns of larger establishments only, i.e. those employing more than 25 persons.

125. The demand for hardstone suitable for wearing courses represents about 2 per cent of the total amount of stone used in road construction, Somerset County Council, *Quarrying in the Mendips*, 1971, p. 73.

126. Figures calculated from the overall output figures for Britain, 1969, as supplied by the Department of the Environment, and the total number of quarries as listed by the Quarry Managers' Journal, *Directory of Pits and Quarries*, 20th ed., 1969.

127. Calculated from the *Annual Abstract of Statistics*, **108**, 1971. Table 200, p. 184.

128. Calculated from Department of Trade and Industry, *Digest of Energy Statistics*, 1971, Table 126, pp. 186–7.

129. *Stone and Slate Quarrying and Mining*, op. cit., Table 5 (ii). The term 'roadstone' as used here appears to include other types of aggregates, excluding ballast.

130. Data supplied by the Ministry of Agriculture, Agricultural Lime Supplies, breakdown into broad categories of total lime spread.

131. Calculated from the *Annual Abstract of Statistics*, **108**, 1971, Table 202.

132. *Stone and Slate Quarrying and Mining*, op. cit., Table 5 (ii).

133. Calculated from above.

134. *Industrial Minerals*, **42**, March 1971, p. 43.

135. Data supplied by the Department of the Environment, 29 November 1971.

136. C. L. Keeler, 'Planning and the quarrying industry in Somerset', *Quarry Manager's Journal*, **54** (12), December 1970. Reprint supplied by British Quarrying and Slag Federation.

137. Somerset County Council, op. cit., p. 73.

138. Keeler, op. cit.

139. Somerset County Council, op. cit., pp. 118 and 123.

140. Deduced from data supplied by the Department of the Environment, 29 November 1971.

141. T. M. Thomas, *The Mineral Wealth of Wales and its Exploitation*, Oliver and Boyd 1961, p. 71.

142. Please and Pike, op. cit., Table II.

143. Calculated from Thomas, op. cit., p. 86 and Department of Environment Data, supplied 29 November 1971.

144. Calculated from Department of the Environment data, supplied 29 November 1971.

145. Letter from the County Planning Office, Ross and Cromarty, to the author, 30 April 1971.

146. F. P. Stowel, *Limestone as a Raw Material in Industry*, ICI Ltd., 1963, p. 6.

147. Somerset County Council, op. cit., p. 123.

148. Letter from Kent County Planning Officer, 29 October 1971.

149. *Maidstone Vicinity and Medway Gap Town Maps*, Report on the Survey and Analysis, 1970, p. 42.

150. Somerset County Council, op. cit., p. 117.

151. *Maidstone Vicinity and Medway Gap Town Maps*, op. cit., p. 42.

152. Somerset County Council, op. cit., p. 117.

153. 'The Hopton Wood limestone mine at Middleton by Wirksworth', *East Midland Geographer* **3** (24, 8), 1965, p. 472.

154. J. E. Metcalfe, *British Mining Fields*, Institute of Mining and Metallurgy, 1969, p. 10.

155. Letter from Mr M. R. Lloyds of Lloyds Spar Quarries Ltd., 17 June 1971.

156. Brian G. Fish, 'Quarrying in the 1970s', *Quarry Managers' Journal* **54** (10), October 1970, p. 364.

157. See, for instance, Somerset County Council, op. cit., p. 23.

158. Quarry Managers' Journal, *Directory of Pits and Quarries*, 20th ed., 1969.

159. *Industrial Minerals* **49**, October 1971, pp. 16–18.

160. e.g. by J. E. Carleton, 'The shape of the (aggregates) industry and its trends', *Quarry Managers' Journal* **45** (4), April 1970, p. 145.

161. Fish, op. cit., p. 364.

162. Somerset County Council, op. cit., p. 90.

163. ibid., p. 90.

164. ibid.

165. Department of Trade and Industry, *Digest of Energy Statistics*, 1971, Table 126, pp. 186–7.

166. ibid.

167. Quoted Somerset County Council, op. cit., p. 107.

168. G. J. Mortimer, 'The aggregates industry in the 1970s'. *Cement Lime and Gravel* **45** (7), July 1970, p. 176.

169. ibid.

170. L. M. Dunstan, 'Some aspects of planning in relation to mineral resources', *Cement Lime and Gravel* **41** (9), September 1966, p. 289.

171. 'Tunstead Quarry', *Quarry Managers' Journal* **53** (11), November 1969, p. 408.

172. G. G. Haythornthwaite, 'Cement Works and the Countryside', *Town and Country Planning* **21** (114), 1953, p. 500. However, the adoption in 1971 of the dry process of cement manufacture for the new Hope works has made it possible to deepen the shale quarries to utilize material previously unusable. As a result, the annual take of land for shale has been proportionally reduced.

173. Data made available by the British Quarrying and Slag Federation, 3 November 1971.

174. Haythornthwaite, op. cit., p. 500.

175. Letter from Mr T. M. Thomas, of the Welsh Office, 8 November 1971.

176. Peak Park Planning Board, 18th Annual Report, April 1969–March 1970, p. 34, para. 126.

177. M. S. Barratt, D. B. Courtier, D. O. Hughes and J. M. Robertson, 'Land use planning and mineral resources with special reference to aggregates for the construction industries', in *Geological Aspects of Development and Planning in Northern England*, Yorkshire Geological Society, 1970, p. 62.

178. Associated Portland Cement Manufacturers and East Lothian County Council, *Dunbar Quarry*, 1970, p. 41.

179. Letter from Northamptonshire County Planning Officer to the author, 11 August 1971.

180. Barratt *et al.*, op. cit., p. 62.

181. See Brian J. Greenhead and J. D. Knowles, 'Environmental considerations of quarry blasting', *Quarry Managers' Journal* **54** (10), October 1970, p. 371.

182. Mortimer, op. cit., p. 176.

183. Fish, op. cit., p. 365.

184. Somerset County Council, op. cit., pp. 225–6.

185. Letter from the Director, Peak Park Planning Board, 11 June 1971.

186. Keeler, op. cit.

187. Somerset County Council, op. cit., p. 44.

188. A. H. M. Morris, 'Quarrying and the Public Image', *Quarry Managers' Journal* **54** (12), December 1970, p. 467.

189. Somerset County Council, op. cit., p. 88.

190. Keeler, op. cit.

191. Somerset County Council, op. cit., p. 157.

192. W. I. Stanton, 'The impact of limestone quarrying on the Mendip Hills', *Proceedings of Bristol Speleological Society*, II, part I, 1967; and Somerset County Council, op. cit., appendix 4; *W. I. Stanton, Limestone Reserves in the Preferred Areas—Sub-Water-Table Working*.

193. Stanton, 'The impact of limestone quarrying on the Mendip Hills', op. cit., p. 62.

194. Somerset County Council, op. cit., p. 205.

195. Fish, op. cit., p. 370.

196. Report of the Second International Surface Mining Conference, *Quarry Managers' Journal* **53** (1), January 1969, p. 31.

197. ibid., summary of paper of E. P. Pfleider, Chairman of Committee on Rapid Excavation, entitled 'Rapid underground excavation as an alternative'.

Igneous and metamorphic rocks

198. The *Census of Production*. The Ministry of Technology *Digest of Energy Statistics* and the *Annual Abstract of Statistics* also include felspar.

199. S. I. Tomkeieff, 'The economic geology of quarried materials. 2, igneous and metamorphic rocks', *Quarry Managers' Journal*, March 1964, p. 85.

200. ibid., pp. 86–8.

201. ibid., p. 88.

202. ibid., p. 93.

203. ibid., p. 94.

204. Report of the *Census of Production, 1968*, 3, 'Stone and slate quarrying and mining', HMSO 1971: calculated from Table 5 (ii), pp. 3–9. Larger establishments are those employing 25 or more persons.

205. Calculated from above.

206. Calculated from above.

207. G. Hughes and W. Gilbert, 'Some experiments in the use of basalt in the refractories industry', *Refractories Journal*, August 1967, pp. 272–84.

208. A. Please and D. C. Pike, *The Demand for Road Aggregates*, Road Research Laboratory report LR 185, 1968, Table 11, p. 26.

209. Calculated from the *Census of Production*, op. cit., Table 5 (ii), 3/9.

210. Road Research Laboratory, Road Note no. 24, Roadstone Test Data presented in tabular form, HMSO 1959.

211. J. R. Hosking, *Synthetic Aggregates of High Resistance to Polishing*, 1, 'Gritty aggregates', Road Research Laboratory report LR 250, 1970, p. 19.

212. ibid., p. 1.

213. Somerset County Council, *Quarrying in the Mendips*, 1971, figure 6, p. 68.

214. Calculated from the *Census of Production*, op. cit., Table 5 (ii), 3/9.

215. *Annual Abstract of Statistics*, **108**, 1971, Table 200, p. 184.

216. Quarry Managers' Journal, *Directory of Quarries and Pits*, 20th ed., 1969.

217. Calculated from data supplied by the Department of the Environment, 29 November 1971.

218. Interview, Leicestershire County Planning Office, July 1971.

219. Please and Pike, op. cit., Table 11, p. 26.

220. Somerset County Council, op. cit., p. 117.

221. Interview, Leicestershire County Planning Office, July 1971.

222. Calculated from data supplied by the Department of the Environment, 29 November 1971.

223. Quarry Managers' Journal, *Directory of Quarries and Pits*, 20th ed., 1969.

224. Calculated from the total British output as in data supplied by the Department of the Environment and total number of quarries as in the *Directory of Quarries and Pits*, op. cit.

225. Interview, Leicestershire County Planning Office, July 1971.

226. Quarry Managers' Journal, *Directory of Quarries and Pits*, 20th ed., 1969.

227. It is impossible to be absolutely specific about this in view of the Ministry's grouping of outputs by counties; it is however likely that output from Cornwall exceeds that from Shropshire or Staffordshire, the two main contenders, in view of what is known of individual quarry output.

228. Somerset County Council, op. cit., p. 74.

229. Data supplied by Mr M. S. Mason Smith of Associated Roadstone Corporation, South-Western Division, 7 July 1972.

230. ibid.

231. ibid.

232. ibid.

233. Calculated from the Quarry Managers' Journal, *Directory of Pits and Quarries*, 20th ed., 1969, and data supplied by the Department of the Environment, 29 November 1971 (output figure for Cornwall, assuming an output of 508 000 tonnes for Somerset).

234. Data supplied by the Department of the Environment, 29 November 1971.

235. ibid.

236. Data supplied by the British Quarrying and Slag Federation, 3 November 1971.

237. ibid.

238. T. M. Thomas, *The Mineral Wealth of Wales and its Exploitation*, Oliver and Boyd, 1961, p. 98.

239. Data supplied by Mr R. M. Ogston of Kingston Minerals Ltd., 21 August 1972.

240. Data supplied by the Quarry Manager, Penmaenmawr Quarry, July 1972.

241. Calculated from Thomas, op. cit., p. 98.

242. Calculated from data supplied by the Quarry Manager, Penmaenmawr Quarry, July 1972.

243. Reprint of 'A notable granite quarrying operation in North Wales', part 1, *Quarry Managers' Journal*, July 1962, p. 5; 1971 rate of output supplied by the Quarry Manager, Penmaenmawr Quarry, July 1972.

244. Calculated from Thomas, op. cit., p. 98.

245. Data supplied by the Quarry Manager, Penmaenmawr Quarry, July 1971.

246. Thomas, op. cit., p. 93.

247. Calculated from the output figure for Wales, 1969, supplied by the Depart-

ment of the Environment and the output figure for the UK, 1969, in the *Annual Abstract of Statistics*, no. 108, 1971, Table 200, p. 184.

248. Calculated from the output figure for Scotland, 1969, supplied by the Department of the Environment and the output figure for the UK, 1969, in the *Annual Abstract of Statistics*, no. 108, 1971, Table 200, p. 184.

249. Data supplied by the Department of the Environment, 19 November 1971.

250. ibid.

251. ibid.

252. Calculated from the total number of Scottish quarries as in the *Directory of Pits and Quarries*, 20th ed., 1969, and the output figure for Scotland, 1969, as supplied by the Department of the Environment.

253. Letter of Mr John R. Mutch of John Fyfe Ltd., 25 February 1972.

254. Letter of Mr John R. Mutch of John Fyfe Ltd., 31 August 1972.

255. Calculated from the total number of Aberdeen and Angus quarries 1969 as in the *Directory of Pits and Quarries*, 20th ed., 1969, and the output figure for these counties as supplied by the Department of the Environment.

256. Data supplied by the Department of the Environment, 29 November 1971.

257. Calculated from the total number of quarries for these counties as in the *Directory of Pits and Quarries*, 20th ed., 1969, and the total output for these counties as supplied by the Department of the Environment.

258. Letter from Mr J. Lockie of Wimpey Asphalt Ltd., 30 November 1972.

259. Data supplied by the Department of the Environment, 29 November 1971.

260. G. P. Wibberley, *Agriculture and Urban Growth*, Michael Joseph, 1959, p. 188.

261. Letter from Renfrewshire Director of Planning and Engineering, 27 July 1971. Recent applications for working in this county, where 975 000 tonnes of igneous and metamorphic rocks (mainly basalt) were produced in 1969, have been in the range of 6–12 hectares and upwards.

262. Letter from Caernarvonshire County Planning Officer, 15 April 1971.

263. Report of Survey, East Lothian County Council, 27 April 1971; and of Dunbarton County Council, 28 April 1971.

264. Letter from Westmorland County Planning Officer, 30 April 1971.

265. e.g. Report of Survey, Stirling County Council, 23 April 1971; and Argyll County Council, 10 May 1971.

266. Letter from Herefordshire County Planning Officer, 19 April 1971.

267. Interview, Leicestershire County Planning Office, July 1971.

268. ibid.

269. ibid.

Sandstone

270. S. I. Tomkeieff, 'The Economic Geology of Quarried Materials, 5, Sandstones', *Quarry Managers' Journal*, October 1964, p. 399.

271. The *Annual Abstract of Statistics*, HMSO, source of total figures given in this chapter, includes silica stone, ganister, grit and conglomerate under the heading 'sandstone'. The Ministry of Technology *Digest of Energy Statistics* uses the same classification. The Ministry of Transport includes quartzite, gritstone, freestone, flagstone, chert, flint and pennant under the general heading of sandstone. The Board of Trade *Census of Production*, HMSO, groups together sandstone, quartzite and ganister.

272. Tomkeieff, op. cit., pp. 401–2.

273. Data supplied by the British Quarrying and Slag Federation, 3 November 1971.

274. Department of Trade and Industry, Business Statistics Office, *Report of the Census of Production, 1968*, 3, 'Stone and slate quarrying and mining', HMSO 1971, Table 5 (ii), 3/9. Larger establishments are those employing more than 25 persons.

275. Road Research Laboratory, Road Note no. 24, roadstone test data presented in tabular form, HMSO 1959.

276. See J. R. Hosking, *Synthetic Aggregates of High Resistance to Polishing*, part I, 'Gritty aggregates', Road Research Laboratory report LR 350, 1970.

277. Calculated from *Report of the Census of Production*, op. cit., Table 5 (ii), 3/9.

278. Calculated from the total annual output figures given in the *Annual Abstract of Statistics*, **108**, 1971, Table 200; and the total numbers of quarries given in the *Directory of Quarries*, Quarry Managers' Journal, 20th ed., 1969.

279. Calculated from the *Report of the Census of Production 1968*, op. cit., Table 5 (ii), 3/9.

280. *Annual Abstract of Statistics*, no. 108, HMSO, Table 200.

281. Calculated from ibid.

282. *Scottish Abstract of Statistics*, HMSO, 1970, Table 81, p. 92; *Digest of Welsh Statistics*, no. 9, HMSO 1962, p. 45, and no. 17, 1970, p. 82; *Annual Abstract of Statistics*, op. cit., Table 200.

283. Data supplied by the Department of the Environment, 29 November 1971.

284. S. H. Beaver, *The Geology of Sand and Gravel*, Sand and Gravel Association, 1968, p. 62.

285. Quarry numbers as given in the *Directory of Quarries*, op. cit., county total from data supplied by the Department of the Environment, 29 November 1971.

286. Somerset County Council, *Quarrying in the Mendips*, 1971, p. 123.

287. M. S. Barratt, D. B. Courtier, D. O. Hughes and J. M. Robertson, 'Land use planning and mineral resources with special reference to aggregates for the construction industries' in *Geological Aspects of Development and Planning in Northern England*, Yorkshire Geological Society, 1970, p. 58.

288. Quarry numbers as given in the *Directory of Quarries*, op. cit.; county total from data supplied by the Department of the Environment, 29 November 1971.

289. Beaver, op. cit., p. 59.

290. *Directory of Quarries*, op. cit.

291. K. C. Edwards, *Extractive Industry in Nottingham and its Region*, British Association for the Advancement of Science, 1966, p. 296.

292. *Directory of Quarries*, op. cit.

293. Letter from Lancashire County Planning Officer to the author, 13 March 1972.

294. Information supplied by Lancashire County Planning Office, 29 August 1974.

295. Letter from Warwickshire County Planning Officer to the author, 29 March 1972.

3. UBIQUITOUS NON-METALLIFEROUS MINERALS (II)

Chalk

1. Calculated from the *Annual Abstract of Statistics*, no. 108, 1971, Table 200, p. 184.
2. Data supplied by the British Quarrying and Slag Federation, 3 November 1971.
3. Calculated from the *Annual Abstract of Statistics*, no. 108, 1971, Table 202, p. 185.
4. *Industrial Minerals* **49**, October 1971, p. 13.
5. P. H. Grimshaw, The 'UK Portland Cement Industry', *Geography* **53**, 1968, p. 81.
6. ibid., p. 82.
7. Somerset County Council, *Quarrying in the Mendips*, 1971, p. 124; A. W. Parsons, *Earthworks in Soft Chalks, a Study of some of the Factors affecting Construction*, Ministry of Transport, Road Research Laboratory report no. LR 112, 1967.
8. Central Unit for Environmental Planning, *Humberside, a Feasibility Study*, HMSO 1969, 9.28.
9. Figures supplied by the Ministry of Agriculture, November 1971.
10. In 1969 chalk for agricultural liming cost about £1·97 per tonne, delivered and spread, compared with £2·41 of ground limestone for the same purposes.
11. Data supplied by the British Quarrying and Slag Federation, 3 November 1971.
12. A. Coleman, 'Landscape and planning in relation to the cement industry of Thamesside', *Town Planning Review*, **25**, 1954, p. 218.
13. Blue Circle Group, *A Review of 1969*, May 1970, p. 8.
14. Associated Portland Cement Manufacturers and East Lothian County Council, *Dunbar Quarry*, 1970, p. 1.
15. Letter from Rear Admiral C. K. T. Wheen of the Cement Makers' Federation, 20 December 1971.
16. Blue Circle Group, *A Review of 1969*, May 1970, p. 16.
17. ibid., p. 8.
18. Letter from Mr M. J. Greer, of Associated Portland Cement Manufacturers Ltd., 25 February 1972.
19. Blue Circle Group, *A Review of 1969*, May 1970, p. 8.
20. ibid. Exports of ground and unground Portland cement in fact rose to 732 858 tonnes in 1970. (Data supplied by H.M. Customs and Excise, Southend, 2 August 1972.)
21. Ministry of Works and Buildings, *Report of the Committee on Cement Production*, HMSO, May 1941.
22. Data supplied by Dr G. Marshall of Associated Portland Cement Manufacturers Ltd., 3 February 1972.
23. Letter from Mr M. J. Greer of Associated Portland Cement Manufacturers Ltd., 24 February 1972.
24. John Taylor, 'Cement and the countryside', *Town and Country Planning* **21** (111), 1953, p. 308.
25. Central Unit for Environmental Planning, op. cit., para. 9.27.
26. Chilterns Standing Conference, *A Plan for the Chilterns*, 1971, p. 71.
27. Data supplied by the British Quarrying and Slag Federation, 3 November 1971.
28. ibid.

29. Quarry Managers' Journal, *Directory of Quarries and Pits*, 20th ed., 1969.

30. Central Unit for Environmental Planning, op. cit., para. 9.28.

31. Report and Analysis of the First Review of the County Development Plan, Surrey County Council, 1965, ix–19.

32. Deduced from the British Quarrying and Slag Federation Directory of Members, 1970.

33. Chilterns Standing Conference, op. cit., p. 6.

34. Data supplied by the British Quarrying and Slag Federation, 3 November 1971.

35. Reports of Survey, Kent, East Riding, Surrey, Hampshire, Wiltshire and Isle of Wight County Councils.

36. Letter from East Sussex County Planning Officer to the author, 19 October 1971.

37. ibid.

38. *Sunday Times*, 6 December 1970.

39. Reports of Survey, West Sussex, Isle of Wight, Surrey, Hampshire and East Riding County Councils.

40. See Jeremy Bugler, *Polluting Britain*, Penguin, 1972, pp. 8–31.

41. Chilterns Standing Conference, op. cit., p. 10.

42. Calculated from data supplied by the Department of the Environment, 29 November 1971.

43. Letter from Kent County Planning Officer to the Secretary of the Standing Conference on London and South-East Regional Planning, 17 September 1971.

44. ibid.

45. For map, see A. Coleman, op. cit., p. 219.

46. As classified by D. Stamp, the Land Utilization Survey.

47. Although Coleman (op. cit., p. 229) contends that there are compensating advantages in terms of variety of terrain and the breathing space which the pits provide in an area of otherwise dense urban settlement.

48. Letter from Kent County Planning Officer, 29 October 1971.

49. Coleman, op. cit., p. 219.

50. North-West Kent Draft Town Map, Draft Report, 1971, 8.3.4.

51. ibid., 8.1.3.

52. Letter of Kent County Planning Officer to the Secretary, Standing Conference on London and South-East Regional Planning, 17 September 1971.

53. Interview, Bedfordshire County Planning Office, 17 September 1971.

54. Chilterns Standing Conference, op. cit., p. 71.

55. ibid.

56. ibid.

Brick clays

57. Pamela R. Healey and E. R. Rawstron, 'The brickworks of the Oxford Clay Vale', *East Midland Geographer*, **4**, December 1955, p. 4, comment that brickworks, except those using clay from coalmines, are usually within 100 metres of the working face, but Michael B. Gleave, 'Some contrasts in the English brickmaking industry', *Tijdschrift voor Economische en Sociale Geografie* **56**, March/April 1965, p. 55, noted that in the West Riding and Oxford Clay Vale material was transported to works in areas where the immediate reserves had been exhausted or sterilized.

58. National Brick Advisory Council, *Clay Brickmaking in Great Britain*, HMSO 1950, table I, pp. 6–7.

59. ibid., Table 3, pp. 10–11.

60. ibid., appendix, p. 76.

61. Letter from Mr Michael Drown of the London Brick Company, 8 November 1971.

62. Data supplied by the Brick Development Association Ltd., February 1972.

63. 'National Federation of Clay Industries Report, 1969–70', *Refractories Journal*, September 1970, p. 28.

64. Gleave, op. cit., p. 56.

65. Healey and Rawstron, op. cit., p. 46.

66. Report of Survey, Hertfordshire County Council, 28 April 1971.

67. K. C. Edwards, 'Extractive industry', in *Nottingham and its Region*, British Association for the Advancement of Science, 1966, p. 294.

68. Letter from Mr Drown, 8 November 1971.

69. L. B. Collier, 'The world's largest brickworks', *Bedfordshire Magazine* **9**, 1963, p. 20.

70. Letter from Mr Drown, 8 November 1971.

71. Healey and Rawstron, op. cit., p. 47.

72. For an analysis of the marketing regions of the bricks of the Oxford Clay Vale, the West Riding of Yorkshire and of Kent and Surrey see Gleave, op. cit., pp. 58–9.

73. ibid., p. 55.

74. National Federation of Clay Industries, *How Bricks are Made*, pp. 1 and 3.

75. Production of clay roofing tiles fell from 2 916 000 square metres in 1963 to 1 131 000 square metres in 1969. *National Federation of Clay Industries Annual Report*, 1969–70.

76. L. Dudley Stamp and S. H. Beaver, *The British Isles*, 6th ed., Longmans 1971, p. 366.

77. Healey and Rawstron, op. cit., p. 44.

78. ibid., p. 47.

79. Letter from Mr Drown, 8 November 1971.

80. Surrey County Council, Report and Analysis of Survey, First Review of County Development Plan, 1965, paras. 9–17.

81. Somerset County Council, County Development Plan, First Review, 1964, p. 50.

82. Quoted Greave, op. cit., p. 56.

83. Somerset County Council, op. cit., p. 50.

84. Kent County Council, Revision of County Development Plan, 1967, paras. 388–9.

85. Geoffrey Cowley, *Bedfordshire Brickfield*, Bedfordshire County Council, October 1967, p. 5.

86. ibid., p. 10.

87. ibid., pp. 14 and 16.

88. Report of Survey, Huntingdon and Peterborough County Council, 23 April 1971. The London Brick Company total of excavated areas in Huntingdon and Peterborough at December 1971 was *716 hectares*. (Letter from Mr Michael Drown of the London Brick Company, 16 June 1972.)

89. Letter from Mr Michael Drown of the London Brick Company, 16 June 1972.

90. Jeremy Bugler, *Polluting Britain*, Penguin 1972, p. 115.

91. Letter from Mr. Michael Drown of the London Brick Company, 4 July 1972.

92. Bugler, op. cit., p. 124.

93. John Barr, *Derelict Britain*, Penguin 1969, p. 168.

94. This is due to a combination of slower growth in the electricity industry since the 1950s, greater utilization of gas and oil firing, and increasing sales of pulverized fuel ash for aggregates.

95. Data supplied by Buckinghamshire County Planning Officer, 28 October 1971.

96. ibid.

97. Cowley, op. cit., p. 6.

98. ibid.

99. Bugler, op. cit., p. 129.

100. Cowley, op. cit., p. 10.

101. Notably Barr, op. cit., and Bugler, op. cit.

102. Cowley, op. cit., p. 40.

103. ibid., p. 36.

104. Transcript of the address of Mr J. P. Bristow, Deputy Chairman of London Brick Company, to the Brickfield Conference, 1968, supplied by the London Brick Company.

105. Interview, Bedfordshire County Planning Office, 17 September 1971.

106. *The Times*, 21 October 1970.

107. Notably Bugler, op. cit.

108. Ministry of Housing and Local Government, *The Control of Mineral Working*, revised ed., 1960, pp. 5–6.

Slate

109. S. I. Tomkeieff, 'The Economic Geology of Quarried Materials, 7, Slate', *Quarry Managers' Journal*. February 1965.

110. ibid., p. 73.

111. J. E. Richey and J. G. C. Anderson, *Scottish Slates*, wartime pamphlet no. 40, Department of Scientific and Industrial Research, Geological Survey of Great Britain, Scotland, May 1944.

112. Ministry of Works, *The Welsh Slate Industry* (the Rees Report), HMSO 1947, p. 5.

113. ibid.

114. ibid.

115. *Annual Abstract of Statistics*, no. 108, 1971, Table 200, p. 184.

116. Calculated from Department of Trade and Industry, *Digest of Energy Statistics*, 1971, Table 126, p. 187.

117. Letter from Mr Eric L. Calver of Sir Alfred McAlpine and Sons Ltd., 26 November 1971.

118. Calculated from the *Census of Production, 1968*, **31**, 'Stone and slate quarrying and mining', HMSO 1971, Table 3/9.

119. Letter from Mr J. A. Kent of the Old Delabole Slate Co., 23 December 1971.

120. Board of Trade, Overseas Trade Statistics of the UK, December 1970, HMSO 1970, Table VI, 273.11 and Table VII, 661.33.

121. Data supplied by the Broughton Moor Green Slate Quarries Ltd., 5 January 1972.

122. Letter from Mr Eric Calver of Sir Alfred McAlpine and Sons Ltd., 26 November 1971, and data supplied by the Broughton Moor Green Slate Quarries Ltd., 5 January 1971.

123. Data supplied by the Broughton Moor Green Slate Quarries Ltd., 5 January 1972.

124. Data supplied by Mr J. A. Kent of the Old Delabole Slate Co., 23 December 1971.

125. 'Penrhyn expands production of slate powder and granules', *Industrial Minerals* **4**, January 1968, p. 39.

126. Quarry Managers' Journal, *Directory of Quarries and Pits*, 20th ed., 1969.

127. Ministry of Works, op. cit., p. 1.

128. *Annual Digest of Welsh Statistics*, no. 16, HMSO 1969, p. 69; *Annual Abstract of Statistics*, no. 108, 1971, table 200, p. 184.

129. Data supplied by the Department of the Environment ⌐29 November 1971.

130. Data supplied by Mr J. A. Kent of the Old Delabole Slate Co. Ltd., 23 December 1971.

131. Letter from Mr J. W. Roberts of Penrhyn Quarries Ltd., 13 September 1972.

132. These figures are arrived at on the basis of information obtained by various sections of the trade and are approximations only.

133. Letter from Caernarvonshire County Planning Officer, 15 April 1971.

134. *Penrhyn Slates*, Penrhyn Quarries Ltd.

135. Data supplied by the Department of the Environment, 29 November 1971.

136. Quarry Managers' Journal, *Directory of Quarries and Pits*, 20th ed., 1969.

137. Ministry of Works, op. cit., p. 8.

138. Letter from Mr J. W. Roberts of Penrhyn Quarries Ltd., 9 August 1972.

139. ibid.

140. Mines Inspectorate Division, Miscellaneous List of Mines in the United Kingdom at 30 September 1970, typescript.

141. Trevor M. Thomas, 'Wales, land of mines and quarries', *Geographical Review* **46**, 1956, p. 67.

142. Lucien Myers, *Selling Slate across the World*, Broughton Moor Green Slate Quarries Ltd., 1972.

143. Broughton Moor.

144. Report of Survey, Lancashire County Council, 26 April 1971.

145. Letter from Harold Ogden, Broughton Moor Green Slate Quarries Ltd., 11 September 1972.

146. Data supplied by Westmorland County Planning Officer, 30 April 1971.

147. M. S. Barratt, D. B. Courtier, D. O. Hughes and J. M. Robertson, 'Land use planning and mineral resources with special reference to aggregates for the construction industries', *Geological Aspects of Development and Planning in Northern England*, Yorkshire Geological Society 1970, pp. 52–3.

148. Data supplied from the trade.

149. Letter from Harold Ogden, Broughton Moor Green Slate Quarries Ltd., 11 September 1972.

150. Lucien Myers, op. cit.

151. ibid.

152. Data supplied by Broughton Moor Green Slate Quarries Ltd., 5 January 1972.

153. Quarry Managers' Journal, *Directory of Quarries and Pits*, 20th ed., 1969.

154. E. A. Edmonds, M. C. McKeown and M. Williams, *British Regional Geology, South West England*, 3rd ed., HMSO 1969, p. 32.

155. Richey and Anderson, op. cit., p. 9.

156. ibid., p. 8.

157. *Directory of Quarries and Pits*, op. cit.

158. C. T. Crompton, 'The treatment of waste slate heaps', *Town Planning Review* **37**, 1966–7, p. 291.

159. Letter from Mr J. A. Kent of the Old Delabole Slate Co., 23 December 1971.

160. Ministry of Works, op. cit., p. 20.

161. *Industrial Minerals* **40**, January 1971, p. 37.

162. Letter from Mr J. W. Roberts of Penrhyn Quarries Ltd., 13 September 1972.

163. See Department of Scientific and Industrial Research, Technical Note A 84, June 1960.

164. Crompton, op. cit.

165. ibid., p. 292.

166. Lake District National Park, 26 August 1971 and 29 August 1974.

167. Crompton, op. cit., p. 295.

168. ibid.

169. Letter from Mr J. W. Roberts of Penrhyn Quarries Ltd., 13 September 1972.

170. Letter from Caernarvonshire County Planning Officer, 15 April 1971.

171. Letter from Mr J. W. Roberts of Penrhyn Quarries Ltd., 13 September 1972.

172. Data supplied by Broughton Moor Green Slate Quarries Ltd., 5 January 1972.

4. LOCALIZED NON-METALLIFEROUS MINERALS

China clay

1. Letter from Mr N. R. Leonard of English China Clay to the author, 30 June 1970.

2. Institute of Geological Sciences, Mineral Resources Division, *Statistical Summary of the Mineral Industry, 1964–9*, HMSO 1970, p. 69. This is an unofficial statistic; the official statistics group together china clay and china stone.

3. China Clay Council, 'The china clay industry, proposed long-term development strategy', printed in the *Cornish Guardian*, 13 January 1972.

4. Letter from Miss Clare Bradley of English China Clays to the author, 5 April 1972.

5. T. G. Pleasants (Marketing Director ECLP), 'Marketing: realizing our resources', *Financial Times*, 18 April 1969.

6. H. M. Barton, *A History of the Cornish China Clay Industry*, Truro 1966, p. 84.

7. Kenneth Hudson, *The History of English China Clays*, David and Charles 1970, pp. 62–9.

8. Board of Trade, Working Party Reports, *China Clay*, HMSO 1948.

9. Pleasants, op. cit.

10. Board of Trade, Working Party Reports, *China Clay*, HMSO 1948, p. 22.

11. *Industrial Minerals*, **15**, December 1968, p. 17.

12. N. J. G. Pounds, 'The china clay industry of Southwest England', *Economic Geography* **28**, 1952, p. 23.

13. **15**, December 1958, reprint.

14. April 1965.

15. D. C. Corner and D. C. Stafford, *China Clay Sand*, Devon County Council 1971, p. 12.

16. T. G. Skelton (Works Director, ECLP), 'The Winning of China Clay', *Financial Times*, 18 April 1972.

17. ECLP Information Sheet; T. G. Skelton, op. cit.

18. *English China Clays Review of 50 Years*, Spring 1969, p. 35.

19. Corner and Stafford, op. cit., Table 2–1.

20. China Clay Council, op. cit., 'Short- and long-term development plans'.

21. *Pottery Gazette and Glass Trade Review*, vol. KC1, no. 1072, October 1966, p. 1047.

22. *Refractories Journal*, December 1971, p. 27.

23. S. F. Brailsford, 'Clay in the Paper and Board Industry', *Financial Times*, 18 April 1969.

24. *Guardian*, 3 December 1971.

25. Brailsford, op. cit.

26. English China Clays, Annual Report, 1970, p. 8.

27. Claim made at the Planning Inquiry, Salisbury, June 21–2, 1967.

28. China Clay Council, op. cit.

29. Corner and Stafford, op. cit., p. 6; chart 1–2.

30. Institute of Geological Sciences, Mineral Resources Division, op. cit., p. 70.

31. p. xii.

32. Corner and Stafford, op. cit., table 1–4.

33. ibid., p. 7.

34. Institute of Geological Sciences, Mineral Resources Division, op. cit., p. 70.

35. Corner and Stafford, op. cit., p. 5.

36. ibid., pp. 6–7.

37. op. cit., p. 1.

38. ibid., p. iv.

39. Pounds, op. cit., p. 25.

40. op. cit., p. iv.

41. *Industrial Minerals*, op. cit.

42. China Clay Association, Report on the Disposal of Micaceous Residues, vol. I, September 1969, p. 18.

43. Corner and Stafford, op. cit., p. 15.

44. ibid., p. 26.

45. ibid., p. 26.

46. ibid., p. 16.

47. op. cit., pp. i and iv.

48. Daphne du Maurier, *Vanishing Cornwall*, Penguin 1972, p. 152.

49. John Bart, *Derelict Britain*, Penguin 1969, p. 187.

50. China Clay Council, op. cit., p. iv.

51. Ministry of Housing and Local Government, China Clay Standing Conference, Report of the Conference, October 1955.

52. China Clay Association, op. cit., vol. I, p. 3.

53. China Clay Association, op. cit., vols. I and II.

54. China Clay Council, Press Release, 20 May 1971.

55. China Clay Council, op. cit., 'Short- and long-term development plans', p. iv.

56. In February 1968 a regular service of clay freight trains transporting the material in slurry form was started from Cornwall to Bowaters paper mill at Sittingbourne in Kent.

57. e.g. *New Statesman*, 30 January 1970.

58. Corner and Stafford, op. cit., Table 2–1.

59. ibid., p. 80.

60. ibid., p. 14.

61. ibid., p. 26.

62. ibid., p. 18.

63. The Report was at pains to point out that the concept of shortage only had relevance at a given price, p. 34.

64. ibid., p. 81.

65. ibid., p. 82.

China stone

66. Data supplied by ECLP, 17 January 1972.

67. Henry Dewey, *British Regional Geology, South West England*, HMSO 1948, 2nd ed., p. 37.

68. *Industrial Minerals* **12**, September 1968, p. 11.

69. ibid.

70. Data supplied by ECLP, 17 January 1972.

71. ibid.

72. Kenneth Hudson, *The History of English China Clays*, David and Charles 1970, p. 90.

73. Quoted ibid., p. 91.

74. Data supplied by ECLP, 17 January 1972.

75. Letters from Miss Clare Bradley of ECLP, 17 January 1972.

76. *Industrial Minerals*, op. cit., p. 11.

77. ibid.

78. Letter from Miss Clare Bradley of ECLP, 17 January 1972.

79. Letter from Miss Clare Bradley of ECLP, 5 April 1972.

80. Data supplied by the Highlands and Islands Development Board, 20 August 1974.

81. *Industrial Minerals* **42**, March 1971, p. 43.

82. *Refractories Journal*, December 1971, p. 36.

83. ibid.

Ball clay

84. A. Scott, 'Ball clays', *Memoirs of the Geological Survey*, vol. xxxi, HMSO 1929.

85. D. A. Holdridge, 'Ball clays and their properties', *Transactions of the British Ceramic Society*, **55**, 1956, p. 369.

86. Report of the Inquiry on the Ball Clay Industry, Board of Trade, HMSO 1946, pamphlet number 7032, p. 4.

87. Letter from Mr C. D. Pike of Watts Blake Bearne and Company to the author, 29 December 1971.

88. Daniel Lysons, *Magna Britannia*, vol. VI, ccxci, 1882.

89. ibid., p. 249.

90. Report of the Inquiry on the Ball Clay Industry, op. cit., p. 10.

91. 'Buoyant market for ball clays', *Industrial Minerals* **17** (2), February 1969, p. 10.

92. ibid.

93. Kenneth Hudson, *The History of English China Clays*, David and Charles 1970, p. 121.

94. Letter from Mr N. R. Leonard of English China Clays Ltd. to the author, 31 March 1971.

95. *Industrial Minerals*, op. cit., p. 11.

96. ibid.

97. ibid., p. 12.

98. Letter of Mr W. J. B. Watts of Watts Blake Bearne and Company to the author, 8 April 1970.

99. 'Ball clay production in south Devon', *Quarry Managers' Journal*, August 1964.

100. Letter of Mr W. J. B. Watts, 8 April 1970.

101. *Quarry Managers' Journal*, op. cit.

102. J. D. Cooper, 'Ball clays', *Financial Times*, 18 April 1969.

103. Figures supplied by Watts Blake Bearne and Company, April 1970.

104. ibid.

105. *Industrial Minerals*, op. cit., p. 9.

106. Letter of Mr N. R. Leonard, 31 March 1971.

107. *Pottery Gazette and Glass Trade Review*, June 1969.

108. Letter of Mr C. D. Pike, 29 December 1971.

109. English China Clays Ltd., Chairman's Report for the year ending 30 September 1969.

110. Letter of Mr N. R. Leonard, 31 March 1971.

111. Letter from the Dorset Planning Officer to the author, 18 May 1971.

112. Devon County Council, *Man and the Devon Environment*, 1970, p. 30.

113. Letter of Mr C. D. Pike of Watts Blake Bearne and Company to the author, 2 November 1971.

Fuller's earth

114. Interview, Bedfordshire County Planning Office, 17 September 1971.

115. First Annual Report of the Secretary for Mines, HMSO 1922, Table 1.

116. *Industrial Minerals* **24**, September 1969, p. 16.

117. ibid.

118. ibid.

119. ibid., p. 17.

120. *Industrial Minerals* **28**, January 1970, p. 37.

121. Institute of Geological Sciences, Mineral Resources Division, *Statistical Summary of the Mineral Industry, World Production, Exports and Imports, 1964–9*, HMSO 1970, p. 48.

122. Letter from Mr R. M. Raikes of Laporte Industries Ltd. to the author, 10 January 1972.

123. *Industrial Minerals* **24**, September 1969, p. 16.

124. *Industrial Minerals* **28**, January 1970, p. 37.

125. *Industrial Minerals* **42**, March 1971, p. 43; Interview, Bedfordshire County Planning Office, 17 September 1971.

126. *Industrial Minerals*, **24**, September 1969, p. 15.

127. Letter from Mr R. M. Raikes, 10 January 1972.

128. Interview, Bedfordshire County Council, 17 September 1971.

129. *Industrial Minerals* **24**, September 1969, p. 16.

130. Report and Analysis of the First Review of the Surrey County Development Plan, 1965, p. 81. For probable extent of reserves, see county map appended to this report.

131. First Review of Somerset County Development Plan, 1964, p. 117.

132. *Industrial Minerals* **24**, September 1969, p. 19.

133. Institute of Geological Sciences, Natural Environment Research Council, Report on Fuller's Earth in the Fernham Area, 1970.

134. Interview, Berkshire County Planning Office, 15 September 1971.

Salt

135. Cheshire County Council, 'The Cheshire Salt Field and its Planning Problems' typescript, 1969, p. 2.

136. W. B. Evans, A. A. Wilson, B. J. Taylor and D. Price, 'Geology of the country around Macclesfield, Congleton, Crewe and Middlewich, *Memoirs of the Geological Survey*, HMSO 1968, pp. 140–1.

137. Since salt does not outcrop in the normal sense, the mineral 'outcrop' has conventionally been shown in those areas where undissolved rock salt abuts against overlying collapsed strata. See B. J. Taylor, P. H. Price and F. M. Trotter, 'Geology of the country around Stockport and Knutsford', *Memoirs of the Geological Survey*, HMSO 1963, pp. 78–9.

138. E. G. Poole and A. J. Whiteman, 'Geology of the country around Nantwich and Whitchurch', *Memoirs of the Geological Survey*, HMSO 1966, p. 13.

139. ibid., pp. 101–2.

140. ibid., p. 102.

141. ibid.

142. ibid.

143. Evans, op. cit., p. 262.

144. Cheshire County Council, op. cit., p. 2.

145. Pennycuyck V. C., Lotus v. British Soda, *Solicitors Journal,* 1970, p. 885.

146. Letter from Staffordshire County Planning Officer to the author, 13 January 1972.

147. Interview, Worcestershire County Planning Office, July 1971.

148. Cheshire County Council, op. cit., p. 2.

149. Data supplied by Cheshire County Council, 20 August 1974.

150. Data supplied by the Department of the Environment, 29 November 1971.

151. ibid.

152. Cheshire County Council, op. cit., p. 3.

153. ibid., p. 11.

154. ibid., p. 3.

155. ibid., p. 11.

156. ibid., p. 11.

157. Data supplied by the Department of the Environment, 29 November 1971.

158. J. E. Metcalfe, *British Mining Fields*, Institution of Mining and Metallurgy 1969, p. 48.

159. *Industrial Minerals* **41**, February 1971, p. 33.

160. ibid.

161. Letter from Mr K. A. Whittaker of Cheshire County Planning Office to the author, 13 March 1972.

162. Cheshire County Council, op. cit., p. 4.

163. ibid., p. 17.

164. Cheshire County Council, op. cit., p. 6.

165. Cheshire County Council, op. cit., p. 13.

166. Private information, Mr Harris, Lancashire County Planning Office, January 1972.

167. Letter from Mr K. A. Whittaker of Cheshire County Planning Office, 13 March 1972.

168. Letter from Staffordshire County Planning Office, 13 January 1972.

169. Letter from Mr K. A. Whittaker of Cheshire County Planning Office, 13 March 1972.

170. Cheshire County Council, op. cit., p. 16.

171. ibid.

Gypsum and anhydrite

172. *Industrial Minerals* **42**, March 1971, p. 43.

173. *Annual Bulletin of Construction Statistics*, **12**, 1970, Department of the Environment, HMSO, Tables 51 and 52.

174. Data supplied by British Gypsum Ltd., 14 September 1971.

175. *Annual Abstract of Statistics*, **108**, 1971, Table 202.

176. 'Special reports on the mineral resources of Great Britain, iii, gypsum and anhydrite', *Memoirs of the Geological Survey*, HMSO 1918, 2nd ed., preface.

177. ibid.

178. K. C. Edwards, 'Extraction industry', in *Nottingham and Its Region*, British Association for the Advancement of Science, 1966, p. 285.

179. Letter from Mr D. Skilton of British Gypsum Ltd. to the author, 12 March 1971.

180. East Midlands Economic Planning Council, *The East Midlands Study*, HMSO 1966, p. 44.

181. H. P. Moreland and J. P. Graham, 'Gypsum mining in Nottingham', *The Chartered Surveyor* **101**, 5, 1968, p. 238.

182. Report of Survey, Nottingham County Planning Department, 7 May 1971.

183. Moreland and Graham, op. cit., p. 238.

184. Data supplied by British Gypsum Ltd., 14 September 1971.

185. J. E. Metcalfe, *British Mining Fields*, Institution of Mining and Metallurgy, 1969, p. 77.

186. Data supplied by British Gypsum Ltd., 14 September 1971.

187. ibid.

188. Report of Survey, Cumberland County Planning Department, 3 May 1971.

189. Data supplied by British Gypsum Ltd., 14 September 1971.

190. ibid.

191. ibid.

192. Metcalfe, op. cit., p. 75.

193. *Industrial Minerals* **35**, August 1970, p. 34.

194. Metcalfe, op. cit., p. 54.

195. Letter of Mr D. Skilton of British Gypsum Ltd., 12 March 1971.

196. Moreland and Graham, op. cit., p. 238.

197. P. B. Ellis and V. Turnock, 'Gypsum Mining in the High Weald', *Geography* **49**, 1964, op. 127.

198. ibid.

199. Data supplied by British Gypsum Ltd., 14 September 1971.

200. ibid.

201. Ellis and Turnock, op. cit., p. 128.

Celestite

202. Data supplied by Mr H. C. Brooksbank of Rogers and Cooke (Salisbury) Ltd., 13 January 1972.

203. ibid.
204. First Annual Report of the Secretary for Mines, HMSO 1922, Table 1.
205. W. R. Jones, *Minerals in Industry*, 4th ed., Penguin 1963, p. 239.
206. Data supplied by Mr H. C. Brooksbank, 13 January 1972.
207. *Industrial Minerals* **42**, March 1971, p. 45.
208. Institute of Geological Sciences, Mineral Resources Division, *Statistical Summary of the Mineral Industry, 1964–9*, HMSO 1970, p. 343.
209. Data supplied by Mr H. C. Brooksbank, 13 January 1972.
210. *Industrial Minerals* **26**, November 1969, p. 37.
211. ibid.
212. ibid.

Fluorspar

213. *Industrial Minerals* **33**, June 1970, p. 9.
214. ibid.
215. ibid.
216. *Industrial Minerals* **34**, July 1970, p. 11.
217. ibid.
218. ibid.
219. ibid.
220. ibid.
221. *Mining Annual Review*, June 1970, p. 105.
222. P. R. Cote, *Fluorspar*, Mineral Resources Branch of the Canadian Department of Energy, Mines and Resources, *Mineral Review* Reprint no. 20, 1969.
223. B. L. Hodge, 'The UK fluorspar industry and its basis', *Industrial Minerals* **31**, April 1971.
224. *The Times*, 30 April 1971.
225. K. C. Dunham, *Fluorspar*, Memoirs of the Geological Survey, Special Reports on the Mineral Resources of Great Britain, vol. IV, 4th ed., HMSO 1952, p. 12.
226. Hodge, op. cit., p. 26.
227. ibid.
228. ibid., p. 35.
229. ibid.
230. *Mining Magazine* **113** (4), October 1965, p. 277.
231. First Annual Report of the Secretary for Mines for the Year Ending 31 December 1921, HMSO 1922, table 1, p. 79.
232. Dunham, op. cit., p. 4.
233. Mineral Resources Consultative Committee, Mineral Dossier no. 1, *Fluorspar*, HMSO 1971. Deduced from table 2, p. 20.
234. *Mining Annual Review*, June 1970, p. 104.
235. Dunham, op. cit., p. 80.
236. Hodge, op. cit., p. 29.
237. ibid.
238. Interview, Derbyshire County Planning Office, 28 July 1971.
239. Letter of Dr J. V. Bramley of Laporte Industries Ltd. to the author, 10 November 1971.
240. Hodge, op. cit., p. 29.
241. *Industrial Minerals* **33**, June 1970, p. 15.
242. *Industrial Minerals* **30**, February 1970, p. 25.

243. ibid.

244. *The Mining Magazine* **122** (2), February 1970, p. 133.

245. Hodge, op. cit., p. 29.

246. Letter from the Director, Peak Park Planning Board to the author, 11 June 1971.

247. *Industrial Minerals* **33**, June 1970, p. 15.

248. *The Times,* 16 February 1971.

249. Letter from Mr C. Dawson of the British Steel Corporation to the author, 25 March 1971.

250. Dunham, op. cit., p. 51.

251. Memoirs of the Geological Survey, Geological Survey of Great Britain, *Geology of the Northern Pennine Orefield,* vol. i, HMSO 1948, p. 226.

252. Dunham, op. cit., p. 30.

253. Letter from Mr C. Dawson, 25 March 1971.

254. Dunham, op. cit., p. 30.

255. Letter from Mr C. Dawson, 25 March 1971.

256. Dunham, op. cit., p. 63.

257. *The Times,* 16 February 1971.

258. ibid.

259. Department of Trade and Industry, Mines Inspectorate Division, List of Miscellaneous Mines in Britain as at 30 September 1970, typescript.

260. Hodge, op. cit., p. 34.

261. J. T. Coppock, 'The recreational use of land and water in rural Britain', *Tijdschrift voor Economische en Sociale Geografie,* May/June 1966, p. 85.

262. Letter from the Director, Peak Park Planning Board, 11 June 1971.

263. The Peak District National Park, 18th Annual Report of the Planning Board, April 1969–March 1970, para. 127.

264. ibid.

265. ibid.

266. ibid., para. 122.

267. Letter from Dr J. V. Bramley, 10 November 1971.

268. Letter from the Director, Peak Park Planning Board, 11 June 1971.

269. ibid.

270. Letter from Dr J. V. Bramley, 10 November 1971.

271. *The Observer,* 28 March 1971.

272. ibid.

273. Hodge, op. cit., p. 35.

274. Interview, Derbyshire County Planning Office, 28 July 1971.

275. e.g. by the Reclamation Office of Durham County Planning Departmentin an address to the British Association, Durham, September 1969. (Private view.)

276. Mineral Resources Consultative Committee, op. cit., p. 11.

277. ibid.

Barium minerals

278. W. R. Jones, *Minerals in Industry,* Harmondsworth 1963, 4th ed., pp. 54–5.

279. Memoirs of the Geological Survey, *Geology of the Northern Pennine Orefield,* vol. i, 1948, p. 95.

280. Memoirs of the Geological Survey, Special Reports on the Mineral Resources of Great Britain, *Barytes and Witherite,* 2nd ed., 1916, p. 2.

281. First Annual Report of the Secretary for Mines for the Year Ending 31 December 1921, HMSO 1922, p. 79, Table 1.

282. *Geology of the Northern Pennine Orefield*, op. cit., p. 343.

283. *Industrial Minerals* **22**, July 1969, p. 29.

284. Ministry of Technology, *Digest of Energy Statistics*, HMSO 1968–9, and 1969–70.

285. Letter from Mr E. J. Deas, last Managing Director of Settlingstones Mine, to the author, 27th April, 1971.

286. *Industrial Minerals*, op. cit., p. 29.

287. Letter from Mr E. J. Deas, 27 April 1971.

288. ibid.

289. *Mining Annual Review*, June 1970, p. 108.

290. ibid.; *Industrial Minerals* **32**, May 1970, p. 11.

291. *Industrial Minerals* **32**, May 1970, p. 15.

292. ibid.

293. Data supplied by Athole G. Allen Ltd., 19 April 1971.

294. ibid.

295. ibid.

296. ibid.

297. ibid.

298. ibid.

299. ibid.

300. ibid.

301. ibid.

302. *Geology of the Northern Pennine Orefield*, op. cit., p. 316.

303. *Mining Annual Review*, June 1970, p. 449.

304. Special Reports on the Mineral Resources of Great Britain, op. cit., p. 1.

305. *Industrial Minerals* **32**, May 1970, p. 15.

306. Letter from Mr D. H. Nicholson of Laporte Industries Ltd., 2 July 1971.

307. Interview, North Riding County Planning Office, July 1971.

Refractory materials

308. T. M. Thomas, *The Mineral Wealth of Wales and its Exploitation*, Oliver and Boyd, 1961, p. 133.

309. J. Laming, 'Raw materials and refractories performance', *Refractories Journal*, June 1971, p. 7.

310. ibid., p. 8.

311. ibid., p. 7. Firebricks withstand up to 1350–1600° C under load depending on alumina content.

312. *Refractories Journal*, March 1970, p. 7.

313. *Industrial Minerals* **71**, October, 1972.

314. *Refractories Journal*, February 1971, p. 7.

315. Laming, op. cit., p. 7.

316. G. R. Rigby, 'Future trends in refractory materials for steel production', *Refractories Journal*, May 1971, p. 27.

317. J. Gittins, 'Basic Oxygen Steelmaking Refractories', *Refractories Journal*, December 1970, p. 6.

318. H. M. Richardson, 'Production and Use of Refractories in Britain', *Journal of the British Ceramic Society* **7**, 22, 1970.

494

319. *Refractories Journal*, November 1971, p. 7.
320. Letters from Mr E. Jones of Steetley Ltd., 26 July 1972 and 16 August 1972.
321. British Association for the Advancement of Science, *Nottingham and its Region*, K. C. Edwards, 'Extractive Industry', p. 295.
322. Letter from Mr E. Jones, 16 August 1972.
323. D. S. Buist, 'Industrial uses of the magnesian limestone', *Refractories Journal*, December 1970, p. 20.
324. Data supplied by the Iron and Steel Statistics Bureau, 5 January 1972.
325. Buist, op. cit., p. 20.
326. L. Dudley Stamp and Stanley H. Beaver, *The British Isles*, 6th ed., Longmans 1971, p. 376.
327. Letter from Mr C. S. Hedley of Steetley (Mfg.) Ltd., 13 November 1972.
328. *The Steetley Group*, Steetley Company Ltd., 1969, p. 21.
329. Buist, op. cit., p. 21.
330. W. R. Jones, *Minerals in Industry*, 4th ed., Penguin 1963, p. 155.
331. Buist, op. cit., p. 21.
332. *The Steetley Group*, op. cit., p. 21.
333. Buist, op. cit., p. 21.
334. ibid.
335. ibid.
336. Buist, op. cit., p. 21.
337. Letter from Mr J. D'A. Tremlett of Man–Abell Holdings Ltd., 23 March 1972.
338. Jones, op. cit., p. 21.
339. Calculated from the *Annual Abstract of Statistics*, **108**, 1971, Table 200 and *Statistical Survey of the Mineral Industry*, 1964–9, p. 190.
340. Durham County Council, Planning Department, R 12464.
341. Memoirs of the Geological Survey, Special Reports on the Mineral Resources of Great Britain, vol. vi, *Refractory Materials*, 2nd ed., 1920.
342. W. Davies, 'British Resources of Ganister and Silica Rock', *Transactions of the British Ceramic Society* **47**, 1948, p. 55.
343. ibid.
344. ibid., p. 58.
345. Memoirs of the Geological Survey, op. cit., p. 3.
346. Davies, op. cit., p. 53.
347. Thomas, op. cit., p. 150.
348. National Federation of Clay Industries Annual Report, 1969–70, published in *Refractories Journal*, September 1970, p. 30.
349. Davies, op. cit., p. 150.
350. Quarry Managers' Journal, *Directory of Pits and Quarries*, 20th ed., 1969.
351. Davies, op. cit., p. 74.
352. Thomas, op. cit., p. 149.
353. *Directory of Pits and Quarries*, op. cit.
354. ibid.
355. Davies, op. cit., p. 72.
356. *Directory of Pits and Quarries*, op. cit., pp. 464–5.
357. ibid.
358. Edwards, op. cit., p. 295.
359. Letter from the Director of the Peak Park Planning Board, 11 June 1971.
360. Laming, op. cit., p. 7.
361. Thomas, op. cit., p. 157.

495

362. *Annual Abstract of Statistics*, **108**, 1971, Table 200.

363. Letter from Mr B. E. Poole of Johnson Poole and Bloomer, 6 March 1972.

364. Laming, op. cit., p. 7.

365. Report of H.M. Chief Inspector of Mines and Quarries for 1968, HMSO 1969, p. 40.

366. Letter from Mr B. E. Poole, 6 March 1972.

367. Report of H.M. Inspector of Mines and Quarries for 1968, HMSO 1969, p. 40.

368. *Colliery Guardian Guide to the Coalfields*, 1970.

369. Letter from Mr B. E. Poole, 6 March 1972.

370. Letter from the Director, National Federation of Clay Industries, 28 February 1972.

371. Letter from Mr B. E. Poole, 6 March 1972.

372. Interview with Mr Lamb, Secretary to the Opencast Executive, National Coal Board, 21 June 1972.

373. ibid.

374. ibid.

375. Letter from the County Planning Officer to the author, 15 March 1972, indicates that several fireclay operators in Shropshire hold these views: this view is also endorsed, in broadly similar terms, by Mr B. E. Poole, in a letter to the author, 6 March 1972.

376. Interview with Mr Lamb, 21 June 1972.

377. Data supplied by the Department of the Environment, 29 November 1971.

378. Memoirs of the Geological Survey, Special Reports on the Mineral Resources of Great Britain, vol. xlv, *Refractory Materials: Fireclays*, 1920, p. 2.

379. ibid., pp. 148–9.

380. *Colliery Guardian Guide to the Coalfields*, 1970.

381. Data obtained from map showing the main clay/coal workings in the Opencast Executive's Midland Region, supplied by Mr G. Jago, 13 June 1972.

382. Calculated from the *Digest of Welsh Statistics*, 1960 and 1970, and the *Annual Abstract of Statistics*, 1960 and 1970.

383. Thomas, op. cit., p. 155.

384. ibid.

385. ibid.

386. As indicated by the *Colliery Guardian Guide to the Coalfields* (of closure of mines) and confirmed in letter from the Deputy County Planning Officer for Stirling, 23 April 1971.

387. *Colliery Guardian Guide to the Coalfields*, 1960, pp. 93–100.

388. ibid., 1970, pp. 42–5.

389. Memoirs of the Geological Survey, *Fireclays*, op. cit., pp. 215–16.

390. ibid., p. 230.

391. ibid.

392. Data supplied by the Ayrshire County Planning Officer, 15 April 1971.

393. Letter from Stirlingshire Deputy County Planning Officer, 23 April 1971.

394. Letter from Salop County Planning Officer, 15 March 1972.

395. ibid.

396. Letter from the Director, Peak Park Planning Board, 11 June 1971.

397. ibid.

398. Letter from Salop County Planning Officer, 15 March 1972.

399. ibid.

Silica and moulding sand

400. Letter from Mr A. P. Lovat of British Industrial Sand Ltd., 16 December 1971.

401. *Industrial Minerals* **35**, August 1970, p. 13.

402. Letter from Mr A. P. Lovat of British Industrial Sand Ltd., 24 August 1971.

403. *Industrial Minerals*, op. cit., p. 14.

404. ibid., p. 16.

405. Glass Manufacturers' Federation, Press Release, reference no. 375, 30 June 1971.

406. Letter from Mr A. P. Lovat, 16 December 1971.

407. Letter from Mr A. P. Lovat, 11 May 1972.

408. Letter from Mr A. P. Lovat, 16 December 1971.

409. *Industrial Minerals*, op. cit., p. 9.

410. ibid., p. 12.

411. ibid.

412. Data supplied by British Industrial Sand Ltd., 11 May 1972.

413. ibid.

414. *Industrial Minerals*, op. cit., p. 12.

415. Glass Manufacturers' Federation, List of Members, reference 45/437.

416. *Refractories Journal*, March 1970, p. 30.

417. L. Dudley Stamp and Stanley H. Beaver, *The British Isles*, 6th ed., Longmans 1971, p. 590.

418. Letter from Mr A. P. Lovat, 24 August 1971.

419. ibid.

420. Data supplied by British Industrial Sand Ltd., 11 May 1972.

421. ibid.

422. K. C. Edwards, *Extractive Industry in Nottingham and its Region*, British Association for the Advancement of Science 1966, p. 294.

423. Mackay and Schellmann, Report to Cheshire County Council, April 1970.

424. Letter from Mr A. P. Lovat, 11 May 1972.

425. Letter from Mr A. P. Lovat, 24 August 1971.

426. Letter to the author, 5 May 1971. The other district is the gravel field of north-west Surrey.

427. Letter from Cheshire County Planning Director, 30 April 1971.

428. ibid.

429. Report and Analysis of Survey of the First Review of the County Development Plan, 1965, p. 79.

430. Mackay and Schellmann, op. cit.

431. Sand Working in Cheshire, Planning Policy Guide, John Collins, County Planning Director, April 1970.

432. ibid.

433. Letter from Mr A. P. Lovat of British Industrial Sand Ltd., 24 August 1971.

Diatomite

434. Memoirs of the Geological Survey, Special Reports on the Mineral Resources of Great Britain, vol. v, *Diatomite*, HMSO 1917, p. 38.

435. W. R. Jones, *Minerals in Industry*, 4th ed., Penguin 1963, p. 95.

436. Memoirs of the Geological Survey, op. cit., p. 38.

437. *Industrial Minerals*, **18**, March 1969, p. 9.

438. ibid.

439. Letter from Mr P. S. Williams of Cape Insulation Ltd. to the author, 17 August 1972.

440. Letter from Westmorland County Planning Officer to the author, 30 April 1971, and from the Clerk to the Planning Board, 26 August 1971.

441. Letter from Mr P. S. Williams of Cape Insulations Ltd., 17 August 1971.

442. Institute of Geological Sciences, *Diatomaceous Deposits in Snowdonia*, report no. 72/5, 1972.

443. Memoirs of the Geological Survey, op. cit., p. 38.

444. Letter from Mr D. R. Fasham of the Highlands and Islands Development Board, 24 August 1971 and 20 August 1974.

445. *Transactions of the Royal Society of Edinburgh* xxxiii, 1887, p. 419.

446. Letter from Ross and Cromarty County Planning Officer, 30 April 1971.

447. Letter from Mr D. R. Fasham of the Highlands and Islands Development Board, 24 August 1971.

5. METALLIFEROUS MINERALS

1. Memoirs of the Geological Survey, Special Report on the Mineral Resources of Great Britain, vol. viii, *Haemetites of West Cumberland, Lancashire and the Lake District*, 2nd ed., 1924.

2. Memoirs of the Geological Survey, Special Reports on the Mineral Resources of Great Britain, vol. x, *The Haemetites of the Forest of Dean and South Wales*, 1919.

3. United Nations Department of Economic and Social Affairs, *Survey of World Iron Ore Resources*, New York 1970, p. 275.

4. Robert Hunt, *British Mining, A Treatise on the History, Discovery, Practical Development and Future Prospects of Metalliferous Mines in the UK*, 1887, p. 846.

5. J. E. Metcalfe, *British Mining Fields*, Institution of Mining and Metallurgy 1969, p. 21.

6. Robert Rice, 'The problems of reviving non-ferrous metal mining in Britain', *Chartered Surveyor*, January 1970, p. 328.

7. L. Dudley Stamp and Stanley H. Beaver, *The British Isles*, 6th ed., Longmans 1971, p. 468.

8. Cornish Mining Development Association, *Metal Mining in the West of England*, typescript, 1969.

9. Hunt op. cit. p. 838.

10. Stamp and Beaver, op. cit., p. 473.

11. Report of the Commission on Mining and the Environment (the Zuckermann Commission), September 1972, p. 29 and appendix 5.

12. Calculated from Department of Trade and Industry, *Digest of Energy Statistics*, HMSO 1971, table 125, p. 185.

13. W. R. Jones, 'The public ownership of mineral rights in Great Britain' in *The Future of Non-Ferrous Mining in Great Britain and Ireland*, Institution of Mining and Metallurgy 1959, p. 495.

14. *The Times*, 3 January 1973.

15. ibid.

16. W. W. Varvill, 'The future of lead–zinc and fluorspar mining in Derbyshire' in *The Future of Non-Ferrous Mining in Great Britain and Ireland*, op. cit., p. 177.

17. Letter from Mr D. H. Nicholson of Laporte Industries Ltd., 2 July 1971.

18. Letter from Mr A. W. Boustred of the Holywell–Halkyn Mining and Tunnel Co. Ltd., 14 June 1971.

19. Department of Trade and Industry, op. cit., p. 185.

20. Report of the Commission on Mining and the Environment, op. cit., p. 75.

21. Rice, op. cit., p. 328.

22. Report of the Commission on Mining and the Environment, op. cit., p. 65.

23. ibid., p. 66.

24. ibid.

25. ibid., p. 68.

26. ibid., p. 69.

27. A. G. Charles, 'Metal prices' in *The Future of Non-Ferrous Mining in Great Britain and Ireland*, op. cit., p. 543.

28. Rice, op. cit., p. 328.

29. Anton Gray, 'The fourth Sir Julius Wernher memorial lecture' in *The Future of Non-Ferrous Mining in Great Britain and Ireland*, op. cit., p. xvii.

30. K. C. Dunham in *The Future of Non-Ferrous Mining in Great Britain and Ireland*, op. cit., p. 204.

31. R. M. Preston, 'Official opening to the symposium' in *The Future of Non-Ferrous Mining in Great Britain and Ireland*, op. cit., p. 2.

32. J. F. McDivitt, *The Status of Mineral Exploitation in Europe*, OEED, 1964, p. 60.

33. Ministry of Munitions of War, Report of the Controller of the Department for the Development of Mineral Resources in the UK, HMSO 1918, Cd. 9184.

Mines Department, Report by the Advisory Committee for the Metalliferous Mining and Quarrying Industry on the Possibilities of Developing or of Reviving the Working of Metalliferous and Associated Deposits in Great Britain, HMSO 1932.

Ministry of Fuel and Power, Report of the Mineral Development Committee, HMSO 1949, Cmd. 7732.

34. *Mining Journal* **275** (7052), 16 October 1970, p. 336.

35. Report of the Commission on Mining and the Environment, op. cit., pp. 24–5.

36. ibid., p. 25.

Non-ferrous metals: tin

37. Cornish Mining Development Association Annual Report, 1972–3, p. 3.

38. *Metal Mining in the West of England*, Cornish Mining Development Association, 1972.

39. R. Eglin, 'Mr Shore, the miners' friend', *Observer*, 29 June 1969.

40. *The Times*, 23 March 1962.

41. *Metal Mining in the West of England*, op. cit.

42. J. H. Trounson, 'Practical considerations in the development of old Cornish mines' in *The Future of Non-Ferrous Mining in Great Britain and Ireland*, 1959, pp. 371–82.

43. H. G. Dines, *The Metalliferous Mining Region of South-West England*, 1956, p. 8.

44. H. Dewey, *British Regional Geology*, South-West England, DSIR, HMSO, 2nd ed. 1961, pp. 49–50.

45. *Mining Magazine* **108**, 1963, p. 39.

46. P. Lamartine Yates, J. Dewhurst and J. Coppock, *Europe's Needs and Resources*, 1961, p. 631.

47. Cornish Mining Development Association op. cit. p. 3.

48. ibid. p. 6.

49. Cornish Chamber of Mines Report, 1966, p. 21.

50. From the company record of the Grenville United Mines.

51. R. H. Thomas, 'Observations on the Great Flat Lode' in *Royal Cornwall Polytechnic Society 44th Report*, 1886, p. 184.

52. Cornish Chamber of Mines Report, 1966, p. 21.

53. ibid., p. 21.

54. D. B. Barton, *The Mines of West Cornwall*, Truro, 1963, p. 25.

55. Cornish Mining Development Association Annual Reports, 1966–7, p. 3, and 1967–8, p. 3.

56. ibid., 1968–9, p. 4.

57. Barton, op. cit., pp. 27–8.

58. Eglin, op. cit.

59. Cornish Chamber of Mines Reports 1967, p. 11, and 1968, p. 13.

60. Cornish Mining Development Association Annual Report, 1969–70.

61. Cornish Chamber of Mines Report, 1971, p. 15.

62. Barton, op. cit., pp. 38–9.

63. Cornish Chamber of Mines Reports, 1966, p. 17, and 1967, p. 17.

64. Cornish Mining Development Association Annual Report, 1968–9, p. 1.

65. Barton, op. cit., p. 39.

1970–1, p. 8.

66. D. B. Barton, *The Mines and Mineral Railways of East Cornwall and West Devon*, Truro, 1966, pp. 51–3.

67. J. H. Trounson in report to the author, 29 August 1974.

68. Cornish Mining Development Association Annual Report, 1958–9, p. 1.

69. Eglin, op. cit.

70. Cornish Chamber of Mines Report, 1966, p. 13.

71. ibid., 1968, p. 14.

72. Cornish Mining Development Association Annual Report, 1972–3, p. 10.

73. ibid., 1972–3, p. 10.

74. ibid., 1972–3, p. 10.

75. ibid., 1968–9, p. 4.

76. Cornish Chamber of Mines Reports, 1966, p. 19, 1967, p. 19, and 1968, p. 19. Cornish Mining Development Association Annual Report, 1969–70.

77. Based on report and statement of the company for the year ending 31 December 1964.

78. Cornish Chamber of Mines Report, 1968, p. 19.

79. *The Times*, 9 May 1969.

80. Cornish Chamber of Mines Report, 1968, p. 19. Cornish Mining Development Association Annual Report, 1969–70 and 1970–1, p. 7.

81. Cornish Mining Development Association Annual Report, 1972–3, p. 8.

82. ibid. 1966, p. 15, and 1967, p. 15, 1969–70 and 1970–1, p. 6, 1972–3, p. 7.

83. From the company records of the Levant mine.

84. R. H. Garnett, 'Divers investigate the Levant mine', *Mining Magazine* **104**, 1961, pp. 73–5.

85. *The Times*, 7 June 1965.

86. Cornish Chamber of Mines Reports, 1967, p. 15, and 1968, p. 16.

87. Eglin, op. cit.

88. Cornish Mining Development Association Annual Report, 1970–1, pp. 6–7, 1972–3, p. 5.

89. Cornish Chamber of Mines Report, 1968, p. 16.

90. Eglin, op. cit.

91. Cornish Mining Development Association Annual Report, 1972–3, p. 7.

92. ibid., 1966–7, p. 4.

93. ibid., 1967–8, p. 3.

94. ibid., 1965–6, p. 5.

95. ibid., 1970–1, p. 7.

96. Cornish Mining Development Association Annual Report, 1967–8, p. 3.

97. From the company records of Bassett mine.

98. Cornish Mining Development Association Annual Report, 1969–70.

99. Cornish Chamber of Mines Report, 1968, p. 18.

100. Cornish Mining Development Association Annual Reports, 1969–70, and 1970–1, p. 7.

101. ibid., 1965–6, p. 4, and 1964–5, p. 1.

102. Cornish Chamber of Mines Report, 1966, p. 21.

103. Cornish Mining Development Association Annual Report, 1967–8, p. 3.

104. Part of the English China Clays combine based at St Austell in Cornwall.

105. Cornish Mining Development Association Annual Report, 1967–8, p. 4.

106. ibid., 1967–8, p. 3.

107. ibid., 1964–5, p. 1.

108. Barton, op. cit., pp. 10–11.

109. Cornish Mining Development Association Annual Report, 1966–7, pp. 2–3.

110. B. Ritchie, 'Cornwall's old industry is teething again', *The Times*, 5 June 1967.

111. The Mineral Development Acts 1950–60 have permitted not only the application of modern prospecting techniques but in addition they have facilitated the acquisition of land where the mineral developer cannot locate the owner of the minerals or where agreement cannot be achieved with the private mineral owner.

112. *Financial Times*, 17 October 1966.

113. Barton, op. cit., p. 22.

114. From the company records of Great Wheal Vor United Mine.

115. Cornwall County Council Development Plan Survey, 1952, part 1, and appendix 16, pp. 271–5.

116. Cornish Mining Development Association Annual Report, 1963–4, pp. 1–2.

117. Details of the conclusion of this venture were given by the Chairman of the Cornish Mining Development Corporation, J. H. Trounson, in a letter to the author, 22 July 1969.

118. Barton, op. cit., p. 11.

119. *The Times*, 19 January 1961.

120. *The Times*, 11 May 1961.

121. *Mining Magazine*, **106**, 1962, p. 3.

122. J. H. Trounson, in a letter to the author, 22 July 1969.

123. From the company records of the Carnelloe Mine.

124. H. W. J., Hoeck, 'Strategic planning for the coast—the example of Cornwall', *Journal of Town Planning Institute*, 1968, p. 395.

125. ibid., p. 396.

126. Cornish Mining Development Association Annual Report, 1968–9, p. 4.

127. J. H. Trounson, 'Mining in Cornwall', *Observer*, 6 July 1969.

128. *Metal Mining in the West of England*, Cornish Mining Development Association, 1972.

129. A. J. Walter, 'A pattern for the revival of mining exploration in the British Isles', paper 32 in the symposium on the *Future of Non-Ferrous Mining in Great Britain and Ireland*, 1959, pp. 575–83.

130. Royal School of Mines, *Minerals and the Environment*, a submission to the Zuckerman Commission, January 1972, p. 34.

131. ibid.

132. Letter from Mr H. E. Montagu of Consolidated Goldfields Ltd., 22 June 1970.

133. Statement made by Cornish Mining Development Association and the Cornish Chamber of Mines at a meeting convened by the Council for the Protection of Rural England, Truro, 19 November 1971.

134. Cornish Mining Development Association Annual Report, 1967–8, p. 1.

135. Department of Taoiseach, Central Statistics Annual Production Section.

136. *Hansard*, HMSO 21 June 1961, column 1, 514.

137. Cornish Mining Development Association Annual Report, 1970–1, p. 3.

138. J. H. Trounson, letter to the author, 14 December 1972.

Ferrous metals : iron ores

139. Iron and Steel Board, *Development in the Iron and Steel Industry*, Special Report, HMSO 1957, pp. 37 and 40.

140. British Steel Corporation, *Iron and Steel Industry Annual Statistics*, 1969, Table 1.

141. 'Home and imported ore: the UK balance', *Steel Review* **38**, April 1965, p. 12.

142. British Iron and Steel Federation, Development Coordinating Committee, Stage 1 Report, July 1966, p. 55.

143. British Steel Corporation—10 Year Development Strategy, Cd. 5226, HMSO, February 1973.

144. D. C. D. Pocock, 'Britain's post-war iron ore industry', *Geography* **51**, 1966, p. 52.

145. *Mining Annual Review*, June 1970, p. 61.

146. *Mining Journal* **275** (7044), 21 August 1970, p. 149.

147. East Midlands Economic Planning Council, *The East Midlands Study*, HMSO 1966, p. 33.

148. *Steel Review*, op. cit., p. 10.

149. British Steel Corporation supplied information privately, 1971.

150. British Iron and Steel Federation, Development coordinating Committee, op. cit., p. 55.

151. Letter from Mr J. McLaren of the British Steel Corporation, 3 August 1971.

152. British Iron and Steel Federation, Development Coordinating Committee, op. cit., p. 55.

153. *Mining Journal* **275** (7052), 16 October 1970, p. 336.

154. United Nations Department of Economic and Social Affairs, *Survey of World Iron Ore Resources*, New York 1970, p. 275.

155. Memoirs of the Geological Survey, Special Reports on the Mineral Resources of Great Britain, vol. viii, *Haemetites of West Cumberland, Lancashire and the Lake District*, 2nd ed., 1924.

156. ibid.

157. *Sunday Times*, 21 February 1971.

158. *Mining Magazine* **118** (4), April 1968, p. 250.

159. *Iron and Steel Industry Annual Statistics*, op. cit., Table 4.

160. Memoirs of the Geological Survey, Iron Ores, vol. x, *The Haemetites of the Forest of Dean and South Wales*, 1927, p. 60.

161. *Iron and Steel Industry Annual Statistics*, op. cit., Table 4.

162. Memoirs of the Geological Survey, *The Northampton Sand Ironstone: Stratigraphy, Structure and Reserves*, HMSO 1951; *The Liassic Ironstone*, HMSO 1952.

163. J. R. Tomlinson, 'Home ore counter-attacks', *Steel Review* **38**, April 1965, p. 13.

164. L. Dudley Stamp and Stanley H. Beaver, *The British Isles*, 6th ed., Longmans 1971, p. 385.

165. Norman J. G. Pounds, *The Geography of Iron and Steel*, Hutchinson 1966, p. 84.

166. Pocock, op. cit., p. 52.

167. ibid.

168. Eric S. Tonks, *The Ironstone Railways and Tramways of the Midlands*, Locomotive Publication Company, Hampton Court, 1959, pp. 243–6.

169. *Victoria County History of Oxfordshire* ii, Oxford University Press 1907, p. 268.

170. *Iron and Steel Industry Annual Statistics*, op. cit.

171. Proceedings of an Inquiry held at Banbury 8–18 November 1960, typescript, Oxfordshire County Library.

172. ibid.

173. ibid.

174. ibid.

175. ibid.

176. *The Times*, 10 May 1961.

177. Proceedings of an Inquiry held at Banbury, op. cit.

178. *Iron and Steel Industry Annual Statistics*, op. cit., Table 3.

179. D. C. D. Pocock, 'Iron and Steel at Corby', *East Midlands Geographer* **15**, 1961, p. 3.

180. *Iron and Steel Industry Annual Statistics*, op. cit., Table 3.

181. Letter from Mr J. M. Ridgion of the British Steel Corporation, 31 December 1970.

182. Pocock, *East Midlands Geographer*, op. cit., p. 55.

183. Pocock, *Geography*, op. cit., p. 4.

184. Tomlinson, op. cit., p. 13.

185. ibid.

186. Letter of Mr J. McLaren of the British Steel Corporation, 29 April 1971.

187. *Iron and Steel* **43** (6), December 1970, p. 343.

188. Stamp and Beaver, op. cit., p. 387.

189. P. T. Wheeler, 'Ironstone working between Melton Mowbray and Grantham', *East Midlands Geographer* **4** (4, 28), 1967, p. 240.

190. ibid., p. 243.

191. D. C. D. Pocock, 'Iron and steel at Scunthorpe', *East Midlands Geographer* **3** (3, 19), 1963, p. 132.

192. G. D. Elliot, *Ironmaking at the Appleby–Frodingham Works of the United Steel Companies Ltd*, Iron and Steel Institute Special Report, no. 30, 1944, p. 22.

193. National Council of Associated Iron Ore Producers, Memorandum dealing with the working of stratified ironstone in the Jurassic system in England, 1944.

194. Pocock, 'Iron and steel at Scunthorpe', op. cit., p. 133.

195. ibid., p. 129.

196. *Iron and Steel* **42** (5), October 1969, p. 281.

197. The Mining Engineering Company, *Dragonby Mine*, 1957; letter from Mr J. McLaren, 29 April 1971.

198. Letter from Mr J. McLaren, 29 April 1971.

199. S. H. Beaver, 'Changes in Industrial Land Use 1930, 1967' in *Land Use and Resources: Studies in Applied Geography*, Institute of British Geographers Special Publication no. 1., November 1968, p. 105.

200. W. David Evans, 'The opencast mining of ironstone and coal', *Geographical Journal* **104**, 1944, p. 111.

201. *Report on the Restoration Problem in the Ironstone Industry in the Midlands*, Summary of Findings and Recommendations, HMSO 1946, Cmd. 6906.

202. Data supplied by the Ironstone Restoration Fund, 22 August 1974.

203. 'Northamptonshire Reclamation Programme', *Town and Country Planning* **33** (10), 1965.

204. ibid.

205. East Midlands Economic Planning Council, op. cit., p. 79.

206. Proceedings of a Public Inquiry held at Banbury, op. cit.

207. Letter from the County Planning Officer, County of Lincoln, Parts of Lindsey, 21 April 1971.

208. *Humberside, a Feasibility Study*, a Report by the Central Unit for Environmental Planning, HMSO 1969, 9.21.

209. Data supplied by the County Planning Officer, Northamptonshire County Council, 11 August, 1971.

210. Report of Survey, Glamorgan County Council, 14 May 1971.

211. See Council for the Protection of Rural England, Report of Working Party on Mineral Extraction, August 1970, p. 11. Mr J. McLaren of British Steel Corporation in a letter to the author, 29 April 1971, states that 'in general the Ironstone Restoration Fund has operated satisfactorily'.

6. CARBON AND HYDROCARBON FUELS

Coal

1. Ministry of Technology, *Digest of Energy Statistics*, HMSO 1971, Table 15, p. 40.

2. *Annual Abstract of Statistics*, no. 108, 1971, Table 200, p. 184. (Figures exclude marine-dredged sand and gravel.)

3. In December 1971 it was expected that the official forecasts of the rate of growth of demand for sand and gravel would again be revised downwards, to 3·5 per cent. Letter from Surrey County Planning Officer, 2 December 1971.

4. National Coal Board Report and Accounts, 1970–1, vol. ii, p. 3.

5. Ministry of Technology, *Digest of Energy Statistics*, 1971, Table 125, p. 185.

6. Deduced from NCB Report and Accounts, 1970–1, vol. ii, p. 84.

7. ibid.

8. Data supplied by the Mineral Resources Division, Institute of Geologica Sciences, 8 November 1971.

9. Ministry of Technology, *Digest of Energy Statistics*, 1971, Table 1, p. 12.

10. Ministry of Technology, *Digest of Energy Statistics*, 1971, Table 121, p. 176.

11. John Platt, *British Coal*, Administrative Staff College Monograph, 1968, p. 106.

12. Calculated from NCB Report and Accounts, 1969–70, vol. ii, p. 82.

13. E. S. Simpson, *Coal and the Power Industries in Postwar Britain*, Longmans 1966, p. 106.

14. The total proved workable reserves of coal, as estimated in the Regional Survey report of 1945, of the then East Midlands division (Nottinghamshire, Derbyshire and Leicestershire) was 5590 million tonnes.

15. See W. D. Holmes, 'The Leicestershire and South Derbyshire Coalfield', *East Midland Geographer* **10**, December 1958, p. 22.

16. See Ieuan Griffiths, 'The new Welsh anthracite industry', *Geography* **47**, 1962, p. 390.

17. See Trevor M. Thomas, 'Recent development in the South Wales coalmining industry', *Tijdschrift voor Economische en Sociale Geografie* **155**, August/September 1964, p. 189.

18. M. J. Marnell and G. Humphreys, 'Private coal mining in South Wales', *Geographical Review* **55** (3), 1965, p. 336.

19. Lord Robens, 'Size and potential in British coal', *National Provincial Bank Review*, August 1966.

20. Trevor M. Thomas, 'Coal Mining in Britain: A Declining Industry?', *Tijdschrift voor Economische en Sociale Geografie*, October 1961, p. 167.

21. Ministry of Technology, *Digest of Energy Statistics*, 1971, Table 18, p. 43.

22. *Europe's Growing Energy Needs, How They Can be Met*, Organization for European Economic Cooperation, May 1956.

23. Platt, op. cit., p. 47.

24. NCB Report and Accounts 1970–1, vol. ii, Table 11, p. 84.

25. *The Times*, 7 January 1971.

26. White Paper on Fuel Policy, 1967, HMSO, para. 15.

27. Total energy consumption in 1970 was 333 million tonnes of coal equivalent (Ministry of Technology, *Digest of Energy Statistics*, 1971, p. 6). The estimate in the White Paper was 315 million tonnes of coal equivalent.

28. Report of the Association for Coal in Europe, London ed., 1 March 1971.

29. Frank Vogl, 'Bleak days for the German coal industry', *The Times*, 13 July 1971.

30. *Sunday Times*, 6 December 1970.

31. NCB Report and Accounts, 1969–70, vol. I, pp. 25–6.

32. Report of the Association for Coal in Europe, op. cit.

33. Reported in *The Times*, 3 July 1971.

34. *The Mining Annual Review*, June 1970, p. 82.

35. Platt, op. cit., p. 106.

36. ibid.

37. Data supplied by the National Coal Board, 14 November 1971.

38. Lord Robens, Address to the Annual Conference of the National Union of Mine-Workers, mimeographed by the National Coal Board.

39. Lord Robens, 'Size and potential in British coal', *National Provincial Bank Review*, August 1966.

40. *Mining Magazine* **122** (4), April 1970.

41. Gerald Manners, 'Some economic and spatial characteristics of the British energy market' in *Spatial Problems of the British Economy*, ed. G. Manners and M. Chisholm, Cambridge University Press 1971.

42. ibid., fig. 6.3, p. 168.

43. ibid., p. 167.

44. Ministry of Technology, *Digest of Energy Statistics*, 1971, Table 45, p. 79. (These figures include consumption by establishments producing electricity for railways, tramways and trolleybus operation and for groups of factories.)

45. NCB, 5 September 1974.

46. Lord Robens, 'Industry and the use of land', *Journal of Town Planning Institute* **51**, 1966, p. 240.

47. Data supplied by the National Coal Board, 14 November 1971.

48. J. R. Atkinson, 'The industrial landscape', *Journal of Town Planning Institute* **48**, 1963, p. 102.

49. Data supplied by the National Coal Board, 14 November 1971.

50. J. R. James, Sheila F. Scott and E. C. Willatts, 'Land use and the changing power industry in England and Wales', *Geographical Journal* **127** (3), September 1961, p. 290.

51. Quoted in *Guardian*, 23 November 1970.

52. Address by Sir H. Houldsworth, July 1954, NCB pamphlet no. 8.

53. Data supplied by the National Coal Board.

54. ibid.

55. ibid.

56. *The East Midlands Study*, The East Midlands Economic Planning Council, HMSO 1966, p. 79.

57. K. C. Edwards, 'Extractive industry' in *Nottingham and its Region*, British Association for the Advancement of Science, 1966, p. 276.

58. ibid.

59. H. J. Lowe, 'Planned dereliction', *Town and Country Planning* **35** (2), 1967, p. 88.

60. East Midlands Economic Planning Council, op. cit., p. 79.

61. H. J. Lowe, 'Colliery waste, a national or a local problem?', *Town and Country Planning* **34** (12), December 1966, p. 551.

62. *A Review of Yorkshire and Humberside*, Yorkshire and Humberside Economic Planning Council, HMSO 1966, p. 5.

63. Quoted John Barr, *Derelict Britain*, Penguin 1969, p. 45.

64. Letter from Durham County Planning Officer to the author, 29 December 1970.

65. James *et al.*, op. cit., p. 290.

66. John F. Davis, 'Recent changes in the Bristol Somerset coalfield', *Goegraphy* **41**, 1956, p. 57.

67. NCB Report and Accounts, 1971–2, vol. i, p. 9.

68. ibid. p. 13, data supplied by the Brick Development Association Ltd., 20 August 1974.

69. NCB Report and Accounts, 1969–70, vol. I, p. 13.

70. Data supplied by the National Coal Board.

71. Anthony Tucker, 'A Tip Worth its Weight in Gold', *Guardian*, 24 September 1971.

72. ibid.

73. ibid.

74. Letter from Durham County Planning Officer, 29 December 1970.

75. Geoffrey Cowley, *Bedfordshire Brickfield*, Bedfordshire County Council, October 1967, p. 33.

76. Data supplied by the National Coal Board, 14 November 1971.

77. NCB Report and Accounts, 1969–70, vol. I, Table 5, p. 61.

78. C. H. Shadbolt and W. B. Mabe, *Subsidence Aspects of Mining Development and Planning in some Northern Coalfields*, Geological Aspects of Development and Planning in Northern England, Yorkshire Geological Society, 1970.

79. James *et al.*, op. cit., p. 290.

80. See for instance Alice Coleman, 'Land reclamation at a Kentish colliery', *Institute of British Geographers* **21**, 1955.

81. Trevor M. Thomas, *Coal Mining in Britain, a Declining Industry?*, op. cit., p. 274.

82. NCB Report and Accounts 1968–9, vol. i, p. 14.

83. Data supplied by the National Coal Board, 14 November 1971.

84. Lord Robens, 'Industry and the use of land', *Journal of Town Planning Institute* **51**, 1966, p. 241.

85. Letter from Nottinghamshire County Planning Officer, 6 March 1972.

86. Interview, Derbyshire County Planning Office, 28 July 1971.

87. NCB Report and Accounts 1969–70, vol. I, p. 13.

88. G. P. Wibberley, *Agriculture and Urban Growth*, Michael Joseph, 1959, pp. 189–90.

89. Letter from Mr P. G. Lamb of the National Coal Board Opencast Executive, 3 February 1972.

90. Letter from Mr R. H. Watkins of the Ministry of Agriculture, Fisheries and Food, 25 January 1972.

91. Letter from Miss E. Walpole of the Ministry of Agriculture, Fisheries and Food, 20 January 1972.

92. National Coal Board Opencast Executive, 30 August 1974.

Hydrocarbons

93. Peter Hinde, *Fortune in the North Sea*, Foulis 1966, p. 2.

94. P. E. Kent, 'Extractive Industry' in *Nottingham and its Region*, British Association for the Advancement of Science, 1966, p. 299.

95. R. G. W. Brunstrom, 'Recently discovered oilfields in Britain', Proceedings of the Sixth World Petroleum Congress, Frankfurt-am-Main, section, 1 paper 49, 1963 (reprint London 1963).

96. Kent, op. cit., p. 301.

97. Trevor H. Thomas, 'The North Sea and its environs future reservoir of fuel' *Geographical Review* **56**, 1966, p. 22.

98. Information supplied by the Petroleum Information Bureau, 21 September 1970.

99. E. S. Simpson, *Coal and the Power Industries in Postwar Britain*, Longmans 1966, p. 97.

100. Petroleum Information Bureau, *Oil—United Kingdom*, 1968, p. 8.

101. Data supplied by the Department of Trade and Industry, March 1971.

102. However, in August 1966 Esso Petroleum, which was proposing to drill an exploratory well at Cudham, near Orpington in Kent, was obliged to abandon the project as a result of conditions imposed by Bromley Council Planning Committee.

103. *Sunday Times*, 28 November 1971 (report of a protest meeting at Bridport).

104. ibid.

105. 'North Sea progress', *Esso Magazine* xvii, (3), Summer 1968, p. 8.

106. ibid., p. 8.

107. Hinde, op. cit., p. xiii.

108. T. Gaskell, 'Source of the North Sea Gas', *Geographical Magazine* **39**, 1967.

109. Lord Shawcross, *The Law of the Continental Shelf with Special Reference to The North Sea*, World Land Use Survey, Occasional Papers no. 5, 1964, p. 36.

110. Jean Devaux-Charbonnel, 'Law, oil and the sea today', *World Petroleum*, May 1965, p. 50.

111. *Economist*, 8 August 1970.

112. The 1958 convention did not make adequate provision for the surveying of the sea bed at up to five times the depth of the continental shelf, since made possible by technical advances. In 1970 pilot drilling in 6100 metres of water by an Anglo-American team was reported (*Economist*, 8 August 1970). In that year discussions were under way to establish a world code for the exploitation of the sea bed, outside the limits of the continental shelf.

113. Shawcross, op. cit., p. 39.

114. D. R. Whitbread, 'North-west Britain and Ireland—next step in offshore play', *World Petroleum* **41** (5), May 1970, p. 28.

115. James Law, 'Britain's giveaway petroleum policy', *Guardian*, 28 December 1971.

116. House of Commons paper 122.

117. See Thomas, op. cit., fig. 4, p. 31.

118. Gas Council, *Natural Gas in the Seventies*, 1970, p. 5.

119. *Annual Abstract of Statistics*, HMSO 1970.

120. J. A. Demont, 'The introduction of North Sea gas into the East Midlands', *East Midland Geographer* **4** (7, 31), 1969, p. 379.

121. *The Times*, 17 August 1970.

122. *Geographical Journal* **134** (1), March 1968, p. 83. See also P. R . Odell and F. Thackeray, 'The right price for North Sea gas', *The Times*, 7 December 1966; R. Huddie and R. Murray, 'Pricing policy for North Sea gas', *The Times*, 24 April 1967.

123. *Economist*, 30 May 1970.

124. White Paper on Fuel Policy, HMSO Cmnd. 3438, November 1967.

125. *The Impact of Natural Gas on the Consumption of Energy in the OECD European Member Countries*, HMSO 1970.

126. *Economist*, 3 January 1970.

127. Gas Council, *Natural Gas in the Seventies*, 1970, p. 3.

128. *The Times*, 11 January 1969.

129. P. R. Odell, 'Exporting North Sea gas', *The Times*, 13 August 1970.

130. *The Times*, 14 January 1971.

131. *The Times*, 30 September 1970.

132. A cubic metre of oil contains approximately 1000 times the heat content of a standard cubic metre of natural gas. The heat content of a cubic metre of gas when compressed to a typical line pressure of 345 Newton/sq. cm is increased 35 times, making an oil/gas ratio of about 30:1. At this pressure, a gas pipeline would have to have a diameter approximately 3·5 times that of an oil pipeline to achieve parity. (*Petroleum Review* **25** (294), June 1971, p. 216.)

133. British Gas Corporation, 29 August 1974.

134. Gerald Manners, 'Some economic and spatial characteristics of the British energy market', ed. G. Manners and M. Chisholm, *Spatial Problems of the British Economy*, Cambridge University Press 1971, p. 165.

135. Petroleum Information Bureau, *Oil—The North Sea Search*, April 1968, p. 6.

136. See P. R. Odell, *Growth in the 1970s?*, paper given to the Regional Studies

Association Conference on 'Migration and Development: the Prospects for the North', University of York, 29 March 1967; P. R. Odell, 'What will gas do to the east coast?', *New Society*, 5 May 1966.

137. East Anglia Economic Planning Council, *East Anglia, A Study*, HMSO 1968 p. 16.

138. *The Times*, 15 February 1967.

139. 27 July 1968.

140. F. E. Dean (Technical Liaison Officer, Production and Supply Division, The Gas Council), 'Plans in the pipeline', *Guardian*, 6 November 1970.

141. *Petroleum Economist*, January 1974, p. 15. F. E. Dean, 29 August 1974.

142. *Petroleum Economist*, May 1974, p. 184. All subsequent figures for oilfield capacity are also taken from this source.

143. *Petroleum Economist*, January 1974, p. 14.

144. *Petroleum Economist*, March 1974, p. 97.

145. Whitbread, op. cit. p. 27.

146. *Economist*, 5 January 1974.

147. Scottish Oil, 1973.

148. International Management and Engineering Group, A study of Potential Benefits to British Industry from Offshore Oil and Gas Development, HMSO, 1973.

149. Ibid.

150. *New Scientist*, 7 January 1974.

151. North of England Development Council, *Oilfield*, 1973.

152. Letters from Mr R. G. Shelton of the Fisheries Laboratory, Burnham-on-Crouch, 14 April 1971, and from Mr H. A. Cole of the Fisheries Laboratory, Lowestoft, 16 April 1971.

153. See Ministry of Agriculture, Fisheries and Food, *The Torrey Canyon Disaster and Fisheries*, Laboratory Leaflet (New series) no. 18, 1968.

154. *Economist*, 1 September 1973, p. 71.

155. Scottish Office, *International Coastal Planning Framework*, October 1973.

7. TRENDS IN THE DEVELOPMENT OF THE EXTRACTIVE INDUSTRIES

1. S. H. Beaver, 'Minerals and planning', *Geographical Journal* **104**, 1944, p. 167.

2. Department of Trade and Industry, *Digest of Energy Statistics*, HMSO 1971, Table 125, p. 185.

3. Royal School of Mines, *Minerals and the Environment*, a submission to the Zuckerman Commission, 1972, p. 4.

4. *A Study of Potential Benefits to British Industry from Offshore Oil and Gas Developments*, HMSO 1973.

5. *Quarry Managers' Journal*, January 1969, Report of the Second International Surface Mining Conference at Minneapolis, p. 31.

6. *Industrial Minerals* **49**, October 1971, 'Aggregates in the United Kingdom', pp. 18–19.

7. NCB Report and Accounts, 1970–1, vol. ii, Table ii, p. 84.

8. Reports of the Advisory Committee on Sand and Gravel (the Waters Committee), HMSO 1948–56.

9. Quarry numbers as given by Report of H.M. Inspector of Mines and Quarries for 1971; total output figures calculated from *Annual Abstract of Statistics*, no. 108, 1971, Table 200, p. 184.

10. Brian C. Fish, 'Quarrying in the seventies', *Quarry Managers' Journal*, October 1970, p. 364.

11. Obtained by dividing the total output figures for these rocks as supplied by the Department of the Environment (for England, Wales and Scotland only) by the total number of quarries as listed by the Quarry Managers' Journal, *Directory of Pits and Quarries*, 20th ed., 1969.

12. NCB Report and Accounts 1970–1, vol. ii, Table ii, p. 84.

13. Robert Rice, 'The problems of reviving non-ferrous metal mining in Britain' *Chartered Surveyor*, January 1970, p. 328.

14. Standing Conference on London and South-East Regional Planning, *Sand and Gravel Extraction*, LRP 1640, February 1971, p. 38.

15. *Guardian*, 12 January 1971.

16. See *Evidence submitted by Friends of the Earth Ltd. to the Committee on Minerals Planning Control*, January 1973, p. 21.

17. R. D. Medford, 'Marine mining in Britain', *Mining Magazine* **121**(6),December 1969, p. 477.

18. Report of the Commission on Mining and the Environment, September 1972, p. 30.

19. e.g. The Institute of Geological Sciences, Assessment of British Sand and Gravel Resources, no. 1, The Sand and Gravel Resources of the Country South-East of Norwich, Norfolk, Report no. 71/20. This, the first of a series of reports on the assessment of British sand and gravel resources produced by the Mineral Assessment Unit, is described as 'the application to large areas of methods used commercially for evaluating reserves on small sites'.

20. *Friends of the Earth Ltd.*, op. cit., p. 26

21. Report of the Commission on Mining and the Environment, op. cit., p. 43.

22. *Friends of the Earth Ltd.*, op. cit., p. 38.

23. F. Callot, 'Structure, development and future of the world mining production', paper presented to the VIIth International Mining Congress at Bucharest, September 1972.

24. Report of the Commission on Mining and the Environment, op. cit., p. 66.

25. See ref. Barrett J. Riordan, 'The economics of a quality environment', an address to the Compressed Gas Association, *World Petroleum* **42** (4), May 1971, p. 19.

26. Interview, Derbyshire County Planning Office, July 1972.

27. Report of the Commission on Mining and the Environment, op. cit., p. 39.

28. ibid., pp. 45–6.

29. Council for the Protection of Rural England, Report of the Working Party on Mineral Extraction, August 1970, p. 11.

30. ibid.

31. e.g. the east Sussex–Ouse valley complex of chalk workings for cement manufacture now has planning permission for some 50 years' working.

32. Report of the Commission on Mining and the Environment, op. cit., p. 28.

33. Report of the Urban District Councils Association to the Government Committee on Minerals Planning Control, *Guardian*, 25 November 1972.

34. Somerset County Council, *Quarrying in the Mendips*, 1971, p. 44.

35. Data supplied by the National Coal Board, 1971.

36. D. C. Corner and D. C. Stafford, *China Clay Sand, Liability or Asset?*, Devon

County Council, 1971, p. 78; verbal information, Mr Behrman, National Coal Board Minestone Executive, 22 January 1973.

37. Corner and Stafford, op. cit., pp. 78–9.

38. 'Short- and long-term development plan', China Clay Council, published 13 January 1972.

39. Calculated from the Peak District National Park Planning Board 18th Annual Report, April 1969–March 1970, para. 127.

40. Verbal information, Mr J. Trounson, 30 January 1971.

41. Brian G. Fish, 'Quarrying in the 1970s', *Quarry Managers' Journal* **54** (10), October 1970, p. 370.

42. *Quarry Managers' Journal* **53** (1), January 1969, summary of paper by E. P. Pfleider, Chairman of Committee on Rapid Excavation, entitled, 'Rapid underground excavation as an alternative'.

43. D. I. Roberts, E. Hoek and B. G. Fish, 'The concept of the mammoth quarry', *Quarry Managers' Journal* **56** (7), July 1972, p. 231.

44. Letter from Westmorland County Planning Officer, 30 April 1971.

45. D. I. Roberts, *et al.*, op. cit., p. 231.

46. C. L. Keeler, 'Planning and the quarrying industry in Somerset', reprinted from *Quarry Managers' Journal* **54** (12), December 1970, for the British Quarrying and Slag Federation.

47. Department of the Environment, Press Notice 872M, 3 August 1972.

48. ibid.

49. R. F. Silverlock, 'Planning and the law', *Quarry Managers' Journal* **54** (3), March 1970, p. 96.

51. Report of Committee for Environmental Conservation to the Government Committee on Mineral Planning Control, *Guardian*, 10 January 1973.

52. Report of the Commission on Mining and the Environment, op. cit., p. 47.

53. Quoted in Jon Tinker, 'A mouse that didn't roar', *New Scientist*, 21 September 1972, p. 497.

54. See ibid. and Report of the Commission on Mining and the Environment, September 1972, p. 14.

INDEX

Note: Numbers in italics refer to Figures and Tables.

513

s*